NEUROPSYCHOLOGICAL EVALUATION OF OLDER CHILDREN

Neuropsychological Evaluation of Older Children

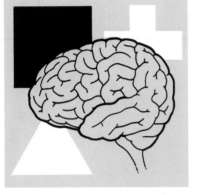

Ralph M. Reitan
Deborah Wolfson

Neuropsychology Press

Neuropsychology Press
2920 S. 4th Avenue
South Tucson, Arizona 85713-4819

602-882-2022

Design and Layout: Dave Fischer
Electronic Type: Casa Cold Type, Inc.

Printed in the United States of America

ISBN 0-934515-10-7

Library of Congress Card Number: 91-68054

 Printed on recycled paper.

Contents

Preface...ix

I.   Development and Current Problems of
      Child Neuropsychology...1

II.   Outcome Following Brain Injury in Childhood...................31

III. Theories of Brain-Behavior Relationships............................47

IV.   Content and Methodological Organization
      of the Halstead-Reitan Neuropsychological
      Test Battery for Older Children...71

V.   Relationship of Specific Tests to the
      Reitan-Wolfson Model...117

VI.   REHABIT: A Structured Program for Retraining
      Neuropsychological Abilities..129

VII. Investigations of the Validity of the
      Halstead-Reitan Neuropsychological
      Test Battery for Older Children...185

VIII. Description of Tests in the Halstead-Reitan
      Neuropsychological Test Battery for
      Older Children...299

IX.   Instructions for Administering and Scoring
      the Halstead-Reitan Neuropsychological
      Test Battery for Older Children...323

X.   Principles and Illustrations of Individual
      Case Interpretations..471

      Sequential Organization of Illustrative Cases....................482

      Neuropsychological Evaluation of Normal Children........483

         Examples of the Range of Neuropsychological
         Findings in Normal Children:

            Case 1 — Terry. A rather typical normal control child........485

            Case 2 — Ben. A control child with mild neuropsycho-
            logical deficits but no expressions of clinical concerns.......497

            Case 3 — Cody. A child who, despite the lack of
            medical evidence of cerebral damage or disease, has
            learning problems and a loss of interest in school..............505

            Case 4 — Denise. A control case until very recent
            events raised a question of clinically significant
            brain dysfunction...516

Neuropsychological Evaluation of Children
with Neurological Conditions as well as
Neuropsychological Problems 526

Neoplasms of the Brain 526

Medulloblastoma 528

Case 5 — *Ann*. A child with a medulloblastoma 531

Supratentorial Brain Tumors in Children 543

Case 6 — *Tom*. A child with a thalamic astrocytoma 548

Cerebral Tumors 561

Case 7 — *Rachel*. A child with an astrocytoma
principally in the right posterior frontal area
(pre- and post-operative results) 563

Pseudotumor Cerebri 579

Case 8 — *George*. A child suspected of having a brain tumor.
This case illustrates the important neuropsychological
differences in cases of cerebral tumors and children
incorrectly suspected of having a cerebral tumor 582

Cerebral Abscess 592

Case 9 — *Cathy*. A child with a left frontal cerebral
abscess 595

Cerebral Hemispherectomy for Intractable Epileptic
Seizures 608

Case 10 — *Donald*. A child who had right
hemispherectomy for intractable epileptic seizures.
Tested pre- and post-operatively 611

Arteriovenous Malformations 626

Case 11 — *Ted*. A child with an AVM of the left cerebral
hemisphere 629

Encephalitis 640

Case 12 — *Cindy*. A child with neuropsychological
problems after encephalitis 643

Epilepsy 655

Case 13 — *Oscar*. A 15-year-old adolescent who had
significant neuropsychological, educational, and
social problems associated with epilepsy 659

Traumatic Brain Injury..672

    Case 14 — Margaret. A child with a closed head injury.
The mother felt that the child was less able than before
the head injury, but the neurosurgeon insisted that
Margaret had no evidence of permanent injury. Initial
neuropsychological examination was done 11 months
after the injury and a follow-up examination another
year later 677

    Case 15 — Millie. A child with a left parietal depressed
skull fracture who was initially tested shortly after her
injury and again 15 months later because she was
encountering difficulties in school. The case is
discussed with relation to the importance of parental
counseling and cognitive retraining..................................694

    Case 16 — Eunice. A child with prior head injuries at
3 and 4 years of age. Neuropsychological examination
was done at 10 years of age because the child was
having problems in school and her parents had begun
to suspect that the earlier injuries had caused brain
damage..711

    Case 17 — Boyd. A boy who had sustained a serious
closed head injury 19 months before neuropsychological
testing. Boyd seemed to be impaired academically and
in other ways, but the medical findings were within
normal limits. Litigation was pending..............................722

The Neuropsychology of Learning Disabilities..................736

    Case 18 — Roger. A child with significant learning
disabilities and behavior problems in whom neuropsychological deficits were a major factor. Consideration is
given to approaches needed in cognitive retraining as
indicated by neuropsychological evaluation......................744

    Case 19 — Steve. A child with increasing resistance and
hostility to academic activities, refusal to accept
suggestions or direction, anger outbursts, and defiant
behavior. Referred to a child guidance clinic and also to
a pediatric neurologist who requested neuropsycho-
logical evaluation 760

    Case 20 — Rudy. A child who seemed to be relatively
normal except for extreme difficulty learning to read
and develop other academic skills. Now in the 5th
grade, Rudy was showing signs of increasing anxiety,
self-doubt, and impairment of his self-image because
of his learning disabilities..774

Behavioral Problems of Children with
Cerebral Damage or Dysfunction..785

    Case 21 — Gary. A child with a life-long history of
    unacceptable social behavior, rage outbursts, striking
    out physically and injuring others, problems with the
    criminal justice system, poor academic performance,
    and probably epilepsy. The neuropsychological test
    findings provide an insight toward understanding this
    child's behavior and approaches to remediation.................789

    Case 22 — Jim. A child with disruptive, negativistic, and
    hostile behavior. The neuropsychological test results
    do not indicate the presence of significant brain damage,
    but do reveal disparities in neuropsychological ability
    structure which, in turn, predispose this child toward
    adverse behavioral adjustments and problems in
    understanding and adapting to environmental stresses.
    A program of remediation oriented toward improving
    child-family interactions in addition to cognitive
    retraining of neuropsychological functions necessary
    to maintain such improvement is also outlined.................. 802

Appendix
    Sample of computerized scoring of the Neuropsychological
    Deficit Scale (NDS) for Older Children 815

Glossary..821

References...839

Author Index..863

Subject Index...869

Preface

The organization and content of this book reflect our dual interest in scientific validation and clinical applications. While it is often said that clinical applications naturally emanate from good science, the fact is that a large gulf often exists between the two that is difficult to bridge. Scientific validation of principles of brain-behavior relationships is imperative, but if the unit of value is the individual person, this validation has little meaning unless methods are developed and tested for accuracy in clinical application. Thus, a major purpose of this book is to translate research findings of brain-behavior relationships into clinical procedures for assessing the individual child.

This volume focusses on both brain and behavior, and in this sense, respects the hybrid term, neuropsychology. The discerning reader will be aware that a great number of past and present studies in the area have been directed toward variables that are only presumed to depend on brain functions, and have gone on to relate these variables to a host of other variables. This is probably not surprising, considering the fact that most professionals in the field have been taught to study behavior, often do not have the opportunity to collect biological or pathological information about the brain, and thus follow their training and experience. They therefore practice psychology rather than neuropsychology. Their approach to neuropsychology is to presume that their tests and observations relate to brain damage or dysfunction, and thereby in effect limit the significance of their findings to only the "psychology" side of the neuropsychology equation. The bridge between brain and behavior, in clinical cases that are not positively identified as having organic brain disorders, is still not adequately constructed and is rarely explicitly studied.

In the early phases of clinical neuropsychology the field was given limited respect by neurologists, neurosurgeons, and other neuroscientists because of an erroneous conception of the inadequacies of neuropsychologists in the *neuro* area of brain-behavior relationships. Persistent work in establishing the dependence of behavior on the brain eventually led to a degree of respectability and recognition of clinical neuropsychology, fostered especially by evidence which showed convincingly that neuropsychological findings were closely related to independently determined brain conditions. At present, however, it appears that the training of psychologists in behavior (and the lack of training and concern for the biological condition of the brain) is again prevailing, and the initial disrespect of neuroscientists for neuropsychology may again emerge. Even though we appear to hold each other in high regard, neuropsychology has not yet fully emerged as a member of the family of neurosciences (although many neuropsychologists who have limited contact with other neuroscientists have little awareness of this fact).

The title of this book might lead the reader to presume that the content exclusively involves children. A consideration of the historical development of child neuropsychology makes it quite clear that brain-behavior relationships in children cannot be adequately understood without knowledge of adult neuropsychology. Since children mature into adults (even though cerebral damage may have a significant effect) comparisons of child and adult neuropsychology were imperative. These comparisons, intended to clarify age-related differences, have in fact led to presentation of more detailed information about adult neuropsychology, based on the contrast with the major differences in adult and child neuropsychology that stem from the effects of brain lesions sustained in infancy or early childhood.

One of the major focuses of this book concerns the effects of damage to the brain early in life. Our research and clinical observations lead to the conclusion that early cerebral damage, regardless of lateralization, results in profound impairment (provided that the lesion is sufficiently pervasive). The determining factors appear to be (1) that localization of function has not yet been established early in life and damage leads to an outcome of generalized neuropsychological impairment, and (2) that the entire mass of cerebral tissue is necessary to subserve eventual normal development.

Our studies have shown that the simple formulations of the past (concrete vs. abstract impairment; figure-ground deficits; hyperactive behavior; perceptual handicaps, etc.) are not adequate and, in fact, minimize the actual problems experienced by children with cerebral damage. It must be recognized that the effects of cerebral damage are complex, variable among subjects, and usually involve many dimensions of neuropsychological functioning. Only if the full range and nature of the deficits are recognized can the individual child be given appropriate assistance. The problem of simplification and premature categorization plagued the area of childhood brain damage for years, and exactly the same trend has more recently appeared in the area of learning disability.

In clinical assessment it is tremendously important to avoid the trap of (1) testing only for specific deficits that relate to circumscribed cerebral areas, and (2) testing for specific neuropsychological deficits as if a general ability factor was not present and neuropsychological functions could be neatly and separately sorted into parcels. Neuropsychologists are strongly motivated to identify specific deficits a child may have, but it must be recognized that general deficits exist (involving the entire cerebral cortex) as well as specific deficits (which may relate to a focal area or region of the cerebral cortex). This is an especially important distinction in child neuropsychology, since regional localization of particular abilities is a gradually developing and age-related phenomenon.

It is incumbent upon the neuropsychologist to know which abilities are generally distributed throughout the cerebral cortex and which abilities relate to more specific areas. In our judgement, an appropriate prescription for cognitive (brain) retraining can hardly be developed without an understanding of the interaction of general and specific neuropsychological impairment. Failure to understand this relationship has led not only to a fractionalization of neuropsychological ability structure, but a fractionalization of the brain itself, with one area in the left hemisphere assigned to speech pathologists, parts of the right hemisphere to occupational therapists, the motor system to physical therapists, etc. The emphasis on specific tests (which emanates primarily from the field of behavioral neurology) as compared with the use of general tests of brain function (which is derived from clinical neuropsychology) has had a profound effect on the entire approach to evaluation and treatment of the brain-damaged child.

In assessing neuropsychological abilities of the individual child, it is imperative to assess the full range of neuropsychological functions in order to evaluate intraindividual differences in brain-related abilities. Many non-brain-damaged persons have below-average abilities, and others have above-average functioning. The same is true for children with known cerebral damage, even though such children tend to score somewhat lower than normal children. The major problem among brain-damaged children often involves striking intraindividual disparities in ability structure, with areas of weakness limiting the functional usefulness of areas of strength. Without an assessment of the complete range of brain-related abilities, no such comparative intraindividual evaluations can be made.

A standardized battery of tests, checked out on hundreds of normal and brain-damaged children, is necessary to achieve this aim. Many neuropsychologists use a casually-composed set of tests, often selected on the basis of presenting complaints (as if brain impairment could somehow be equivalent to a sprained elbow), and do not have any evidence that the tests they have selected either assess all major aspects of brain functions or evaluate them in a comparative manner. The brain should be assessed as an organ, even though additional selected tests may be used to complement the standardized battery. Otherwise, individual strengths and weaknesses may be missed, an imbalanced view of comparative strengths and weaknesses may emerge, brain-behavior functions of the child as an individual may be distorted, and recommendations and plans for remediation may be based only on comparisons of the child against normative data rather than on a realistic understanding of his/her unique ability structure. In this book we have presented results on individual children in order to demonstrate the ways in which the Halstead-Reitan Battery for Older Children permits this kind of analysis.

We feel that it is important in the individual child to be able to identify brain-related deficits as contrasted with normal variability in performances, to identify particular brain-related deviations in the child's ability structure, to evaluate the full range of neuropsychological functions (which requires detailed study of large numbers of normal and brain-damaged children using a standardized battery of tests), and thus be in a position to prescribe and implement an appropriate program of brain training.

We have used case illustrations to communicate information of this type, not only because scientific study in clinical neuropsychology ultimately must focus on the individual human being, but also because some of the most important points regarding the effects of cerebral damage can best be made in the context of case illustrations. The practical and clinical relevance of principles and theory merge, and take on added significance, when they are shown to apply to the individual human being.

As noted in the first paragraph above, a major aim of this book is to translate theory and research into clinical applications for individual subjects. Our substantial use of case illustrations is intended not only to provide the reader with training in clinical interpretation of neuropsychological test results and to provide illustrations of report-writing, but to demonstrate the ways in which principles of clinical neuropsychology apply across a broad range of children with documented cerebral damage as well as children with learning and behavioral disorders. Most readers will find it helpful to use the case-data to test out the principles of child brain-behavior relationships for him/herself. This can be done by performing a point-by-point "blind" interpretation of the test results, utilizing the principles already established, and then comparing this interpretation with the one presented in the book. No other approach to child neuropsychology provides this type of learning opportunity.

Years ago in the area of traumatic brain injury, long before evidence of widespread neuronal shearing and petechial hemorrhages in the brain were known, neuropsychological data from the Halstead-Reitan Battery clearly demonstrated evidence of generalized damage as well as focal effects in persons who had sustained head injuries. In fact, findings of this type served as the basis for identifying traumatic brain damage (in contrast to other etiologies) on the basis of the test results alone (Reitan, 1964). This same situation now exists for many children with learning disabilities and behavioral disorders. The Halstead-Reitan Battery clearly shows evidence of an organic brain disorder and the test results describe relevant neuropsychological correlates. We hope that future research on the underlying neurobiological disorders will soon emerge to add another dimension to our understanding of these conditions.

Finally, this volume emphasizes remediation of neuropsychological deficits. The majority of children with cerebral damage or dysfunction do not represent medical problems (although of course in absolute numbers many do). In most cases the problems of the child are neuropsychological in nature and involve impairment of previously developed abilities or the potential for future development. These deficits have consequences that affect all aspects of the child's life. The first step in treatment of many children is to identify the basic nature of the neuropsychological impairment and then devise a training program aimed to rebuild the child's ability structure. We feel that it is extremely important to couple neuropsychological evaluation with remediation efforts, and for this reason have presented an extensive description of our own cognitive remediation program, REHABIT, together with detailed discussions of applications to individual children.

Additional points should be mentioned to the interested reader:

1. This book contains expanded and detailed instructions for administration and scoring of all of the tests in the Halstead-Reitan Neuropsychological Test Battery for Older Children. Photographs and detailed examples are included to instruct the reader in learning administration and scoring of the tests.

2. The Neuropsychological Deficit Scale (NDS) for Older Children, which promises to be very useful as a guide to clinical interpretation, is described, and research results and scoring procedures and protocols are presented.

3. Recognizing that neuropsychologists vary in their knowledge of neuroanatomy, neurology, and neuropathology, we have presented summaries of these areas as related to the various conditions represented by our case illustrations, thereby providing a concise review of many of the neurologic disorders that affect children. In

addition, an extensive glossary provides definitions of hundreds of neuropsychological and medical terms that may facilitate communication with some of our readers.

4. In our effort to translate theory and research into practical clinical application, we have included numerous examples of children's responses on the Reitan-Indiana Aphasia Screening Test (AST) in order to identify brain-related impairment. These illustrations assist the practitioner in identifying pathognomonic versus deviant but still normal performances on the AST.

5. Our intent has been to provide the reader with an extensive review of research studies concerned with the effects of cerebral damage in children. We hope that this review will help the reader broaden his/her knowledge of childhood brain-behavior relationships, particularly as this knowledge leads to increased competence in clinical practice and in understanding the individual child with impairment of cerebral functions. Considering the importance that has recently been assumed by the legal system in evaluating neuropsychological claims of cerebral damage in children as well as adults, we hope that this volume may contribute a basis for valid resolution of these claims as based, in turn, on valid evaluations by clinical neuropsychologists.

We would especially like to thank Shelly Benezra, MSEd, for her contributions to the production of this book. She read all of the working drafts, the final draft, and the many drafts that followed, offering valuable suggestions with patience and good humor.

Ralph M. Reitan
Deborah Wolfson
Tucson
January 1992

CHAPTER I

Development and Current Problems of Child Neuropsychology

The Historical Background

Every area of inquiry has a long record of investigations that significantly influenced its development, and this is certainly true of the field of child neuropsychology. We tend to identify the modern era of adult neuropsychology as beginning around 1935, when Ward Halstead established the first full-time laboratory for investigating the psychological effects of cerebral lesions. Even though there had been many reports of the consequences of cerebral disease or damage on the behavior of children before 1935, the modern era of child neuropsychology is generally considered to date back to about that same time, beginning with the work of A.A. Strauss and Heinz Werner at the Wayne State Hospital and Training School.

Kessler (1980) refers to these earlier reports as representing the medical era, whereas the contributions made after 1941 were principally from psychologists and educators. (Obviously, there is no perfect distinction in this regard, either in terms of the time frame or the professional training of the contributors.) As Kessler points out, the epidemic of encephalitis lethargica during World War I involved many children as well as adults. In the ensuing years, neurologists and psychiatrists were greatly interested in the behavioral changes and deficits that characterized the post-encephalitic syndrome and several reports appeared (Bender, 1942a, 1942b; Ebaugh, 1923; Gibbs, 1930; Hohman, 1922; Schilder, 1934). A great deal of attention was also given to birth injury (Schilder, 1934) as well as cerebral trauma later in childhood (Blau, 1936; Bowman & Blau, 1943; Strecker & Eubaugh, 1924). Many other conditions were also evaluated, including Down's syndrome (then referred to as "mongolism") and cretinism (Benda, 1949), epilepsy (Schilder, 1934), and cerebral palsy (Benda, 1930; Denhoff & Robinault, 1960).

It can be seen that there has been considerable interest in the behavioral consequences of cerebral disease and damage oriented toward some of the most common types of injuries sustained by children. However, in these earlier reports the definition of the dependent variables was relatively unsophisticated. Although the children had well-defined conditions of cerebral damage, the clinical reports by physicians were consistently impressionistic in nature and were based upon interviews and other forms of gross observation. The physicians rarely employed any techniques or procedures that were designed to meet laboratory standards of replicability and, as a result, the accuracy of the diagnosis was heavily dependent upon the clinical acumen and observational capabilities of the reporting physician.

The Beginnings of Child Clinical Neuropsychology

As we noted previously, the beginnings of child clinical neuropsychology may be attributed to the collaborative efforts of A.A. Strauss, a psychiatrist, and Heinz Werner, a psychologist. These two men left Germany when Hitler came to power and, after brief stays in other countries, accepted positions in the United States at the Wayne State Hospital and Training School in Michigan.

In this setting Strauss and Werner had an opportunity to study mentally retarded children and became interested in the challenge of determining the types of deficits that were attributable to cerebral damage. In order to pursue this aim, it was necessary to identify the children who had cerebral damage and differentiate them from children whose mental retardation was due to limited education, background, training, or other environmental factors. Strauss and Werner defined familial or hereditary mental deficiency as an endogenous retardation in which there was presumably no structural defect of the brain. Mental deficiency of the exogenous type, on the other hand, was presumed to be due to some type of brain lesion even though no gross signs of neurological deficit were present.

Strauss and Werner (1941) proposed criteria for identifying children with *exogenous mental deficiency* (and, therefore, cerebral damage) according to several factors:

1. A detailed review of the child's developmental medical history which documented traumatic or inflammatory damage of the brain before, during, or shortly after birth. (Despite their insistence on this criterion, Strauss and Werner excluded so-called "obvious" cases of developmental brain disease or abnormality, which was referred to as *organic mental deficiency* rather than exogenous mental deficiency. This latter

group included endocrinological disturbances, congenital syphilis, and hereditary diseases of the brain.)

2. Minimal or "soft" neurological signs on clinical examination (even though frank and obvious neurological deficits were not included).

3. Absence of mental deficiency in any other members of the immediate family.

Primary criteria for diagnosis of *endogenous mental deficiency* tended to meet converse criteria. Children were excluded from the exogenous group and included in the endogenous group if there was (1) evidence of mental retardation among other family members, and (2) no evidence of prior injury or disease that might have affected the brain. Strauss and Werner (1941) indicated that 20%–25% of the mentally retarded children at the Wayne State Hospital and Training School met the criteria for inclusion in the exogenous group and therefore "had evidence of brain lesions."

It was obvious to many other investigators that the criteria proposed by Strauss and Werner were hardly adequate for differentiating between mentally retarded subjects who had cerebral damage and those who did not. In fact, the inclusionary criteria for the diagnosis of exogenous mental deficiency (brain damage) were based entirely on clinical examination, the child's history, and the absence of mental deficiency in other family members. Any one of these criteria might be unreliable, at least to a degree, in its determination. For example, many neonates have histories of difficult deliveries and some degree of physiological embarrassment following birth, but are entirely normal in their later development. Although the diagnostic usefulness of "soft" neurological signs found on physical examination has been debated for years, the reason that these signs are called "soft" is to distinguish them from findings which represent hard, irrefutable evidence. Finally, determining the absence of mental deficiency in other family members would require careful examination of each member of the immediate family; many persons who are mentally retarded are in fact able to work and function relatively normally, depending upon the environmental circumstances and the assistance they are given.

Despite the problems with criteria for inclusion in these groups, a considerable amount of experimental investigation was conducted on groups of children identified as having exogenous or endogenous mental deficiency. The differences between the groups laid the initial groundwork for development of the field of clinical child neuropsychology.

At Wayne State Hospital Werner was principally responsible for the experimental psychological studies of endogenous vs. exogenous mental deficiency, at least in terms of devising procedures for examination of individual children. Several investigations were based upon children's ability in the area of visual perception.

Werner and Thuma (1942b) examined 20 children in each of the endogenous and exogenous groups who were between the chronological ages of 11 and 14 years. Both groups had intelligence quotients that were approximately 70. The experimental task involved the perception of apparent movement under a number of stimulus conditions that represented variations of the phi-phenomena. The authors reported that the movement was seen by nearly all of the children in the endogenous group, but by very few children who were classified in the exogenous group.

Additional studies were done with these two groups of children to determine their ability to see and report actual movement. The results indicated that the exogenous group required much greater movement of stimulus figures than did the endogenous group. Werner and Thuma (1942a) also studied critical flicker fusion in two similar groups of children and found that the exogenous group had significantly lower critical flicker frequencies (the point at which fusion occurred) than did the endogenous children.

Werner and Strauss (1941) compared similar groups of children to determine their ability to identify a figure when it was depicted with a distracting background. In other words, the researchers were interested in determining how well the children could differentiate the figure from the ground or, perceptually, their ability to inhibit the distracting influence of irrelevant information. They found that under these circumstances the exogenous group performed much more poorly in identifying the figure than did the endogenous group.

Werner and Strauss (1939) also used a procedure called the Marble Board Test to evaluate the ability of children with endogenous and exogenous mental retardation to perceive various figures or designs and reproduce these figures on another marble board. Again, the results indicated that the children in the exogenous group distorted the figure and performed much worse than the children with endogenous mental retardation.

In summary, in every experiment based upon visual perception, the exogenous children performed much more poorly than the endogenous children. They demonstrated significant losses in perception and, when required to respond in a particular manner, gave responses that the authors described as being slow, oversimplified, inaccurate, and representing what they called an "incoherent approach."

Werner and Bowers (1941) were interested in whether these deficiencies were limited to visual perception or involved other sensory modalities as well. These investigators devised a task in which a musical pattern was played on a piano to the subject, who was then requested to sing the musical pattern. The children with endogenous mental retardation were able to perform relatively well, but those in the exogenous category lost the pattern and relationships and were not able to duplicate the musical pattern. This finding represented still another instance in which perceptual tasks among mentally retarded children with brain damage (exogenous group) were significantly impaired in comparison with mentally retarded children without brain damage (endogenous group), even though their IQ values and chronological age levels were essentially identical.

A number of additional studies were conducted with these children, and probably the most important of these related to the area of concept formation. Strauss and Werner (1942a) devised a sorting procedure similar to the tests developed by Kurt Goldstein (1942a) for his study of adult subjects. They found that exogenously retarded children were not able to develop meaningful principles for grouping of the objects, made frequent errors, and after having devised a principle and finding that it was unrealistic, did not modify their original hypothesis.

On the basis of the experimental results of these various studies and their observation of children in the exogenous group, Werner and Strauss (1940) offered a general conclusion that these children had difficulty perceiving and registering incoming information, were seriously impaired in their ability to differentiate between the essential stimulus features and background information, and were easily distracted by stimuli in the environment which were not essential to the task at hand. Therefore, because of these perceptual and conceptual deficits, their recommendation for these children was that all distractions should be minimized and the environment should consist of the stimulus material relevant to the essential problem. Strauss and Lehtinen (1947) proposed that two approaches should be used in facilitating the psychological development and learning of the brain-injured child: (1) limiting distracting elements of the environment, and (2) helping the child develop attentional capabilities to attend to the relevant and pertinent stimulus material.

The studies by Strauss and Werner and their immediate associates led to a general impression that children with brain damage were generally hyperactive, emotionally labile, perceptually disordered, impulsive, distractible, and abnormally rigid and perseverative. Conclusions of this kind, in turn, led to the development of training and teaching environments in which every effort was made to restrict external environmental cues. For example, the child was taught in a booth that had bare walls and a complete absence of pictures and other objects. In other words, there was nothing to distract the child from the task at hand. The "brain-damaged child" tended to become equated with the "hyperkinetic child," both of whom needed as much freedom from distracting influences as possible.

It must be noted, however, that adequate criteria for establishing brain damage in either of these groups were essentially absent. More critically, as noted by Birch (1964), the diagnoses of brain damage were established largely on the basis of the child's behavioral manifestations rather than by any direct evidence of structural, physiological, or neurochemical abnormalities. Citing Strauss and Lehtinen (1947), Birch commented that, "The 'simplistic' view in its extreme form appears in the work of Strauss and Lehtinen (1947), who have stated that 'all brain lesions, wherever localized, are followed by a similar kind of disordered behavior.'"

Birch indicated that, "In addition to those children who are identified by pathologic patterns of behavior and whose functioning is characterized by difficulties in figure-ground perception, abnormal distractibility, perseverative tendencies, conceptual rigidity, emotional lability, hyperactivity, and motor awkwardness, there are several other varieties of behavioral disturbances that may accompany damage to the central nervous system. These patterns may range from relatively simple subtractive dysfunctions manifested in overall mental deficiency to patterns of personality disturbance arising from difficulties in impulse control or from disturbances in the development of body boundaries that in certain instances result in the development of patterns of dysfunction that in a clinical setting are phenomenally identical with childhood psychoses."

Obviously, by the time Birch made these comments in 1964, it had become necessary to attempt to counteract the impression, engendered initially by the work of Strauss and Werner, that any type of brain lesion in a child resulted in a complex but standard manifestation of behavioral disturbances.

It is interesting to observe how the clinical observations and experimental studies of Strauss and Werner and their associates went directly to classroom application. None of the clinical studies or experimental investigations led to the development of neuropsychological tests or formal examining procedures which could have been applied by the scientific community to many children with cerebral damage (and which, in turn, could have produced a balanced understanding and representation of the types of impairment shown by children with varying neurological conditions). In fact, considering their inadequate criteria to diagnose brain damage, Strauss and Werner actually neglected the question of whether brain damage as an independent variable even existed. In attempting to establish brain-behavior correlations, the early investigators of child neuropsychology essentially ignored the condition of the brain in any rigorous sense. Even though a neurological history was obtained and "soft" signs were considered, the information derived would hardly be a sufficient basis to determine the presence or absence of cerebral damage.

Failure to actually determine which behavioral functions relate to independent biological variables describing the condition of the brain (as contrasted with a hypothetical presumption of how these relationships *should* exist) may have very definite consequences. The writings of Kephart illustrate one of the most striking instances in which brain-behavior relationships were presumed rather than determined empirically.

Kephart had been closely associated with Strauss (Strauss & Kephart, 1955), and along with members of this group had presumed that many of the mentally retarded children who met the criteria for exogenous mental deficiency were brain-damaged children. As we have noted, some of these children undoubtedly did have biological impairment of brain functions; however, among these mentally retarded children it is often impossible to obtain sufficiently detailed information about brain functions to develop independent variables that can be related to behavioral manifestations. Brain damage, as an undivided entity, is entirely too gross a variable to permit understanding of brain-behavior relationships, and more specific information, such as lateralization, localization, type, and process of brain damage is required (Reitan, 1966).

From his observation of children with mental retardation, Kephart presumed that competency in right-left orientation was fundamental to the development of a host of other skills which, in turn, were basic in developing academic abilities. More specifically, he identified right-left orientation as a basic ability underlying the development of perceptual skills generally and the child's ability to deal with temporal and spatial relationships. Kephart presumed that it was perfectly logical that right-left orientation and temporal and spatial abilities were closely intertwined and essentially parts of a single behavioral function. Since he had not studied subjects with documented cerebral lesions, he had no way of knowing that these abilities are quite separate biologically.

The brain clearly distinguishes between these two abilities; right-left orientation is subserved by the left cerebral hemisphere, and skill in dealing with temporal and spatial relationships is subserved by the right cerebral hemisphere (Wheeler & Reitan, 1962). One might, of course, appeal to the integrative function of the two cerebral hemispheres as a basis for relating right-left orientation and ability in temporal and spatial functioning, but one is nevertheless left without documentation of the independence of these two abilities (as demonstrated by their differential dissolution in association with lateralized cerebral damage). In fact, the entire concept of "left brain" and "right brain" has developed on the basis of studying the relationships between the biological functioning of the brain and behavioral manifestations, but these developments were made by researchers in the area of adult neuropsychology who, as we have noted, were much more rigorous in relating brain function to behavior.

We should also point out that Kephart's postulates and conclusions were reached shortly before differences in the function of the two cerebral hemispheres, even among adults, were becoming well recognized. Nevertheless, the presumption that right-left orientation and ability in dealing with temporal and spatial relationships were fundamentally part of the same total process (although the brain treats them as separate entities assigned to each cerebral hemisphere) would scarcely have occurred if there had been a more rigorous requirement of establishing relationships between brain variables and behavioral manifestations.

Kephart (1960) was, in fact, very explicit in his postulates of the relationship between right-left orientation and ability to perform simple tasks such as drawing common figures. He said, "Before he can begin to draw a square, the child must be able to distinguish between his left side and right and to control the two sides of the body separately and simultaneously" (p. 23). After describing the basic steps involved in such a simple task as drawing a square, Kephart commented, "All of these adjustments are problems of laterality." (By laterality Kephart meant right-left orientation.) He went on, "If he is confused as to which is the right side and which is the left side and if he confuses the movement patterns of these two sides, he will have difficulty beginning the task of drawing the square."

Kephart felt that it was necessary to establish competence with right-left orientation in order to develop more extensive abilities in dealing with spatial relationships. He felt that right-left orientation leads to an understanding of directionality, and that kinesthetic awareness of differences of movement of one's body leads to the first appreciation of spatial coordinates, the "chief among these [being] directional differences in the right-left differentiation."

Kephart identified a number of other skills necessary to perform a simple task such as drawing a square, and went on at some length to identify right-left orientation as a fundamental ability that must be learned in order to develop these other skills. In identifying the importance of right-left orientation in this respect he concluded, "The development of laterality is extremely important since it permits us to keep things straight in the world around us."

In addition, Kephart cited the importance of "directionality," which develops from "laterality" as fundamental to learning to read, particularly in terms of the need for differentiating between letters such as *b* and *d*. He stated explicitly that, "Laterality leads to directionality," and went on with a more detailed explanation of the relationship between these variables as follows: "When the child has developed laterality within his own organism and is aware of the right and left sides of his own body, he is ready to project these directional concepts into external space. He learns to translate the right-left discrimination within himself into a right-left discrimination among objects outside himself."

Kephart's book, *The Slow Learner in the Classroom* (1960), was written to assist the classroom teacher in dealing with children who have impaired learning abilities. This volume undoubtedly has been of assistance to teachers. It is entirely possible that specific recommendations for training the child with impaired learning abilities may be effective regardless of whether the conceptual and theoretical notions involved are correct. It is also apparent, however, that it would be desirable to develop theoretical positions that support the facts already known about brain-behavior relationships. In order to achieve this end it is necessary to know what the brain-behavior relationships actually are, rather than only presume them. Nevertheless, the first 25–30 years of the development of modern child neuropsychology was devoted principally to elucidation of the behavioral side of the equation and, judging from the publications in the area, few if any variables related directly to the biological condition of the brain were deemed necessary.

Benton (1959b), in his detailed investigation of right-left discrimination and finger localization, essentially continued the tradition of studying impaired or defective children as contrasted with children having documented brain disease or damage.

As Kephart had done previously, Benton selected the area of right-left discrimination as a topic for study. Instead of relating defective or impaired performances to conditions of brain dysfunction, Benton, in his investigations of right-left discrimination, reported relationships with age, responsiveness to crossed commands, sex, institutionalization, mental level, mental deficiency, handedness, systematic reversals of correct responses in right-left discrimination, and reading disability. He also studied interrelationships among deviant performances, attempting to determine the degree of association or independence of various deficits.

Studying the interrelationships among specific symptoms or deficits without first investigating the general effects of impaired brain functions may well lead to an attribution of a causal relationship between specific deficits, when in actuality a third factor (such as general impairment due to brain damage) may be responsible for both deficits. Obviously, the fact that two deficits may be consistently present in impaired persons does not prove that one deficit causes the other. Thus, there are potential problems in studying specific deficits without establishing a more general context such as the presence or absence of cerebral damage. Benton's comment about the study he did with Kemble (referred to but not referenced in Benton, 1959b) investigating the relationship between right-left discrimination and reading disability exemplifies this problem. Benton (1959b) interprets the results to indicate that, "Much of the deviant responsiveness observed in children with reading disability may be attributable to systematic reversal in right-left discrimination on the part of these children rather than to a basic inability to discriminate between the right and left sides of one's body" (p. 56).

As noted, Benton and his associates studied the relationship between right-left discrimination and a considerable number of factors. In one study, he investigated 158 normal school children (Benton, 1955a) and in another investigation of mental retardation he considered 110 "defective" children (Benton, 1955b). Nevertheless, when discussing children with actual brain damage, Benton (1959b) commented, "My series is as yet too small to provide a stable estimate of the over-all incidence of specific developmental deficit in this category of patient" (p. 54). It was apparent that even though he had no findings or conclusions to report, Benton had begun to realize that it was important to study subjects with known brain lesions (since he at least referred to children in this category).

The same situation existed with Benton's study of finger localization (Benton, 1959a). Variables such as age, sex, mental level, arithmetical ability, mental deficiency, and relationship of finger agnosia to finger praxis were all supported with data and conclusions were reached. However, in reporting on actual brain damage, Benton indicated that this topic ". . . is one of obvious clinical and theoretic interest, but, as proved to be the case with right-left discrimination, there is a dearth of empirical data on it" (pp. 86–87). He went on to say, "Unfortunately, from a quantitative standpoint, my series is as yet inadequate to answer the question of whether an unduly high incidence of impaired finger localization can be expected in this category of patients; hence, the issue of the clinical significance of defective performance in this respect remains open."

Insofar as the results of these investigations are concerned, the issue of right-left discrimination and finger localization as meaningful variables in the area of clinical neuropsychology remained an open question. In spite of the extensive studies that related impairment on these variables to a number of other circumstances and conditions which may or may not have reflected the biological condition of the brain, it was not established whether these variables were valid indicators of impaired brain function.

Benton (1959b) went on to consider the relationship between right-left disorientation and finger agnosia to other types of specific deficits. However, this section of his book was based entirely on a review of adult literature, and therefore had nothing directly to do with child neuropsychology. It is noteworthy, however, that in this section (concerned with acquired rather than developmental impairment) Benton had no material of his own to present, based either on groups or individual cases.

Benton found that both right-left disorientation and finger agnosia, as indicated by the adult literature, were shown by clinical examination to be found frequently in the concurrent presence of some degree of mental retardation, aphasia (with no mention of lateralized cerebral involvement), autotopagnosia or body agnosia, agraphia, acalculia, alexia, constructional dyspraxia, visual disorientation or visuospatial agnosia, color agnosia, and indifference to pain. Benton raised a question of whether this array of deficits might properly be called the "parietal symptom-complex," but he did not mention whether the symptom complex would be associated with left or right parietal damage.

Although Benton reported no studies of his own that were concerned with patients having well-described documented cerebral lesions, he had investigated psychotic patients in addition to the normals and mentally retarded subjects that were previously reported. Benton and Abramson (1952) studied 34 adult psychotic patients, most of whom were schizophrenic, and found no evidence of right-left disorientation or finger agnosia. However, Goodstein (1957), using a more difficult examination for finger localization, found fairly frequent evidence of finger agnosia in a group of 42 schizophrenic patients, but he found only one instance of moderately defective performance concerning right-left discrimination in this group of subjects.

Benton provided a detailed review of the development of ability in right-left orientation and finger localization based on his studies of normal and mentally retarded children. He discussed the influence of determining factors, such as the knowledge of the right-left gradient of the body schema (and finger schema) or defects in symbolic thinking on the developmental course in normal and mentally retarded children. It should be noted again, however, that none of these data, which were concerned with a conceptual understanding of these deficits, was based on children with documented cerebral lesions.

In terms of neuropathological correlates, Benton depended entirely upon the adult literature and presented none of his own data. He concluded that bilateral finger agnosia and a pervasive type of right-left disorientation were associated with bilateral disease of the parietal or parietal-occipital areas. He noted that these conditions might also occur with damage of the "dominant hemisphere" (presumably the left hemisphere), but felt that right-left disorientation, when associated with unilateral cerebral disease or damage, was of a more simple type. He also noted that unilateral finger agnosia might be observed clinically, but in such cases it was related to "a more general psychosensory impairment of the hand and arm." It is interesting that Benton did not relate unilateral finger agnosia to involvement of the contralateral parietal area, but such conclusions would have required data based on subjects with documented brain lesions.

It is clear from this review that in right-left orientation and finger localization a complete dissociation occurred in children as contrasted with adults. Regarding children, Benton had no conclusions to offer about the relationship of the deficit to neurological factors such as localization or lateralization of damage. This was not unexpected, considering the fact that he apparently had no information about the neurological status of the children he studied. When Benton referred to neurological correlates, it was necessary for him to turn entirely to the adult neurological literature (including a study by Heimburger, DeMyer, & Reitan [1964]). It is obvious that Benton's review of the literature, extending over more than half a century, would not provide an adequate basis for consistent or definitive conclusions. For example, there was hardly any mention of the relationship of the deficits in question to lateralization of cerebral functions, and correlations of these conditions were related more closely to concepts such as "knowledge of the right-left gradient of the body schema" or "knowledge of finger schema" than to neurological variables such as left, right, or generalized cerebral damage or even to more specific areas within each cerebral hemisphere.

One must conclude that it is nearly impossible to gain a clear understanding of brain-behavior relationships when only the behavioral aspect of the correlation has been studied and no direct information about the biological condition of the brain is available. Nevertheless, this had been the initial approach in the field of child neuropsychology, and was perpetuated by Benton and others even as late as 1959.

As another example of work being done in child neuropsychology, Taylor (1959) published a volume in which she presented psychological test performances of eight children (Part 1) and an extensive description of a great variety of techniques and tests for psychological examination (Part 2).

The case presentations (or "case portraits," as Taylor called them) included four children with perinatal brain lesions (three cases of cerebral palsy and one case of hydrocephalus) and three children with brain damage sustained after birth (one case each of meningitis at 6 months of age, measles encephalitis at 5 years of age, and head injury at 7 years of age). Follow-up examinations of each of these children were presented, but the principal emphasis was to describe the child's reactions to and performances on a variety of psychological tests. Thus, these case presentations largely reflected the fact that children with cerebral damage may demonstrate a considerable degree of impairment.

Case illustrations may be of value when presented in the context of an organized body of knowledge, especially when the descriptive data is sufficient in and of itself to permit prediction of brain damage or dysfunction on the basis of the neuropsychological measurements alone. In such instances the case presentations serve to validate in clinical application specific features or principles of the organized body of knowledge. Taylor (1959), however, merely demonstrated that a small group of children with heterogeneous brain damage had difficulties on certain psychological tests.

Although current investigative work continues to neglect the *neuro* aspect of neuropsychology, there also have been many recent studies which quite ably relate the biological condition of the brain to behavioral or psychological functions (Chadwick, Rutter, Shaffer, & Shrout, 1981; Chadwick, Rutter, Thompson, & Shaffer, 1981; Klonoff & Paris, 1974; McFie, 1961; Rutter, 1981).

However, investigations conducted by Barbara C. Wilson and her colleagues (Wilson & Risucci, 1986; Wilson & Wilson, 1978) on the neuropsychology of children with developmental language disorder (DLD) still represent the former category. These studies have an organization and approach that are of distinct value in terms of producing psychological knowledge about children with developmental language disorder (DLD), but have no demonstrated neuropsychological value.

Wilson and Wilson (1978) used a number of tests to measure cognitive, linguistic, perceptual, and memory abilities, and devised a method for presenting each child's test results according to ten behavioral "factors." This permitted the construction of a profile for each child which the authors consider to be useful for planning individual treatment and education programs. Thus far the procedure and plan seem very promising. However, a review of the tests on which the ten factors are based reveals that none of the tests has been carefully studied in terms of sensitivity to brain damage or impairment. They are not validated as neuropsychological tests, and essentially no information was derived that relates to brain functions in terms of either general or specific referents.

Wilson and Risucci (1986) proposed the criteria used to identify the children with DLD as follows: Absence of "frank brain damage" such as cerebral palsy, as well as absence of mental retardation, primary emotional disturbance, primary attention deficit disorder, or a hearing impairment sufficiently severe to account for the language deficit. These criteria are all exclusionary except for evidence of limited language skills, and none of the criteria establishes evidence of cerebral damage any more convincingly than did the criteria for exogenous mental deficiency proposed nearly 50 years earlier by Strauss and Werner (1941). Nevertheless, like Strauss and Werner, Wilson and her colleagues discuss their findings in a neuropsychological context, raising such questions as whether " . . . there are subtypes whose primary 'language' deficit is not at the cognitive-linguistic cortical level but, rather at the 'processing' subcortical level" (Wilson & Risucci, 1986). It might have been advisable for these investigators to have first determined that their results were at the "brain level" before raising more specific questions.

In 1951, at the Indiana University Medical Center, Reitan started his laboratory for the study of brain-behavior relationships in both adults and children. Reitan had the advantage of training in methods of adult clinical neuropsychology under the direction of Ward Halstead at the University of Chicago. From the time he started his laboratory in 1935, Halstead had established close working relationships with neurologists, neurological surgeons, and neuropathologists, and he realized that this was necessary in order to obtain the most comprehensive medical information available about the brains of the individuals he studied. As Halstead discussed in his 1947 book, *Brain and Intelligence*, he was able to obtain detailed information about both the type of lesion and its location which, in turn, was carefully mapped in gross terms on brain-lesion charts.

Reitan had therefore been exposed to and appreciated the importance of the contribution made by specialists in the neurological sciences, including careful and detailed histories and physical neurological examinations, findings from specialized neurological diagnostic techniques (such as electroencephalography, air studies, and cerebral angiograms), recorded observations by the surgeon at the time of operation on the brain, detailed mapping of the location of the lesion, examination of tissue specimens by expert neuropathologists to identify the type of lesion involved and, in some cases, examination of the brain and reconstruction of the lesion from information gained at autopsy. These were viewed as standard procedures necessary in order to establish relationships between the condition of the brain and psychological measurements. In fact, the opportunity for collaborative assistance from neurologists, neurological surgeons, and neuropathologists was viewed by Reitan as a primary and necessary condition for establishing a neuropsychological research program. It seemed clear that a meaningful concept of child clinical neuropsychology required detailed information about the biological and pathological condition of the brain as well as extensive evaluations of the individual's behavioral and psychological functions.

In addition to a neurological evaluation, it was important to have an opportunity to perform an extensive series of neuropsychological examinations on every subject in order to reflect the varied abilities that probably were subserved by the brain. Only in this way did it seem likely that neuropsychological methods of investigation could be developed in which respect was shown for the "neuro" as well as the "psychological" factors that were important, together with establishing relationships between these two aspects.

Following Halstead's advice, Reitan accumulated information about the relationships between the brain and behavior of individual subjects by recording postulates or inferences about the condition of the brain based initially on the neuropsychological test results alone. After a "blind interpretation" was written for each individual subject (for a firm documentation), the code was "broken" by turning to the complete neurological and neuropathological information that had been acquired through the diagnostic and therapeutic skills of neurologists, neurosurgeons, and neuropathologists.

In the early phases of this work the inferences regarding the condition of the brain, based on the psychological test results alone, were sometimes in serious error. However, using this procedure helped greatly to identify the aspects of the test results that were of critical (as contrasted with associational) significance in determining the relevant aspects of brain pathology.

During the course of this procedure it was necessary to perform comparable examinations on non-brain-damaged control subjects. These kinds of approaches helped identify principles and methodological approaches that established valid and reliable relationships between the status of the brain and behavioral (neuropsychological) measurements. The data which was collected served as the basis for many formal research studies, many of which are summarized in Chapter VII.

After having developed an understanding of the test results as they related to the condition of the brain and the methodological approaches that complemented clinical interpretation, it became possible to address meaningful neuropsychological research questions concerning other groups of children, such as those with mental retardation and learning disabilities, for whom direct information about the condition of the brain is not available from the neurological sciences. Initially, however, it was imperative that knowledge was developed both in terms of methodological aspects of approach as well as in substantive content regarding brain-behavior relationships before a meaningful neuropsychological approach could be followed in groups of subjects whose diagnostic condition was determined on the basis of behavioral rather than neurological findings. Extension of validated neuropsychological studies to such areas are well illustrated in the area of mental retardation by Matthews (1974), in the area of learning disabilities by the excellent contributions of Gaddes (1980), Knights and Bakker (1976), Rourke, Bakker, Fisk, and Strang (1983), and Rourke, Fisk, and Strang (1986), and in the area of reading disabilities (Doehring, 1968; Doehring, Trites, Patel, & Fiedorowicz, 1981).

Problems in Child Clinical Neuropsychology Which Have Resulted from Inadequate Documentation of the Neurological Bases of Behavior

As we have documented above, brain-behavior relationships in children were studied initially principally in subjects in whom direct knowledge of brain functions was essentially missing. Even in cases in which it was verified that a child had brain damage, conclusions were drawn from behavioral evaluations that represented highly specific or extremely limited types of behavior. The inconsistent and conflicted knowledge derived from these approaches was often then elaborated to represent the neuropsychology of conditions such as minimal brain dysfunction and learning disabilities, thus effectively broadening and spreading the confusion.

After the field was entrenched in generalizations and misconceptions, researchers finally began to pay attention to the "brain" aspect of the brain-behavior equation, and ensured that definitive evidence of cerebral disease or damage was present in the children they compared to normal control children. In addition, a considerable number of behavioral (psychological) tests was included to assess at least a moderate range of abilities and skills of each child. Although the question being investigated concerned brain-behavior relationships, most of the studies in this area done during the first thirty years failed to define adequately either the "brain" or the "behavior" aspects of the question. Retrospectively, it seems hardly surprising that the result of the investigations was confusion, and progress was inadequate until the variables to be related were identified.

The reader may be inclined to wonder if such an indictment of the early researchers in child neuropsychology could possibly be accurate, considering the apparent simplicity of the required approach. Later in this chapter we will review many of the specifics which support such a conclusion. It seems obvious that neuropsychology requires correlation of both neurological and psychological events or variables, but even today an inclination to ignore (or presume) one or more aspects of the problem continues to be prominent in the field (Reitan, 1988). In contrast, the field of adult neuropsychology had beginnings which were firmly and explicitly grounded in both "neuro" and "psychological" variables, and the type of confusion repeatedly

demonstrated in child neuropsychology (regarding categories such as *minimal brain dysfunction* and *learning disabilities*)
has never evolved.

In this introduction we can document the confusion,
briefly and compellingly, by reference to (1) the concept of
minimal brain dysfunction, and (2) the long-term neuropsychological consequences of cerebral damage occurring
early vs. later in childhood.

Pasamanick and Knobloch (1959) observed a range of
clinical manifestations in children, extending from gross
and obvious neurological deficits to behavioral impairment
in which neurological signs were minimal or essentially
absent. These researchers referred to children in the latter
category as having *minimal brain dysfunction.* Shortly afterwards Clements and Peters (1962) published a description
of behavioral disorders that characterized children who had
minimal brain dysfunction.

Kessler (1980) has presented a knowledgeable review of
the development and history of minimal brain dysfunction,
noting that many sentiments of the time led to the proposals
for the term's adoption. Such reasons included rejection of a
persisting tendency to attribute deviant behavior and learning deficiencies to environmental factors (even when no
such specific factors could actually be implicated); a tendency to believe that all complex behavior and learning
skills emanated from brain functions (and therefore disorders of many kinds could be attributed to brain impairment); and even a desire to absolve parents of blame in
instances where their influences upon the child did not
seem adverse.

As Kessler (1980) points out, even organized scientific
and educational activities, such as those sponsored by the
National Institute of Neurological Diseases and Blindness
(Clements, 1966; de la Cruz, Fox, & Roberts, 1973), had a
considerable influence on adoption of the term *minimal brain
dysfunction.* While serving on a planning committee for a

major meeting on minimal brain dysfunction sponsored jointly by two of the National Institutes of Health and the New York Academy of Sciences, one of the authors (RMR) proposed that the members define the condition in question before planning the details of a conference on the condition. The response from a pediatrician, who was a high ranking government health official, was representative of the group: "Oh, don't start that. We all know who these children are."

Nevertheless, some researchers (Benton, 1973) protested that the diagnosis should be *major* rather than *minimal* brain dysfunction (considering the severe behavioral disorders frequently included) and others suggested that the term *minimal* might be considered to relate to evidence of brain dysfunction as compared with behavioral dysfunction (Gomez, 1967). The diagnosis became relatively entrenched, and many studies of minimal brain damage appeared (de la Cruz, Fox, & Roberts, 1973).

Finally, in 1980 the *Handbook of Minimal Brain Dysfunctions: A Critical View* (Rie & Rie, 1980) was published. The editors prefaced the volume by stating, "It is now painfully obvious that no single minimal brain dysfunction exists and that the literature is characterized by a plethora of unsubstantiated assumptions and, relatively speaking, a dearth of fact. Few foci of professional interest have generated such strength of feeling and such diverse response. In contrast to those who write confidently about the nature and treatment of MBD, others urge that we discard the designation as useless and misleading, if not destructive . . . There is no *syndrome* of minimal brain dysfunction; there are any number of determinants of hyperactive behavior; learning disorders occur for many different reasons."

It would appear that the diagnostic classification *minimal brain dysfunction* was proposed without adequate documentation of criteria to support the diagnosis, either in terms of the "brain" or "behavior" aspect of the designation. While the efforts of individual scientists were responsible for the creation of the diagnosis initially, organizational and institutional efforts fostered and nourished the presumed condition of minimal brain dysfunction. As noted earlier, major resources of the National Institutes of Health were devoted to a large professional meeting and a resulting publication about this syndrome, a syndrome which Rie and Rie (1980) later concluded does not exist.

Even though lacking something in timeliness, it should be noted that the volume edited by Rie and Rie did include a great deal of useful information about behavioral problems and learning disorders in children. However, it took us nearly 20 years to learn how little we knew about a major diagnostic category (minimal brain dysfunction). One must wonder about the base of knowledge that permits such scientific fumbling for so many years.

Even today, do we really have a base of knowledge about the psychological consequences of neurological disorders in children? It continues to be painfully clear that in order to gain reliable knowledge of the neuropsychology of children it is necessary to develop an understanding of the relationships between the brain and behavior by using well-defined groups of children with cerebral damage or disease and contrast and compare them with children having normal brain functions.

Of course, procedures such as positron emission tomography (PET) can identify important aspects of brain function in normal children. But it is critical to identify the relevant dimensions of brain functions in children in order to correlate them with behavioral manifestations.

The second issue that we wish to consider, especially concerning differences in opinions or conclusions, is the matter of plasticity and potential for recovery of functions following cerebral damage early in childhood vs. later in childhood. Kennard (1936, 1938, 1940, 1942) reported that following imposition of cerebral cortical damage, relative sparing of deficit and recovery of motor functions occurred much more readily in infantile monkeys than in adult monkeys. This phenomenon, known as the "Kennard Principle," led Teuber (1976, cited in Rudel, 1978) to comment during a conference on the effects of head trauma in human beings that if it were necessary to sustain brain damage as a result of a head injury, one would be wise to have the head injury in childhood rather than in adulthood in order to escape deleterious effects.

As we will discuss in Chapter II, plasticity of brain functions is an extremely complex issue that involves many variables. It is a critically important issue in the field of child clinical neuropsychology, but researchers investigating this problem have reported quite different conclusions.

In the *Journal of Consulting and Clinical Psychology*, Chelune and Edwards (1981) published a review of the literature that focused on the effects of early vs. later brain lesions. In their discussion of plasticity and recovery of function they concluded, "The earlier brain damage is sustained in life, the less deleterious its eventual impact on behavior than similar damage incurred by the mature brain." To substantiate their claim they referred to "excellent reviews" by Kertesz (1979), Stein, Rosen and Butters (1974), and Hécaen and Albert (1978).

These authors did note, however, that many variables could influence the eventual outcome of early-vs.-late-occurring lesions, citing Reitan (1974), whose studies documented that early brain lesions interfere with normal acquisition of skills during the developmental years, and lesions sustained by adults tend to result in the loss of previously acquired skills. Reitan's investigations clearly documented that lesions sustained early in life may have an especially devastating consequence on the eventual acquisition of higher-level psychological functions; the damaged brain has a limited potential to acquire such skills. Despite this evidence, the central theme of Chelune and Edward's review, at least in this respect, is essentially in agreement with the Kennard principle.

In the same issue of the *Journal of Consulting and Clinical Psychology,* Satz and Fletcher (1981) present a discussion of the review by Chelune and Edwards. They point out that, "[the authors] present the traditional view that brain lesions in young organisms are associated with better behavioral recovery because the immature brain is more 'plastic' than the mature brain." Satz and Fletcher express concern about using age as a relevant variable rather than the pathological characteristics of the lesion and the types of physiological reactions, both adverse and reparative, that occur following a biological insult (see Reitan & Wolfson, 1988b for a more complete description of reaction to injury and the processes of repair and biological recovery).

Satz and Fletcher (1981) also objected to use of the term *plasticity* without a more compelling definition than the one provided by Chelune and Edwards. In fact, they cite St. James-Roberts (1979) as having noted that, "The authority with which the plasticity viewpoint is endowed stands in marked contrast to the equivocality of the evidence on which it is based." They also note that Isaacson (1975) described recovery from brain damage early in childhood as a "myth." In conclusion, Satz and Fletcher state that it is clear that recovery of function following damage early in childhood as compared with later in life is much more controversial than implied by Chelune and Edwards.

This brief review of plasticity of brain functions makes it quite clear that professional opinions about this topic, expressed even in the same issue of a particular journal, stand in rather striking contrast. While there has been a great amount of animal work devoted to this problem (beginning with the studies of Kennard and followed by many additional investigations [as reviewed by Reitan, 1985]), there are few studies comparing neuropsychological outcome at a given age among children who sustained cerebral damage early in life with children who sustained cerebral damage at an older age. Obviously, the question is an empirical one which could be answered by appropriately designed experimental investigations.

Curiously, in the area of child clinical neuropsychology, important issues of this kind seem to be dealt with by force of argument and the authority of cited opinions. In Chapter II of this volume we will provide the reader with additional information regarding the brain's potential for recovery and contrast the neuropsychological consequences of cerebral damage sustained by young children, older children, and adults.

In our judgment, the field of child neuropsychology had an unfortunate beginning which has placed it at a disadvantage as compared with adult neuropsychology. First, as we have stressed repeatedly, in its very beginnings adult neuropsychology emphasized the importance of describing and delineating the independent variables which reflect the biological condition of the brain and thereby permit correlation of dependent (behavioral and/or psychological) variables with brain status. Admittedly, the pathological conditions that occur in children may not generate the range of categories that occur in adults, and the problem of developing brain-related abilities during the early years also complicates (if not obfuscates) establishment of brain-behavior relationships. Nevertheless, such problems scarcely represent an excuse for failing to delineate the *neuro* aspect of the neuropsychological equation.

The psychological part of this equation (represented by dependent variables) may constitute an even more significant reason for the inadequate beginning and development of child neuropsychology. First, the psychological manifestations of supposedly impaired brain functions were shown almost exclusively in the form of experiments (experimental child neuropsychology) as opposed to standardized testing procedures that can be widely used and replicated repeatedly (clinical child neuropsychology). Experimental neuropsychology has been extremely valuable in the adult area (see the review of Teuber's work on traumatic brain injury in Reitan & Wolfson [1986]), but experimental work alone would never have had the impact necessary to develop the field without the emergence of standardized clinical tests which could be used in the same way by hundreds of different clinicians.

Reitan (1966, 1988) has previously compared and contrasted the aims and contributions of experimental and clinical neuropsychology. While these two areas are quite different in many respects, they can and should have a strong complementary force. In child neuropsychology standard tests were essentially not available until Reitan began developing the Battery described in this volume. In the meantime, experimental child neuropsychology, principally of Strauss and Werner, was far overreaching its validity in application unchecked by the balances, imposed by the scientific community, that arise from widespread use of formal clinical tests.

We recognize that there is merit in experimental as well as clinical child neuropsychology; however, either area can get significantly out of balance without the other, resulting in a serious distortion of the dependent variables in the brain-behavior equation.

■

CHAPTER II

Outcome Following Brain Injury in Childhood

Plasticity of the Immature Brain

Finger and Stein (1982) have written extensively on the biological effects of brain damage, including primary and secondary effects, progressive changes at the molecular level, and behavioral recovery. In discussing the physiological plasticity of the brain, they say, "Although there are many changes in cerebral function and anatomy that follow injury, there is no certainty that *any* [italics added] of the morphological alterations that do occur are related to functional recovery" (p. 103).

The question of "plasticity" concerns the potential for adaptation from insult. The biological changes associated with many types of brain lesions have been studied in detail (e.g., neoplasms: Butler, Brooks, & Netsky, 1982; cerebral vascular disease: Barnett, Mohr, Stein, & Yatsu, 1986; degenerative disease: Katzman, Terry, DeTeresa, et al., 1988). In discussions of plasticity the major condition that receives

31

attention is traumatic injury or insult, because of the recovery potential that exists. In many other conditions the pathological involvement is an ongoing disease process which, by reason of its pathological nature and the lack of effective treatment, limits or precludes adaptation or recovery.

The primary and secondary effects of brain trauma have been extensively reviewed at both a gross and cellular level in terms of morphological and functional (electrophysiological and biochemical) changes (Becker, Miller, Young et al., 1982; Finger & Stein, 1982; Miller & Becker, 1982; Reitan & Wolfson, 1988b). At this point we will review briefly the primary and secondary effects of brain trauma and the biological mechanisms involved in the recovery process.

Primary and Secondary Effects of Brain Trauma

Primary or direct damage to brain tissue occurs as a result of the initial impact to the cerebrum and is represented by injury to neurons, supporting cells, and blood vessels. Significant blows to the head routinely cause generalized and widespread cerebral damage as well as focal damage. Primary damage may result from penetration, pressure gradients, and rotational and shearing forces (especially involving areas where the brain is compressed within the skull or where the brain has been torn over rough surfaces on the inner surface of the skull).

Secondary effects of primary damage may also occur and result in further serious and significant damage. Secondary damage is caused by bleeding and edema. Bleeding may be focal, as in hemorrhages and contusions, or may be in the form of widespread petechial hemorrhages. Brain edema may be relatively focal and clearly involve one cerebral hemisphere more than the other, but often the swelling is widespread in nature.

Because the skull is an inflexible structure, swelling of cerebral tissue in one area displaces tissue in some other area and may result in permanent and even fatal consequences. Tearing of brain tissue over the tentorium as a result of brain edema, compression of tissues, and even displacement of brain tissues through the foramen magnum all represent important mechanisms of secondary damage. Obviously, the primary and secondary effects of traumatic injury determine the severity of the damage and thus are highly pertinent to the potential for recovery.

In addition to the primary and secondary pathological effects of brain trauma, adverse influences on cellular mechanisms may also occur. These involve particularly the interruption of axonal transport and axoplasmic flow within the neuron. This impairment of normal metabolic functions causes changes within the cell body and degeneration of axons and dendrites. These metabolic changes may be sufficiently severe to cause death of the neuron.

Impairment of function or death of the neuron affects synaptic interactions by limiting mediation of both electrical signals and nutritive (trophic) interactions between neurons. Damage to the neuron as well as impairment of its synaptic interactions may result in atrophy and degenerative changes in other neurons that receive synaptic transmission from the damaged neurons. As researchers have demonstrated (particularly in the sequence of neurons that constitute the visual system), these transneuronal changes may have adverse effects at distant sites.

Mechanisms of Recovery Following Brain Trauma

Mechanisms of Short-Term Recovery

Supporting cells, which consist mainly of glial cells (oligodendrocytes, astrocytes, ependymal cells, and microglia), proliferate following an injury and are involved in absorbing the cellular debris and toxic products of degeneration and necrosis. These cells function as phagocytes, and in this sense have the positive effect of removing damaged and necrotic tissue.

However, the proliferation of these supporting cells also may create a problem. Within the central nervous system there is a tendency for neurons to regenerate and attempt to re-establish connections that were disrupted by the injury, and this proliferation of glial cells tends to block effective restoration of synaptic connections. In other words, the rapid proliferation of glial cells interferes with the ability of damaged neurons to re-establish their prior connections.

This fact has led to the often-stated conclusion that functional regeneration within the central nervous system is not possible. Nevertheless, there definitely are short-term recovery functions represented by biological repair (especially in the form of redevelopment of vascularization and diminution of swelling) that may lead to a restoration of physiologic processes. Restored vascularization particularly may result in improved cerebral oxygenation and recovery of tissue that has been damaged but not destroyed.

Thus, the short-term biological recovery and repair processes definitely can serve as a basis for improvement of function of the damaged brain tissue. However, these processes are essentially completed in a relatively short time, usually within the first month post-injury. In fact, in many persons who have sustained a brain injury, these short-term recovery processes are probably essentially complete either by the time the patient is ready for discharge from the hospital or soon afterwards. Nevertheless, as experienced clinicians have observed, the recovery of functions and general improvement of intellectual and cognitive abilities continues for a much longer period of time.

Mechanisms of Long-term Recovery

Several types of biological response to injury have been proposed, including (1) sprouting, (2) incomplete destruction of the damaged system, (3) generation of new electrical potentials through activation of "latent" synapses or a compensatory increase of excitability, and (4) the concept of redundancy, or the existence of alternate systems or circuits in the brain which can "take over" the impaired functions.

Sprouting of the severed end of the proximal portion of a sectioned neuron has been observed some time after degeneration of the distal portion of the axon has been completed. In the peripheral nervous system these sprouts at the end of the severed axon grow, and apparently guided by Schwann cells, may eventually reach the original effector organ and bring about restitution of the original function. Even though sprouts are emitted from severed axons in the central nervous system, the same mechanism leading to functional reconnections does not seem to occur. The proliferation of glial cells in response to injury and tissue destruction interferes with the functional growth necessary to re-establish the original connections. Even though sprouting of severed central axons may establish some connections, the original input may be lost, the organization of neurons is frequently incorrect, and physiologically functional reconnections are probably minimal.

The complexity of the interconnections of the central nervous system is immense, and even axons which are close to each other may have quite different functions. Thus, even when an axonal sprout does re-establish a connection, a different neurological function might be produced, and rather than achieve restoration of the initial function there might actually be an introduction of a deviant or even disadvantageous function. Although sprouting of severed central axons occurs, and this mechanism must be considered as a possible biological basis for recovery, little information is known about its actual role.

The second basis for recovery concerns the possibility of incomplete destruction of a damaged area or system. Most brain lesions are probably similar in terms of having an area of principal destruction and pathology and a peripheral area of damaged but not totally destroyed tissue which eventually extends into normal tissue. This is almost certainly true, despite the definite distance effects which occur on a transneuronal basis or, with many lesions, on a secondary basis. Even conditions which are not represented by focal lesions must be considered to have the potential for impairment of nerve tissue with eventual return of function.

The basis for this type of recovery, however, concerns repair processes which depend upon vascular and metabolic functions. These changes involve short-term repair and recovery processes which are probably essentially completed within weeks of the initial damage. Thus, this mechanism would not explain the long-term improvement over several months shown by many persons with cerebral injury.

A possible mechanism of activation of "latent" synapses or a compensatory increase of excitability may represent a response to injury that is relevant to recovery of functions. Experiments by Wall and his colleagues (Dostrovosky, Millar, & Wall, 1976) illustrate this phenomenon. In studying the function of cells within the spinal cord after cutting peripheral nerve fibers, these investigators have found evidence that circumstances which decrease input activity may result in a compensatory increase of excitability. In other words, it may be possible that synapses which have not been destroyed by a lesion can be brought to a state of increased action through mechanisms which are not fully understood.

It appears that there is some type of homeostatic mechanism whereby a partial loss of input produces a compensatory reaction which permits the diminished input to have an increased synaptic effectiveness. Regardless of whether this increase is brought about by morphological change, a change of substances transported along the axon, or other physiological mechanisms, an increased excitability within the central nervous system, instigated by a decrease of input activity, would represent an adjustment that could be of considerable significance concerning the recovery process.

None of the preceding mechanisms would appear to differ in the immature vs. the mature brain. The concept of redundancy of brain tissue, however, based upon the postulate that alternate circuits or systems exist in the brain which may assume the function of the destroyed tissue, *may well differ in children* as compared to adults. This notion, in turn, relates to the frequent contention that only a small fraction of the large number of neurons in the brain is actually used. The redundancy concept presumes that there is a substantial number of neurons essentially "in reserve," ready to become active when the original system of neurons is damaged or destroyed.

There is, in fact, evidence indicating that such a system, which implies a significant degree of plasticity or interchangeability of functions for neurons in various parts of the brain, may exist in the developmental process of the immature organism. Thus, children with a totally atrophic or amputated cerebral hemisphere may still develop some of the cognitive functions that would normally be subserved by the absent cerebral hemisphere. In other words, the neuropsychological effects of a damaged or limited immature brain may be quite different from the effects of a lesion imposed on a mature or adult brain. In addition, the process of developing cognitive abilities with a damaged or limited brain is quite different from the process of developing such abilities with a normal brain (Reitan, 1985).

Although the immature brain appears to have a greater degree of flexibility in developing neuropsychological functions than the more crystallized adult brain, our clinical observations suggest that the "redundancy" hypothesis (in the sense that otherwise unused cerebral cortex assumes the function of the impaired cortex) is not supported. The price paid for functional flexibility in the immature brain seems to be a generalized limitation of abilities, including those abilities which in the adult would be associated with the undamaged portions of the cerebral cortex. (See Reitan and Wolfson [1988b] for a more detailed explanation of these possible mechanisms regarding the biological bases of plasticity or potential for recovery of function.)

Age-Dependent Differences in Plasticity of Cerebral Functions

The concept of plasticity of cerebral functions in the immature vs. mature human brain appears therefore to relate to the flexibility among children in the extent to which the cerebral cortex can assume functions normally subserved by a damaged area (or even hemisphere) as contrasted with a more crystallized organization of abilities, characterized by regional-localization, in the adult brain.

The concept of plasticity of cerebral functions, insofar as it implies potential for recovery and development of normal neuropsychological functions, places the immature human brain at a distinct disadvantage (as will be shown in the following pages). The child with perinatal cerebral damage usually fares very poorly in development of higher-level brain functions as a result of having a damaged brain as compared with a normal brain to subserve this development. A reduced amount of cerebral cortex appears to result in a general reduction of neuropsychological abilities, regardless of the greater degree of flexibility of the remaining cortex in assuming various functions.

The Kennard Principle. We referred to the Kennard Principle in Chapter I, noting that there was a definite disagreement about its validity. Margaret Kennard had observed that lesions imposed on the brains of infant monkeys resulted in relative sparing of motor functions, whereas similar lesions imposed on the brains of adult monkeys caused pronounced motor deficits. She concluded that brain lesions were much better tolerated by the immature brain than the mature brain, and postulated that the immature brain had a degree of plasticity which permitted very rapid recovery following damage.

As we noted in Chapter I, Chelune and Edwards (1981), after citing several "excellent reviews," concluded that the earlier brain damage is sustained in life, the less deleterious the eventual impact will be on behavior as compared with the effects of similar damage sustained by the mature brain. However, these authors did note that Reitan (1974) had pointed out that brain lesions sustained by human beings early in life interfere with normal acquisition of skills during the developmental years. Satz and Fletcher (1981), in a discussion of the article by Chelune and Edwards (1981), refer to their position as the "traditional view." They cite Isaacson (1975) and others who suggest that the idea of a rapid and nearly complete recovery from brain damage sustained in early childhood is a myth, and conclude that recovery of function, in accordance with the age at which the lesion was sustained, is a very complex and controversial issue.

Finger and Wolf (1988) have considered Kennard's publications and many other investigations concerned with this question, especially in a historical context. They reviewed experiments concerned not only with evaluation of movement capabilities, but also involving decerebrate rigidity in animals following transection of the brainstem, and evaluated reports of the influence of cerebral lesions on speech and language functions in children as compared with adults. The report by Finger and Wolf makes it clear that many investigators believe that following brain damage children suffer less impairment than adults.

However, as is generally true in neurological (as contrasted with neuropsychological) studies, the focus of attention in this area relates to specific functions rather than to general development of brain-behavior relationships. Motor functions and decerebrate rigidity in animals can hardly be considered comparable to the higher-level brain functions that constitute the most significant aspects of neuropsychological functioning in human beings. The observation that specific aphasic deficits are rarely (if ever) long-term deficits in children as compared with adults does not necessarily imply anything about the consequences of cerebral damage on the development of verbal intelligence of children as they grow into adulthood. Thus, the neurological literature does not serve as an adequate guide for answering this question, and does not controvert neuropsychological evidence of severe impairment in brain-damaged children, as compared with controls, on a wide range of neuropsychological measures.

In a review of studies concerned with recovery potential of the immature as compared with the mature brain, Reitan (1985) noted that it was difficult to believe that the answer to this question, as presented in the literature and apparently as accepted by many clinicians, had depended so heavily upon the results of animal experiments. Although animal studies may be valid and advantageous in answering certain types of questions, the extremely pronounced differences between the ability structure (particularly those abilities concerned with higher-level functions) of lower animals and human beings is tremendous. Animals do not approach human beings in the most significant aspects of brain-related behavior.

There have been relatively few studies comparing children who have sustained cerebral lesions early in life with children who have experienced lesions at a later age. Woods and Carey (1979) compared children who had sustained brain lesions before the age of one year with a group of children who had sustained brain lesions at a mean age of 5.7 years. They found that there were residual deficits even in the group that had sustained brain lesions very early in life.

A second line of evidence concerns comparing brain-damaged children and control children with comparable studies of persons who had not sustained brain lesions until adulthood. Boll (1974) performed such a study among children in the 9- through 14-year age range. He did not deliberately vary the duration of cerebral damage in his experimental group, but many of the children had sustained brain lesions early in life and had acquired intelligence, as measured by the Wechsler Scale, with a damaged brain. The results reported by Boll are shown in Table 2-1.

TABLE 2-1

Summary of Wechsler IQ values reported by Boll (1974) for groups of brain-damaged and control children who were comparable in chronological age (9 through 14 years).

		Brain-damaged	Controls	Mean Difference
Verbal IQ	Mean	79.78	104.89	25.11
Performance IQ	Mean	87.56	109.96	22.40
Full-scale IQ	Mean	81.36	108.22	26.86

The mean IQ values of the brain-damaged children were much lower than the mean IQs of the non-brain-damaged (control) children. The brain-damaged children had a mean Full Scale IQ of 81.36, which was 26.86 points lower than the mean for the controls. The difference between mean values for Verbal IQ was nearly as large, and the difference for Performance IQ was only somewhat smaller. It should be noted that these brain-damaged children were not selected because of severity of damage.

The conditions of these children ranged from quite mild cerebral lesions to seriously destructive lesions, but the criterion was only that every child in the brain-damaged group had definitive evidence of cerebral damage or disease. Conversely, the control group was not selected to be especially competent, and available evidence suggested that the socioeconomic background of the two groups was approximately equivalent. Similar results have been reported by Reitan (1974) for brain-damaged and control children in the 5-through 8-year age range. It would therefore appear that children with independent neurological evidence of brain disease or damage have much lower IQ values than do control children.

Considered by itself, this finding does not contribute to an understanding of the possible differences between adults and children who have sustained cerebral damage. However, we have done a great number of similar studies with adults who had the advantage of normal growth and development prior to sustaining cerebral damage (Dikmen & Reitan, 1976; Doehring & Reitan, 1961; Doehring, Reitan, & Kløve, 1961; Finlayson, Johnson, & Reitan, 1977; Fitzhugh, Fitzhugh, & Reitan, 1962; Herring & Reitan, 1986; Reed & Reitan, 1963; Reitan, 1955a, 1959a, 1960, 1970, 1985b; Reitan & Boll, 1971; Reitan, Reed, & Dyken, 1971). A review of these many studies consistently indicates that the brain-damaged group earns IQ values that are significantly lower than those earned by the controls, and the difference in IQ values customarily is about 10 to 12 points.

The differences in IQ scores noted above for children were customarily more than twice as large as those for adults. Why should brain-damaged children perform so much more poorly as compared with controls than comparable groups of adult subjects? The answer almost certainly lies in the fact that in the studies cited above the brain-damaged adults had normal brains with which to gain their neuropsychological abilities, and their impairment (as compared with adult control groups) reflected a *loss* of previously acquired intellectual functions. Among children, however, the problem is more one of impairment of competence in *acquisition* of intellectual functions as a result of a damaged brain. The difference in level of performance between brain-damaged and control groups of children is certainly not restricted to measures of intellectual function (Wechsler Scale), but is also shown on an extensive range of additional neuropsychological measures (Boll, 1974; Reitan, 1974).

As an additional approach to this question, we went to our files of children with brain damage which had been documented by a complete neurological evaluation. We proceeded through this file to identify the first ten children who, on the basis of the neurological history and findings, had brain injury that dated back to the time of birth. The Full Scale IQ values for these ten children were as follows: 34 (est.), a child that was too impaired to test, 91, 46, 82, 46, 52, 73, 57, and 50. Omitting the child that was so impaired that it was not possible to test him, these values yield a mean Full Scale IQ of 59. For these children the mean Verbal IQ was 63.56 and the mean Performance IQ was 60.44.

Even though this selection of ten children with evidence of perinatal brain damage does not constitute a proper scientific investigation, it certainly does suggest that many children who have definite brain damage at birth demonstrate limited intelligence when tested between the ages of 9 and 14 years. We should note that one of these ten children actually fell within the lower limit of the Average range and another child was in the lower part of the Low Average range. In all of the other eight instances, however, IQ values ranged from the fourth percentile and down. This finding hardly seems consistent with the Kennard Principle, and negates the contention that, if given the choice, it would be wise to sustain brain damage early in life rather than in adulthood in order to escape deleterious effects.

Secondly, when information is sought about neuropsychological development, either among normal or brain-damaged children, it would seem advisable to obtain the appropriate and necessary measurements on human beings rather than upon lower animals. The Kennard Principle was established through study of monkeys, flourished for about forty years, and only at the present time seems to be coming into perspective.

This question concerning neuropsychological development is too important to have been treated with such an incompetent approach. It appears that the long-term outcome in young brain-damaged children relates principally to their ability (or lack of ability) to acquire future neuropsychological functions. In adults the situation principally concerns a loss or impairment of previously developed abilities following brain damage and, to a lesser degree, the acquisition of additional abilities.

Our evaluations of brain-damaged persons over the years suggest that children who sustain brain damage initially in the 9- through 14-year age range have already acquired brain-related abilities to a significant degree in the course of normal development. Thus, they are in a position to suffer impairment of previously existing abilities. However, since the course of normal physical growth and maturation has not been completed, they also are at risk for being able to normally complete their neuropsychological growth.

Although we can propose a general principle only tentatively, our observations strongly suggest that early brain damage usually puts a child on a course of neuropsychological development that runs below that of normal children. The duration of brain damage during the developmental years (or the earlier time at which brain damage occurred) determines the general degree of impairment or deviation from normal children. Among older children there is both a loss of previously acquired abilities and an impairment in the ability to normally acquire future neuropsychological skills. However, the older child suffers less in this latter respect because he/she had the opportunity for normal development during the earlier years.

Factors of this kind seem certainly to have significance, but it must also be remembered that in the individual case cerebral damage is extremely variable and depends on factors such as location, type, extent, and severity of the lesion. Such factors also influence the status of neuropsychological functions for the individual child, with the end result necessarily representing a considerable degree of overlap in neuropsychological abilities with earlier and later cerebral damage.

■

CHAPTER III

Theories of Brain-Behavior Relationships

We have previously reviewed and compared a number of theories of brain-behavior relationships (Reitan, 1988; Reitan & Wolfson, 1988b) and have briefly traced the nature and development of theories over more than the last 100 years (Reitan & Wolfson, 1992a). Our present purpose will be to review certain recent theories that are cast in a developmental framework and to describe the theory of Reitan and Wolfson (Reitan, 1988; Reitan & Wolfson, 1985, 1986, 1988a, 1988b, 1992a) because of its integral relationship to the tests which compose the Halstead-Reitan Neurpsychological Test Battery for Older Children and their clinical interpretation.

The specialized functions of the left and right cerebral hemispheres have had a very pronounced influence on the general concept of brain-behavior relationships (to the detriment of a full appreciation of the critically important non-lateralized neuropsychological functions [see Reitan, Hom & Wolfson, 1988]), and have had a profound influence, to the extent of preoccupation, on developmental theories and the ways in which the specialized functions of the brain develop during the maturational process. Older theories of brain-behavior relationships, such as those of Halstead (1947) and Luria (1970), were proposed before popular attention was so much engaged by right-brain/left-brain differences; consequently, these theories rely upon more general consideration of brain-mediated processes which intervene between stimulus and response.

Review of Specific Neuropsychological Theories

Goldberg and Costa's Theory. Goldberg and Costa (1981) have proposed a neuropsychological theory of brain-behavior relationships that emphasizes the individuality of the left and right cerebral hemispheres. Initially, they review the evidence of neuroanatomical differences between the cerebral hemispheres. Although the two hemispheres appear remarkably similar in gross aspects of structure and are much more alike than they are different (von Bonin, 1962), many studies have indicated that there are fairly consistent anatomical differences between the two cerebral hemispheres. These differences, in turn, provide a temptation for the theorist to search for an anatomical basis for obvious neuropsychological and behavioral differences in the functions of the two cerebral hemispheres.

It must be recognized, however, that it is an extremely difficult task to establish valid relationships between the anatomical uniqueness of each cerebral hemisphere and corresponding behavioral functions. Before one can draw causal connections between two sets of events, it is necessary at least that the data representing those two sets of events be available for the same individuals. This condition is difficult to achieve, because in many respects the anatomical uniqueness of individual brains cannot be well observed without autopsy studies, and behavioral data must be obtained while the subject is alive.

Nevertheless, in their statement of neuropsychological theory, Goldberg and Costa note that fundamental neuro-anatomical differences between the hemispheres can lead to a wide range of cognitive consequences, and that they have explored one of them which appears to be of considerable importance. They propose theoretically that the left cerebral hemisphere ". . . achieves superiority in the utilization of a multiplicity of descriptive systems which are fully formed in an individual's cognitive repertoire and which are relevant to specific classes of materials or tasks." Conversely, the right hemisphere was described as being most crucial in the processing of materials to which none of the descriptive systems pre-existing in a subject's cognitive repertoire is readily applicable and in assembling new descriptive systems.

This conceptualization describes the left cerebral hemisphere as being more capable of unimodal and motor processing as well as storing compact codes, and the right cerebral hemisphere is supposedly more able in performing intermodal integration and in processing novel stimuli. When the individual is involved in the process of acquiring a new descriptive system, the right cerebral hemisphere plays a critical role in the initial stages of acquisition. The left cerebral hemisphere is more able in utilizing codes that are already well-routinized.

These authors become much more specific in attempting to relate the anatomical peculiarities of the left cerebral hemisphere to various aspects of language acquisition. They note that in the left cerebral hemisphere there is a relatively greater representation of the temporal planum, parietal operculum, and pars opercularis of the inferior frontal gyrus, and that these anatomical differences "account for its relatively strong predisposition for elemental phonetic processing." In the right cerebral hemisphere there is a "greater representation of associative zones of intermodal integration," and this presumably "accounts for its relative importance in the formation of the referential basis of semantics."

Syntax may be said to occupy an intermediate position, in that "it is involved in both coordination of the elements of surface structure (for which unimodal learning may be proposed) and also serves a functional role, mastery of which may involve intermodal integration." The necessary but difficult requirement of relating unique aspects of anatomical structure and elements of language acquisition in the same subjects must again be emphasized, especially since it was totally ignored in the above theoretical statement.

Although Goldberg and Costa identify many studies which support their theory, it is important to note that the results of these studies, even when reaching statistical significance, include a very substantial degree of overlap among groups of subjects. In other words, although independent variables may be exclusively represented among the groups used, the results of dependent variables show a great deal of variability within and between groups, even in instances that achieve statistically significant intergroup differences. Therefore, it is an error to treat the conclusions drawn from individual studies as if they were absolute and not subject to a great deal of variability among the subjects on which the principles were established.

Secondly, it is perhaps only natural to select particular points of information from the literature that support one's theoretical position. In one instance, for example, Goldberg and Costa refer to the findings of Semmes (1968) to support their proposed functional differences between the left and right cerebral hemispheres. They state that Semmes proposed that cognitively similar units are represented compactly in the left cerebral hemisphere in contrast to their intermixed representation in the right hemisphere. They use this information with relation to their review of neuroanatomical differences to suggest that these differences "extend to the storage of sets of cognitive elements which may be defined other than on the basis of their sensory modalities."

Certain specific points regarding the study by Semmes are relevant and should be noted. In her study of tactile functioning of the left hand as compared with the right hand and her resulting presumptions concerning responsible cerebral lesions, Semmes used patients with penetrating brain wounds. It is well known that persons with such lesions have extensive and widespread cerebral damage in addition to any evidence of focal involvement (Jennett & Teasdale, 1981). In this kind of material it would be extremely difficult to use findings described as reflecting "compact representation of similar units" vs. "intermixed representation" in the two cerebral hemispheres, with relation to the possible anatomical bases.

To provide further evidence supporting the differential nature of information processing of the two cerebral hemispheres, Goldberg and Costa also use findings derived from the study of patients with commissurotomies as well as persons with congenital absence of the corpus callosum. The authors make no reference to the fact that the brains of most of the commissurotomized patients had evidence of disease or damage early in life, a factor which in its own right may very well have influenced the organization of behavioral correlates of the two hemispheres.

Data from patients with agenesis of the corpus callosum can hardly be thought of as a reflection only of an abnormality of the corpus callosum, with a presumption that the two cerebral hemispheres are normal in other respects. A review of studies of patients with callosal agenesis (Russell & Reitan, 1955) consistently showed that such persons have failed to develop normally, and in addition to having a partial or complete absence of the corpus callosum, demonstrated evidence of generalized impairment of cerebral functions. Case studies reflecting such pathological conditions are hardly appropriate for providing evidence pertinent to theories of normal brain functions.

As noted, Goldberg and Costa cite many additional studies in support of their theory. At this point we cannot undertake to review the relevance of each citation and its limitations, but we must caution the reader that building a theory on the basis of reports in the literature is filled with many hazards. We should also note that this particular theory, even though presented in a developmental context, presents another example of attempting to explain only the specialized functions of the two cerebral hemispheres and certain aspects of their interrelationships.

Goldberg and Costa note that it is an oversimplification to treat the brain as consisting of two separate processors and that they have a "full appreciation of the fact that interaction of the hemispheres occurs in every on-line process . . ." Nevertheless, they feel that it is necessary to specify the roles of the two cerebral hemispheres before building composite models, and that any concept of interaction would have very little value until "it is clearly established what each element is doing in the ensemble."

A "full appreciation" of the interaction of the two hemispheres, claimed by these authors, may be an overstatement when their concept of the generalized aspects of neuropsychological functioning still refers only to "interaction of the hemispheres," and there is no apparent evidence that any effort has been made to discover the types of neuropsychological functions which are diffusely represented throughout the cerebral cortex regardless of which hemisphere is considered.

Rourke's Theory. Rourke (1982) has also proposed a developmental model of brain-behavior relationships, and acknowledges the theory of Goldberg and Costa (1981) as the principal stimulus for his theoretical position. Reitan (1985), in an earlier comment on Rourke's theory said,

"Although Rourke notes that serious students in the area would not contend that an adequate or complete theory of brain-behavior relationships in children is yet possible, he proposes that the right cerebral hemisphere precedes the left cerebral hemisphere in acquisition of abilities." Along with Goldberg and Costa, Rourke believes that the right cerebral hemisphere has a critical role in the initial stages of the acquisition of information, and that the left cerebral hemisphere deals with the details which he identifies as "utilization of routinized codes that flow from the initial acquisitions."

Rourke's theory is embodied in five postulates:

1. An ontogenetic progression occurs in a developmental context for right cerebral functions.

2. Children's conceptualizations progress from global to specific in accordance with the ontogenetic processing between the hemispheres of the brain.

3. Right hemisphere functions must develop initially for adequate functions.

4. Concept formation also follows this right hemisphere-left hemisphere progression, with the right hemisphere involved in the formation of concepts and the left hemisphere in their articulation, elaboration, and stereotypic application.

5. Impairment of right cerebral hemisphere functions is of special significance in limiting the development of adaptive abilities.

These are interesting postulates and are supported in part by some of Rourke's findings in his study of children with learning disabilities. He and his colleagues have reported findings which postulate two groups of learning-disabled children (Rourke & Finlayson, 1978; Rourke & Strang, 1978, 1983). In addition, Rourke reported results which he believes suggest that children with certain types of disabilities (presumably related to the right cerebral hemisphere but not actually so demonstrated) have special problems with the Category Test (Strang & Rourke, 1983).

Rourke has also found that certain reading, spelling, and arithmetical deficits fall into differential patterns for various groups of children with learning disabilities. Although not having direct biological evidence, Rourke has implied that these patterns of deficits relate to differential impairment of the left and right cerebral hemispheres.

Concerning the five postulates that serve as the basis of Rourke's developmental neuropsychological theory, it may be that right cerebral functions must be trained before left hemisphere functions become operative in a practical sense. In support of this proposition, one could refer to the historical development of kindergarten training procedures as a forerunner to education in the use of language symbols for communicational purposes. In all probability, the brain of the young child is more amenable to training and modification in manipulatory and visual-spatial tasks than to training in reading, spelling, writing, and arithmetic. The first point of Rourke's theory seems to be based upon general experience and common sense, even though there is no rigorous scientific evidence to support it.

The second postulate in Rourke's theory, concerned with conceptual development from global to specific in association with right to left hemisphere development, is less well supported. As noted previously, Doehring and Reitan (1962) found that in adult subjects (who might represent the ultimate criterion for conceptual development) with either a right or left cerebral lesion there were no differences in level or pattern of results on the Category Test. This type of evidence, based on persons with documented brain lesions and emanating from what Rourke describes as the "first phase of neuropsychological theorizing," would seem to be quite important in maintaining contact with the neurological bases of behavior.

The third postulate in Rourke's theory, that development of right hemisphere functions is a prerequisite for adequate development of left hemisphere functions, appears to be a restatement of the first point.

The fourth postulate, that concept formation is basically dependent upon the right cerebral hemisphere and the elaboration of such concepts is dependent upon the left cerebral hemisphere, stems principally from Rourke's findings that children with specific arithmetical deficiencies performed more poorly on the Category Test than children who had relatively good arithmetical abilities but were impaired in dealing with language symbols (Rourke, 1982).

It must be noted again that these studies by Rourke and his colleagues were not based upon subjects with any documented brain damage or brain lesions whatsoever; they were based upon children with learning disabilities, and most children in this category have relatively normal neurological findings. Therefore, one must question whether the conclusion of Rourke et al. has any empirical basis concerning the "neuro" aspect of neuropsychology.

As mentioned above, Doehring and Reitan (1962) found that in terms of concept formation there were no differences in the effects of actual lesions of the right and left cerebral hemispheres. McFie and Piercy (1952) found that Weigl's sorting test was failed by a significantly larger proportion of patients with left hemisphere lesions than patients with right hemisphere lesions. Goldstein (1936), using similar abstraction tests, felt that impairment of abstraction ability could result from any cerebral lesion, but that frontal damage had the most adverse effects. Rylander (1939) found no difference in performance of various abstraction tests among persons with left and right cerebral lesions. Halstead (1940) also failed to find any laterality effects when comparing patients in their ability to group heterogenous objects according to organizing principles. Each of these investigators based his conclusions about brain-behavior relationships on subjects who had documented brain lesions.

Finally, Rourke's fifth postulate is concerned with the significance of limitation of adaptive abilities in persons with right cerebral dysfunction. Rourke is careful to use the term "right-hemisphere systems" rather than "right cerebral damage" because his data do not refer to persons with documented right cerebral lesions. Therefore, Rourke's inferences are based upon types of impairment or patterns of disability that *he* believes may be related to right cerebral functions. In fact, there is no adequate scientific evidence to support the hypothesis that significant impairment of "adaptive abilities" is specifically related to right cerebral damage, although this certainly is an open question.

In conclusion, one may view Rourke's theory as being of interest, but it is related almost exclusively to the "specialization" concept of cerebral functions. The theory considers general characteristics of brain functions on the basis of integration of lateralized functions through the commissural structures. As we previously noted, the abilities of the individual that nature has represented diffusely in both cerebral hemispheres, merely in terms of their more generous anatomical distribution, may be more significant than those that are specialized or limited to either the left or right hemisphere (or areas within each cerebral hemisphere).

Kolb and Whishaw's Theory. Kolb and Whishaw (1980) have proposed a theory which is based on the premise that early in the course of development abilities are relatively simple in nature and become more complex in a cognitive sense as the individual matures. The essential feature of this theory is concerned with the organization of the brain as it subserves simple and more complex cognitive functions.

The authors postulate that simple cognitive functions are initially represented bilaterally, but particular abilities develop an increased dependence on one of the cerebral hemispheres as the neuropsychological functions of the individual develop and become more complex.

According to these authors, simple cognitive functions presumably are not lateralized, but are generally distributed throughout the brain; more complex cognitive abilities (such as language and visual-spatial skills) are differentially lateralized. As determined by the eventual outcome, Kolb and Whishaw's theory proposes that language functions become increasingly represented in the left cerebral hemisphere during the course of neuropsychological maturation and spatial and manipulatory abilities relate more closely to the right cerebral hemisphere. Recognizing that the "association" areas of the cerebral cortex are not already committed to primary or secondary sensory and motor functions, Kolb and Whishaw's theory postulates that these association areas are especially involved in complex cognitive functions and serve as the principal location of higher-level brain functions.

The developmental context in which this theory is based would then presume that young children have a general representation of their relatively simple abilities throughout the cerebral cortex, and the specialized functions of the left and right cerebral hemispheres develop as the child grows older and cognitive skills become more complex. A considerable amount of evidence is available to support the contention that brain functions in the young child are not well localized; a focal lesion does not necessarily give rise to highly specific neuropsychological deficits. Secondly, lateralized cerebral damage in a young child does not totally preclude development of abilities that would normally be associated with the damaged area. For example, children who have sustained lateralized cerebral lesions early in life and have undergone hemispherectomy are not totally devoid of language functions even when the left cerebral hemisphere has been removed.

Available evidence suggests that regardless of the location or lateralization of the tissue, the potential of cerebral cortical tissue to subserve particular abilities is much greater early in life than after physical maturation. It would seem likely, in accordance with the theory of Kolb and Whishaw, that there may be a progression from diffuse to more specific representation of particular abilities. It is certainly apparent that intellectual and cognitive abilities develop in complexity as the child grows into adulthood. There appear to be some features of the Kolb and Whishaw theory that relate to known events of the developmental sequence.

It is possible to examine the postulates of this theory in more detail, particularly with relation to simple cognitive functions. According to the theory, simple cognitive tasks presumably are not well localized in the cerebral cortex. However, even a cursory review of the literature indicates that some of the most simple types of cognitive tasks are very closely dependent upon one of the cerebral hemispheres.

It has long been known, for example, that relatively simple tactile cognitive functions, such as finger localization and object identification (stereognosis), are closely dependent upon the intactness of the contralateral parietal area. In tactile finger localization the usual testing procedure involves touching one of the subject's fingers and asking the subject to discern which finger was touched. Quite clearly this is not a complex cognitive task, but involves a simple cognitive function. On the basis of the Kolb and Whishaw theory, one would presume that such a simple cognitive function was diffusely represented in the cerebral cortex.

Research results have shown not only that ability in tactile finger recognition is dependent upon the parietal area, but that a distinct lateralization effect is also present (Hom & Reitan, 1982). Damage of the left parietal area tends to impair this simple cognitive function for fingers of the right hand; damage of the right parietal area impairs performances on the left hand. In fact, when groups of persons with distinctly lateralized lesions are composed, tactile finger localization abilities on the left and right hands show a relatively strong inverse coefficient of correlation (Reitan, 1984a).

Many other simple cognitive tasks are distinctly lateralized and localized. Aphasic manifestations (such as naming deficits) in right-handed adults who have developed cerebral functions normally are almost invariably associated with damage of the left cerebral hemisphere (Wheeler & Reitan, 1962). Motor deficits of a relatively simple nature have also been shown to have distinct lateralization effects, as demonstrated by evaluation of performances with the Purdue Pegboard (Costa, Vaughn, Levita, & Farber, 1963).

Even in young children these simple types of cognitive performances are distinctly related to the left or right cerebral hemisphere. In fact, in interpreting results from the Halstead-Reitan Battery, the methodological approach that serves most effectively to identify children with lateralized cerebral dysfunction is concerned with intraindividual differences on the two sides of the body in a variety of simple cognitive performances. Higher-level neuropsychological abilities may be more diffusely represented in the brains of young children than among adults, but the lower-level neuropsychological functions, which require only simple cognitive abilities, appear to be heavily dependent upon the anatomical organization of pathways within the nervous system and in turn have essentially a similar relationship in children and in adults.

A second approach toward testing the theory of Kolb and Whishaw would be to determine whether there are complex cognitive tasks which are diffusely represented in the cerebral cortex and not differentially dependent upon the left or right cerebral hemisphere. The Kolb and Whishaw theory postulates that more complex cognitive abilities, which develop over time, become increasingly specialized in their cerebral lateralization or localization.

One of the most complex higher-level neuropsychological tests is the Category Test, which measures abilities related to reasoning, abstraction, logical analysis, and concept formation. Prior evidence has indicated that this test is very sensitive to the biological condition of the cerebral cortex (Reitan, 1955b and many ensuing studies). Results on the Category Test have also been investigated in subjects with lateralized cerebral lesions (Doehring & Reitan, 1962). The findings indicate that performances on the Category Test are quite independent of a lesion's lateralization or localization. In fact, the pattern of errors on individual subtests was remarkably similar for groups with left or right cerebral lesions as compared with control subjects.

There appear to be quite complex cognitive abilities that are not lateralized or localized in the cerebral cortex, but instead are diffusely represented throughout the cerebral cortex. Although language skills become increasingly specialized during the course of development and localize in the left cerebral hemisphere and spatial and manipulatory skills become increasingly dependent upon the right cerebral hemisphere, in developing a theory of brain-behavior relationships it is important to recognize that other abilities, including some that are quite complex in nature, are diffusely distributed throughout the cerebral cortex.

In a biological sense, these diffusely distributed abilities, which involve the function of the entire cerebral cortex (including areas that are also devoted to specialized abilities), may be the most important. Nearly every adult with cerebral damage, either focal or diffuse, shows significant evidence of impairment in abstraction and reasoning abilities, regardless of whether specific deficits (such as aphasic manifestations or constructional dyspraxia) are concurrently present. As might well be expected from results on the Category Test, persons with cerebral damage much more regularly demonstrate generalized deficits rather than specific deficits which are manifested in measures that are sensitive only to a lesion in either the left or right cerebral hemisphere.

A basic problem with the theory proposed by Kolb and Whishaw concerns not only the fact that simple cognitive functions are often specifically lateralized and localized and that more complex cognitive abilities are in some instances diffusely represented, but that the theory itself is essentially locked into a concern for explaining the specialized (lateralized) functions of the two cerebral hemispheres. The dramatic differences in functions of the two cerebral hemispheres have been well publicized, but the types of abilities generally dependent upon the entire cerebral cortex, regardless of lateralization or localization, have not received as much attention.

There is a tendency to presume that if an area of the cerebral cortex is clearly related to a specific type of ability (e.g., language and related verbal skills), it does not subserve other neuropsychological functions (such as abstraction and reasoning), even when not in a verbal context. This tendency probably is related to the inclination of some theorists to assign higher-level neuropsychological functions to the "association" areas, essentially because of the availability of these areas.

In developing a neuropsychological theory of brain-behavior relationships, however, it is important to consider the entire range of abilities critically dependent upon the brain. In evaluating human brain-behavior relationships this criterion cannot be met through knowledge derived only from animal studies. A review of the publications cited by Kolb and Whishaw to their own work in their textbook, *Fundamentals of Human Neuropsychology*, indicates that their published research has been essentially limited to animal studies.

Reitan-Wolfson Theory. We will not review additional theories of brain-behavior relationships, such as those of Luria and Halstead, since these theories have been reviewed and compared quite recently in other publications (Reitan, 1988; Reitan & Wolfson, 1988b). However, the neuropsychological theory proposed by Reitan and Wolfson (1985, 1986, 1988b, 1992a) will be described briefly because of its specific relevance to the content, composition and clinical interpretation of the Halstead-Reitan Neuropsychological Test Battery for Older Children and its relationship to the content and procedures used in REHABIT (see Chapter VI) for training brain functions and remediating neuropsychological deficits.

We believe that any theory of brain-behavior relationships must necessarily recognize both receptive and expressive aspects of brain functions to determine the adequacy and efficiency with which the brain receives information and engages in responses. Luria proposed that the ascending reticular activating system represented the electrophysiological basis for the readiness of the brain to register incoming information, but we prefer to avoid postulating any such specific mechanism.

Earlier work on the ascending reticular activating system as an arousal and alerting mechanism for the cerebral cortex, which appeared initially to hold such exciting promise, has not had the clinical impact that was anticipated. Halstead's theory, which predated knowledge of the ascending reticular activating system (Moruzzi & Magoun, 1949), did not relate the energy source to registration of incoming material; instead, Halstead postulated a power source for intellectual functions directly.

We feel that integration of receptive and expressive functions with central processing is important and must be considered within the total context of brain-behavior relationships, but development of detailed knowledge about these functions is probably best left to specialists in sensory and muscle physiology. However, implementation of a neu-ropsychological theory definitely requires that the functional adequacy of the primary receptive areas of the cerebral cortex be assessed, and to evaluate these areas the Halstead-Reitan Batteries include a number of tests of simple tactile, auditory, and visual functions.

Motor functions warrant similar attention, and the Halstead-Reitan Batteries include measures of primary aspects of motor function (Finger Tapping and Grip Strength) as well as tests of complex integration of motor functions with sensory input and significant problem-solving requirements (such as the Tactual Performance Test). However, important as motor and sensory functions may be, the major challenge for a neuropsychological theory of brain-behavior relationships concerns central processing.

The Reitan-Wolfson model of brain-behavior relationships requires initially that information arrive at the cerebral cortex via the various sensory avenues. Primary sensory areas are located in each cerebral hemisphere, indicating that this initial level of central processing is generally represented in the cerebral cortex, but involves the temporal, parietal, and occipital areas particularly.

Neuropsychologically, the first level of central processing involves alertness, attention, registration of incoming information, continued concentration, and screening of incoming information in relation to prior experiences (immediate, intermediate, and remote memory). It is apparent that the adequacy with which the brain registers incoming information determines the usefulness of the information and the ways in which the brain can utilize it. Persons with cerebral damage vary greatly in this respect. Severe and extensive cerebral lesions often cause such generalized impairment of alertness, attention, and concentration that the subject has no prospect of being able to function adequately. This type of generalized cerebral impairment is frequently identified clinically as a "memory loss."

When registration of incoming information is so deficient that the individual is not able to relate it to past experiences, it may appear that memory is the basic deficit. It must be recognized that registration plays a major role in the initial aspects of memory function and memory, in turn, is represented in neuropsychological functioning by reference to the content of the task at hand. For this reason we have chosen to respect "memory" as being represented throughout a broad range of neuropsychological measurements. Memory is depicted as a generalized cerebral function rather than a separate type of function susceptible to measurement by "memory" tests (the approach of experimental psychology).

Persons with severe and striking impairment at this first level of central processing tend to do very poorly on almost any task presented to them. Such subjects fail to show striking patterns and relationships among higher-level test findings (such as differences between verbal and performance intelligence), even when a lateralized lesion may be present in addition to diffuse involvement. It may be possible to identify *specific* deficits in these patients, which in turn may permit inferences regarding lateralization of focal cerebral damage; however, this approach requires methodological implementation through use of specific tests (as compared with general measures) (Reitan, 1986).

The first level of central processing, represented by alertness, attention, concentration, and memory, interacts with the differential functions of the two cerebral hemispheres. For example, persons with generalized involvement as well as severe destructive lesions of the left cerebral hemisphere may be considerably less alert in dealing with verbal and language information than in dealing with visual-spatial problems.

In our theory of brain-behavior relationships we propose various levels of central processing, but it is also important to recognize that throughout the model an interaction occurs among various levels. The first level of central processing is rather generally represented in the cerebral cortex and other functions are more explicitly lateralized or localized, and an interaction occurs between selective deficits (often associated with strictly focal lesions) and generalized impairment (often associated with diffuse damage).

After an initial registration of incoming material, the brain proceeds to process verbal information in the left cerebral hemisphere and visual-spatial information in the right cerebral hemisphere. At this point the specialized functions of the two cerebral hemispheres become operational. Although anatomical pathways representing vision, audition, and tactile perception appear generally to be equivalently represented on the two sides of the brain, verbal information — especially through vision (reading) and audition (listening) — reaches the left cerebral hemisphere and visual-spatial (and probably temporal-sequential) information is processed by the right cerebral hemisphere.

As noted elsewhere in this chapter, many studies in the literature support the differential dependence of verbal and visual-spatial information on the two cerebral hemispheres, but the exact process by which incoming information is routed to one hemisphere or the other is poorly understood. A considerable amount of evidence suggests that differential routing is less firmly established early in life than when the individual is older, and is apparently dependent upon a maturational development of brain-behavior relationships. There is, however, evidence which suggests that such a predisposition may exist even in infancy (Molfese, 1977).

The differential functions of the two cerebral hemispheres are quite distinctly established, as shown by the nearly perfect specialization of verbal functions in the left cerebral hemisphere and the preponderant tendency toward localization of spatial abilities in the right cerebral hemisphere, especially in right-handed adults who have had the advantage of normal development of brain-behavior relationships (Wheeler & Reitan, 1962).

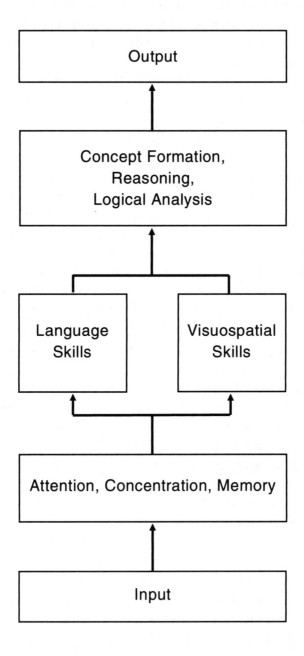

Fig. 2-1. A simplified graphic representation of the Reitan-Wolfson model of neuropsychological functioning.

At this point we should note again that clinical observation indicates that among persons who are grossly impaired at the first level of central processing, higher-level verbal and visual-spatial functions may not show any decided lateralization effect, even in instances of lateralized cerebral lesions. These persons have such impaired registration of incoming material that the higher-level processing functions, concerned with differential verbal and visual-spatial content, have limited opportunity to function.

In the Reitan-Wolfson theory, the highest level of central processing is represented by abstraction, reasoning, concept formation, and logical analysis. Research evidence indicates that these functions are also generally represented throughout the cerebral cortex (Doehring & Reitan, 1962), although particular tasks (depending upon their verbal or visual-spatial content), may establish a lateralizing effect. The Category Test, the best measure of this function in the Halstead-Reitan Batteries, does not show any lateralizing effect even though the content of the test is entirely nonverbal. In addition, the Category Test is *not* exclusively sensitive to anterior frontal lesions, as presumed by some investigators. Persons with nonfrontal lesions as well as individuals with frontal lesions demonstrate definite impairment on this measure.

The sensitivity of the Category Test to cerebral cortical damage regardless of localization probably accounts for the remarkable ability of this test to reflect cerebral damage. The Category Test is definitely a general test of the adequacy of cerebral cortical functioning, and any person with diffuse (generalized) or localized (focal) involvement is likely to demonstrate impairment on this test when compared with the performances of control subjects.

Impairment at the highest level of central processing has profound implications concerning the adequacy of neuropsychological functioning. Persons with such deficits have lost a great deal of capability to profit from experiences in a meaningful, logical, and organized manner. In casual social contact, such persons may appear to be relatively intact. However, because of the close relationship between organized behavior and memory, these persons often complain of memory deficits and are grossly inefficient in practical, everyday tasks. They are not able to organize their activities properly, and frequently direct their energy to elements of the situation that are not appropriate to the nature of the problem.

This nonappropriate activity, together with an eventual withdrawal from attempting to deal with problem situations, constitutes a major component of what is frequently and imprecisely referred to as "personality" change. Upon inquiry such changes are often found to consist of erratic and ill-considered behavior, deterioration of personal hygiene, a lack of concern and understanding for others, etc. When examined neuropsychologically, it is usually found that these behaviors are largely represented by cognitive changes at the highest level of central processing rather than by emotional deterioration.

Clinical evaluation of the individual subject with relation to this neuropsychological model requires an understanding of the integrative aspects of central processing at the various levels. The emphasis on the specialized functions of the two cerebral hemispheres has tended to detract from the other levels of central processing which are more generally distributed throughout the cerebral cortex.

For example, a person may have a focal lesion of the left cerebral hemisphere that has resulted in pronounced dysphasic manifestations. If this subject is evaluated only for dysphasia, the generalized aspects of neuropsychological dysfunction may be neglected, regardless of how completely the dysphasic difficulties are assessed and described.

A therapeutic approach that centers only on the specific deficits, neglecting the more general characteristics of impairment, is likely to be grossly inadequate. Speech therapy may improve some aspects of the dysphasic manifestations, but the patient may be so significantly impaired in abstraction, reasoning, and concept formation abilities that it is impossible to attain normal functional levels.

Evaluation of a broad range of patients, whose collective deficits covered the entire range of neuropsychological impairment, in terms of type and severity as well as corresponding brain lesions, were considered in the development of the Halstead-Reitan Batteries. This process led to an integration of the various aspects of central processing in clinical assessment. The importance of evaluation and its relationship to all of the elements of neuropsychological functioning cannot be overemphasized when attempting to gain a full understanding of brain-behavior relationships for the individual subject.

The operational definition of this neuropsychological model of brain-behavior relationships is based upon the individual tests in the Halstead-Reitan Batteries, and clinical implementation depends upon administration of these tests and interpretation of their results. The extremely close relationship between the Halstead-Reitan Batteries and the neuropsychological model stems from the fact that the tests were developed to reflect the full range of brain functions and their interrelationships and this in turn led to development of the model.

Remediation approaches (as represented by REHABIT) also relate explicitly to the theoretical model, its clinical exposition in the individual case with the test results of the Halstead-Reitan Battery, the interdependent interpretation of specific and general deficits, and the organization of training materials required for remediation of the particular deficits of the individual subject within the general framework of brain-behavior relationships (see Chapter VI).

The central features of the Reitan-Wolfson theory emphasize (1) an initial registration of incoming material and integration of this material with the individual's past experiences, (2) a second level of processing depending largely upon content of incoming material and organized according to the lateralized functions of the cerebral hemispheres, and (3) a third stage of central processing, especially directed to more complex and difficult tasks, and thereby representing perhaps the highest features of human brain functioning, consisting of concept formation, reasoning, and logical analysis.

Although these stages of central processing have a directional organization, we also postulate that a breakdown in neuropsychological functioning may occur at any level, and that interactions between the levels of central processing may occur in either direction, gradually leading to a more competent solution and response. However, some tasks, by their very nature, require careful and detailed registration; other problems will be processed principally by one cerebral hemisphere; and other tasks, depending upon their degree of complexity, will require sorting according to their elements into conceptual categories and careful logical analysis.

In terms of its anatomical representation, the Reitan-Wolfson theory includes a combination of hypotheses relating to equipotentiality of cerebral cortical tissue and of regional-localization. The first and third stages of central processing relate to the principle of equipotentiality; the middle stages, relating to lateralization of functions and specialization of abilities, fall within the purview of a regional-localization hypothesis.

■

CHAPTER IV

Content and Methodological Organization of the Halstead-Reitan Neuropsychological Test Battery for Older Children

In clinical neuropsychological examination of individual children it has become customary to evaluate three broad areas of functioning: (1) general intelligence, (2) brain-behavior relationships, and (3) academic achievement. The Wechsler Intelligence Scale for Children-Revised (WISC-R) is frequently the instrument of choice in assessment of general intelligence because it has been evaluated in far more detail and over a considerably longer period of time than other instruments (such as the Kaufman Assessment Battery for Children [K-ABC]). As we will describe in later chapters, our evaluation of brain-behavior relationships in children uses an extensive series of neuropsychological tests that are essentially similar to the tests used in the

Halstead-Reitan Neuropsychological Test Battery for Adults. Many instruments are available to evaluate academic progress and achievement, and we have customarily used the Wide Range Achievement Test (WRAT) because of brevity in administration. However, we realize that in many instances the individual child may require a considerably more extensive and comprehensive evaluation in this area.

Personality and emotional characteristics among children with cerebral damage or dysfunction have not been studied systematically or extensively, and the relative absence of research in this area is probably the principal reason that such areas are frequently not evaluated in the typical neuropsychological examination. In our assessment of adult subjects many years ago we routinely began administering the Minnesota Multiphasic Personality Inventory (MMPI), recognizing the clinical importance of performing at least a screening assessment of personality and emotional problems. (The MMPI is not considered to be a neuropsychological instrument in the sense that it directly reflects adequacy or inadequacy of brain functions.)

Among children, however, we were constrained from using questionnaire procedures because of advice issued to us by the National Institutes of Health concerning the possibility of sensitive or objectionable content in questionnaires. It is likely that instruments currently available might be used to contribute to knowledge about emotional and personality problems experienced by children with cerebral disease or damage, and may be used by psychologists familiar with such instruments.

In addition to evaluating the above areas of function, it is common to administer surveys of lateral dominance, especially to determine hand preference. Eyedness and footedness are also sometimes determined. Fig. 4-1 presents a recording form which lists the tests used to assess brain-behavior relationships in older children.

The Halstead-Reitan Neuropsychological Test Battery for Older Children

Name _____ Age _____

Gender _____ Education _____ Handedness: RH ____ LH ____

Neuropsychological Deficit Scale (NDS) Summary

Level of Performance	Subject's score	Mean for controls	Mean for brain-damaged	Cut-off score
Motor Functions	____	6.29	14.05	
Sensory-perceptual Functions	____	5.15	10.77	
Attention and Concentration	____	1.91	3.78	
Immediate Memory and Recapitulation	____	2.23	3.31	
Visual-spatial Skills	____	4.06	7.69	
Abstraction, Reasoning, Logical Analysis	____	2.63	6.03	
Level of Performance–Total	____	22.27	45.63	33/34
Dysphasia and Related Variables	____	1.37	7.97	3/4
Right / Left Differences	____	6.79	13.74	9/10
Total NDS Score	____	30.43	67.34	43/44

WISC-R

VIQ _____
PIQ _____
FS IQ _____

Verbal Subtests

Information _____
Similarities _____
Arithmetic _____
Vocabulary _____
Comprehension _____
(Digit Span) (_____)

Performance Subtests

Picture Completion _____
Picture Arrangement _____
Block Design _____
Object Assembly _____
Coding _____
(Mazes) (_____)

WRAT

Grade Equivalent
Reading _____
Arithmetic _____
Spelling _____

Strength of Grip

Dominant hand ( ) _____ kg
Non-dominant hand ( ) _____ kg

Name Writing

Dominant hand ( ) _____ sec
Non-dominant hand ( ) _____ sec

Category Test

Number of errors _____

Tactual Performance Test

Dominant hand ( ) _____
Non-dominant hand ( ) _____
Both hands _____   Total Time _____
                          Memory _____
                          Localization _____

Seashore Rhythm Test

Number correct _____   _____

Speech-sounds Perception Test

Number of errors _____

Finger Tapping Test

Dominant hand ( ) _____   _____
Non-dominant hand ( ) _____

Trail Making Test

Part A _____ sec _____ error(s)
Part B _____ sec _____ error(s)

Bilateral Simultaneous Sensory Stimulation

RH ____ LH ____   Both: RH ____ LH ____
RH ____ LF ____   Both: RH ____ LF ____
LH ____ RF ____   Both: LH ____ RF ____

RE ____ LE ____   Both: RE ____ LE ____

RV ____ LV ____   Both: RV ____ LV ____
____ ____   ____ ____
____ ____   ____ ____

Tactile Finger Recognition

RH 1 ___ 2 ___ 3 ___ 4 ___ 5 ___   RH ___ / ___
LH 1 ___ 2 ___ 3 ___ 4 ___ 5 ___   LH ___ / ___

Finger-Tip Number Writing

RH 1 ___ 2 ___ 3 ___ 4 ___ 5 ___   RH ___ / ___
LH 1 ___ 2 ___ 3 ___ 4 ___ 5 ___   LH ___ / ___

Tactile Form Recognition Test

Dominant hand ( ) _____ sec _____ error(s)
Non-dominant hand ( ) _____ sec _____ error(s)

Fig. 4-1. Summary sheet used to record test scores of older children.

We will not describe either the Wechsler Intelligence Scale for Children-Revised or the Wide Range Achievement Test-Revised in this chapter; such descriptions and instructions for administration have been published elsewhere and are readily available for the interested reader. In this chapter we will describe the tests included in the Halstead-Reitan Battery in terms of their essential requirements and conceptual organization as measures of brain-behavior relationships. The individual tests will again be discussed in Chapter VIII with an orientation directed toward practical points of information that relate testing procedures and scores to the interpretation of the results. Chapter IX will provide specific and detailed instructions for the administration and scoring of each test.

Assessment of General Intelligence

The WISC-R provides information about verbal and performance intelligence, which is often helpful in determining the child's general level of capability. In contrast to the fairly definite information about lateralization and localization of cerebral damage that may often be derived from results on the Wechsler Adult Intelligence Scale (WAIS), our studies have not indicated any basis for concluding that subtest patterns in the WISC-R have any such specific meaning.

The child neuropsychologist should be aware that in children differences between Verbal and Performance IQ scores do not appear to be consistently related to lateralization of cerebral damage. Our surveys of results on children with neuropsychological impairment suggest that up to 70% of these children have somewhat lower Verbal IQ than Performance IQ values. It is not uncommon, however, to encounter children with definite and destructive left cerebral lesions who are impaired on both Verbal IQ and Performance IQ but have a Verbal IQ which is somewhat higher than the Performance IQ. Thus, while the WISC-R provides an indication of general level of intellectual ability, subtest variability or pattern seems to have little specificity regarding the condition of the brain.

In clinical evaluation it is important to compare the level of general intelligence (as shown by the WISC-R) with results obtained in more direct evaluation of brain-behavior relationships. Among children with perinatal brain lesions or lesions sustained early in life, it is not uncommon to see a very serious failure of acquisition of abilities (as reflected by the WISC-R), even though results on other neuropsychological measures may be at a somewhat higher level. Conversely, children with recent cerebral damage may have premorbidly developed fairly adequate levels of general intelligence, and reveal significant impairment on neuropsychological measures (similar to the pattern that is frequently observed in adult subjects).

As we have noted in the prior chapter, as the child matures there appears to be a gradual development of verbal and performance intelligence which in turn becomes differentially dependent upon the left and right cerebral hemispheres. An older child with a recently sustained lateralized lesion might therefore actually show a differential relationship between Verbal and Performance IQ values in accordance with expectation based on the hemisphere involved. Thus, it is sometimes possible to compare WISC-R scores to other neuropsychological measures in order to draw significant inferences regarding brain-behavior relationships for the individual child. However, in most cases the major contribution of the WISC-R to neuropsychological assessment of the child is in determining the general level of intellectual functions.

Assessment of Academic Achievement

In some instances it is possible to use measures of academic achievement in a manner similar to the one in which we use WISC-R scores. For example, a child with recently sustained cerebral damage may score at a relatively high level in terms of academic achievement (with the scores reflecting past abilities), even though results on neuropsychological tests demonstrate relatively profound cognitive impairment.

General and Specific Neuropsychological Tests

We have often discussed the importance of including both general and specific neuropsychological tests in a comprehensive evaluation of the individual subject (Reitan & Wolfson, 1988b). This is equally true for adults and children. General neuropsychological measures are those tests that reflect impairment due to a brain lesion, regardless of whether the damage is focal or diffuse and regardless of the particular area involved by a focal lesion. In other words, general neuropsychological tests reveal the types of dysfunction that are associated with brain lesions regardless of their characteristics. In contrast, specific neuropsychological tests are much more closely related to the area of involvement, or localization of cerebral damage.

In evaluation of children, the most reliable specific neuropsychological tests are related to assessment of motor and sensory-perceptual capabilities through comparison of performances on the two sides of the subject's body. Significant impairment on such tests on the left side of the body are frequently associated with right cerebral lesions; conversely, impairment on the right side of the body often reflects a left cerebral lesion. Results on general neuropsychological tests more adequately reveal the overall level of neuropsychological impairment; findings on specific tests assist in lateralization and localization of maximal cerebral damage in addition to identifying deficits in the important areas of motor and sensory-perceptual skills.

Methods of Inference Regarding Brain-Behavior Relationships

We have previously described the four major methods of inference employed in the analysis of neuropsychological test data in drawing clinical conclusions about the individual subject (Reitan, 1967; Reitan & Wolfson, 1985, 1986, 1988b). In essence, each of these four methods of inference requires evaluation of neuropsychological data for the individual subject from a different point of view.

First, it is necessary to evaluate the *level of performance* in order to discern the degree of deficit shown by the individual child in comparison with normative groups. This approach is principally dependent upon the use of general neuropsychological tests, and obviously is based upon interindividual performances.

A second approach that has been incorporated into the Halstead-Reitan Neuropsychological Test Battery is the identification of specific deficits or *pathognomonic signs* of cerebral damage. It must be recognized that such signs are easier to identify among adult subjects because of the greater frequency of normal development of abilities to adulthood, coupled with striking specific deficits that are incompatible with prior normal development. However, among children it is quite common to find instances of longstanding cerebral damage that has tended to limit normal development. As a result, abilities are frequently impaired on a widespread basis generally, and indications of specific deficit are difficult to discern. Nevertheless, in individual instances errors in performance sometimes occur that are scarcely within the range of expectation for children with normal brain functions, and the pathognomonic sign approach is of value.

The third method of inference, *patterns and relationships* among higher-level neuropsychological test results, is rarely useful in neuropsychological evaluation of the individual child. There is clearly a tendency for brain-damaged children to perform simpler tasks more normally than tasks which are more difficult, and to demonstrate a deterioration of abilities as the demands of the task increase. However, this is a general manifestation of neuropsychological deficit among children with brain damage or dysfunction rather than a basis for differential neuropsychological diagnostic conclusions.

As mentioned above, patterns and relationships among subtest scores on the WISC-R are usually not helpful in assessing the neurological correlates of neuropsychological deficits. While the approaches based upon level of performance and pathognomonic signs require evaluation of the child's performances in accordance with normative data (an *inter*individual comparative approach), the patterns and relationships approach represents a method that compares the individual with him/herself on various measures (an *intra*individual approach).

Intraindividual inferential methodology has a particular strength inasmuch as the individual is compared with him/herself, thereby bypassing the variability implicit in any normative group. In fact, the subject serves as his/her own control, thus making intraindividual comparisons quite powerful as a neuropsychological inferential method. Unfortunately, however, among children the significance of this method is greatly attenuated in evaluating higher-level neuropsychological functions because of the generalizing effect even of focal cerebral lesions in children during the course of development as well as other maturational factors.

The final method of inference used to evaluate brain-behavior relationships, *right-left differences*, compares the subject's performances on essentially identical tasks on the two sides of the body. This is obviously another intraindividual comparative approach. Deliberately included in the HRB are a number of testing procedures involving motor and sensory-perceptual abilities from which this kind of comparison can be made. Interpretation of such data still requires an understanding of the expected relationships of performance on the two sides of the body, especially for tasks that are affected by hand preference.

Lateral Dominance

Lateral dominance is much more of a systematic factor in interpretation of motor functions than sensory-perceptual skills. In other words, although a child may be strongly right-handed for expressive or motor tasks (which will definitely be reflected in the complex and skilled unimanual performances for which the preferred hand is used), differential performances in favor of the preferred hand are much less marked for tasks that depend upon input of information to the brain. It is therefore important to realize that finger tapping speed generally should be about 10% faster for the preferred hand than for the nonpreferred hand. Results for the Tactual Performance Test generally are reduced in time by about one-third between the first trial (preferred hand) and the second trial (nonpreferred hand) and reduced again by one-third between the second trial and the third trial (both hands). Obviously, in order to use the inferential method based upon right-left differences in performance, it is necessary to have determined the child's handedness by using the Reitan-Kløve Lateral Dominance Examination.

Content of the Halstead-Reitan Neuropsychological Test Battery for Older Children

More detailed information regarding the description, administration, and scoring of each test is given in Chapters VIII and IX. The description given below is intended to provide only an overview of the content and organization of tests in the Battery.

The content of the HRB for Older Children follows the orientation of the Reitan-Wolfson model of neuropsychological functions. As we have previously discussed (Reitan & Wolfson, 1988b), all theories of brain-behavior relationships include a provision for the brain to receive incoming stimuli from the external environment (a receptive factor) and a provision for response mechanisms (an expressive factor).

Intervening between the receptive and expressive factors is a complex set of functions referred to as *central processing*. Central processing of incoming information requires several functions: (1) registration of information delivered through the various senses, (2) coding of the information and intersensory integration, (3) analysis of the information and problem-solving, (4) organization and formulation of the response, and (5) direction of the response in order to achieve an appropriate or adaptive end result.

The interaction between sensory input, processing of sensory information, intermodal sensory integration, analysis of the significance of the information registered in the brain, and final organization of the response is undoubtedly complex in terms of effecting a total process. Admittedly, this brief statement of central processing certainly does not do justice to the complexity of the analytical and adaptive abilities of the brain. Nevertheless, the neuropsychologist must be aware that a battery of tests organized to produce a comprehensive neuropsychological examination must evaluate the integrity of each of these areas.

The HRB for Older Children uses a number of tests to evaluate motor and sensory-perceptual functions. The developing specialization of the cerebral hemispheres is also recognized by including in the Battery measures which evaluate both simple and relatively complex verbal and language skills (left cerebral hemisphere) and visual-spatial and manipulatory functions (right cerebral hemisphere). Finally, the analytical and executive functions of the brain are evaluated by tests that relate to abstraction, reasoning, logical analysis, and planning abilities. Obviously, there is a close and integral organization of the tests included in the HRB and the Reitan-Wolfson neuropsychological model, thereby allowing the test results to be organized for clinical interpretation within the framework and context of a conceptual model of brain-behavior relationships.

In the discussion of the tests that follows we have not attempted to give complete descriptions of the tests, the equipment, the testing conditions and procedures, or instructions for administration and scoring. For information of this type, the reader is referred to Chapters VIII and IX.

Tests of Sensory-perceptual Functions

A number of tests have been devised and included in the HRB essentially to reflect disorders in primary registration of simple incoming information through the senses, emphasizing tactile, auditory, and visual modalities. The delivery of simple information through the senses is tested in a manner which allows comparison between the functional status of homologous areas of the two cerebral hemispheres. Primary incoming visual information is processed in the posterior (occipital) parts of the cerebral hemispheres, auditory information in the temporal lobes, and tactile input in the parietal areas.

Although it is believed that the incoming tactile information anatomically crosses to the contralateral cerebral hemisphere, anatomical representations of the auditory system suggest a more substantial bilateral representation. In practice, however, with the auditory tests used in the HRB, lateralized deficits on one side, in the absence of impairment of auditory acuity or deafness of one ear, almost always imply involvement of the contralateral hemisphere.

The visual system is considerably more complex in terms of projections from various parts of each retina to the striate cortex, with each retina being represented on each side of the brain. Although available evidence suggests that a relatively constant representation from receptive neurons to the cerebral cortex occurs within the visual system (Reitan & Wolfson, 1992a), in routine clinical practice it is difficult to take advantage of this situation in complete detail. Nevertheless, tests for tactile, auditory, and visual imperception of simultaneously administered stimuli have proved quite successful in reflecting lateralized cerebral damage.

Tests for Perception of Bilateral Sensory Stimulation

In tests of bilateral simultaneous sensory perception, the first step is to determine the minimum stimulus necessary to elicit a reliable response from the subject. Thus, if the tactile avenue is being evaluated, the examiner would determine the lightest touch that could be correctly identified by the subject. In the actual test the procedure is to administer unilateral stimuli through the appropriate sensory modality and then, without warning, intersperse trials in which the stimuli are given bilaterally. The subject's task is to identify the side of the body stimulated or to recognize that stimuli have been given bilaterally.

In evaluating tactile function, various combinations of stimuli are administered to the hands and face in such a manner that an error on one side of the body has significance for the contralateral cerebral hemisphere. Visual stimuli are administered in the upper, middle, and lower parts of the visual field with the subject's gaze fixated on the examiner's nose. Although the visual examination cannot be done if the subject has homonymous visual field defects, it is not uncommon to find instances of failure to report the stimulus on one side when stimuli are administered bilaterally. Deficits of this kind occur nearly always in subjects with unilateral cerebral lesions.

In practice, it is interesting to observe a subject's ability to report a unilateral stimulus and fail to appreciate the same stimulus when it is given simultaneously with a stimulus on the opposite side of the body. For example, a subject with a right cerebral lesion may report the stimulus when it is given by itself (unilaterally) on the left side. However, when stimuli are administered to each side simultaneously, the subject may consistently fail to report the stimulus on the left side, perceiving the stimulus only on the right side. Physiologically, it appears that a damaged cerebral hemisphere can register simple incoming information when not distracted by a similar type of processing by the other cerebral hemisphere. However, when stimuli are delivered bilaterally and both cerebral hemispheres are involved in processing the simple incoming information, the damaged hemisphere is not able to register the incoming stimulus.

Some subjects consistently fail to report visual stimuli on the entire half of each visual field, involving both left halves or both right halves. Clinical experience suggests that such instances correspond with relatively large lesions. In other instances, however, the imperception with bilateral simultaneous stimulation occurs only in one quadrant (the lower or upper part of each visual field). Clinical experience has demonstrated that when the defect is in the lower quadrants the corresponding lesion is frequently in the contralateral parietal area. When the upper quadrants are involved the lesion tends to be in the contralateral temporal lobe.

It is not uncommon for individual subjects to demonstrate lateralized deficits through all three sensory modalities that are tested; again, such findings tend to correspond clinically with larger lesions. In some subjects, however, selective deficits may occur which involve only the tactile, auditory, or visual aspects of the tests. In these persons the lesions tend to be principally represented in the expected area, depending upon the sensory modality principally involved (auditory/temporal, tactile/parietal, or visual/occipital).

Tactile Finger Recognition

An additional measure concerned with the brain's ability to register simple incoming information is the finger localization test. The subject's task is to identify each finger as it is touched by the examiner. Twenty trials (four trials on each finger) are given to each hand. Subjects with generalized or bilateral cerebral involvement frequently make essentially an equivalent number of errors on each hand, but persons with lateralized lesions (particularly when they involve the parietal area) tend to make more errors on one side of the body than the other. The errors have significance for damage of the contralateral cerebral hemisphere.

Fine Tactile Discrimination
(Finger-tip Number Writing Perception)

Another test that often helps with detection of lateralized deficits, and relates especially to the parietal area contralateral to the hand tested, is a procedure based upon perception of numbers written on the fingertips. This test integrates attention and alertness with fine tactile discrimination and is not perfectly compatible with Tactile Finger Recognition (although the results are often correlated). Four numbers are used as stimuli and each finger is tested four times, producing twenty trials for each hand. The total number of errors differentiates children with brain damage from normal children. Significantly more errors on one hand than the other implicates the cerebral hemisphere contralateral to the impaired side.

Possible Influences of Primary Sensory Deficits

Sensory-perceptual deficits that result from peripheral involvement may complicate the interpretation of the tests described above. However, particularly concerning vision and hearing, it is often possible for the examiner to observe obvious impairment. In fact, it is the examiner's responsibility to note any apparent deficits in sensory function that might possibly interfere with generation of valid test results.

Although most of the visual stimulus material in the HRB is large enough to be seen easily by the child, there may still be instances in which a loss of visual acuity may affect the outcome of certain tests (e.g., the Speech-sounds Perception Test). Peripheral limitations of visual perception, relating to a loss of visual acuity, rarely if ever interfere significantly with the administration of the test for perception of unilateral and bilateral simultaneous visual stimulation.

In the test for auditory stimulation, unilateral impairment of auditory acuity (or unilateral deafness) may affect perception of the stimulus to the impaired side with either unilateral or bilateral simultaneous stimulation. Inferences can be drawn from the actual recording of the data in this regard, but it is also helpful if the examiner has made a notation of any deficits that were observed during the testing session or of any complaints offered by the subject.

There are many examples of persons with significant peripheral impairment of sensory functions who have excellent neuropsychological abilities. Nevertheless, delivery of information to the brain by the senses undoubtedly represents a highly significant basis for problem-solving capabilities, particularly through the modalities of vision and hearing. Considering the extensive array of behaviors in which tactile perception represents contact with the environment, it must also be recognized that tactile perception is fundamental to efficiency of performance in a large number of practical, everyday situations.

It is not surprising that tests of tactile capability, as related to the brain, have a long history in medicine and psychology. In the 1940s, Bender and Teuber (1946) studied perception of simultaneous bilateral tactile stimulation. Examination of tactile finger recognition has an even longer history as one component of the Gerstmann syndrome (Gerstmann, 1927). Fine tactile perception, which is probably fundamental to adequacy in stereognosis, is basic to performing many practical activities in daily living. Even brief consideration permits documentation of the many significant limitations that would be experienced by a person whose tactile-perceptual limitations prevented efficient use of implements and tools in adapting to the environment.

Tactile Form Recognition

The final test in the HRB that is concerned with sensory perception, the Tactile Form Recognition Test, focuses particularly on tactile form discrimination. This test requires the child to identify flat, plastic geometric shapes (square, circle, triangle, and cross) through touch alone. Using a screen to prevent visual identification, the plastic shapes are placed one at a time in each of the subject's hands. Each hand is tested separately. The subject's task is to identify the object placed in his/her hand and use the other hand to point to the same shape shown in a display of the four objects. Results of this test are evaluated both in terms of accuracy of identification of the geometric forms as well as the speed of response.

This test measures tactile form recognition (stereognosis) with each hand and provides a basis for identifying impairment with one or both hands. Lateralized impairment is frequently found in the hand contralateral to a damaged cerebral hemisphere or, more specifically, contralateral to a damaged parietal lobe. Dysstereognosis, or impairment of tactile form recognition, is of special significance when the preferred hand is involved, but considering the frequency with which a person reaches for various objects with either hand, often without the assistance of visual guidance, impairment in stereognosis obviously has significant practical consequences.

We should note that the various tests included in the HRB that measure sensory-perceptual abilities have been devised deliberately to include a decision-making component. In the Tactile Form Recognition Test, for example, each trial requires the subject to determine, through touch alone, the shape of the figure and differentiate between the four alternatives (cross, triangle, square, circle). Tactile Finger Recognition requires a deliberate decision about which finger was touched among the five alternatives on each hand. Finger-tip Number Writing Perception requires very close attention and identification of the number written on the fingertip. Even the tests of unilateral and bilateral sensory stimulation require recognition of the location of the stimulus (hand or face) and determination of whether the stimulus occurred on only one side or bilaterally.

The decision-making requirement of these tasks was deliberately included in order to evaluate a cerebral component in the testing process as contrasted with a task oriented more toward the function of peripheral receptor mechanisms. These tests of sensory-perception were obviously designed to reflect neuropsychological functions rather than to emphasize sensory physiology.

Evaluation of Motor Functions

The HRB includes a number of tests that measure motor speed and fine co-ordination (finger tapping test), motor strength (grip strength), performance of a familiar motor task (name writing), and motor performances in solution of a complex, problem-solving task (Tactual Performance Test). The subject uses his/her hands individually for each task, which provides a basis for comparing lateralized performances. Specific instructions for administering and scoring these tests are given in Chapter IX.

Finger Tapping Test

The Finger Tapping Test uses a standardized tapping device to measure the speed of tapping with the index finger of each hand. This test is relatively specific in terms of its cerebral correlate, reflecting particularly the functional adequacy of the motor area of the contralateral cerebral hemisphere. The results reflect (1) the subject's ability in primary motor speed and fine co-ordination of alternating movements, and (2) the functional adequacy of the brain area responsible for the performance. In this manner one can derive a fairly direct comparison of the adequacy of the homologous areas of the two sides of the brain, taking into account the fact that the preferred hand customarily is about 10% faster than the nonpreferred hand.

Grip Strength Test

Grip strength is evaluated using a Smedley Hand Dynamometer, which can be adjusted to fit large and small hands. Two trials are administered on each side of the body and a mean score is computed for each side. This test measures motor strength of the upper extremities, and the result clearly reflects the differential status of the two cerebral hemispheres as well as muscular aspects of body composition. It is expected that there will be gender differences in addition to a considerable degree of variability within gender related to muscular development, body size and weight, etc. Gender differences in finger tapping speed have been reported in the literature (Dodrill, 1979) and have long been clinically observed (Reitan, 1959b), but clearly would be more pronounced in grip strength.

Considerations of muscle mass and tone, body size, exercise and conditioning activities clearly attenuate the significance of grip strength measurements as a direct manifestation of brain functions. Nevertheless, the test is often extremely useful in evaluating differences on the two sides of the subject's body. Customarily a difference of about 10% is expected in favor of the preferred side. When differences exceed this amount substantially, and particularly when concurring evidence is derived from additional tests, the results may be representative of dysfunction of the contralateral cerebral hemisphere.

Unilateral impairment on the Finger Tapping Test and the Grip Strength Test often occur concurrently for the individual subject, but there are occasional instances in which only one of these functions is impaired by damage of the contralateral cerebral hemisphere. In clinical practice we have therefore found it valuable to use both measures.

Name Writing Test

The Name Writing Test is extremely simple to administer. The subject is merely requested to write his/her full name on a sheet of paper. The hand used provides an indication of lateral preference. In administering this test the subject is not told to write quickly and no specific directions are given concerning the hand that is used. Following completion of the task, the subject is requested to perform the task again, writing his/her name in exactly the same manner, but using the other hand. Again, no mention is made that the subject should write quickly or in any other way alter the conventional manner of writing his/her name. Scores derived from this procedure include (1) the time required in seconds for writing the name with each hand, and (2) the difference in time between the two hands.

Name-writing is probably one of the most over-practiced of all motor tasks (at least with the preferred hand). Research studies (reported in Chapter VII) indicate that even such a simple procedure as name-writing yields quite consistent differences between children with and without cerebral damage or dysfunction. Brain-impaired children customarily require a longer time for name-writing with each hand, and the relationship between performances with the two hands tends to be deviant compared with normal children.

Some children with left cerebral hemisphere damage continue to be right-handed, but actually perform quite poorly with the right hand as compared with the left hand. More frequently, however, brain-impaired children perform poorly with their own nonpreferred hand as compared with their preferred hand. In this instance it appears that the brain-impaired child has practiced sufficiently to develop some skill with the preferred hand; but, when required to perform the task with the nonpreferred hand (for which practice has not previously been a factor), he/she performs very poorly. Normal children, even though they have not had practice with their nonpreferred hand, can adapt to the task much more readily.

Tactual Performance Test

The final test included in the section on motor functions is the Tactual Performance Test (TPT). This test is a measure of complex psychomotor ability that includes a significant problem-solving component. The material required for the test includes a six-figure formboard and six blocks. Each block fits into one of the spaces on the formboard. The child is blindfolded before the task of placing the blocks in their proper spaces is begun. The instructions (Chapter IX) include communication to the child that she/he is to depend upon touch alone to perform the task, which necessitates use of the blindfold.

A series of three trials is given. The first trial is done with the preferred hand, the second with the nonpreferred hand, and the third trial with both hands. The scores of the test are the times required to complete the task on each of the three trials. The sum of the three trials yields a Total Time score.

From a psychological point of view, the Tactual Performance Test provides a considerable amount of information about the child's ability to use his/her hands in a complex problem-solving situation. If the task were performed with the use of vision, it could be completed quite successfully and easily, even by impaired children. However, the blindfold requires the subject to adapt to distinctly limited sensory (tactile) cues. This testing procedure was developed in accordance with a hypothesis that a child with a normal brain would be able to adapt to these disadvantageous circumstances much more readily and with more facility than a child with a damaged or impaired brain.

The Tactual Performance Test is a complex type of performance task. Even though visual sensory input is excluded, input via tactile, proprioceptive, and kinesthetic modalities is available and must be integrated with motor dexterity to solve the problem. The problem-solving elements of the task are also relatively complex, and performance is facilitated by developing familiarity with the shapes of the objects involved, their locations, and integration (immediate recall) of the correlation between particular blocks and their appropriate spaces.

There is no doubt that in terms of its requirements the Tactual Performance Test is complex both neurologically and psychologically. In fact, with relation to other motor measures described above, the Tactual Performance Test reflects one of the recurring principles in the HRB of progression from rather simple tasks within a particular functional area to complex and more difficult problems. This approach definitely contrasts with other neuropsychological batteries which are composed of an extensive series of basically simple procedures in which an overall indication of performance is obtained only through addition of scores on the simple procedures (as contrasted with individual tasks that range from simple to complex skills).

We should also comment on the neurological model represented by the TPT. As noted above, the child is instructed to perform the task initially with the preferred hand, and the examiner provides no information that further trials will be required. However, after completing the task with the preferred hand, the child is instructed to perform the same task again using only the nonpreferred hand. Finally, a third trial is given and the child is permitted to use both hands.

In terms of the neurological model involved, input information through the haptic senses is first delivered from the preferred hand to the contralateral cerebral hemisphere, where the incoming information is registered. Because of intracerebral and intercerebral connections, the incoming information permeates the entire brain, which then becomes involved in solving the problem. Presuming that the child is right-handed, the initial incoming information would be registered in the left cerebral hemisphere and, if there were impaired left cerebral functioning, the child might do quite poorly on the task.

On the second trial the situation would be reversed, and information from the left (nonpreferred) hand would be registered in the right cerebral hemisphere. Again, intracerebral and intercerebral connections would permit the entire brain to be involved in solution of the task. However, if the right cerebral hemisphere were impaired in its registration and distribution of incoming material, one could expect a poor performance with the left hand.

Research results on normal children have shown that a substantial degree of bilateral transfer (positive practice-effect) occurs from the first to the second trial. Customarily, the individual's time on the second trial is reduced by about one-third, clearly indicating that experience gained on the first trial has an effect of reducing the time required on the second trial. Taking into account the expected reduction in time on the second trial, it is easily possible to determine for the individual subject whether any striking deviation from expectancy has occurred. If the time is very slow with the preferred hand, a postulate could be proposed that the contralateral cerebral hemisphere was inefficient in solving the task.

Results obtained on the third trial, when using both hands, often reflect impedance resulting from involvement of an impaired hand in the total task. Conversely, some subjects refrain from using their impaired hand even though use of both hands is permitted. In this latter instance, it is not unusual for a substantial improvement in speed of performance to occur, even though only one hand is used for the task. Thus, particularly on the third trial, it is often advantageous for the examiner to observe the procedure carefully in order to determine whether the overall performance is impeded by the subject's use of the hand that does not perform well, or whether the task is facilitated by use of only the proficient hand.

Following completion of the three trials of the Tactual Performance Test, the board and blocks are removed from the room before the subject removes the blindfold and has an opportunity to see the test. The subject is then provided with a sheet of paper and asked to draw a picture of the board, including all of the blocks that can be remembered, and to place the blocks in their correct positions. This procedure evaluates immediate and incidental memory, and is described in the next section.

Central Processing

For a longer period of time than the term clinical neuro-psychology has been in general use, differentiation has been made between lower and higher brain functions (Halstead, 1945). Lower brain functions have customarily included sensory-perceptual and motor skills, although psychomotor tasks (which involve substantial problem-solving components) have often been included among higher brain functions. Higher brain functions have included areas such as attention, concentration, memory, language and verbal functions, visual-spatial problem-solving skills, and abstraction, reasoning, logical analysis, and planning abilities. In fact, the major subject matter of clinical neuropsychology is principally represented by the area of higher brain functions.

In terms of organization of lower and higher brain functions, the various elements of central processing (higher brain functions) have consistently intervened between input or receptive aspects of brain functions (sensory-perceptual processes) and output or expressive aspects of brain functions (motor response mechanisms). Although a comprehensive neuropsychological assessment necessarily includes evaluation of lower brain functions, the principal emphasis in clinical neuropsychology has usually been directed toward evaluation of higher brain functions. The major aspects of the HRB, to be described below, are concerned with central processing abilities of the brain.

Attention, Concentration, and Recapitulation of Past Experiences (Memory)

The first level of central processing involves alertness, attention, registration of incoming information, continued concentration, and screening of incoming information with relation to prior experiences (immediate, intermediate, and remote memory). The adequacy with which incoming information is registered in the brain determines the usefulness of the information for additional aspects of central processing. If the information is inadequately registered or distorted, the prospects for meaningful organization, analysis, and integration in order to achieve an appropriate or adaptive response are seriously limited, regardless of the integrity of the remaining elements of central processing. In practice, basic abilities in alertness and concentration usually withstand brain impairment more effectively than the highest level functions of abstraction, reasoning and logical analysis.

Persons with cerebral damage tend to vary considerably in their first-level abilities in central processing. When the cerebral lesion is severe and extensive, generalized impairment of alertness, attention, and concentration may render the subject unable to function adequately. This type of generalized cerebral impairment is frequently identified clinically as "memory loss," particularly because of the close association and dependence between memory and initial registration and continued concentration.

Registration of incoming information is sometimes so deficient among children with impaired brain functions that the individual is not able to relate the information to past experiences, and it may appear that memory is the basic deficit. However, registration plays a major role in the initial aspects of memory function; in turn, memory is represented neuropsychologically by reference to the content of the task which is the focus of attention at the moment. Observation of individual subjects suggests that it is necessary to view memory as being represented throughout a broad range of neuropsychological functions.

Our experience therefore has led us to view memory as a generalized cerebral function rather than as a separate type of function susceptible to specific measurement. In fact, having done a considerable amount of experimentation with "memory" tests, as they are used in either the context of experimental and cognitive psychology (Squire, 1975) or clinical evaluation (Russell & Nathan, 1946), we have certainly learned that memory may be impaired significantly in persons with cerebral lesions. However, any contribution to clinical assessment made by memory tests tends already to have been demonstrated by impaired scores on a range of other neuropsychological measurements. In other words, it appears that memory tests rarely contribute unique information or provide a basis for clinical conclusions that were not already well established by the results obtained on other measures in the HRB. Of course, a major basis for this conclusion may well relate to a general factor of abilities, in the sense that there is a substantial correlation and overlap between most tests of higher brain functions (Reitan & Wolfson, 1986).

Severe and profound impairment at the first level of central processing is often associated with acutely destructive or progressive cerebral lesions or conditions of severe, chronic generalized cerebral damage. Children with such impairment tend to do very poorly on almost any task that is presented to them. Although patterns and relationships among higher-level test findings are not pronounced even among children who have destructive or focal cerebral lesions, one can hardly expect to find patterns that have clinical meaning when the first level of central processing is significantly impaired. Patterns and relationships fail to emerge because registration of incoming material, regardless of its particular content (left or right cerebral hemisphere) is ill-defined, and the child's performances tend to be poor across the board.

Two tests have been included in the HRB that have proved specifically helpful in assessing basic competence in attention and concentration. These measures are the Seashore Rhythm Test and the Speech-sounds Perception Test.

Seashore Rhythm Test

The Rhythm Test measures the ability to discriminate variations in rhythmical patterns. The test consists of thirty pairs of rhythmical patterns presented on a standardized tape recording. The child is asked to listen carefully to the stimuli in each pair and to judge whether the second stimulus is the same as the first or is different. The test consists of a total of thirty pairs organized into three groups of ten items each. There is a progression of complexity of the rhythmic beat from one series of ten items to the next.

There is no question that the Rhythm Test requires close attention and concentration to the stimulus material. However, considering the fact that the test has been found useful in evaluating musical talent, it is likely that the results are not totally dependent upon adequacy of brain functions. Although there has been a definite tendency in the literature to attribute deficient performances on the Seashore Rhythm Test to impairment of the right cerebral hemisphere (or more specifically, to the right temporal lobe), available empirical data definitely indicates that equally deficient results are obtained with either right or left cerebral damage (Karzmark, Heaton, Lehman, & Crouch, 1985; Milner, 1971; Reitan & Wolfson, 1989).

Speech-sounds Perception Test

The Speech-sounds Perception Test consists of sixty test items. The subject listens to a series of nonsense syllables presented on a cassette tape recording and is required to correlate them with alternatives printed on the answer form. The test therefore measures the subject's ability to match a spoken sound to the correct alternative among a group of similar printed sounds.

The double vowel *"ee"* is in the middle part of every stimulus syllable. The child determines the correct response by discriminating and matching the consonant or combination of consonants at the beginning and end of each syllable. Since it is necessary for the child to register incoming information through the auditory avenue and correlate that information with printed material through a series of sixty items presented in rather rapid succession, it is apparent that a substantial degree of attention and concentration is necessary to achieve a successful performance.

As with most neuropsychological tests which require attention and concentration, the content of the test and the difficulty level may also be factors in the score obtained. Children with limited academic aptitude or achievement, for example, certainly can be expected to perform poorly on this task. Recent studies (Reitan & Wolfson, 1988c; Chapter VII of this volume) have demonstrated that children with learning disabilities often perform quite poorly on the Speech-sounds Perception Test as well as on the Seashore Rhythm Test. The fact that very poor performances tend to occur on both of these tests suggests that the particular content (verbal vs. nonverbal) is not the responsible factor but, instead, that the children's difficulty relates to impairment of attention and concentration.

This finding is quite consistent with many other reports in the literature which indicate that children with learning disabilities have a basic problem at the first level of central processing. The advantage of using the HRB in this respect, however, is that the degree of deficit shown by the individual child in this area is subject to immediate and direct comparison and evaluation with performances in other significant areas of neuropsychological functioning.

Memory Functions

As noted above, our clinical and research experience has suggested that memory functions are generally distributed throughout the cerebral cortex, and tend to be reflected in clinical evaluation in a manner that is seen on many other measures. Thus, in terms of brain functions, it appears that memory is an ability that is integrally associated with other types of skills. Among adult subjects, for example, Fulbright and Hom (1987), Hom (1992), and Storrie and Doerr (1980) have found that patients with Alzheimer's disease, whose principal complaints were "memory" deficits, performed just as poorly on many other tests as they did on "memory" tests.

In neuropsychological terms, it would appear that the child who appears in practical circumstances to have a poor memory actually has significant impairment of basic abilities on which memory depends (Crook, Bartus, Ferris, Whitehouse, Cohen, & Gershon, 1986). It is also interesting to note that most of the training procedures advocated for improving memory functions depend basically on the development of organizational and associational techniques. The fact that neuropsychological deficit may involve significant impairment in initial registration, alertness, and concentration suggests that these problems may also be significantly related to memory impairment.

A practical approach to the clinical assessment of subjects who complain of memory disorders would be to perform a comprehensive evaluation of higher-level brain functions in order to understand the basic nature of the problem. When experimenting with a variety of tests in the development of the HRB, we found that "memory" tests added time to the evaluation, but contributed little useful information that was not already explicit in the results of other tests already included in the Battery. Two tests specifically related to memory are included in the HRB: the Memory and Localization components of the Tactual Performance Test.

Memory and Localization Components of the Tactual Performance Test

After the three trials (preferred hand, nonpreferred hand, and both hands) of the Tactual Performance Test have been completed, the child is asked to recapitulate the experience by drawing a diagram of the board, reproducing as many of the shapes as possible, and placing them in their correct positions. No forewarning is ever given about this drawing, and the result is dependent upon incidental learning. However, every subject has the opportunity to be exposed to the stimulus material and to reach a criterion with respect to solution of the problem, regardless of whether the performance was done efficiently or in an impaired manner.

Halstead's initial hypothesis about this procedure was that the person with a damaged or impaired brain would be less capable of recapitulating the immediately past experience than would a person with a normal brain. The subject's drawing is scored for both the number of shapes remembered and the number of shapes placed in approximately their correct location. Obviously, there is an experimental dependence between these two scores, inasmuch as the child must be able to remember a particular shape before it can be localized correctly.

The results of this two-phase assessment of memory performances bear an interesting relationship to differences between normal and brain-damaged children. The first phase of the memory task (remembering the shapes) does not differentiate between these two groups as well as the second phase, which requires the shapes to be correctly localized. This finding probably is a reflection of the sequential phase of the two tasks, demonstrating that a normal brain incidentally registers and recapitulates complex situations more comprehensively than does a damaged brain.

In our judgement, memory studies of this type would appear to have more significant implications concerning behavior in practical situations than tasks such as repetition of digits or establishment of word associations. The results of the Memory and Localization components of the Tactual Performance Test suggest that brain-damaged children may be able to remember obviously relevant aspects of a situation; however, taking the next step and deciding how to use recalled information in a practical and appropriate manner constitutes a more significant (and perhaps more debilitating) problem.

Evaluation of Verbal and Language Skills

There is no need to justify inclusion of tests that measure verbal and language skills as part of a comprehensive neuropsychological evaluation and, considering the emphasis placed on these abilities by many neuropsychologists, there is probably even relatively little need to discuss them in any detail.

During the last century investigators from many scientific disciplines have studied the relationship between language and thinking. The problem has also been considered by philosophers and poets not only recently, but in the earliest recorded writings. Meyers (1948) published an excellent review of the background of the problem, and describes the continuing historical interest that identifies this problem as one that has persistently concerned people in their attempt to understand themselves.

John B. Watson, generally regarded as the father of behavioristic psychology, proposed the most intrinsic of relationships between language and thinking — the idea that thinking is subvocal speech (1924). His influence on this topic is quite pronounced in the writings of most present-day psychologists, although few would accept the implication that thinking is impossible without speech. Nevertheless, one frequently encounters statements such as, "Language is inseparably bound up with thinking and other symbolic behavior (Kimble, 1956), and" . . . we must admit that the symbols which represent most of the world are language symbols (verbal, gestural, or written) and that most of our thinking appears to be an internal manipulation of such symbols" (Munn, 1951).

Meyers (1947) has pointed out that investigation of dysphasia offers ". . . a singular opportunity to inquire into the language-thought relationship" (p. 65). In the neurologic literature, however, the question has been stated principally with respect to the integrity of language functions in relation to intelligence. Another review (Reitan, 1953) indicated the diversity of opinion concerning the possible reciprocal significance of aphasia and intellectual impairment. A comment by Weisenburg and McBride (1935) summarizes the problem: "The extent to which intelligence may be said to be affected is a moot point. Some investigators have held that intelligence suffers because speech is disturbed while others have held that speech is disturbed because of the intellectual disorder."

In neurobiological terms, however, verbal and language abilities may not actually have the importance that has been assigned to them historically. In their careful mapping of electrophysiological correlates of verbalization, Penfield and Roberts (1959) found the language area to be heavily represented in the left cerebral hemisphere, occupying an area of cerebral cortex that represented approximately one-fifth of the gray matter in total. It should be pointed out that in some cases they found evidence of electrical changes even in the right cerebral hemisphere. In recent investigations of brain activity, in which verbal abilities were correlated with results of positron emission tomography and evidence of cerebral blood flow, an interesting interaction of functional areas has been found that involves a larger area of the left cerebral hemisphere. Nevertheless, in neurobiological terms, the available evidence suggests that language is something of a specialized function subserved largely by the left cerebral hemisphere and involving only certain areas of the left cerebral cortex.

If language is relatively restricted in terms of its relationship to brain functions, the obvious question must be directed toward the neuropsychological abilities subserved by the rest of the brain. It is clear that a comprehensive neuropsychological evaluation could scarcely be conducted using verbal and language tests as the sole or even principal component of the battery. As we have learned through investigative efforts over the years, and as represented in models of brain-behavior relationships as well as in the HRB, a broad range of neuropsychological functions must be evaluated in order to even approach an adequate representation of abilities subserved by the brain. A balanced representation of measurements across this wide range of abilities, which obviously would be necessary in order to effect a meaningful intraindividual characterization, is even more difficult to achieve.

Although it is certainly necessary to include verbal and language functions in any comprehensive neuropsychological evaluation, the history and probably even the current clinical emphasis in this area serves as a basis to caution neuropsychologists not to overemphasize the importance of language and verbal functions. It is interesting to observe that in comparison with other neuropsychological adaptive functions (as represented by neurobiological studies of the brain), programs of academic instruction, which depend so heavily upon both receptive and expressive verbal communication, are out of balance with the importance of verbal abilities.

In this regard it should also be mentioned that the areas of the cerebral cortex that are involved in verbal and language abilities are not devoted exclusively to these functions. While damage to the language areas may well produce significant impairment of basic abilities in language use (dysphasia) or differential impairment of verbal and performance intelligence among adults (Reitan, 1955a), lesions that cause these deficits are also associated with a broad range of other neuropsychological deficits, represented particularly by general (as opposed to specific) neuropsychological tests.

In one study (Reitan, 1960), a group of adult dysphasic subjects was matched for gender, age, education, and type of lesion (but obviously not location of lesion) with a group of nondysphasic brain-damaged subjects. Results showed that both groups were distinctly impaired compared with a non-brain-damaged control group, but there were no differences between the dysphasic and nondysphasic brain- damaged groups except on tests that explicitly required receptive or expressive language abilities. This evidence strongly suggests that verbal and language abilities should be considered as somewhat specialized neuropsychological functions (in the tradition of Kurt Goldstein [1948]), rather than as an expression of general neuropsychological functions (Marie, 1906).

We feel that in clinical evaluation it is important to examine the basic abilities that deal with simple aspects of language symbols for communicational purposes (dysphasia) as well as more complex verbal abilities such as those represented in verbal intelligence tests. Among younger children we have been less inclined to include measures of verbal intelligence as indicators of adequacy of brain functions, because of the extent to which such measures can be influenced by cultural and educational experiences and the great variability that exists among younger children in these respects.

Some younger children receive a considerable amount of training in academic subject matter, even before entering the first grade; other children, with equivalent ability and brain functions, receive very little training of this type. Among older children such influences have probably tended to balance out to some extent. Nevertheless, in the general evaluation of adequacy of brain functions provided by the Neuropsychological Deficit Scale (NDS) (see Chapters VIII and IX), we have elected not to include results of

Verbal subtests from the WISC-R. Instead, the adequacy of skills in the language and verbal area, as far as the NDS is concerned, is reflected by results from the Reitan-Indiana Aphasia Screening Test (Reitan, 1985).

The Reitan-Indiana Aphasia Screening Test

The Reitan-Indiana Aphasia Screening Test includes simple examinations for a number of basic language abilities, simple drawing skills, arithmetical abilities, identification of body parts, and right-left orientation. The child is required to name common objects, perform simple spelling, reading, and writing tasks, identify numbers both in arabic and in verbal representation, recognize individual letters of the alphabet, enunciate relatively complex words, and comprehend verbal communications. Except for ability in drawing simple spatial configurations (constructional praxis), all of these measures (including enunciation, recognition of the symbolic significance of individual numbers, arithmetical calculations, right-left orientation, and identification of body parts) have been shown in adult subjects to be much more closely related to the functional integrity of the left cerebral hemisphere than the right (Reitan 1984b, 1985).

The Aphasia Screening Test was not devised to be a comprehensive neuropsychological examination, even with respect to the full range of verbal abilities. For purposes of clinical interpretation, we include the Verbal subtests of the WISC-R as additional measures of possible relevance, in spite of the fact that they may very well be influenced by cultural factors and academic opportunities. As mentioned above, in computing the Neuropsychological Deficit Scale score (Chapter IX) we have elected to include input only from the Aphasia Screening Test, because deficits shown on this instrument are probably much more directly and closely related to the integrity of the brain than are the results from the Verbal subtests of the WISC-R.

In Chapter IX we will present detailed guidelines and many individual examples for identifying adequate and impaired performances on the Aphasia Screening Test. We do not recommend formal scaled scoring of these performances because, as manifestations of impaired brain functions, they either fall into the normal range or demonstrate cerebral impairment and therefore are abnormal. In fact, in some instances, formal scoring would tend to violate this dichotomous characterization because certain performances, even though quite characteristic of the kinds of deficits that occur with brain damage, may appear in total to be better performances than some of those that fall at the lower end of the normal range. Because of this, it is important for the neuropsychologist to refer closely and carefully to the examples of adequate (within the normal range) and inadequate (characteristic of brain damage) examples.

Evaluation of Visual-Spatial and Sequential Abilities

The ability to deal with visual-spatial and sequential tasks has long been recognized as an important neuropsychological skill. In adults the ability to perform these types of tasks has been well documented as being principally dependent upon the biological integrity of the right cerebral hemisphere (Reitan, 1955a; Wheeler & Reitan, 1962). It is somewhat curious, however, that certain nonverbal tasks that appear to be essentially concerned with spatial distributions do not show a specific dependence upon the right hemisphere. For example, among the Performance subtests of the WAIS, adult subjects with right cerebral damage demonstrate the most serious and consistent indications of impairment on the Picture Arrangement and Block Design subtests. Object Assembly, which is equally oriented toward visual-spatial relationships, tends to be differentially impaired with right cerebral lesions as compared with left cerebral lesions, but is not as consistent an indicator as Picture Arrangement and Block Design.

The Picture Completion subtest is even less consistent as a right cerebral indicator, although this may be because a verbal response is required in addition to visual perception of the spatial (pictorial) material. In addition, however, considering the fact that Picture Completion is a comparatively weak discriminator of right cerebral damage, it is entirely possible that the nature of the task is not as heavily demanding of adequate brain functions as are some of the other subtests.

The Digit Symbol subtest, for example, distinguishes quite effectively among adult subjects with cerebral damage, regardless of whether the left or right cerebral hemisphere is involved (Reitan, 1955a). Considering the requirements of the test, it is understandable that Digit Symbol would reflect both left and right cerebral damage. First, in order to complete the task, it is necessary to deal with symbolic material, but it is equally necessary to draw various spatial configurations as the response requirement. Thus, both symbolic comprehension and visual-spatial responsiveness is required, with both left and right cerebral functions being involved in producing the final result.

Speed of performance is also a significant variable, and efficiency of functioning per unit of time has frequently been found to relate to adequacy of brain function. Thus, in terms of its requirements, Digit Symbol is a relatively stern test of brain functions. It utilizes abilities dependent upon each cerebral hemisphere in a unified and co-ordinated performance.

Perhaps even more surprising is the fact that performances on the Tactual Performance Test are not consistently and regularly more impaired in persons with right cerebral damage than in persons with left cerebral damage. As we have noted, performance with the hand contralateral to a damaged hemisphere is frequently significantly impaired. However, the total time required for completion of this spatial problem is generally approximately equivalent for persons with right and left cerebral damage. No verbal skill or fluency is required, and the entire task is a nonverbal, spatial problem. In addition, the Memory and Localization components, which again are represented entirely by spatial configurations and their organization, are general rather than lateralized cerebral indicators.

It is apparent from these findings that some tests which appear to be strongly (if not exclusively) spatial in nature fail to demonstrate a special dependence on the integrity of the right cerebral hemisphere. The reasons for findings of this kind are subject only to speculation at the present time, but it is likely that additional aspects of the task, such as the full range of abilities required or the extent to which it is demanding with regard to brain function, may be of significance.

According to empirical data, the Tactual Performance Test is quite a demanding test in a neuropsychological sense, considering the fact that it shows excellent differentiation between groups with cerebral damage and non-brain-damaged controls. In this case the likely explanation for failure of the results to reflect the spatial requirements of the task would be based on a presumption that the task may be more critically dependent upon other abilities which relate to the adequacy of both cerebral hemispheres. As we mentioned in our description of the Tactual Performance Test, it seems to be a very complex type of task that involves a number of aspects of sensory input which must be organized and integrated with relation to the response component. Further, there undoubtedly is a pronounced general problem-solving component to this task in terms of remembering shapes of blocks and spaces, organizing them and relating them to each other, and maintaining efficiency of performance over time.

Although some subjects with severely destructive right cerebral lesions and gross impairment of ability to deal with visual-spatial relationships find that the Tactual Performance Test is too difficult to do even with the comparatively good hand (and in these cases problems in dealing with spatial relationships appear to be of overriding significance), the majority of subjects probably find the limiting aspects of the task to relate to the generalized rather than specialized requirements. It is clear from results of this kind that any neuropsychologist who presumes that a particular task has lateralizing significance without actually testing the hypothesis in groups with left as compared with right cerebral lesions may be seriously in error.

Many of the tests in the HRB involve spatial elements and/or sequential elements. It is important to recognize that some of these tasks are quite simple in nature (such as copying the shape of a square or triangle), whereas others place greater requirements on cerebral functioning (Block Design). The tests included in the HRB that deal particularly with evaluation of spatial abilities are the drawings from the Aphasia Screening Test (the square, cross, triangle, and key), three subtests from the WISC-R (Picture Arrangement, Block Design, and Object Assembly), and Part A of the Trail Making Test. As mentioned above, it is likely that these tests include additional elements and requirements over and beyond spatial abilities, but consistency either in demonstration of impairment or adequacy of performance should provide a fairly valid assessment of impairment in this area in the individual child.

We have mentioned that differential levels of Verbal IQ and Performance IQ on the WISC-R do not correlate closely with lateralized cerebral damage in children. In addition, there appear to be no consistent or reliable subtest patterns which result from focal lesions within each cerebral hemisphere. Among children the differential rates of development of lateralized (specialized) abilities seem to limit the extent to which these types of tests may be used clinically to lateralize cerebral damage.

Nevertheless, visual-spatial and sequential skills undoubtedly represent a basis for general efficiency in neuropsychological performances. There is reason to believe that even the initial aspects of development of number and letter recognition necessarily depend upon having developed the ability to appreciate the differential spatial configurations represented by individual numbers and letters. Children must be able to recognize and differentiate numbers and letters in terms of their spatial configurations before they can attach a differential symbolic significance to these shapes.

Reading ability is dependent upon the development of a high degree of rapid and accurate competence in differentiating letters on the basis of their visual-spatial appearance. Time-tested methods of training in the area of reading readiness customarily focus heavily on development of skills in visual form discrimination. Thus, in terms of the necessary developmental sequence in the acquisition of various neuropsychological abilities, it would appear that visual-spatial and sequential tasks are a major component.

As noted in Chapter III, theorists who have considered developmental models of brain-behavior relationships have even postulated that specialized abilities of the right cerebral hemisphere must be developed before the specialized abilities of the left cerebral hemisphere can be trained (Goldberg & Costa, 1981; Rourke, 1982). While this postulate certainly seems reasonable, there is little empirical evidence to support it, since younger children with lateralized lesions do not show selective or specialized deficits (either visual-spatial or verbal), but instead appear to have rather generalized impairment. Evidence suggests that in the initial stages of neuropsychological development the brain functions as a more homogeneous unit and that the specialized and differential functions of the right and left cerebral hemispheres gradually evolve as verbal and visual-spatial abilities become over-learned.

Evaluation of Abilities in Abstraction, Reasoning, Logical Analysis, Flexibility and Planning

Neuropsychological functions represented by this set of complex and interrelated abilities are heavily involved in organization and expression of adaptive, relevant, and efficient responses of the individual. They have sometimes been called the "executive functions of the brain," a reference that in many instances has not fully represented the significance of these abilities. Our clinical work and research in the area of brain-behavior relationships has led to the conclusion that these abilities are among the most important for an individual to be able to produce meaningful and plausible behavior, and for this reason the Reitan-Wolfson model of brain-behavior relationships represents them at the highest level of central processing.

Our best measures of these functions are the Category Test, Part B of the Trail Making Test, and the Coding subtest from the Wechsler Scale. These tests approach this area, which emphasizes integration of neuropsychological functions as well as basic problem-solving skills (as contrasted with learned, content-oriented abilities), in a somewhat different but complementary manner.

The Category Test requires the subject to view a series of designs, discern common as contrasted with varying elements, identify those elements that form the basis for a consistent application of an organizing principle, and finally, apply the principle to the apparently diverse stimulus configurations. This test heavily emphasizes abstraction, reasoning, and logical analysis, and is strictly a power rather than a speed test.

Part B of the Trail Making Test requires the subject to keep the alphabetical and numerical sequences in mind, shifting back and forth while integrating them and simultaneously searching the page for the correct stimulus item, all under the pressure of doing the task as rapidly as possible (and thus measuring efficiency of performance per unit of time). This test emphasizes flexibility in organizing stimulus material, keeping two sequences in mind at the same time, and accomplishing the task quickly.

The Coding subtest is also scored in terms of efficiency (speed) of performance, and achieves its organizational component from the requirement to observe, select, and match stimuli (numbers and spatial configurations) that come from rather different domains.

The abilities represented by these three tests clearly complement each other, even though they are often all impaired when brain functions are compromised.

When these higher-level abilities are significantly or seriously impaired, the subject is often described as having profound "personality changes," a characterization that essentially fails to recognize that these abilities are among the most important cognitive functions of the brain. In fact, these abilities are among those most susceptible to impairment whenever brain damage or dysfunction occurs. Among adult subjects we have found that these functions are generally represented throughout the cerebral cortex (Doehring & Reitan, 1962; Reitan, 1955b, 1959a), *including* those parts of the cerebral cortex that are also heavily involved in more specialized and specific functions relating to primary sensory-perceptual, motor function, language abilities, etc. Although some studies in the literature have implied that analytical abilities are particularly dependent upon the left cerebral hemisphere, our review of such reports strongly suggests that conclusions related to lateralization effects have been heavily influenced by the particular content of the abstraction, reasoning, and analytical tasks that have been used in the research.

For example, results on the Category Test do not show any lateralizing effect, even though the test is generally recognized as a measure of abstraction, reasoning, and logical analysis skills. This occurs despite the fact that the procedure is entirely nonverbal in nature. Part B of the Trail Making Test, which clearly involves flexibility in thought processes, also shows no lateralizing effect, even though the task employs both verbal and numerical symbols. Thus, when the major requirement of a test (and the factor that customarily limits performance in brain-damaged subjects) is concerned with abstraction, reasoning, flexibility in thought processes, and organization of stimulus material, it appears that the entire cerebral cortex is involved in solution of the task, and that damage is costly in terms of adequacy of performance regardless of whether pathological involvement is diffuse or focal.

All of these observations complement clinical evaluations of individual subjects, indicating that abilities in this area are particularly critical, both in terms of biological representation as well as in practical aspects of behavior. Deficits in abstraction, reasoning, logical analysis and flexibility in thought processes — even though often subtle and difficult to observe — have extremely pervasive and limiting effects on the overall efficiency of neuropsychological functioning.

Persons with such deficits frequently display one or more of the following behaviors: (1) an inability to be able to understand the relationships between various elements of complex situations; (2) an impairment in their ability to gain fundamental insights and understanding about the essential nature of the problem; (3) an inability to profit from experiences in a meaningful, logical, and organized manner; and, (4) a complaint of memory deficits and gross inefficiency in practical, everyday tasks (because of the close relationship between organized behavior and memory). People with striking impairment in this area are not able to organize their activities properly, and frequently direct their energy to elements of the situation that are not appropriate to the solution of the problem. In time these nonappropriate activities may lead to withdrawal even from attempting to deal with problem situations.

It is clear from these observations that impairment at the highest level of neuropsychological functioning represents subtle but profound cognitive changes that lead to ineffective and maladaptive behavior. In our attempts to retrain cognitive functions among persons with cerebral damage it is frequently necessary to begin training in the area of abstraction, reasoning, and logical analysis, not only because of the frequency of impairment in this area, but also because of the importance of the need for the impaired subject to "learn how to learn" before being able to acquire more specific abilities.

With respect to this latter point, it is interesting to note that a large proportion of children with learning disabilities demonstrate definite deficits in the area of abstraction, reasoning, logical analysis, and ability to formulate and organize problem-solving approaches. Often the degree of deficit shown by the child in this particular area has essentially gone unidentified, and training efforts are being directed to the acquisition of specific academic skills before the child has developed any ability in learning how to learn.

Unless these deficits in abstraction and reasoning are identified, and the child is taught how to think and understand relationships and to appreciate the meaning of specific observations, it will continue to be difficult for the child to make any progress except on a very rote basis. Because of the fundamental impairment in this area, the child is not able to generate a self-sustaining degree of efficiency of performance, continues to be impaired in comprehending and understanding complex situations, has little insight into appreciating the relevance of his/her personal activities to the overall scheme, and has difficulty following the sequential aspects of a problem as it develops.

The Category Test is the instrument used principally to evaluate abstraction, reasoning, organizational abilities, and planning skills. In fact, this test represents a standardized and controlled experiment in abstract learning capability (in contrast to many psychological tests in which the problem is structured for the subject and only a response is required). The Category Test requires the subject to (1) observe stimulus material, (2) identify recurring similarities and differences, (3) formulate hypotheses related to the organization of the stimulus material, and (4) test these hypotheses with relation to reality considerations (in this case a bell for the correct response and a buzzer for an incorrect response).

In many respects the Category Test simulates real-life circumstances in which the subject must observe the many elements of the problem, determine which elements are of critical significance, and formulate an appropriate and effective response on the basis of logical analysis, abstraction, and reasoning processes. Subjects who are impaired in this type of neuropsychological functioning frequently are inappropriate in their responses, demonstrate inefficiency when determining which elements of a situation need attention, "forget" important and necessary aspects of the total situation, reach incorrect conclusions and engage in inappropriate behavior, and in general do not function very efficiently as human beings.

As noted above, additional tests that are relevant in this area include Part B of the Trail Making Test and the Coding subtest of the WISC-R. Although the Trail Making Test takes only a few minutes to administer, solving Part B, which involves both numbers and letters, requires a considerable degree of concentration and flexibility in thought processes. The subject is required to deal both with symbolic representations (numbers and letters) as well as the spatial distribution of the stimulus material, thus apparently utilizing abilities of both the left and right cerebral hemispheres for successful completion of the task. The Coding subtest of the WISC-R is essentially similar in requiring an integration of left and right cerebral functions. Both of these tasks also require efficiency of performance for successful solution.

■

Relationship of Specific Tests to the Reitan-Wolfson Model

The neuropsychological model proposed by Reitan and Wolfson (1985, 1986, 1988a, 1988b, 1992a) was described in Chapter III. To recapitulate briefly, it includes six factors: (1) input or sensory (receptor) modalities, (2) output or motor (response) modalities and the intervening aspects of central processing, (3) attention, concentration and memory, (4) verbal functions and language skills, (5) visual-spatial, sequential, and manipulatory abilities, and (6) abstraction, reasoning, logical analysis and planning.

The nature and usefulness of this neuropsychological model can be illustrated by considering its relevance to various individual tests. For example, the Speech-sounds Perception Test and the Seashore Rhythm Test serve their principal functions in the Halstead-Reitan Battery as measures of alertness, attention, and ability to maintain concentration over time. Sherer, Parsons, Nixon, and Adams (1991) have recently recommended that these tests be omitted from the Halstead-Reitan Battery because they are not more sensitive to brain damage than other tests. Such a recommendation reflects the authors' lack of awareness and understanding of the ways in which the Speech-sounds Perception Test and the Rhythm Test supplement and complement other measures in the overall assessment of human brain-behavior relationships.

The Speech-sounds Perception Test requires the subject to listen to a tape recording of a series of nonsense words and, after perceiving the sounds through hearing, to select the matching printed word from three alternatives on the answer sheet. In the Seashore Rhythm Test the subject listens to pairs of rhythmic beats and records whether the beats in each pair were in the same sequence or a different sequence. There are sixty items in the Speech-sounds Perception Test and thirty items in the Rhythm Test. It is therefore necessary for the subject to listen to repeated stimuli and make a rather straightforward judgment. The tests are well-defined, examples are given before the subject begins the test so that he/she knows exactly what to expect, and the task essentially requires only continued attention to verbal (Speech-sounds Perception Test) or nonverbal (Rhythm Test) stimuli.

In most cases, the results on these tests do not give specific information about the competence of the subject in any particular area of content, although the Speech-sounds Perception Test has been shown to have a correlation of .73 with Verbal IQ (Reitan, 1956). Research has demonstrated that some adults with left cerebral vascular lesions make more errors on the Speech-sounds Perception Test than comparable subjects with right cerebral lesions or diffuse damage (Reitan & Wolfson, 1990).

Although many people have presumed that the Seashore Rhythm Test relates to the functional integrity of the right temporal lobe (presumably because the test involves nonverbal stimuli perceived through the auditory avenue), Reitan and Wolfson (1989) found no significant intergroup difference. Since some authors have explicitly stated that the Seashore Rhythm Test is a right hemisphere indicator, in spite of the fact that there is apparently no data to support this contention, we must emphasize that *experimental results comparing groups with left and right cerebral lesions show no lateralizing significance for this test.* In fact, in the Halstead-Reitan Battery the principal use of both the Speech-sounds Perception Test and the Seashore Rhythm Test relates to production of good scores rather than poor performances.

Although both the Speech-sounds Perception Test and the Rhythm Test show highly significant differences between groups with heterogeneous brain damage and non-brain-damaged control subjects, the greatest importance does not lie in the fact that such differentiations occur. On these tests subjects with chronic, static conditions of biological dysfunction of the brain perform relatively better than subjects with acutely destructive lesions. Acute destructive lesions have an impact on brain functions that is quite impairing to overall organizational function, and persons with such lesions frequently demonstrate significant neuropsychological impairment, even at the first level of central processing. However, when brain damage has become relatively chronic and stabilized, the first level of central processing (attention and concentration) is often more intact than the second level (specialized functions) or, especially, the highest level (abstraction and reasoning). Therefore, when the Speech-sounds Perception Test and the Seashore Rhythm Test have reasonably adequate scores (even though they may fall in the brain-damaged range), they provide information that permits more explicit interpretation of the deficits occurring at the second and third levels of central processing.

It is apparent that the principal requirement of each of these tests relates to attention, alertness, and concentration. In some subjects with serious lateralized damage involving the left cerebral hemisphere, the verbal component of the Speech-sounds Perception Test is the limiting factor, but the nonverbal content of the Rhythm Test is not sufficient to produce lateralizing implications that are statistically significant. Neither the Speech-sounds Perception Test nor the Rhythm Test requires a high degree of abstraction and reasoning skills. Instead, each test demands close attention to the specific stimulus material, an immediate judgment, prompt execution of that judgment, and attention to the next stimulus.

Nevertheless, we would postulate that the Speech-sounds Perception Test requires some ability at the third level of central processing, because the auditory stimulus must be evaluated in relation to three printed alternatives and a judgment must be made to select the correct answer. Therefore, it is likely that this test does require a minimal element of comparative reasoning (probably exceeding any such requirement in merely defining words, for example).

Reitan, Hom, and Wolfson (1988) evaluated this neuropsychological model among adult subjects by using a verbal test that required a considerable degree of abstraction and reasoning ability (the Word Finding Test) and another test that had minimal requirements of this type (the Vocabulary subtest from the Wechsler Scale).

The Word Finding Test consists of twenty items, and each item consists of five sentences. In each sentence there is a nonsense word ("grobnik"), and the subject's task is to learn the meaning of this nonsense word. In each item there are five trials to determine the meaning of the word, and each succeeding sentence offers additional clues. The subject must listen to each sentence, formulate a hypothesis, and record his/her response. Each successive sentence provides additional information, and subjects may change their answer in light of the new information received. The meaning is clear to most persons by the fifth sentence in each item. The test score is the number of correct responses.

The Vocabulary subtest was administered in the standard manner according to Wechsler's criteria.

Our postulate was that the Word Finding Test would require scarcely more attention and concentration than the Vocabulary subtest, and that both tests were strictly verbal in terms of content. Therefore, the first level of central processing would probably not be a limiting factor with respect to the scores obtained. Because of the verbal content of these tests, the second level of central processing might well reflect an impairment in persons with left cerebral damage. However, persons with right cerebral damage should probably not be significantly impaired at either the first or second level of central processing. We postulated that subjects with left cerebral damage would perform significantly worse on the Word Finding Test than on the Vocabulary subtest, not because of deficits occurring at the first two levels, but instead because the Word Finding Test had the additional requirement of inferring the meaning of the nonsense word from the context.

In terms of predictive results, we felt that subjects with right cerebral lesions would have scores on the Vocabulary subtest that were essentially similar to scores obtained by the control subjects. (All three groups were comparable in terms of age and education.) However, because the Word Finding Test had a much greater requirement of abstraction and reasoning skills (third level of central processing) than the Vocabulary subtest, we postulated that the group having right cerebral lesions would do worse than the control subjects on this test.

The hypotheses were confirmed nearly perfectly. The group with left cerebral lesions performed worse than the group with right cerebral lesions on both the Word Finding Test and the Vocabulary subtest, emphasizing the relevance of the verbal content of these tests. The group with right cerebral damage did not perform any worse than the control subjects on the Vocabulary subtest, but scored significantly worse on the Word Finding Test. Finally, in the context of performance for all three groups (demonstrated by T-score transformations of the data), the group with left cerebral lesions had lower scores on the Word Finding Test than on the Vocabulary subtest.

As another example we might consider the Coding subtest from the Wechsler Scale as it relates to the neuropsychological model. Among adults Digit Symbol has been consistently identified as the most sensitive of the Wechsler Scale subtests to cerebral impairment, regardless of whether the damage involves the brain diffusely or principally the left or right cerebral hemisphere. Digit Symbol seems to be sensitive regardless of lateralization (Reitan, 1955a), having the lowest mean score of the eleven subtests in each of these three groups of subjects (diffuse cerebral damage, left hemisphere damage, and right hemisphere damage).

We would therefore postulate that this subtest permeates the entire neuropsychological model and performances could be limited at any level of central processing. For example, a child might do poorly on Coding if he/she were impaired in alertness, attention, concentration to the task, or quickness in performance. This would represent a deficit at the first level of central processing.

The second level might also represent a limitation in performance, regardless of whether the child had a lesion of the left or right cerebral hemisphere. Subjects with left cerebral lesions could be limited in their performances by the requirement to match symbols and numbers (the symbolic aspect of the task); persons with right cerebral damage could be limited by the requirement of drawing unfamiliar spatial configurations.

Finally, the task requires integration of stimuli (numbers and symbols), and the subject must have a certain amount of organizational skill to accomplish this transformation successfully (skills represented by the third level of central processing). On the basis of the neuropsychological model alone, then, one would predict that (1) Coding requires adequacy of brain-behavior relationships generally, (2) the complex nature of the subtest could limit the performance of the individual brain-damaged subject regardless of the specificity of the impairment, and (3) subjects with either left, right, or diffuse cerebral damage would perform worse than control subjects.

The Similarities subtest of the Wechsler Scale is often referred to as a measure of verbal abstraction. This test does not have a significant requirement for attention and concentration capability, because each item contains only two words for comparison and these are generally understood without any difficulty. However, the test is strictly verbal in nature, and the subject must explain how the words in the pair are alike. The presumption is that the words themselves are within the vocabulary range of most of the subjects.

The attribution of abstraction to the Similarities subtest is based upon the requirement that the subject has to group the words into a single broader category in order to express their similarity. However, we would contend that third level of central processing (abstraction and reasoning) is not a particularly substantial element of this task. It may be more important for the subject to be able to define the words and, if he/she can give an adequate definition of the words, it is entirely possible to score relatively well on this test. In fact, in three different age groups Wechsler reports coefficients of correlation between Similarities and Vocabulary subtests ranging from .72 to .78. In a group of normals we found a correlation of .54 between Similarities and the Category Test (an abstraction and reasoning measure). In a group of brain-damaged subjects, we found a correlation of only .20 between these latter variables.

There may be reason to consider the Similarities subtest of the Wechsler Scale to be more of a test of verbal abilities than abstraction and reasoning skills, and this may explain why this verbal test produces a relatively weak (although significant) differentiation between persons with left and right cerebral damage.

The Block Design subtest of the Wechsler Scale has been identified as an excellent indicator of right cerebral damage, particularly in subjects with lesions in the posterior part of the hemisphere. This subtest also has been described as a nonverbal abstraction test. It must be noted that Block Design is not only nonverbal, but is explicitly concerned with organization of spatial relationships, a type of function related closely to the status of the right cerebral hemisphere. In addition, Block Design would appear to involve an element of abstraction and organizing ability. Even though the items are presented individually and may not require continued attention and concentration, it appears that Block Design depends heavily upon the specialized visual-spatial functions of the right cerebral hemisphere as well as the general functions of abstraction, reasoning, and logical analysis. It is therefore not surprising that Block Design is effective as a test of adequacy of right cerebral functions (Reitan, 1955a) in addition to having some validity as a general indicator of brain functions (Reitan, 1959a).

The five measures in the Halstead-Reitan Battery most sensitive to brain damage generally considered are:

1. the Neuropsychological Deficit Scale (NDS)
2. the Impairment Index
3. the Category Test
4. Part B of the Trail Making Test
5. the Localization component of the Tactual Performance Test.

Considering their relationship to the neuropsychological model, the sensitivity of these tests is hardly surprising.

The NDS and the Impairment Index derive their sensitivity from being average scores (and therefore presumably being more reliable), as well as being based upon a fairly extensive series of measures that may be adversely affected at any of the three levels of central processing. Therefore, there are many check-points at which the performances of individual brain-damaged subjects might be limited.

The Category Test requires close attention and concentration because the subject must review a series of stimulus figures, discern any similarities and differences that may be of critical significance, and relate these observations to each other through short-term memory. The Category Test has been referred to as a nonverbal abstraction test, and then gratuitously presumed by the uninformed to be a measure of right cerebral functions. There is, in fact, an element of the test that is in a sense similar to Coding: the subject is required to translate observations of visual-spatial configurations into a numerical representation ranging from one to four as a basis for giving a response. It would appear, then, that both of the specialized (second level) areas of central processing may be involved. Regardless of ability at the first or second levels of central processing, the subject must also analyze the nature of the stimulus material, draw reasonable conclusions on the basis of these observations, and apply these conclusions to specific stimulus material in the form of particular responses. The design of the Category Test obviously pervades the entire neuropsychological model, and has potential limitation of performances at each level of central processing.

Part B of the Trail Making Test yields a better differentiation between groups of persons with and without cerebral damage than does Part A (Reitan, 1958b). This finding is not surprising, when one considers how the two parts of this test relate to the neuropsychological model. Part B requires the subject to deal with both numbers and letters (symbolic material that is considerably more complicated than dealing with numbers alone, as in Part A). The subject must scan the sheet visually in order to find the next item to which a line is to be drawn (visual-spatial searching), and simultaneously keep both the alphabetical and numerical series in mind with respect to proper organization (analysis and reasoning). Like the Category Test, Part B of the Trail Making Test also obviously pervades the entire neuropsychological model and fulfills the requirements of a generally sensitive test of brain functions.

Finally, the Localization component of the Tactual Performance Test probably derives its sensitivity (at least in part) from the fact that short-term memory processes pervade the higher levels of central processing, even though in this test the subject is not alerted to this requirement beforehand. The presumption is again sometimes made that both the Memory and Localization components of this test relate to right cerebral functions because of the visual-spatial nature of the figures involved. We should again emphasize that empirical studies do not support this presumption; clinical investigations have demonstrated that the Memory and Localization components are sensitive to brain damage generally, regardless of whether the right or left cerebral hemisphere is exclusively involved. In addition, these tasks require the subject to organize the relationships of the figures while he/she is taking the test. The general sensitivity of these measures to heterogenous brain damage almost certainly stems from overwhelming requirements at the first and third levels of central processing.

It is obviously a mistake to interpret neuropsychological tests in terms of their apparent or face validity. Some tests are general indicators of cerebral functions, either because of procedural aspects or because they require a number of different types of brain functions in order to produce a correct solution to the task. Other tests, because they are considerably simpler in nature, are indicators of specific cerebral functions, and correlate much more closely with localized lesions of the brain (which is true of many of the items in the Luria-Nebraska Battery). The Halstead-Reitan

Battery has achieved a practical balance between general *and* specific neuropsychological measures. This did not occur because the Battery was specifically planned to do so, but instead because these were the testing procedures which turned out to be necessary to produce the type of data that would allow prediction of the independently established neurological variables for the individual subject.

■

CHAPTER VI

REHABIT: A Structured Program for Retraining Neuropsychological Abilities

REHABIT — Reitan Evaluation of Hemispheric Abilities and Brain Improvement Training

Although many specific procedures for training brain-based abilities of children and adults have been developed over the years, few have been organized around any meaningful conceptualization of human brain-behavior relationships. The Halstead-Reitan Neuropsychological Test Batteries provide a solution to this problem by identifying the individual subject's impaired or deficient neuropsychological functions in the framework of a model of brain-behavior relationships, thereby producing an evaluation on which a remediation program can be developed and prescribed. This procedure makes it possible to tailor the training program to the specific needs of the individual person.

Rehabilitation of neuropsychological impairment in both children and adults is viewed within this same theoretical framework. Differences in neuropsychological evaluation of children and adults must be recognized, primarily because children are in a developmental phase of achieving brain-related abilities. However, if a child sustains neuropsychological impairment in a particular area, the basic functions of that area tend to be the same as the functions in which an adult may have deficiencies. In the REHABIT program the rehabilitation materials are essentially similar for children and adults, but in many instances the training begins at a more simple level for the child.

Verbal and language functions are customarily related to the integrity of the left cerebral hemisphere, and visual-spatial and manipulatory skills are dependent on the status of the right cerebral hemisphere. However, children gradually achieve these specialized functions during the course of their development. In fact, recent investigations have emphasized the specialization of brain functions in association with the cerebral hemisphere involved to the relative neglect of the nonspecialized types of abilities which are dependent upon the brain *generally*. Since the abilities that characterize brain functions generally involve all cerebral tissue rather than focal, specialized areas of the brain, it might be reasonable to postulate that these general abilities could be more important than the skills that are represented by only one-half or even a lesser proportion of the brain.

The highest level of neuropsychological functioning, which covers the broad range of abstraction abilities, represents cerebral cortical functioning generally. In terms of their representation in the brain, it can be postulated that abstraction, reasoning, logical analysis, and planning abilities may be more fundamental than the specialized skills. This is an interesting point to consider when evaluating the criteria that contribute to our customary educational values which emphasize, to such a great degree, the functions of the left cerebral hemisphere. In contrast to many rehabilitation programs, the REHABIT program does not use a "shotgun" approach to brain retraining; instead, it has specifically been organized to remediate the individual's neuropsychological deficits, as determined by an evaluation with the Halstead-Reitan Battery.

Recognizing the importance of abstraction abilities and their central role in brain training, five tracks of remediation materials have been established in REHABIT:

1. *Track A* contains equipment and procedures that are specifically designed for developing expressive and receptive language and verbal skills and related academic abilities.

2. *Track B*, which also specializes in language and verbal materials, additionally integrates abstraction, reasoning, logical analysis, and organization skills.

3. *Track C* includes various tasks that focus upon reasoning, organization, planning, and abstraction skills, and do not emphasize any particular content.

4. *Track D* emphasizes abstraction abilities while focusing on materials that require the subject to use visual-spatial, sequential, and manipulatory skills.

5. *Track E* specializes in tasks that require the subject to exercise fundamental aspects of visual-spatial and manipulatory abilities.

Regardless of the content of the training materials being used for the individual subject, every effort is made to emphasize the basic neuropsychological functions of attention, concentration and memory.

With many children and adults it is necessary to provide training in each of these five tracks of REHABIT. In some instances, a person's particular pattern of deficits (as identified by an evaluation with the HRB) indicates that one track should be emphasized much more than the others. A unique feature of REHABIT is that the many items which compose the program were carefully selected by the authors from thousands of training procedures that were reviewed. We would estimate that despite their possible general educational value, about 90% of items considered for inclusion were rejected because they were not the kinds of specific training activities needed by persons with impairment of the type caused by brain damage or dysfunction.

The selection of the items included in REHABIT and the integration of the cognitive retraining with neuropsychological theory and assessment contribute to the uniqueness of the REHABIT approach. Although the theoretical background and practical application of REHABIT overlap with many other educational and professional approaches, the REHABIT program differs from other approaches in both content and procedure. For example, Track A overlaps with both conventional and special education training procedures, but differs from them in its emphasis on verbal, language, and academic skills as they relate to the complete configuration of neuropsychological abilities and deficits shown by the individual. The same point applies to cognitive training using REHABIT and the approaches customarily employed in speech therapy. Activities of occupational therapists often overlap with the content of Tracks D and E, but in the individual case the REHABIT training is integrated with the more general needs of the subject. In addition, the REHABIT program emphasizes higher-level neuropsychological functions much more than customarily occurs in rehabilitation settings. Finally, the strong emphasis on abstraction, reasoning, and logical analysis tasks in Tracks B, C, and D give REHABIT a unique character with regard to cognitive retraining. Thus, although REHABIT shares some characteristics with other approaches in the general field of brain training, it clearly differs from them in the way it has been designed to remediate specific neuropsychological deficits and impairment related to brain damage and dysfunction.

TRACK A

Track A of REHABIT consists of training materials which develop cognitive abilities in the area of verbal, language and academic competence. A considerable number of items in this track are used to train the individual in basic aspects of academic performance, especially in reading, writing, and arithmetic. We have not emphasized rote training in spelling, but many aspects of Track A provide the opportunity for developing competence in this area.

The basic segments of Track A include materials used to (1) develop preliminary reading skills (learning the alphabet; developing familiarity with consonant and vowel sounds; phonetics; vocabulary building; practice with word beginnings, word endings, and the use of contractions; compound words; synonyms, antonyms, and homonyms; practice in the use of words in sentences; and an introduction to simple reading), (2) develop reading comprehension skills, (3) provide training in both printing and cursive writing, (4) increase auditory verbal comprehension skills, (5) develop competence in following verbal and written instructions, and (6) introduce numbers, number concepts, counting, addition, subtraction, multiplication and division.

Finally, Track A also includes material specifically developed for retraining aphasic subjects, concentrating on the areas of word-finding, reading, writing, arithmetic, verbal comprehension, and memory.

As a first step in cognitive remediation, we strongly recommend that careful consideration be given to training the subject in the area of auditory verbal comprehension. Many children and adults, including those with subtle dysfunction of the left cerebral hemisphere, have significant difficulty in auditory verbal comprehension. As we have noted, this type of deficit is common among aphasic adults.

Obviously, if the subject fails to understand the verbal information coming into the brain, it becomes very difficult for him/her to respond appropriately. Initial training in perception and understanding of auditory verbal communications is often a prerequisite for additional remediation in this area. Of course, appreciation of visual input stimuli in reading is equally important, and this aspect is emphasized in the REHABIT materials oriented toward reading-readiness and training in reading and arithmetical procedures.

Materials for Developing Auditory Verbal Comprehension and Integration with Appropriate and Responsive Performances

Impairment in the area of auditory verbal comprehension is prominently documented among aphasic patients. In fact, one of the major categories of aphasia includes fluent aphasic deficits that are closely related to specific impairment in the ability to understand spoken language (Reitan, 1984a). Curiously, however, in programs of remediation and rehabilitation the expressive components of language functions seem to be principally emphasized.

Research based on neuropsychological test results has documented that difficulty in registration of incoming material through the auditory avenue is also a prominent characteristic of learning-disabled children. Nevertheless, among school children with learning deficiencies it is not uncommon to refer to difficulties in spelling, writing, and reading as if the deficits were entirely related to failures in expression.

In our conceptualization of the neuropsychological model we have emphasized that input, central processing, and output are necessary to describe the neuropsychological behavioral cycle. Children with a reading deficiency are often described as if reading output is their only limitation, when input mechanisms through the visual avenue and central processing deficits may in fact represent the major limitation. It must be recognized, therefore, that impaired appreciation of input, or receptive stimuli coming to the brain, can have a very limiting effect upon the adequacy of responses in any behavioral situation.

This input deficit frequently occurs in the auditory avenue, and it is not at all uncommon to encounter complaints from parents that "Johnny just won't listen." In a great number of instances in which complaints of this nature are prominent, our neuropsychological examination has revealed that the child shows substantial (though perhaps subtle) indications of left cerebral dysfunction. Although the deficits are not sufficiently pronounced to be identified as "fluent aphasia," they are still quite clearly brain-related and represent a significant receptive problem.

In many such instances the child is blamed for having a poor attitude, not being properly motivated, being uncooperative, or having personality problems. In situations of this kind we often have found that the child has never received even routine training in listening skills, and the unrecognized impairment of left cerebral receptive functions has created a serious problem (even though the child may be of average intelligence or above).

As we have remarked previously, the first step in the neuropsychological behavioral cycle is the input of stimuli to the brain. It is then necessary for the brain to register and comprehend the input material before an appropriate response can be generated. Because of this sequential relationship, we have included in REHABIT a substantial number of items dealing specifically with training in the area of auditory verbal comprehension. It is only reasonable to teach the subject to register, process, and appreciate incoming stimuli fully and adequately before requiring comprehension of the material and/or an appropriate response. Impairment of input (receptive) skills often goes unrecognized in the classroom or the home and creates problems that frequently are interpreted as lack of co-operation, impaired motivation, or personality problems.

Because many children will show evidence of mild left cerebral dysfunction, it is important initially to perform a complete neuropsychological evaluation of brain-behavior relationships. These children frequently have auditory verbal comprehension problems and difficulties in making satisfactory academic progress. Even when there have been no specific complaints relating to auditory verbal comprehension or academic progress, we find that children with mild left cerebral dysfunction frequently show these types of difficulties.

We recommend that every child who has difficulties with academic subject matter and demonstrates evidence of learning disabilities that appear on neuropsychological examination to be brain-related receive specific training with the auditory verbal comprehension materials in Track A. This material will help increase the child's capability to register incoming stimuli and appreciate the symbolic significance of auditory verbal communications.

Several items in Track A use tape cassettes and worksheets to present a variety of instructions to the subject. The subject is asked to listen to the information presented on the tape, which presents explicit instructions for the subject to follow. For example, the worksheet may show a number of various objects familiar to the subject. The recorded instructions tell the subject to perform a certain action related to one of the figures, such as, "Use your red crayon to draw a circle around the animal you might see in a circus." The subject is required to listen carefully and follow the instructions given on the tape.

A similar format is used with other materials in Track A. It is often necessary to use these cassettes a number of times before the subject develops a full understanding and recollection of the stimulus material, and the tapes should be interspersed with other training materials that are included in Track A.

Track A also includes a number of workbooks in which the subject is given instructions and asked to carry them out. The instructions in the books range from relatively simple to quite complex. Many of the responses deal with visual-spatial relationships, and the subject responds by performing an activity rather than by responding verbally. The tasks therefore provide an opportunity for integrating right and left hemisphere functions. The responses may require tracing and coloring of figures, free-hand drawing, production of figures according to printed instructions, or cutting out figures. Depending on the subject's individual requirements, the technician may ask the subject to read the instructions him/herself or may read the instructions to the subject to provide experience in auditory training.

The principal requirement of this material is for the subject to listen carefully and follow the instructions. This provides experience in responding to an extensive range of verbal communications perceived through vision and hearing.

The material is organized according to difficulty level for the auditory instructions that are communicated. The most simple level in the series begins by presenting a pair of pictures, and the subject is instructed to draw a line of a particular color through the picture identified either first or last. The task progresses in complexity to include three pictures and the response requires drawing a line above the picture identified first, second, or third, etc. The subject must not only comprehend the instructions given but must remember the instructions with relation to the specific aspects of the required response.

Other training materials included in this sequence require the subject to deal with figure-ground relationships among auditory stimuli. In other words, background noises are present that interfere with perception of the stimulus material, mask the stimulus sound, and distract the subject.

These materials provide the subject with extensive experience in focusing her/his auditory attention on the stimulus even though the background provides distraction. Relatively simple responses are required which establish that the subject has understood the verbal communication. The principal requirement, however, concentrates on auditory verbal perception.

Additional materials require the subject to correlate pictures (using various methods of response) with the sound delivered on the tape. For example, if the tape presents the sound of ringing bells, the subject is required to identify a picture of the bell. These procedures gradually become more difficult and complicated as the task proceeds.

A second phase of the stimulus material is concerned with identification and differential selection of initial and final consonants. Recognition of consonants is particularly important in speech-sound perception, because the consonants (as contrasted with the vowels) carry the major communicational information.

Another cassette program requires the subject to identify consonant sounds and blends and to indicate whether they occur at the beginning, middle, or end of each given word. At this point, the training material has progressed from more general verbal communication to perception of details of individual words.

Additional cassettes present a verbal description of an object and the subject is required to listen carefully and select the target object from various alternatives that are presented. The training material continues with this type of problem through various levels of difficulty, and requires auditory comprehension of the verbal material communicated, visual scanning of the stimulus material, recognition and differentiation of visual-spatial configurations, and correlation of the verbal description with the visual-spatial material. The input requirements relate to auditory verbal comprehension functions of the left cerebral hemisphere, whereas the output (or response) requirements are designed to depend principally on right cerebral functions. Rather than rely upon very simple responses (such as pushing a button, a response commonly employed in computer presentations of training material), we have emphasized the practical importance in cognitive remediation of requiring active involvement of both cerebral hemispheres in the training activity.

The training activities in this area were selected to effect an integration of right and left cerebral functions, giving the subject training and experience in integration of brain functions generally as well as an opportunity to demonstrate through performance his/her understanding of the verbal communications.

The amount of material provided under this general heading of *Auditory Verbal Comprehension* is quite extensive, and ranges from very simple procedures to tasks that are relatively complex. In addition, the material is sufficiently broad to provide an opportunity for varied presentation. Although it is desirable to repeat exercises that the subject has not performed adequately, it is not necessary to repeat them so frequently that positive practice-effect becomes a significant factor. It is advisable to keep a record of the adequacy of the subject's responses so that the types of activities that are particularly difficult for an individual may be repeated until a satisfactory level of skill is achieved.

Academic Readiness Training

Another set of materials in Track A is concerned with a large number of procedures and exercises aimed toward establishing the foundation for developing skills in reading, spelling, and writing. Despite its routine nature, it is necessary initially in every area of endeavor to begin by communicating rotely some basic information. In other words, if a subject is going to learn to recognize the symbolic significance of letters of the alphabet, it is necessary that he/she gain familiarity with the differential spatial configurations represented by the various letters.

As the child begins to develop competence in identifying individual letters, it is important that the "sound" of the letter be communicated. Therefore, one of the items in this section uses alphabet flash cards that depict upper- and lowercase letters of the alphabet together with a picture of an object that begins with the letter shown. The opposite side of the card includes several words that begin with a different letter. This material may be used when the child has developed some skill in reading words. Some of the flash cards include uppercase letters on one side and lowercase letters on the other side. Cards that present the entire alphabetical series are also included.

Since children are able to identify pictures by name earlier than they can recognize letters of the alphabet or be aware of their sounds, it is important to begin with verbal identification of the picture. At this point the cognitive retraining technician should communicate to the child the name of the letter and associate the sound of the letter with the picture. This material can thereby serve as an introduction to phonics.

After the child has learned to identify the letter and the letter-sound in association with the picture of an object, the technician should use flash cards that contain only the target letters and no pictures. For subjects who have developed preliminary reading skills, the reverse side of the cards can also be used to identify the words. Cassette programs which present the alphabet and phonics are also included in this section.

Many children have not been given an adequate basic training in identification of letters and their corresponding sounds as a basis for learning to read. Thus, it is likely that even a number of older children will need rehearsal of the letters, the phonics involved, and the use of letters to create words.

There is a considerable degree of variability among children concerning the amount of training needed to learn consistently to identify letters of the alphabet correctly. The technician should remember that the letters of the alphabet represent an extensive series of spatial configurations, and for the beginner in this task (or the severely brain-damaged subject), the problem is not only one of learning the symbolic association of letters, but also of learning to differentiate various spatial representations.

Occasionally children with excellent verbal capabilities have difficulty with this task because of the visual form perception requirements. For example, we have observed extreme disparities between verbal and visual-spatial abilities in the individual child who has a high Verbal IQ but fails to learn to read because of difficulty in visual processing of spatial configurations represented by letters of the alphabet. The initial phase of reading, in which the subject must learn to recognize individual letters, requires a considerable degree of overtraining. In our rehabilitation procedures we emphasize the importance of a serial progression from initial to more advanced skills in developing reading ability.

We have also included a considerable diversity of material to be used in helping the child develop familiarity with letters of the alphabet and their sounds. In this way it is possible to move from one item to another in order to give the child the experience of dealing with different material, through the visual, auditory, and tactile avenues, even though the basic intent is the same. The material in this section provides the subject with a basis for developing familiarity with letters of the alphabet, selected digraphs, and words. Subjects with little prior experience or training may need close supervision in the initial stages of teaching with this material. The tasks provide an opportunity for developing appropriate associations between basic language symbols, words, and pictorial representations as well as contributing to the development of color and number concepts.

An even simpler procedure in this section uses rubber inlay puzzles for both upper and lower case letters. Depending upon the needs of the subject, the material can be used in a number of different ways.

First, the subject can practice learning to identify individual letters. The training technician should be especially alert to making sure that the subject can differentiate between the letters that often get confused (such as "B," "P," and "D," "E" and "F," etc.)

As another activity, the subject can sort the vowels from the consonants and learn to identify them.

The letters of the alphabet can also be associated with their sounds, providing basic training in phonics, and the letters can be selected to spell simple words. All of these activities relate to the identification of letters and their use as verbal symbols.

This stimulus material can also be used to develop skill in motor co-ordination as well as abilities that represent brain functions more generally. The subject can practice placing the letters in their proper positions on the board, thereby developing improved motor co-ordination skills and hand-eye co-ordination.

Secondly, the subject can practice identifying letters through touch alone and obtain additional sensory appreciation of the individual letters. As a more complicated aspect of this procedure, the subject can work at placing the letters in their individual positions either with his/her eyes closed or when blindfolded. This is a rather difficult task; if mastered it will bring about a detailed appreciation of the sequence of the letters that will add much to a "rote" verbal recitation of the alphabet. This latter procedure will also contribute to ability in dealing with spatial relationships.

As the subject practices working either blindfolded or with eyes closed, he/she will gradually gain an understanding of the spatial location of the individual letters ("A" in the upper left-hand corner, "Z" in the lower right-hand corner, etc.). This latter type of knowledge relates specifically to this particular formboard and has little if any generalized significance for the symbolic meaning of individual letters; however, such an exercise can contribute to the development of right cerebral functions. Therefore, the training opportunities implicit in the use of these letter formboards extend through the entire neuropsychological model of brain-behavior relationships. The difficulty level may range from simple to moderately complex, depending upon how the stimulus material is used.

As we have noted previously, the stimulus material has been selected to represent an integration of the specific content of each item with brain functions more generally. In the training process we encourage the cognitive training technician to relate the specific content to various sensory avenues, and also to engage manipulatory skills and performance activities (right cerebral hemisphere) and abstraction and reasoning activities (general aspects of cerebral cortical functions) in exercises using the particular stimulus material (in this case, letters of the alphabet).

The remaining training material selected for laying the groundwork for development of academic skills consists of various phonetic exercises to give the child a further introduction to vowel and consonant sounds, short words, more difficult words that use only a single vowel but have various consonant combinations, familiarity with words that use blends, consonant digraphs, and finally, simple reading.

Additional material provides training in use of contractions, compound words, synonyms, antonyms, and homonyms. Emphasis has also been give to vocabulary building, based upon selection of words from lists of the most commonly used words. These words are also presented individually, so the child can select words needed to express a thought and thereby learn to build sentences.

This same material can be used with persons who have already developed preliminary academic skills by selecting words that represent certain parts of speech or words that must be used in conjunction with the punctuation included.

High-use words are also presented, together with pictures, to teach the dual meanings of common homonyms. Additional stimulus material is oriented toward developing an appreciation of synonyms, using the same appropriate picture to establish pairs of words that have essentially the same meaning.

Many adults and older children with cerebral damage resulting in impairment of basic language and verbal skills will be able to review these simple materials quite quickly. However, such individuals often have specific lacunae in their language structure and sometimes encounter unexpected difficulties with apparently simple items, and there are a number of items available in this section to remediate such deficits.

Finally, there are items in this section which include books and cassette tapes to assist in developing auditory discrimination, reception, association, and memory. These materials provide exercises in the area of verbal reasoning using comprehension types of questions, inferences regarding what must necessarily have occurred between the beginning and end-point based on information provided, answering who, when, where, what, and why questions, and other exercises to help the subject to not only comprehend verbal material, but to develop and use verbalizations to give meaningful explanations.

Material for Developing Reading Skills

The items in this section of Track A were selected specifically to develop reading skills. Some of the material overlaps with items in the preceding section, but is at a somewhat more advanced level.

In order to establish a solid foundation in basic training of English principles, Track A also contains workbooks developed to provide basic understanding and enrichment in both written and oral English. A variety of content areas is integrated to create high-interest reading themes.

Several workbooks cover basic grammatical concepts. Rules and directions are simply stated, and the topics covered include usage of nouns, verbs, modifiers, pronouns, simple punctuation, and ability to use and identify the different types of sentences. Other workbooks emphasize adjectives, adverbs, articles, the many different verb forms (action, regular, irregular, main and helping), simple punctuation, review of sentence types, an introduction to sentence fragments and run-on sentences, and the skills involved in paragraph writing. The types of exercises are imaginative and varied and include cloze and modified cloze activities, circling, and decoding. The skills are presented in a developmental fashion, and the retraining technician will be able to choose the appropriate sequence based upon the subject's level of readiness for each activity.

Another set of workbooks in this series consists of beginning, intermediate and advanced texts for fourth to fifth grade readers. Sentence identification now includes exclamatory sentences, which requires development of auditory identification techniques, and training in verbal skills. Numerous grammatical points and parts of speech are incorporated into the skill objectives. Writing activities are expanded, and the subject is required to write short paragraphs, reports, and letters.

In additional workbooks the usage and expression exercises contain practice with the concepts involved with reading, writing and understanding job descriptions, newspaper headlines, advertisements, taking notes, and writing outlines. For example, the specific punctuation rules for quotation marks are presented and the subject is provided with numerous different types of activities to experiment with the new facts.

Another series of workbooks contains high-interest, low-vocabulary stories, designed to increase the subject's motivation for reading. The workbooks feature diversified subject matter and include current personalities, popular sports figures and events, ghosts, monsters, mysteries, visual and performing arts, and amazing facts in science and nature.

After the subject reads the story, his/her comprehension can be tested and increased with the various questions which follow it. The cognitive retraining technician can explore the subject's understanding of the article by follow-up questions which review the main idea, determine the significant details, identify word meanings from context, draw inferences, and determine relationships between events.

Another reading comprehension series is comprised of hundreds of reading paragraphs. Each paragraph is printed on the front of a card and is placed in one of ten different boxes which are categorized by specific reading skill. The topics covered in this series include Understanding Sentences, Finding Cause and Effect, Predicting Outcomes, Making Inferences, Reading Phrases, Getting the Main Idea, Noting Details, Drawing Conclusions, Using Context Clues, and Finding the Sequence.

There are questions for each paragraph on the reverse side of the cards. Answers are provided on separate cards, which make this activity both self-directed and self-checking. The individual nature of the readings and follow-up activities will aid the cognitive retraining technician in determining specific areas for successful independent level work and on which types of comprehension skills to provide additional instruction.

More advanced readers in Track A provide practice in following details, drawing conclusions, predicting results, and determining cause-and-effect relationships.

The subject is first allowed to read the story up to the point where a question is presented. If the subject chooses the wrong answer, the technician should discuss the reasons why the answer was chosen and help the subject arrive at the correct response. The cognitive retraining technician and the subject can explore the various possibilities together, and specific strengths can be reinforced and specific weaknesses can be reduced.

Many of the workbooks have accompanying audio-cassettes, and present situations such as buying a car, balancing a checkbook, dealing with a family illness, etc. The material is organized to facilitate reading comprehension through a systematic approach that consists of finding the main ideas, understanding details, understanding where, understanding when, understanding why, understanding how things are alike or different, reading between the lines, reading many kinds of writing, reading and understanding new words, and finally reading for purposes of studying.

As additional basic training in reading we have included within REHABIT training material which begins with reading readiness exercises and goes on to develop familiarity with consonants, vowels, initial blends, initial digraphs, and final digraphs; fundamental aspects of word building; familiarity with the role of vowels and silent consonants in words; development of spelling skills; and recognition of the parts of sentences and the use of punctuation.

One set of material consists of cassette tapes, each side containing a separate lesson, and corresponding activity sheets for each lesson. Each lesson is approximately 20 minutes in length and instructions are provided throughout the tape. Lesson 1 is devoted to the recognition and differentiation of the different types of nouns (i.e., common, proper, and plural) and the activity sheet contains five rules for using singular and plural nouns. The subject is asked to use these rules to change the singular nouns to plurals after the voice on the tape explains what a common noun is and how to transform it to represent more than one.

The speaker on the tape works along with the subject as he/she completes each exercise. The lesson continues on pages two and three with a progression from identifying common and proper nouns to circling the nouns which require capitalization.

Lesson 2 presents varying noun forms and offers tips to easy identification, which tends to add a practical side to English grammar. The subject is instructed to circle nouns and underline noun signals. This activity requires the subject to be able to register the incoming verbal information, interpret the explanations previously given, comprehend the specific commands which follow, and be able to distinguish nouns and their signals from the other words in each of the sentences.

The next activity explains the use of number words. Again, concentration and focus are necessary elements of the task as the voice on the tape provides explanation and reinforcement. Pages two and three introduce and review the concepts of possessive nouns and exact nouns. The voice on the tape explains how to create nouns which show possession and what they mean.

The next tape requires the subject to rewrite sentences, substituting pronouns for nouns and then recognize pronouns as objects of verbs. Page three assigns a numerical value to the pronouns and requires the subject to list the amounts and then total them.

The objectives of Lesson 4 include increased ability to discern possessive pronouns, practice substituting possessive pronouns for possessive nouns, and a review of substituting possessive pronouns for objects of prepositions.

The remaining tapes explore the roles of verbs, adjectives, adverbs, with a review found in Lessons 11 and 12. The multi-sensory approach continues as the subject is presented with reading and listening comprehension activities, including crossword puzzles and sentence completion activities.

Practice in word-building is important as a basis for developing an understanding of both simple and complex verbal communication. Some of the word-building material included in REHABIT consists merely of individual letters from which the subject can make selections to form particular words. Other word-building materials are designed to develop familiarity with beginning and ending consonant blends.

Being able to recognize verbal sequences enables one to organize and retrieve information, understand subtle differences in meaning, and recognize chronological order. In the *Verbal Sequences* workbooks, two of the three words in a series suggest what the degree, size, rank, or order of the third word should be. If the subject knows the meanings of some words in the sequence, he/she can infer the meaning of the missing item.

Letter additions, another form of verbal sequencing, builds new words by adding prefixes or suffixes, and by adding letters which change the root of the word. This exercise develops the subject's vocabulary in a game-like format.

Exercises in these workbooks require the subject to add letters to form new words, determine degree of meaning, and identify chronological order of common sequences.

Other workbooks in this section promote categorization skills and vocabulary development. Verbal classification is the ability to group words which have a shared meaning, use, or characteristic. While classification is a fundamental concept-building skill in all academic disciplines, verbal classification fosters the correct understanding and grouping of words, a skill useful in writing and organization of thoughts.

The ability to categorize words is essential in learning to form adequate definitions. When asked to define a noun, students often give only a synonym or characteristic. For example, a bicycle is a two-wheeled vehicle driven by pedals. Students describe wheels, handbars, and pedals, but the key category "vehicle" may be unstated or unformed in the learner's ability to verbalize the concept. A definition of a noun contains a category ("vehicle") and qualifiers ("two-wheeled," "driven by pedals"). In some exercises in this series subjects are asked to identify key categories (class) and recognize subtle differences among words in that category, learning that common words can be classified in many ways.

The workbooks in this series contain the following types of exercises: (1) determining how groups of words are alike, (2) selecting the name for a class of words, (3) selecting the correct class name and adding another word in the same class, (4) determining how one group of words is related to a second group, (5) sorting words by class, (6) finding the exception to a class, and (7) completing word classification matrices.

We have learned that rote practice in spelling is also necessary for many subjects. We have therefore included a number of workbooks that concentrate specifically on spelling of individual words. The material in this section is quite extensive, and includes flash cards, workbooks, and audiocassettes for various levels of training.

Initially, the cognitive retraining technician reads the spelling words for the lesson and the subject writes them as well as he/she is able. Words that are misspelled are identified and must be written correctly. The next step is for the subject to use the spelling words for the lesson in an appropriate manner in sentences that are given. Next, the subject repeats the words from dictation and writes them. Then the subject alphabetizes the spelling words for each lesson and writes them down correctly. Finally, the spelling words for the particular lesson are again read to the subject and written. These procedures provide a considerable amount of practice and rehearsal with individual selected words that increase in complexity. This type of presentation provides the subject with training in spelling as well as in auditory verbal comprehension, vocabulary, sentence building, and writing.

Development of Skills in Printing and Cursive Writing

Track A also includes several training materials to facilitate development of printing and writing skills. The initial set of items includes laminated plastic cards that can be written on with a crayon and wiped clean. Each card contains a capital letter of the alphabet. The initial procedure is to have the child trace over the letter to give practice in learning to make the letter. In addition, each card includes an indented representation of the letter so the child can use his/her finger to draw the shape of the letter, following the indentations as a guide. Finally, space is provided on the card for the child to write the letter independently, attempting to copy the letter as shown.

The second set of materials includes identical material, except that the letters of the alphabet are written in cursive script. This material serves as an excellent introduction to developing initial skill in writing and printing letters of the alphabet. Use of plastic cards encourages the development of the kinesthetic skills integral to legible writing. In addition, the cognitive retraining technician can encourage the child to learn the names of the letters as well as the sounds represented by the various letters. Practice of this kind is very useful as an introduction to independent writing of letters and, eventually, words.

Training in Number Concepts and Arithmetical Skills

This section of Track A includes an extensive set of materials for training in arithmetic-readiness and provides specific training in addition, subtraction, multiplication, and division. The training in arithmetic-readiness uses a number of procedures for communicating the symbolic significance of numbers and for developing an understanding of number concepts and relationships.

Other material concentrates on combinations of stimulus configurations in order to provide training in counting and to develop basic concepts of arithmetic, and a number of procedures teach the concept of fractions. The items in this section include various geometric figures (such as squares and circles) subdivided into component parts to establish a basic understanding of the concepts involved in addition, subtraction, multiplication, and division.

In addition to the material which provides basic training in readiness for arithmetical procedures, a number of the items include specific exercises in arithmetical operations. Flash cards that cover the basics in addition, subtraction, multiplication and division are included to consolidate the child's understanding of arithmetical procedures and to develop memory functions to the point that the basic processes become automatic and ingrained. Flash cards are always a useful way to determine whether a subject is able to respond immediately to simple arithmetical problems. Despite the emphasis on reasoning and logical analysis, rote memorization is fundamental to development of academic skills, including arithmetic.

If the subject has difficulty with immediate responses to flash cards, it is apparent that a search must be instituted to find the basis of the problem. Sometimes the difficulty relates to a failure to appreciate the arithmetical process involved, and in other instances basic aspects of memorization have not been mastered. In some cases the subject may be impaired in the ability to recognize the spatial configuration of one number as compared with another. If a subject has problems with the simple processes involved in giving answers to flash cards, the nature of the problem must be discerned. It may become apparent that training with materials included in Tracks D and E is needed in order to establish basic abilities in differentiating spatial configurations as a prelude to developing arithmetical skills.

After the subject has mastered the basic flash cards, he/she may be introduced to materials which require speed as well as accuracy of response. One set of materials in Track A consists of four sets of practice sheets and accompanying arithmetic drill cassette tapes. The subject is tested on twenty-five basic facts per content area and given four seconds to respond to each equation. The cognitive retraining technician may introduce the tapes individually as a pretest to determine the subject's mathematical baseline and then provide remediation and enrichment using the appropriate skill and ability level practice exercise and cassette. The answer sheets present the problems horizontally and vertically, and the tapes advance in complexity as the subject progresses through the assignments.

These materials provide multisensory study for the subject. He/she is required to listen to the tape, register and process the instructions, perform the necessary computation, and verbalize the response or complete the practice sheet. The technician can determine the method of responding based upon the subject's specific impairments.

Another set of materials provides basic operation mathematical problems presented on eight cassette tapes and a series of worksheets. Some exercises on the tapes require multiple steps for solution, such as " How much is 8 plus 6 times 4?" The subject must listen carefully, record his/her answer, and be ready to deal with the next problem presented on the tape. Upon completion of a drill, the subject can check his/her answers by listening attentively to the speaker on the tape. Subjects who have auditory verbal comprehension difficulties can benefit significantly from these types of exercises.

Other arithmetic-readiness procedures begin with items that identify numbers from one to ten and associate the numbers with an appropriate number of pictorial objects as well as the written number. This material is useful in establishing the notion of quantity with the symbolic representation of the number.

The training material includes additional items that provide opportunities for counting. The items provide practice in using the sequence of numbers, such as counting pennies and the addition of pennies to identify nickels. The procedures continue with games that are based upon numbers, quantities, and sums.

In this section we have also included the Hainstock Blocks, which permit association of numerical figures with the number of plastic balls in each cell. The subject can shake the block, dividing the number of plastic balls into two segments for each number. For example, in one instance there may be six balls in one section and one ball in the other section, corresponding with the number "7." When the block is shaken a second time, there may be four balls in one section and three in the other. The subject is thereby able to discern that the number "7" corresponds with seven balls, regardless of their particular division. The training material goes on with specific tasks involved in addition, initially using sums only through 10.

The arithmetic-readiness material also includes a number of items that encourage the subject to develop an appreciation of fractions, extending from whole figures up to fractions of one-sixth. Manipulation of this material, together with use of counting skills, demonstrates that the whole figure may consist of one or more parts, depending upon how the figure is subdivided. Exercises with this set of stimulus figures establishes the groundwork, using pictorial representations, for learning to "take away" or subtract.

Several workbooks are included which are devoted basically to exercises consolidating counting activities and rehearsing the groundwork for addition and subtraction. Remaining manuals in this section of REHABIT extend through the full range of problems involved in basic arithmetic, including adding, subtracting, multiplying, and dividing fractional and mixed numbers, applying these arithmetical procedures with decimals, and finding percentages and dealing with problems which involve percentages. The material gradually extends from simple to more complex arithmetical procedures, and includes instruction and practice with linear measurement, balancing a checkbook, and establishing a budget.

The final material included in Track A was intended for persons who had developed language and numerical skills but who, as a result of cerebral damage, had lost these abilities and become aphasic. The material is organized in much the same way as the training material used for teaching young children.

A basic difference between children and adults concerns deficiencies of initial acquisition (among children) and a loss of previously acquired abilities (among adults). This difference requires determination of comparative deficits (or neuropsychological needs) of impaired versus unimpaired abilities among adults. Thus, a complete neuropsychological evaluation is imperative.

The training material in this final section, even though devised for adult aphasia rehabilitation, may be useful for children as review material and for consolidation of basic abilities that were previously developed.

This brief and selective review of the extensive materials included in Track A is intended to give the reader a conceptualization of the content, organization, and use of

Track A for brain-related training. The content obviously relates to left hemisphere functions principally, but the full requirements of the tasks and the subject's responses require a degree of organization which is aimed at integrating left hemisphere abilities with brain functions more generally.

Fig. 6-1.   Examples of materials in Track A. This is the most extensive Track in REHABIT, containing over 200 training items.

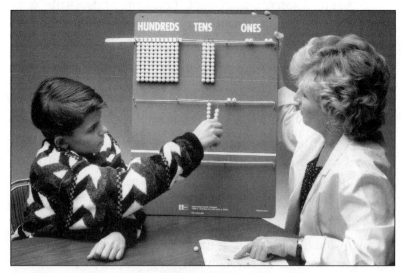

Fig. 6-2.   A REHABIT session using material from Track A.

TRACK B

Materials included in Track B were carefully selected to emphasize tasks with verbal and language content. The items, which range from very simple to complex tasks, are related to the materials in Track A, but require more general problem-solving, abstraction, reasoning, and memory skills. A number of training tasks and procedures from Track B are described below.

One of the items in Track B is a very simple procedure in which numbers are associated with pictures which vary in the number of objects depicted. The numbers themselves are locked into sequence by being pieces of a jigsaw puzzle. As the subject solves the jigsaw puzzle he/she can be instructed about the word that identifies each number (what the number is called), and the sequence of numbers from 1 to 10 according to the way in which they fit into the puzzle.

The next step is to dissemble the jigsaw puzzle made up of numbers, placing each number on the appropriate picture according to the number of objects shown. For example, the number "1" would be placed on the picture of a pail, the number "2" is placed on the picture of two teddy bears, and number "3" on the picture of three balloons, and so on. This exercise helps the subject associate the symbolic representation of numbers with the number of objects depicted, contributing to an appreciation of the quantitative significance of the numerical symbols.

Another item in Track B is also oriented toward developing an association between printed numbers and the number of objects depicted. However, a somewhat different approach is used. The subject is provided with the individual pieces of a jigsaw puzzle. The clues for solving the puzzle are represented not only by the pictorial material, but also by the sequence of numbers from 1 to 10. When the puzzle is solved, the subject can be instructed to observe that the number "1" is beside a single scarecrow, the number

"2" is beside two sunflowers, the number "5" is beside five rabbits, etc.

In addition to providing information about the sequence of numbers from 1 to 10 and their quantitative representation, this task exercises brain functions more generally through the use of the jigsaw puzzle. In order to solve the puzzle the child must learn to observe pictorial elements in detail, and relate them in a meaningful way through use of spatial configurations. Besides numerical content, the task involves recognition of nonnumerical objects and integration between visual-spatial representations and the symbolic meaning of numerals.

The second part of this particular item in Track B involves the same type of task with letters of the alphabet as the significant content. It consists of a jigsaw puzzle in which the solution is dependent upon clues received from nonverbal pictorial representations and letters of the alphabet. When the puzzle is solved the child will discover that the letter "A" is next to a picture of ants, the letter "B" is next to a bear, the letter "L" is next to a lion, and so on. This task, which is designed to develop familiarity with individual letters of the alphabet and their sequence and serve as an introduction to phonics through association with pictures, can be used in conjunction with many of the items in Track A.

The training material in this section gradually increases in complexity. Another item in Track B provides training in recognition and identification of various geometric configurations after a delay interval that may vary in length. For example, on one card is a circle and a plus sign serving as the stimulus figures. After the subject has had an opportunity to view this particular spatial configuration, the card is covered, and after an interval the subject is asked to identify the stimulus figures from a set of four configurations shown on another card.

The tasks increase in difficulty to the point that a series of five geometric shapes must be registered initially and identified not only according to the five different shapes involved, but also according to the sequence and color in which they appeared on the stimulus card.

Although it may seem that training in the ability to identify sequences of geometric shapes is principally a right hemisphere activity, it is important to recognize that verbal and numerical symbols also are represented by spatial configurations. This task therefore proceeds to use letters of the alphabet in the same role that geometric shapes had previously been used. The subject is required to look at a configuration of letters and, after an elected interval, identify the letters that have been observed on a card that includes a number of alternative configurations. The training material then moves on to using words as the stimulus configuration.

If the child has developed simple reading ability and can conceptualize the set of letters as a word, identification of the corresponding word obviously becomes much easier. In fact, the cognitive training technician can use this type of material to provide an introduction to initial phases of reading. For example, the stimulus configuration "trace" must be identified after initially seeing the word among four alternatives consisting of "crate," "trace," "react," and "cater."

The material can be made more difficult by increasing the interval between exposure of the stimulus configuration and exposure of the alternative items from which selection is to be made. The stimulus material itself continues with various combinations of letters of the alphabet and words in cursive writing. The entire process permits an extension from initial registration and recognition of sequence of nonverbal geometric configurations to printed letters of the alphabet, printed words, cursive letters of the alphabet, and cursive words.

The material in Track B contains progressively more difficult verbal material, with the tasks selected according to a theme that requires complex abstractions and reasoning abilities. For example, one of the items is made up of a series of sentences with a key word omitted. Four alternatives are given for each of the missing words. Sometimes more than one word is missing in a sentence and the subject must read the sentence and select the appropriate word among the four alternatives to complete the sentence. This procedure is similar to the Word Finding Test, which has been shown to be extremely sensitive to impairment of left cerebral functions (Reitan, Hom, & Wolfson, 1988) as well as brain functions generally (Reitan, 1972).

An important and practical aspect of having developed familiarity with the symbolic significance of numbers relates to telling time; therefore, several of the items included in Track B are specifically concerned with learning to tell time and concepts about time. One of these items consists of an extensive group of cards on which clock faces are depicted. The face of the clock is identical in each picture, but on each card the background appearance of the clock surrounding the face is different. The child must learn to tell the time shown on the face of the clock regardless of the variability of the rest of the configuration. A similar item is a domino game in which the subject is required to match various time faces, using arabic numerals, roman numerals, and digital faces.

The second item concerned with telling time consists of a clock-face with movable hour and minute hands which can be manipulated by either the child or the technician. The full combination of 12 hours and 60 minutes can be utilized. In using this procedure we recommend that the child be taught not only how to tell time from a clock-face, but that activities which normally occur at various times of the day be associated with the particular times depicted.

To expand the subject's understanding of the concept of time, three additional workbooks are included in this segment. In the first workbook, the subject is introduced to activities which require identification of tenses (past, present, future), synonyms for "before" and "after," cycles of the clock, and the concepts of afternoon, midnight, morning, noon, AM, PM, and scheduling.

The second workbook includes reading a calendar, understanding the concepts of weekdays, weekends, fortnight, and the seasons. The subject is introduced to the concepts of decade, score, century, centennial, millennium, era, and time sequences.

The exercises in the third workbook require the subject to write schedules and work multiple-step problems involving the various concepts of time.

As an additional example of the requirement for reasoning and logical analysis in Track B, one of the items includes thirty pictures representing fifteen pairs of cause-and-effect relationships. For example, one picture shows a man diving into a lake with his clothes on, and the printed question on the back of the card asks, "Why is the man diving into the water with his clothes on?" The subject's task is to sort through additional cards until he/she finds a picture that appears to provide an appropriate answer. The correct picture is of the man swimming to rescue another person. On the back of the second card is the statement, "The man is diving into the water because he wants to help the person who's drowning."

This set of materials can be used either through use of the pictures alone, the printed sentences alone, or finally, through an integration of the pictures and the printed sentences. Although the material is intended to help develop language skills and vocabulary, achievement of this goal is gained through establishing cause-and-effect relationships as well as a description of sequential aspects of behavior. The desired outcome is not only to assist in developing verbal abilities, but to integrate verbal abilities with pictorial representations in a manner designed to promote skills in logical thinking.

The material included in Track B also was selected to train the subject in quantitative relationships as a basis for developing a more sophisticated understanding of the meaning of numbers and fractions. One of the manipulatives intended for this purpose uses interlocking plastic cubes. The cubes can be connected to construct figures of various lengths. This material allows for a great number of activities, all directed toward developing concepts of size and quantitative relationships.

As a simple procedure, the cubes can be connected into rods which can be organized in length from the shortest to the tallest. The subject can then determine how many cubes are required to match the length of a longer rod, and the concept of fractions can be introduced. Combinations of cubes can be assembled to demonstrate that two-fourths are equal to one-half, for example, and that three-fourths plus one-fourth equals the full extent of a given figure.

This material can be used at a very simple level, in terms of matching, and can teach the basic concepts of addition, multiplication, division, and fractions. A number of activity cards are included in this section, and introduce activities which teach addition, subtraction, numerical order, counting, and set. As the subject masters these concepts, additional activities provide training in classification, one-to-one correspondence, conservation, and recognition of patterns.

More advanced concepts can also be taught with this material. Through manipulating the cubes into various shapes described on the activity cards the subject can gain experience in interpreting two-dimensional drawings into three-dimensional objects. Other activities introduce the concepts of volume, ratios, and co-ordinates.

In accordance with our desire to increase motivation by including games or game-like activities in REHABIT, many of the items in Track B are domino-type games, in which the figures are represented by triangles and must be matched in accordance with the two numbers along each side.

For example, if a "4" and a "1" were printed along one side of the triangular figure, it would be necessary to match with a figure that has the same number. The game requires the subject to observe the available stimulus material, organize it as needed for selection, and relate the stimulus material to the configuration that is being formed in the process of the game.

It is obvious that many of the tasks in Track B do not relate exclusively to left cerebral functions. In fact, the items in Track B were deliberately selected to effect an integration of basic neuropsychological functions relating to materials in Track A to materials in Tracks C, D, and E. Besides including elements of numerical or verbal symbols, the material in Track B frequently requires a degree of logical analysis in addition to skill in spatial and sequential elements. A number of the workbooks in Track B emphasize exercises which involve understanding pictorial representations.

In Track B we have emphasized especially the association of pictorial (nonverbal) material with numerical and verbal symbols in order to achieve a degree of integration between these various tracks. Thus, many of the individual items include requirements of a perceptual or performance nature that extend across the entire range of the neuropsychological behavioral model described above.

Fig. 6-3.   Examples of materials in Track B of REHABIT.

TRACK C
Sorting, Classification, Reasoning, Logical Analysis, Planning and Abstraction

Many investigators of intelligence, including some who related intellectual impairment to cerebral damage, have concluded after years of study that abstraction and reasoning abilities represent the fundamental nature of intelligence. Although one might question how thoroughly such abilities are represented by the Stanford-Binet Intelligence Scale, Terman assigned abstraction, reasoning, and concept formation a central role in his definition of intelligence. In the clinical tradition of evaluation of brain-behavior relationships, Gelb, Kurt Goldstein, and others reached the conclusion that abstract (as contrasted with concrete) thinking was the essential characteristic of normal brain functions.

Goldstein carried this distinction to the point that he was far less interested in whether a task could be completed successfully than in how the task was done. If the task was completed through use of concrete thinking approaches, he characterized the performance as defective. He felt that there was no overlap between the abstract and the concrete approach, believing that they were essentially different processes, and that one represented normal behavior while the other indicated impaired brain functioning.

Halstead, in this theory of biological intelligence, identified the use of abstraction, reasoning, and logical analysis — when integrated with input and output — as constituting intelligent behavior. Through years of research and clinical evaluation of individual subjects with and without cerebral damage, our experiences have led to a similar conclusion. In the Reitan-Wolfson neuropsychological model, abstraction and reasoning have been assigned the highest level of central processing, but it is important to recognize that these abilities are integrally associated with the specialized functions of the two cerebral hemispheres. The specialized functions (right-brain and left-brain abilities) relate principally to the content of the material being processed (verbal and language functions versus manipulatory skills and spatial relationships) and these in turn must be analyzed, organized, and understood through abstraction processes. This conceptualization is further supported by evidence that the specialized functions are subserved by the two cerebral hemispheres (Sperry, 1974; Wheeler & Reitan, 1962), whereas abstraction abilities are represented in all areas of the cerebral cortex, including the parts in each hemisphere that are principally involved in the specialized functions (Doehring & Reitan, 1962).

REHABIT, as a brain retraining program, must deal necessarily with the specialized neuropsychological abilities of the brain. In addition, it must effect an integration of these specialized abilities with the general functions of abstraction, reasoning, and logical analysis. Track C therefore represents a central feature of REHABIT, concentrating on basic abilities in abstraction and reasoning while establishing a linkage with verbal and language skills for the left cerebral hemisphere and spatial and manipulatory abilities with the right cerebral hemisphere. The training materials included in Track C were selected to emphasize abstraction and reasoning abilities and place lesser emphasis upon the content of the task.

Because impairment of abstraction, reasoning, concept formation, and analytical abilities is such a common feature among persons with impaired brain functions, it is often necessary to begin brain retraining using the materials found in Track C. Our experience indicates that training of the general aspects of brain functions is usually a prerequisite to training in the specific skills.

Even though the learning-disabled child's limitations are classified as difficulty in the area of academic proficiency and progress, on neuropsychological testing many of these children demonstrate generalized impairment of brain functions. However, it is important to recognize that in practice often the area of academic competence is the only area that is actually tested. These children also show many additional brain-related deficiencies which often go unrecognized unless they are evaluated more generally with neuropsychological testing.

In the individual case, any aspect of impaired brain functions may be sufficient to cause limited academic ability, but failure in the area of abstraction and reasoning is often of major importance. Children need the ability to understand the general context in which they are trying to master specific skills in order for the training to have practical meaning.

It is often stated that individual children have *specific* learning disabilities but, on examination with the Halstead-Reitan Battery, by far the majority of such children have *general* as well as specific deficits. Even the field of learning disabilities seems to be developing an awareness of this fact, which has been known for many years by those who have practiced comprehensive neuropsychological assessments. A recent issue of the *Journal of Learning Disabilities* featured a series of articles oriented to the question of just how specific the deficits actually are in children with specific learning disabilities (1989). Until the child develops sufficient ability in the area of abstraction and reasoning and has a general ability to understand complex situations, it frequently is of limited value to attempt to accomplish training in the basics of academic skills.

One can teach the learning-disabled child rote behavior related to language and numerical symbols, but the potential for development, growth, and generalization of these experiences may be limited. For these children, we have found that initial training with Track C is frequently required, with an approach to the more specific skills represented in Tracks A and E achieved only through an integrative approach using Tracks B and D.

Content of Track C

As in the other Tracks, the items in Track C extend from very simple materials to tasks that are relatively complex. However, especially in Track C, it is important to recognize that even very simple material can be used for training of relatively complex skills in abstraction and reasoning.

The initial step required to develop abilities in this area depends upon careful and accurate observation of recurring similarities and differences in stimulus material. The basic processes of sorting and classifying depend upon such observations. However, even using only a few physical stimulus dimensions, it is possible to develop relatively complicated problems requiring abstraction and logical analysis skills for solution. By adapting the nature of the task to the individual's specific needs and level of competence, many of the very simple items in Track C can be used for rather high-level training.

We will try to indicate some of the ways in which this can be accomplished, but we would also appeal to the ingenuity of the neuropsychologist and the cognitive training technician in developing varied uses for each item. It should always be kept in mind that a particular item may be used at a very simple level of training at one point in the training process and that the same item may be used at a later time in a much more complicated format.

For example, Track C includes a number of bead-stringing activities. One set of material consists of a number of beads of different sizes, shapes, and colors and two stringers. The material can be used to develop motor and manipulatory skills, but it can also be used in a much more complex way to develop higher-level abilities.

The first step in using this item should be to instruct the subject to place the beads on the stringer in order to develop initial familiarity with the material. Since the beads come in various sizes, shapes and colors, a number of additional activities are possible. The next step would be for the technician to string a set of beads, using one of the stringers, and have the subject emulate this procedure using another stringer. Gradually, as the subject develops confidence and familiarity, principles of organization can be introduced.

One procedure might be to sort the beads by color and string all beads of a certain color before another color is added. Another procedure might be to sort the beads by shape, and string all beads of one shape before another shape is started. Another principle might be to string the beads in a sequence so that no two beads of the same color are adjacent to each other. This notion can be further complicated by stringing the beads in a specific size, color, and shape sequence so that the same sequence is repeated in consecutive series.

From these few illustrations it is apparent that a considerable range of sorting and organizing activities is possible. Although the technician should provide examples for the subject initially and guide the subject in using different principles for sorting and stringing the beads, it is desirable to encourage the subject to initiate and develop principles of sorting and to carry out these principles independently whenever possible.

A final activity using this item should lead to comprehension of a principle and recapitulation of a performance in accordance with the principle rather than having to depend upon specific memories. For example, the technician can string beads according to a principle communicated to the subject as the beads are being strung. Then, after having completed the activity, the technician removes the stimulus material. At this point the subject should be given an opportunity to repeat the performance of the technician. Help should be given as necessary to relate the principle involved to the actual activities in order to guide the subject's performance.

The initial phases of this kind of training should be quite simple in nature and adapted to the abilities of the subject. For example, the stringing process might call for the use of two beads of the same color, followed by two other beads of a different color, and so on. The technician should discuss the principle with the subject when the beads are being sorted into their proper groups as well as during the stringing activity. Finally, after the subject has completed the task, the string of beads completed initially by the examiner should be brought out for careful comparison with the string completed by the subject.

It is apparent that even such a simple procedure as stringing beads can be used quite effectively by increasing the organizational complexity of the task. The technician may wish to use beads and stringers at a very simple level in one instance and return to the task at a more complex level, using memory of organizing principles based on color, size and shape when the subject has progressed to a higher ability level. Much of the material in Track C is of such a nature that the task can be adapted to the ability level of the subject.

A number of workbooks in Track C provide exercises in visual perceptual discrimination and categorization of objects. One workbook provides line-drawings with several of the objects in a row being identical except for one of the objects being turned in the wrong position. The subject must identify the identical figures as well as the one that is different from the others. Using this material, he/she is given an opportunity to observe the significance of minor differences in similar spatial configurations and develops an appreciation of the directionality of the figures depicted. In addition, the material provides preliminary training in grouping and classification through questioning the subject about the ways in which the pictures are different and the ways in which they are alike. As the subject is encouraged to identify and explain the characteristics of the various figures, he/she should gradually be helped to appreciate that certain things may simultaneously possess same and different properties and learn ways to categorize and organize based on these features.

Another simple training exercise consists of thirty cards, depicting fifteen pairs of things that go together (such as a hammer and nail, a bat and ball, and a lock and key). When these cards are spread out before the subject, they provide an opportunity for careful inspection and review of the details of the picture, followed by selection of pictures that go together. In this exercise the subject should be questioned about his/her rationale for associating the two objects, regardless of whether the answer is correct or incorrect.

In addition, this material can also be used to facilitate the development of vocabulary and verbal communicational skills. For example, when the subject selects the two pictures that depict a hammer and nail, he/she should be asked questions such as, "What is a hammer used for?" As the child (or dysphasic adult) develops familiarity with the stimulus material, a memory aspect of the task may be introduced. For example, the child can be presented with a picture of a bat and asked to recall by name (either verbally or in writing) the object with which the bat is associated and then proceed to find the correct picture.

A somewhat more complicated task involves discerning the missing object in a given picture. One task in Track C consists of a stimulus card with different types of objects depicted in each of the four quadrants on each card. However, each quadrant is missing one object because a total of four objects is used. In one quadrant a picture may be shown of a lemon, an apple, and a nut. However, the four objects used in total also include berries. On one card the berries are missing. To solve the problem the child must inspect each of the quadrants, determine the missing item by observing the content in the other quadrants, and select the missing item from a series of cards.

On other cards four items are included in each quadrant but one of the items clearly does not belong with the others. It often is easier for a young child, or a person with impaired abstraction and grouping abilities, to respond to an inappropriate item than it is to respond to a missing item. This material provides excellent practice in exercises of this type, ranging from quite simple to somewhat more complex problems.

Using this same task, a memory component may be introduced by using the white circles that are included with the material. One of the circles can be used to conceal or block out individual items in the pictures. When a particular object (such as an apple or a lemon) is covered, the child can be asked to discern from the content of other pictures on the same card which object is missing. These exercises encourage close observation of visual material, identification of the pictures with respect to meaning, and logical reasoning, based upon observation of additional pictures, to effect grouping of objects into meaningful categories.

Another type of organizing procedure that we have found helpful requires the child to use cues to place objects appropriately in a printed grid. One item, for example, consists of a board with 16 squares and a margin around the entire grid. Additional stimulus material consists of cards that vary in color and content. Some of these cards are marked with an outside black border and these cards are used as the "cue" cards to be placed in the margin around the grid.

Such a card containing a blue spot might occupy a certain position and all of the figures that were included in the corresponding row of squares would have to contain the color blue. The additional details relating to a particular square on the grid would require consideration of the coordinates involved. If a cue card in a particular row was identified by the number "3" and a corresponding cue card above a particular column was represented by a flower, the child would have to find a card that contained three flowers to place in the intersecting square.

In this task the variability of the "cue" cards is quite extensive, permitting a great number of organizing possibilities. The material extends from quite simple to relatively complex tasks and is useful in training preschool children with normal brain functions as well as older children and adults who have impaired abstraction and reasoning abilities.

Track C also contains a considerable amount of material that requires the child to establish associations between pictures according to their content. Simple sorting activities may be performed to organize the pictures that belong together, but it is also important to give the child practice in identifying pictures that do not belong with others according to the category represented by the group.

Still other pictures depict activities divided into two phases. For example, the first card may show a picture of a particular type of activity and a second card must be selected to complete the activity. Selection of pairs of pictures, in accordance with the activity involved, assists the child to develop a logical association between the pictures in terms of content and action.

Some of the training materials in Track C are composed principally of a large number of stimulus materials that can be sorted, classified, and grouped in various ways. One item in Track C consists of stimulus figures and sorting trays. The figures vary in color and shape. It is possible to sort the figures according to any number of principles, based upon single characteristics or combinations of characteristics. In addition, these objects can be used to integrate the classification skills of Track C with those of Track A for purposes of counting, basic addition and subtraction principles, naming, spelling, and writing.

The exercises in Track C range from very simple procedures to tasks that are relatively complex. The basic purpose of the material, however, is to permit development of problem-situations for the subject to solve according to an organizing principle. This material is intended to provide training in memory tasks that are integrated with organizing principles in order to permit deduction to facilitate the memory process.

A considerable number of tasks in Track C can be used with subjects who are impaired in maintaining alertness and attention. The basic mechanism in central processing is oriented toward registering incoming stimuli and relating them to prior experiences and skill (as well as memory of previous experiences).

A simple exercise of this type is to underline the number "4" whenever it appears on a page of numbers. It is necessary for the subject to proceed in an orderly fashion, and be alert continuously to identify the number "4." The exercise can also be performed using different numbers (or combinations of numbers) which are selected for the individual exercise. The subject should repeat this task many times in total, with practice being distributed over various training sessions. Gradually, even the brain-impaired subject who initially has great difficulty paying attention to specific stimulus material will begin to develop improved skills (unless there is an underlying disease process that causes progressive pathological deterioration of the brain).

Additional training material is provided for the same type of task using geometric figures, nonsense designs, complex designs, letters of the alphabet, combinations of letters in meaningless configurations, and combinations of letters to form simple words. Obviously, the material extends from simple to complex content requirements, but is consistently organized in a manner that requires alertness, close attention, and continuous concentration. These abilities, which are often impaired in persons with compromised brain functions and in children with learning disabilities (Reitan & Wolfson, 1988c), are fundamental to eventual successful use of the higher skills in central processing. As an additional dimension to the task, the technician may time each performance in order to gain a quantitative record of improved efficiency as practice progresses.

For some subjects it may be necessary to use these focused activities to improve alertness and concentration skills before proceeding to other types of tasks. This determination can usually be made by considering the test scores on the Speech-sounds Perception Test and the Seashore Rhythm Test in the context of other results of the Halstead-Reitan Battery. Poor scores on these tests suggest that these type of activities may provide an appropriate starting point for cognitive rehabilitation.

A number of workbooks included in Track C are appropriate for subjects who require more advanced training in the use of abstraction, reasoning, and logical analysis. Skills that are targeted in these workbooks include the following activities: identifying premises and conclusions, identifying relevant and irrelevant information, recognizing words taken out of context, and identifying a conclusion that does not follow from the given evidence. Mastery of these types of activities allow the subject to communicate more effectively and make reasonable choices based on various kinds of evidence.

People often think that when two events happen almost simultaneously, they must somehow be related. This kind of thinking often results in falsely concluding that one of the events must be the cause of (or the effect of) the other. (I had a bad cold, so I stayed in bed for a week, and the cold got better. Therefore, staying in bed will cure a cold.)

Another rather common error is to mistake an effect for a cause or a cause for an effect. (Every city which has crime has a police force. So if we'd get rid or our police forces, we'd abolish crime.)

The fallacy of false cause can assume other forms, as well as the two forms mentioned above: (3) Mistaking coincidence for cause and effect. (I walked under a ladder, and five minutes later I almost got hit by a car. So walking under a ladder causes bad luck.) (4) Mistaking sequential events for cause and effect. (I heard tires screeching. I looked up and two cars hit each other. So screeching tires cause car accidents.) (5) Mistaking related events for cause and effect. (I saw Canada geese flying northward. Within a week, my daffodils bloomed. Therefore, the geese caused the daffodils to bloom.)

Track C contains several workbooks designed to help the subject learn to distinguish between events which have a cause-and-effect relationship, and events which are merely simultaneous, sequential, coincidental, or somehow related.

When using REHABIT it is important to keep in mind the sequential nature of central processing activities of the brain as represented in the Reitan-Wolfson neuropsychological behavioral model. Incoming stimuli require attention and concentration for initial registration before the specialized or higher aspects of brain function can effectively be utilized to produce an appropriate behavioral response.

Fig. 6-4.   Examples of materials in Track C of REHABIT.

TRACK D

Track D emphasizes the importance of right hemisphere functions in the development of abilities that we believe are important in the practical aspects of everyday living. These functions center particularly around visual-spatial, tactile-spatial, and sequential tasks. While the specialized functions of the left cerebral hemisphere facilitate and abet communicational skills, the functions of the right cerebral hemisphere permit the individual to function efficiently in space and time.

Although the academic orientation and value system of our society places great value on verbal, language, and communicational skills, individual efficiency of performance is heavily dependent upon right cerebral functioning. Nevertheless, the role of the right cerebral hemisphere in behavior seems to be relatively neglected (and probably undervalued) in our society, apparently because of the strong emphasis on proficiencies related to academic training and language. (Obviously, some of the types of training available in an academic setting relate to right hemisphere activities as well, but priority has been given to left hemisphere skills.)

A question has sometimes been raised about whether left or right cerebral lesions are more disabling in human beings. As with many "either-or" questions, the answer may be relatively meaningless because of the different functions subserved by each cerebral hemisphere. In other words, the answer may well be "both." A question of this type probably cannot be answered unless a procedure were available for assigning equal weight and relevance to the functions subserved by each cerebral hemisphere. The Halstead-Reitan Neuropsychological Test Battery was devised according to procedures which might achieve this end, and the Left and Right Neuropsychological Deficit Scales (Reitan & Wolfson, 1988b) might provide a practical answer, but at this time these Scales have not been studied in this respect.

For reasons that recognize the importance of the right cerebral hemisphere, Track D has been developed in considerable detail, especially because the usual academic setting appears to do relatively little to develop abstraction and reasoning abilities in the context of visual-spatial tasks, skills involving sequential elements, and activities requiring performance of problem-solving activities.

The types of training activities included in Track D are relatively familiar to most neuropsychologists, either through their use in various psychological tests of a performance nature or in training and rehabilitation activities. In fact, some of the types of items included in Track D are similar to certain items previously described in other tracks, but are used in a different manner in Track D.

The emphasis in Track D is on the visual-spatial skills in a context of abstraction, reasoning, and logical analysis. Nearly every item in Track D permits development of skills in naming shapes and colors, counting, sorting and grouping, and reproduction after an interval, to stress the integration of memory and visual-spatial organization principles.

Despite the selective nature of the material in Track D, we again emphasize the importance of using the material in as broad a manner as possible, depending upon the needs of the individual subject. In other words, if the subject has difficulties in counting or naming, the stimulus material should be used to assist in developing these abilities. In addition, the difficulty level of the task can be sharply increased by requiring the subject to reproduce various items from memory.

Much of the material in Track D can be used in conjunction with items in other Tracks to increase the subject's reading and writing readiness skills. A number of activities require the subject to observe stimuli carefully and discriminate between similar looking objects, letters (b and d, p and q, etc.), and simple words (was and saw, on and no, etc.).

A large part of the content of Track D makes use of block-design types of tasks. In these tasks the subject is provided with colored blocks or blocks which have designs on each side and is instructed to reproduce a pictured design or pattern using the blocks. The training material includes two- and three-dimensional block design tasks. Some of the material extends to picture designs in which various surfaces of the block contain parts of a picture which must be assembled in order to reproduce the whole picture. With older children and adults it is often useful to allow the subject to study the pattern on the stimulus card in detail and then reproduce the figure without referring to the stimulus card.

Verbal skills can also be integrated into the tasks involving cubes. For example, the subject could choose one of the design cards and hold it out of the technician's line of vision. Then, by giving only verbal information, the subject should instruct the technician about how to produce the figure. Such an activity will provide experience in observing, planning, giving instruction, evaluating how clear the instructions are to other persons, and evaluating the final product.

Other block-design tasks use blocks in the shape of various geometric forms rather than cubes, and these must be combined to reproduce the entire configuration. Items of this type include the familiar parquetry figures and designs that have frequently been used in rehabilitation and brain retraining programs, thereby extending the content and configurations into many kinds of constructional tasks.

Track D also makes extensive use of formboard puzzles of various types. For more impaired or younger subjects, we recommend that these formboards be performed with the use of vision. However, as with the Tactual Performance Test in the Halstead-Reitan Battery, it is very instructive for many subjects to solve the formboard (by placing the appropriate pieces in their proper spaces) with their eyes closed or while wearing a blindfold. This latter procedure also emphasizes the integration of tactile perception and problem-solving of a spatial nature.

As with the other tracks, the training material is generally organized from simple to more complex tasks. However, in Track D we have included a number of tasks in which a single type of training material may be used in different ways to progress from quite simple to more difficult tasks.

For example, sequential picture cards are used quite extensively in Track D. These tasks involve sets of pictures that must be organized in sequence in order to depict an unfolding activity or successive aspects of a story. They are basically similar to the Picture Arrangement subtest of the Wechsler Scales.

In order to maintain organization of the material, one item in Track D includes several sets of such pictures, extending from very simple to relatively complex sequences. Arrangement of pictures in sequence according to a logical principle or analysis of the stimulus material is a very important training activity because of the extent to which it requires initial registration of the stimuli, detailed analysis of visual-spatial information and logical thinking ability to place the cards in the proper sequence.

Track D also includes jigsaw puzzles as a training aid in the use of cues involving various types of spatial relationships to facilitate right hemisphere abilities. One of these jigsaw puzzles, which is relatively simple in nature, must be fitted together in a sequence of pieces that tell a story, integrating an understanding of spatial relationships and sequential organization.

Other stimulus materials in Track D consists of blocks in the shapes of cubes, cylinders, and triangular prisms. Activities on the accompanying workcards involve duplicating patterns and sequences, sorting, categorizing and creating sets, identifying solid and plane shapes, size and property comparisons, and the exploration of two- and three-dimensional representation.

Track D also includes several workbooks that provide a wide range of exercises in dealing with spatial relationships. We feel strongly that actual manipulation of objects is important in brain training (as contrasted with the types of responses usually employed to respond to stimuli on a computer screen), and that neither workbooks nor computer screens alone provide the range of flexibility that is required. However, workbooks do have the advantage of providing an extensive range of exercises, and can be particularly useful in providing material for visual form perception when integrated with actual hands-on exercises.

A final aspect of Track D emphasizes visual-spatial input (or receptive functions) in specific detail. Every item in Track D requires perception of the stimulus material, a degree of central processing, and expression of a response. However, since so many training items emphasize the response aspect (in terms of drawing, manipulating objects, forming and completing designs with objects, etc.), we deliberately included several tasks that depend mainly upon visual form perception. This type of training is particularly important for some children in order for them to develop the basic skills necessary for the visual form discrimination requirements (differential recognition of letters) in reading.

One of these tasks requires the subject to sort objects in accordance with a guide that is provided. The subject must examine each object carefully, determine whether it is the same or different as compared with a number of objects used as guides, and accomplish the sorting on this basis.

Another procedure requires the subject to view complex designs and select from alternatives the design that matches the target figure. Other activities require the subject to observe the stimuli carefully and make decisions about the characteristics of the designs: which figures are similar, larger, taller, in the same position, etc. The technician can greatly expand the utility of these exercises by asking the subject to draw the designs (either using the stimulus figure or from memory), describe them orally and in writing, produce them in three dimensions, etc.

A number of activities in this Track involve the use of grids. The activities provide step-by-step instructions such as, "Move your pencil one space left, up two spaces, left one space," etc. until the subject has created a picture. For reinforcement of the concept of directionality, the technician may include other REHABIT materials. Additional skills involved in these exercises include counting, manual dexterity, auditory verbal comprehension, and following directions.

Fig. 6-5. A REHABIT session using material from Track D, which emphasizes visual-spatial tasks requiring abstraction and reasoning skills.

TRACK E

Track E contains training materials that were selected to provide basic experience in the fundamentals of spatial relationships. Since the problem-solving element was extensively represented in Track D, problem-solving activities in the context of spatial relationships are not emphasized in Track E. Although much of the material in Track E is relatively simple in nature, some of the items explore more complex aspects of spatial configurations.

A number of items provide the opportunity for learning to draw various shapes. For persons with very limited drawing abilities, the beginning exercises should be those which provide dotted lines for the subject to draw over. In other exercises the subject is required to independently reproduce the figure in freehand as exactly as possible. The training material can also be used for drawing figures and designs for which a target figure (sample) has not been provided.

Another item uses a set of cards to illustrate spatial relationships of a relatively simple nature, including over and under, above and below, on and off, next to or beside, in front of, in back of or behind, between objects, through objects, and within objects. Adults usually have no difficulty with simple relationships of this kind unless there is severe damage of the right cerebral hemisphere. In young children, however, rehearsal of these relationships is sometimes highly useful.

Track E also includes a considerable amount of material for basic practice in block-design activities and in solution of simple jigsaw puzzles. As we have noted previously, subjects who are quite limited in their ability to deal with spatial relationships should begin by solving the puzzles with the use of vision. As the individual becomes more proficient in visual-spatial skills, the technician may require the subject to perform the task while blindfolded. Another dimension may be added by asking the subject to complete the task by using only one hand and/or timing the performance.

Pegboard activities are also a component of Track E, using pegboards with a large number of holes and variously colored pegs. Pattern cards provide target stimuli for the subject to reproduce. The training technician may also find it valuable to compose patterns on the pegboard, have the subject observe and review the pattern carefully in order to discern underlying principles, and reproduce the pattern after a delay. This type of task also encourages development of visual-motor skills, directionality (up, down, left, right), color identification, and memory.

Some of the material in Track E was selected to provide training in visual perception of details. In one item a series of pictures are presented on cards, each depicting a scene that includes a great number of details. Target details are identified for the subject and he/she must search each card in order to find them. This activity is intended to develop ability in visual form perception and attention to individual details in the context of distracting figures. In many instances the subject is able to identify the target figure but does not approach the problem of searching for the stimuli with an efficient method. The technician should use these exercises as an additional opportunity to evaluate the subject's problem-solving skills and discuss various ways of completing the task more effectively and efficiently.

Many years ago Strauss and Werner (1941) emphasized the importance of impairment in appreciation of figure-ground relationships among children (see Chapter I). Although this is only one of the many ways in which impaired neuropsychological functions may be manifested behaviorally, it does represent an important area of visual perception.

Summarical Comments

It is important to emphasize that the design and content of REHABIT were carefully developed to relate to both the content of the Halstead-Reitan Battery and the theory of neuropsychological functioning that is implicitly represented by the assessment procedures. Thus, the sequence progresses from a theoretical model of brain-behavior relationships to assessment (diagnosis) of the individual person to treatment (brain retraining) through use of REHABIT. The general characteristics of the theoretical model provide a description of the neuropsychological strengths and weaknesses for the individual subject, and the results of this evaluation serve as a foundation for prescribing a brain-retraining program, using REHABIT, to improve brain functions for each subject. This approach, which integrates theory, assessment and remediation, obviously is distinctly antithetical to assessment procedures which are casually composed by the neuropsychologist according to the subject's own personal evaluation (complaints) and in which areas of training are determined without a full and balanced evaluation of intra-individual strengths and weaknesses.

The integration of theory, neuropsychological assessment, and prescription of a brain-retraining program for the individual subject obviously requires the attention and services of a well-trained and experienced clinical neuropsychologist. A cognitive retraining technician may be of great help in carrying out specific training activities, but close and continued supervision by the neuropsychologist is absolutely necessary.

■

CHAPTER VII

Investigations of the Validity of the Halstead-Reitan Neuropsychological Test Battery for Older Children

Methodological Considerations

Although the Halstead-Reitan Battery for Older Children had been composed as early as 1955, we decided to gain extensive clinical experience with it before performing the first validation study. It was apparent to us that neuropsychological evaluation of the immature brains of children differed in a number of ways from comparable evaluations of adult brains, and that the influence of impaired brain functions on the development of neuropsychological abilities (which was much more a factor among children than adults) was of great significance. We therefore felt that such factors required evaluation through extensive clinical study of individual cases before formal research studies should be carried out.

Considering the fact that during the formative years these abilities are in the process of developing to adult levels, it seemed reasonable to presume that the brain-related performances of adults and children would be represented by essentially the same neuropsychological abilities. We felt that the overall content of the Older Children's Battery should be similar to the Adult Battery, and that the range and type of abilities assessed by each of these Batteries should be essentially identical. In addition, the methodological considerations that had been so important in developing a basis for clinical conclusions about the individual subject would obviously need to be included in the Older Children's Battery. In other words, besides evaluating level (or adequacy) of performance, the Older Children's Battery would also need to (1) identify specific tasks of a simple nature than might have pathognomonic significance for cerebral damage, (2) investigate differential levels of performance as they might relate to the functional adequacy of various parts of the cerebral cortex, and (3) include procedures that permitted testing of the same type of performance on the two sides of the body in order to evaluate comparatively the functional status of homologous areas within each cerebral hemisphere.

These presumptions required a substantial degree of similarity both in content and in methodological aspects of approach in the Older Children's Battery and the Adult Battery. Nevertheless, it must be recognized that before any test (or battery of tests) can be considered to be neuropsychological in nature (as contrasted with being psychological or falling within some other specialty area of psychology), they must be shown to demonstrate sensitivity to the biological status of the brain. As noted in the first chapter of this volume, failure to meet this requirement in the area of child neuropsychology — as contrasted with adult neuropsychology — resulted in significant confusion and seriously limited the progress of understanding children's brain-behavior relationships. Unfortunately, continued neglect of this obvious requirement still constitutes a significant problem in the field of child clinical neuropsychology.

In researching the Older Children's Battery, our first formal step was to compare results obtained by normal children with results of children having documented cerebral disease or damage. We were also well aware that the behavioral correlates of brain functions were represented by a broad array of abilities rather than by only a single test (Bender, 1956) or a limited number of tests measuring selected functions (Werner & Strauss, 1939, 1940, 1941). In effect, it was not our purpose to devise or identify a "test for brain damage," as had been done in many clinically-oriented studies. Instead, our aim was to evaluate the entire spectrum of neuropsychological functions as they related to the biological condition of the brain, and such an approach obviously required that the Battery represent the full range of abilities subserved by the brain.

In terms of an orderly exposition of research findings, we felt that it was necessary first to gain a comprehensive understanding of the tests in the Battery as they related to cerebral damage generally considered. This overall view would provide a framework within which more specific studies of selected functions could be evaluated. In this manner we hoped to achieve a balanced representation of brain-behavior relationships, one which would clearly involve both behavioral and neuropathological variables and categories. In terms of the general representation, our first purpose was to learn the ways in which the full range of tests included in the Battery related to a heterogeneous representation of cerebral damage.

More specific questions concerning selected neuropsychological variables or more specific neuropathological conditions were obviously important to recognize, and their meaning would be enhanced if they could be placed in the context of a comprehensive framework. This approach represents a fundamental difference between the areas of clinical neuropsychology and behavioral neurology. As pointed out by Reitan and Wolfson (1992a) and Rourke and Brown (1986), the methodology of clinical neuropsychology utilizes measurement techniques and assessment approaches that include continuous distributions (that present the general picture) as well as dichotomous distributions (that reflect specific deficits).

The field of behavioral neurology is oriented toward evaluation of specific deficits and their cerebral localization and is limited in its representation of the general neuropsychological functions of the cerebral cortex. The field of clinical neuropsychology has recognized that general functions must be assessed to provide a context within which to evaluate the significance of specific deficits (Goodglass & Kaplan, 1979). While this approach was implicit in the original development of the Halstead-Reitan Batteries for both adults and children and was designed to provide a more meaningful assessment of the individual subject, the same approach applies to the sequence of development of research findings.

Validity Studies

Our initial study (Reed, Reitan, & Kløve, 1965) was an overall investigation of an extensive number of tests in the Older Children's Battery to determine each test's sensitivity to cerebral damage. In this study 50 brain-damaged children ranging in age from 10-14 years were matched for chronological age with 50 control children. It was possible to match the subjects quite closely; no pair of children differed in age by more than three months. Diagnoses of brain damage were based upon a complete neurological evaluation of each subject, and children were included in the study only if they had a documented neurological diagnosis.

A broad range of neurological diagnoses was deliberately included to ensure that any deficit shown on the neuropsychological measures would represent general brain pathology rather than a selective kind of deficit that might be associated with some specific condition. Diagnoses of children in the study included the following major categories of cerebral disease or damage: neoplastic disease, closed and penetrating traumatic brain injuries, infectious involvement of the brain (including both viral and bacterial infection), vascular malformations, idiopathic epilepsy, epilepsy with known etiology, degenerative nervous system disease, and developmental malformations. Some additional children with definitive brain pathology were included in the study, even though the etiology was uncertain.

The control children were volunteer subjects. Complete anamnestic information was obtained for each child, and there was no evidence suggesting that brain damage had been sustained. In order to ensure that this group had normal brain functions, a neurologist obtained complete history information and performed neurological examinations on about one-half of the children, and findings were normal in each case. On this basis we presumed that each of the 100 children included in the study had been given an equivalent basis for classification to the brain-damaged or control group (depending upon the neurological findings obtained), and that a perfect differential classification had been made with respect to the independent variables.

The groups were essentially identical for chronological age; each group had a mean age of 12.48 years. Since the children were closely matched in pairs, this was expected. Although educational achievement and grade placement are often adversely affected by brain damage, the brain-damaged group had a mean grade placement of 5.33 years and the controls had completed 5.96 grades. This difference was statistically significant ($p. < 05$), but the fact that the brain-damaged children were not far behind the normal control group suggests that in general these children were not grossly impaired in terms of grade placement. However, the two groups showed striking and highly significant differences between Wechsler Full Scale IQ values. The brain-damaged group had a mean FSIQ of only 84 as compared with a FSIQ of 106 for the control subjects. These latter data strongly suggest that brain damage had a strikingly adverse effect on development of general intelligence.

The two groups of children were compared on an extensive series of tests, including summary variables as well as each individual subtest from the Wechsler Scale, the Trail Making Test (Parts A and B), the Category Test, the Tactual Performance Test (Total Time, Memory, and Localization components), the Seashore Rhythm Test, the Speech-sounds Perception Test, the Finger Tapping Test (dominant and nondominant hands), and other measures.

The results demonstrated a substantial difference between the two groups, with the brain-damaged children performing more poorly than the controls on every measure. Statistical comparisons of individual variables indicated that only two tests (the Picture Completion subtest of the WISC and the Memory component of the Tactual Performance Test) failed to reach statistical significance beyond the .01 level. The findings in this study therefore demonstrated that heterogeneously considered, the effects of cerebral damage are essentially equally heterogenous and diversified in their neuropsychological manifestations. Compared with results obtained in comparable studies of adult subjects, however, the findings indicated that on tests that were directly dependent upon language functions, children showed greater impairment than adults (who tend to show a greater degree of deficit on tests that require immediate problem-solving capabilities).

It is well known that among adult subjects, tests of verbal abilities are usually considered to reflect stored experience and consolidated, long-term memory functions.

These abilities, which develop over the years, are generally more resistive to the effects of cerebral damage than relatively complex tasks for which immediate past experience is not directly relevant. However, among children, in whom the limiting effect of brain damage may be more heavily imposed upon acquisition of neuropsychological skills, verbal tests (including measures such as Vocabulary) were among the measures most seriously affected by brain damage. Despite this observation, the more striking result of the study was that cerebral lesions tend to manifest themselves neuropsychologically along an extensive variety of dimensions, tending to modify the relevance of conclusions concerned with comparative strengths and weaknesses.

We should note that for every test there was a degree of overlap between the two groups, with more than one in ten brain-damaged subjects excelling his/her matched control on each measure except for the Coding subtest from the WISC. This finding indicates that using only a single test for diagnostic purposes would be an unacceptable and inaccurate practice, although the area of clinical neuropsychology appears to have developed sufficiently at this point so that recognition is given to the aim of evaluating brain-behavior relationships generally rather than to effect a diagnostic classification based on a single measure.

Boll (1974) performed a replication and extension of the study by Reed, Reitan, and Kløve (1965). He compared 27 brain-damaged children with 27 control children who had no past or present evidence of cerebral damage or disease. The groups were matched for age, race, sex, and handedness. Each group included 16 males and 11 females. The brain-damaged subjects had a mean age of 146.59 months (SD, 19.19) and the controls had a mean age of 143.15 months (SD, 18.92). This difference did not approach statistical significance.

The brain-damaged children in this study represented a variety of neurological diagnoses, including neoplasms, traumatic injuries, congenital vascular anomalies, inflammatory and infectious involvement, and perinatal lesions. The diagnosis for each child was based upon a complete neurological evaluation and was entirely independent of results obtained on neuropsychological testing. The control subjects were volunteers. The tests were individually administered by carefully trained neuropsychological technicians who did not know either the diagnoses of the children or the purpose or design of the study.

Boll used a more extensive series of tests than Reed, Reitan, and Kløve (1965). He included Grip Strength with both hands, the Tactile Form Recognition Test with both hands, the Tactile Finger Recognition Test, Finger-tip Number Writing Perception, the Name Writing Test with each hand, and the Reading and Spelling scores from the Wide Range Achievement Test (WRAT). In addition, handedness, footedness, and eyedness were determined using the standard procedures of the Halstead-Reitan Battery for Older Children.

As might well be expected, the results of this study indicated striking differences between the two groups. However, certain tests — including the Picture Completion subtest of the WISC, the Memory and Localization components of the Tactual Performance Test, and results on the Tactile Form Recognition Test — failed to reach acceptable probability levels for statistically significant differences between the two groups. Other measures that did not reach statistically significant levels included Finger-tip Number Writing Perception with each hand and Tactile Finger Localization with the left hand.

The principal generalization based upon the data analysis and group comparisons was that the brain-damaged group demonstrated extensive impairment that covered a broad range of neuropsychological abilities. Considering the overall results, Boll concluded that the areas of deficit included verbal intelligence, performance intelligence, pure motor skill, motor problem-solving functions, visual-motor problem-solving skills, tactile perception, academic progress, verbal and nonverbal aspects of auditory perception, visual-motor reaction functions, incidental memory and alertness, concept formation, and even such a simple task as name writing speed with the preferred hand as compared with the nonpreferred hand.

Although in this volume we will not review formal research results concerned with the effects of cerebral damage for children in the 5- through 8-year-old age range, we can comment that essentially similar results have been obtained when comparing brain-damaged and control children in this age group (Reitan, 1974; Reitan & Boll, 1973). On the great majority of measures used in any single study, children with cerebral damage show evidence of generalized impairment and perform more poorly than control subjects.

Additional investigations were done which further documented the generalized impairment of children with cerebral damage (Selz & Reitan, 1979a, 1979b). These studies used groups of 25 control children, 25 learning-disabled children, and 25 brain-damaged children. The purpose of these studies was to identify the unique neuropsychological features of children with learning disabilities compared with control and brain-damaged groups. However, these investigations also demonstrated the striking and consistent differences between control children and brain-damaged children, and identified certain consistent characteristics that were relatively unique to the group with learning disabilities. For our present purposes, we will review the data relevant to the effects of documented brain damage.

The 25 control subjects in the Selz and Reitan studies were volunteers from two school systems; 15 children came from a small-town school and 10 were from a suburban school. None of these children had evidence of brain dysfunction, and all were functioning normally without any academic problems or complaints. Obviously, this does not mean that every child was performing ideally, but none of the children had evidence of past or present cerebral disease or damage and all were progressing adequately within their normal class placement. The mean age of this group was 138.16 months (SD, 13.08).

Among the brain-damaged children, 9 attended city schools, 7 attended suburban schools, and 9 were enrolled in small-town schools. The subjects were selected on the basis of compelling evidence derived from neurological examination (including specialized neurological diagnostic procedures), and each child had independent and documented evidence of structural brain damage or a clinically significant brain disorder. Selection of these children (as well as the control children) was entirely independent of psychological test performance. No attempt was made to select brain-damaged children according to location, type, or severity of cerebral damage, and it appeared that the total group represented heterogeneous brain involvement. The entire group included cases of intracranial tumor, both open and closed head injuries, arteriovenous malformation, encephalitis, cerebral abscess, idiopathic epilepsy, and birth injuries. The mean age of the brain-damaged group was 133.8 months (SD, 17.31).

In this study the dependent variables included Verbal IQ, Performance IQ, Full Scale IQ, and the results of tests included in the Halstead-Reitan Battery for Older Children (including the Reitan-Indiana Aphasia Screening Test). Multivariate analysis of variance indicated that the mean values were not the same for all three groups, yielding a highly significant difference. Using the three diagnostic categories, a discriminant analysis based on only 13 of the measures correctly classified 23 of the 25 controls, 19 of the 25 children with learning disabilities, and 18 of the 25 children with brain damage.

Four of the children with brain damage were very mildly impaired, and from the statistical analysis, appeared to be control subjects. A certain degree of overlap of this kind is to be expected, but the results indicated quite clearly that the test results, generally considered for the children in the three groups, permitted differential classification into their appropriate categories. This study demonstrated that children with learning disabilities tended to be intermediate to the other two groups.

The outstanding finding of this investigation, however, was that the children with cerebral damage performed much more poorly than the control subjects. In fact, among the three groups, discriminant analysis yielded an overall correct classification of 80% (although it must be recognized that these findings stand in need of cross-validation). When the group with learning disabilities was deleted from consideration, it appeared that differentiation between the control and the brain-damaged subjects was achieved with a hit-rate of about 87% correct classifications.

These various studies provide an unequivocal answer to the first question that must be asked: Does the Halstead-Reitan Neuropsychological Test Battery for Older Children provide a valid and sensitive procedure for differentiating between children with normal brains and children with damaged brains? This is a question that is critical to the utilization of the test battery, and the answer clearly is positive.

The same data provide a basis for offering an answer to a question that is clinically significant for the groups involved: Is the Halstead-Reitan Neuropsychological Test Battery for Older Children sensitive to generalized neuropsychological impairment in groups of heterogeneous brain-damaged children? The answer is again unequivocally positive. The results of these studies therefore provide the framework and establish the foundation for further investigations of specific questions concerned with brain-behavior relationships in children.

In studies of the neuropsychological correlates of cerebral damage in adult subjects, it has been observed that relatively complex and demanding tasks, particularly when they require the subject to adapt to novel circumstances, are more sensitive to cerebral damage than tests which use familiar, routine, and over-practiced subject matter or performances. For example, the Verbal subtests of the WAIS tend to reflect impairment less effectively than tasks that are not dependent upon prior learning or stored information. Among children, however, studies have shown that there are striking degrees of impairment among brain-damaged groups, especially on the Verbal subtests of the WISC-R. This clear disparity between the consequences of cerebral damage among adults and children may very possibly represent the adult's resistiveness to lose acquired abilities compared with the child's difficulty acquiring the same type of neuropsychological abilities. In other words, once these complex developmental skills are eventually acquired and mastered, they seem to be relatively resistant to the effects of cerebral damage.

In order to pursue this question further, a study was done to determine the differences between brain-damaged and non-brain-damaged children on a heavily practiced task (Reitan, 1971a). We decided to investigate facility in name writing, presuming that children had probably as much experience with this task as with any other skilled performance. The study was conducted using two groups of children aged 5, 6, 7, and 8 years. One group had documented evidence of cerebral damage and the other group was composed of normally functioning children who had no past or present evidence of cerebral disease or damage. There were two dependent variables: the time required for name writing with each hand measured separately, complemented by the difference in time between the two hands. Therefore, three scores were produced by each subject.

Three hypotheses were proposed as a basis for comparing the performances of the two groups: (1) on the average, normal subjects using their preferred hand would complete the task more rapidly than would the brain-damaged subjects, (2) the normal subjects would also perform the task better with their nonpreferred hand, and (3) the difference in time between the preferred hand and the nonpreferred hand would be less for normal subjects than for brain-damaged subjects, and would show a greater degree of variability in the brain-damaged subjects.

Even though brain damage may be diffusely represented and involve both cerebral hemispheres, it is not uncommon for one cerebral hemisphere to be more involved than the other. If the left cerebral hemisphere (across from the right hand) were principally involved, it seemed likely that impairment of the right upper extremity might ensue, and as a result the subject might become left-handed. In this case, we would expect the nonpreferred (right) hand to perform quite poorly, because initially the impairment on that side had been sufficiently severe to cause a change in handedness. In some instances it was likely that even with left cerebral damage a child might continue to be right-handed, and would demonstrate a degree of impairment on the preferred (right) side. In these cases, however, the comparative performances of the two hands would also be deviant compared to normal performances, with the nonpreferred (left) hand performing almost as well as the preferred hand.

Our hypothesis about a difference in performance between the two hands was therefore based upon an expectation of deviant performances among the brain-damaged children, in many instances with the nonpreferred hand performing quite poorly compared to the preferred hand; however, in a few instances, we predicted that the reverse effect would occur. Of course, these were specific hypotheses falling within the context of our general interest in whether the effects of brain damage might be sufficiently pervasive to manifest themselves even on a highly-practiced performance.

The results of comparisons of the two groups were quite striking. Writing their names with either their preferred or nonpreferred hand, the brain-damaged subjects required nearly twice as much time as the normal subjects. The time difference between the two hands was also distinctly deviant for the brain-damaged group, with a tendency toward a bimodal distribution. In most cases, however, the nonpreferred hand was slow compared to the preferred hand, suggesting that the brain-damaged child had special difficulty adapting to the task with the hand that had not had much previous practice. However, since some differences were in the negative direction (with the preferred hand actually performing worse than the nonpreferred hand), a parametric statistical approach to the data was not appropriate. In fact, to convert raw scores to scaled scores, we devised a rule system which reflected deviant performances in the same direction quantitatively, essentially in accordance with our hypotheses.

Scores for individual subjects in the two groups, based upon these converted scores (which are essentially similar to those used in computing the Neuropsychological Deficit Scale [see Reitan & Wolfson, 1988b for adults and this volume for older children]), yielded a correct classification of individual subjects to their appropriate groups in a total of approximately 80% of the cases. Thus, the general hypothesis of this study was quite clearly answered. The results indicated that the effects of cerebral damage permeated even such an overly-practiced task as name writing, a finding which strongly suggests that among children neuropsychological impairment is not at all limited to types of tasks that are novel or complex.

Following completion of the above study, we were aware that despite the clear differentiation between groups of brain-damaged and non-brain-damaged children, the results might possibly have been caused, at least in part, by another factor: a lack of development of skill in name-writing, especially since the children ranged in age mainly from six to eight years. Conceivably, brain-damaged children in this age range have had less of an opportunity than normal children to learn to write their names and to perform this task with skill. Therefore, we decided to replicate the study using children in the 9- through 14-year-old age range (Reitan, 1971b).

In this study, 35 children with independent neurological evidence of cerebral damage were compared with non-brain-damaged control subjects. The children were matched in pairs for race, gender, and chronological age. The brain-damaged children were selected from patients who had been referred to the hospital because of documented brain disease or damage rather than because of other problems (such as learning deficiencies or behavioral disorders). These latter types of difficulties may have been present in the brain-damaged group, but they did not serve as selective factors in composition of the group. All of the children in the non-brain-damaged control group were volunteers from a single school system who had agreed to participate in a study concerned with psychological testing.

The procedure was essentially the same as in the previous study. Each child was asked initially only to write his/her name and was requested to do it in a perfectly normal manner. No mention was made of doing the task either rapidly or slowly. The amount of time required was recorded by the examiner. The subject was then asked to write his/her name in exactly the same way a second time, using the nonpreferred hand. The time required to complete the task with each hand and the difference in time between the two hands served as the sources of data. To convert raw data to scaled scores we used exactly the same rule system that we used in the previous study.

The results indicated that for name-writing with the preferred hand the normal children used significantly less time than did the brain-damaged children. The same result occurred in comparisons of the nonpreferred hand. The brain-damaged subjects required more time than did the control subjects to write their names with their non-preferred hand than with their preferred hand.

Analysis of the data indicated that the results were sharply different between the two groups, and yielded approximately 80% correct classification of control and brain-damaged subjects. In fact, in terms of correctness of classification, the results were essentially identical to those found in the initial study of younger children. Even though the conversion scales had been developed for use with younger children, there appeared to have been no depletion of accuracy of prediction. Thus, the findings indicated that compared with their own matched control subjects, brain-damaged children in the 9- through 14-year age bracket were essentially as deviant in name-writing speed as were younger brain-damaged children.

The findings suggested that the previous results obtained with the younger children did not occur because the subjects had not yet learned adequately to write their names. Instead, the results indicated that brain-damaged children seem to have a tempo that is different from the tempo of normal children. It can probably be safely assumed that children in the 9- through 14-year age bracket have learned to write their names, and that for most of them the task is essentially an over-learned skill. The results have even greater significance in suggesting that brain damage in children permeates and influences even over-learned performances, rather than causing impairment only of novel and complex tasks.

The Significance of Dysphasia in Children

Although the concept of developmental dysphasia (or dysphasia in children) has received considerable attention in the literature, it is nevertheless a concept which is not clearly understood. One would presume that the use of the term *dysphasia* would implicate impaired brain function as a basis for deficient use of language and verbal symbols. By definition, aphasia is considered to be a loss, resulting from cerebral damage, in the ability to use specific language and verbal symbols for communicational purposes.

The problem in applying the term dysphasia to children stems from the fact that in adults this condition has generally referred to a *loss* of previously acquired verbal and language skills. In children, however, the condition relates to a *failure to develop* normal verbal and language skills. In adults, the onset of aphasia is generally relatively sudden and is associated with a cerebral lesion that is subject to unequivocal diagnosis. In children, the limitation of development of language and verbal skills is usually gradual, occurring in the course of acquisition, and in many such instances no definitely discernable cerebral lesion is present.

This latter problem stems, of course, from the fact that development of language and verbal skills is quite variable among normal children (as reflected by the normal probability distribution). It is therefore difficult to differentiate between children whose impaired language functions are due to brain damage and those children whose language abilities fall in the lower part of the normal probability distribution. Considering these circumstances, the concept of developmental dysphasia is not unexpectedly blurred.

Some investigators apparently do not find it necessary to implicate the brain as a condition for diagnosis of developmental dysphasia. For example, Wyke (1978) identifies developmental dysphasia as a deficit in acquiring normal language functions in children who have normal or above normal intelligence and hearing ability which permits the perception of verbal sounds. Zangwill (1978) supports this definition by stating that the term developmental dysphasia refers to children who have limited or faulty development of language, and goes on to say that these children do not otherwise show any gross neurological or psychiatric disability. He suggested that the outstanding handicap in developmental dysphasia is "social and educational rather than physical," and that sensory or motor deficits of any severity are rarely present.

These positions have led to the belief that children with developmental dysphasia are only slow in developing language skills. If a brain-related basis is invoked as an explanation, the reference is to a vague and essentially unexplained concept such as "cerebral immaturity" or "developmental lag." In this sense, a child with developmental dysphasia is only slow in developing language and verbal skills, and therefore essentially comparable to younger children in these abilities. Obviously, this conceptualization of developmental dysphasia differs strikingly from dysphasia in adult subjects, both in terms of the neuropathological condition responsible for the disorder as well as in the behavioral manifestation (which in adults is hardly thought to be only a reduction in level of verbal and language functions).

Rapin and Wilson (1978) felt that some children with developmental dysphasia had impairment of brain functions which was responsible for the condition. They wrote, "Furthermore, it appears that some children who are delayed in acquiring language may not be suffering from a lesion in the central nervous system, but rather from delay in the maturation of relevant neurological systems." This latter group of children, who had "delay in the maturation of relevant neurological systems," would seem essentially to correspond with the children who fall toward the lower end of the normal probability distribution. Obviously, Rapin and Wilson have adopted a position about developmental dysphasia that does little to further an understanding of the interaction between cerebral damage and development, within the lower part of the normal range, of language skills.

Benton (1964) presented a detailed consideration of developmental dysphasia, and proposed that it was a condition in which a child shows a relatively specific failure of the normal growth of language functions, manifested either by disability in speaking (though speech understanding might be essentially normal) or disability both in understanding and expression of speech. He felt that the disability was "specific" in the sense that it could not readily be ascribed to other factors, such as deafness, mental deficiency, motor disability or severe personality disorder. Although difficult in the individual case to identify a specific etiology, Benton felt that there was a steadily growing body of evidence which implicated cerebral damage as an essential causative factor of developmental dysphasia in children.

Gaddes (1980) espoused a position in which he was unequivocal in relating impaired brain function to the development of language skills. His review of the evidence led him to conclude not only that the brain is generally involved in developmental dysphasia, but involved specifically concerning location and severity of damage in the brain centers necessary for language. He felt that mild dysfunction in the language centers will cause a child to have a specific learning disability, whereas more severe damage in these centers will merit a diagnosis of dysphasia. He states explicitly, "It is important to remember that while the child with specific developmental dyslexia is free from gross neurological damage as shown on the neurological examination, this, of course, does not exclude the possibility of very minimal neurological brain dysfunctions. As well, there may be a further possibility of a genetic deficit that somewhat interferes with normal reading" (p. 252).

From even a brief review of the literature, it is clear that it has been difficult to differentiate between cerebral damage which results in impairment of development of language functions and slow or retarded development of language functions by children who merely have lesser aptitude. The situation again represents one in which there is a need for empirical data and direct observation and examination of children with known cerebral damage, children who have learning disabilities but do not show evidence of cerebral damage, and normal control children. Rather than debating the issues, there is much to be said for acquiring the data that might resolve the questions.

Reitan (1985) has presented detailed descriptions of the performances of children with cerebral damage, learning disabilities, and normal brain functions on the Reitan-Indiana Aphasia Screening Test. These were the subjects previously studied by Selz and Reitan (1979a), and their characteristics have been described in an earlier section of this chapter. In summary, the controls consisted of 15 boys and 10 girls, with a mean age of 138 months. The learning disability group was composed of 19 boys and 6 girls, with a mean age of 135 months. The brain-damaged group consisted of 15 boys and 10 girls with a mean age of 134 months. No statistically significant differences were present in the age distributions of the three groups.

The control children were normal volunteers. The learning-disabled children were generally at least two grades behind their expected grade level. In addition, these children had been recognized by the classroom teacher as having significant learning difficulties and had been referred for additional evaluation and remedial help. The third group, consisting of subjects with diagnosed cerebral lesions or significant brain disorders, were diversified in terms of their diagnoses, and not uncommonly were having significant difficulty making normal academic progress. The learning-disabled and brain-damaged groups therefore overlapped with respect to impairment in developing language and academic abilities. The control children and the learning-disabled children had normal results on their neurological evaluation.

Results on the Reitan-Indiana Aphasia Screening Test were evaluated by assigning scaled scores to each deficit that was found, using the method described in this volume in the chapter for administration and scoring of the tests (Chapter IX). A score of 0 was given for performances that fell within the normal range. However, if a particular deficit was found, it was assigned a score of 1, 2, or 3, depending upon the significance of the deficit for cerebral damage. For example, spelling dyspraxia received a scaled score of 1 whereas dysnomia, which is a more definite and significant indicator of cerebral impairment, received a score of 3. Each of the specific deficits that may be discerned from the Reitan-Indiana Aphasia Screening Test, as well as their assigned scaled scores, are discussed in Chapter IX.

This particular study included an approach toward validation of the data that is rarely used; we elected to predict the results that would be found in each group and to compare the predicted result with the actual outcome. This procedure was possible because we had transformed the performances of each child for each variable into a 4-point scale ranging from normal to definitely impaired (scores of 0, 1, 2, and 3).

Having had considerable experience with children in each of the groups, we felt that it might be possible to predict the percentage of children in each group who would show each type of deficit. For example, if we expected none of the control subjects to show evidence of body dysgnosia, the prediction would be that all 25 of these subjects would have a score of 0 for that variable. If we felt that none of the controls would show evidence of dysnomia, all 25 children would be placed in the normal category. Dysnomia occasionally occurs in brain-damaged children, and we actually predicted that 4 of these 25 children (16%) would show this particular deficit. In this manner predictions were made for each variable in each group without knowledge of the actual results.

It is obvious that any attempt to make predictions of this kind necessarily depends upon having had a considerable amount of clinical experience with the broad range of children that fall in each of the three groups being studied, as well as a good deal of knowledge of the types of results that were reflected by the dependent variables. It was therefore possible that such predictions would end up being strikingly deviant from the actual outcome. On the other hand, if the predictions agreed relatively closely with the actual outcome, there would be a very powerful validation of the experimental findings.

We subdivided the 12 types of deficits derived from the Aphasia Screening Test into several groupings for presenting the predicted and actual results. The first grouping consisted of body dysgnosia, auditory verbal dysgnosia, and visual number dysgnosia. These deficits were selected as a group because they occur very rarely among control children, and even rather rarely among brain-damaged children.

As shown in Table 7-1, we predicted that none of the control children would demonstrate these deficits, and the actual outcome data indicated that this prediction was in fact true. We also predicted that none of these deficits would occur among the 25 children with learning disabilities, and this prediction again was confirmed. However, we felt that it was likely that one child in the group of 25 brain-damaged children (4%) would show these deficits. As indicated in Table 7-1, body dysgnosia and auditory verbal dysgnosia were each demonstrated by one child (4%), whereas two children with brain damage (8%) showed evidence of visual number dysgnosia.

TABLE 7-1

Predicted and actual incidence of "rare" aphasic symptoms in control children, learning-disabled children, and brain-damaged children.

Deficit	Control %		LD %		BD %	
	Predicted	Actual	Predicted	Actual	Predicted	Actual
Body Dysgnosia	0	0	0	0	4	4
Auditory Verbal Dysgnosia	0	0	0	0	4	4
Visual Number Dysgnosia	0	0	0	0	4	8

Considering the rare occurrence of these particular deficits, one could question why tests for them were even included in the examination. It is important to recognize that when these particular deficits are present, they have serious implications for impairment of brain functions. From a clinical point of view it is important to discern deficits of this kind, even though they occur rarely.

The next grouping of deficits from the Aphasia Screening Test was composed of the type of disorders frequently manifested by children with learning disabilities. As seen in Table 7-2, these deficits included visual letter dysgnosia, dysnomia, dysgraphia, dyscalculia, and central dysarthria. Table 7-2 also shows that we expected none of the control children to demonstrate visual letter dysgnosia or dysnomia, but we estimated that one child in the control group (4%) would show dysgraphia, dyscalculia, and central dysarthria. The outcome results for the control children were just a little better than we had predicted. One child showed evidence of central dysarthria, but none of the control children manifested any of the other difficulties.

TABLE 7-2

Predicted and actual incidence of aphasic symptoms seen frequently in children with learning disabilities and children with brain damage.

	Control %		LD %		BD %	
Deficit	Predicted	Actual	Predicted	Actual	Predicted	Actual
Visual Letter Dysgnosia	0	0	16	12	16	12
Dysnomia	0	0	16	12	16	12
Dysgraphia	4	0	24	24	24	36
Dyscalculia	4	0	40	40	40	36
Central Dysarthria	4	4	40	40	40	40

Among the children with learning disabilities and brain damage, we felt that these disorders would be more common and comparable in the two groups. As seen in Table 7-2, we predicted an incidence ranging from 16%-40% for these variables. The actual outcome was very close to the predicted frequencies, confirming our estimates of the more common manifestations of dyscalculia and central dysarthria than the other deficits.

We elected to treat dyslexia as a separate variable because of its central role among learning-disabled children, and the predicted and actual incidence of dyslexia is shown in Table 7-3. We felt that one of the 25 control children (4%) would probably show evidence of reading impair-

TABLE 7-3

Predicted and actual incidence of dyslexia.

	Control %		LD %		BD %	
Deficit	Predicted	Actual	Predicted	Actual	Predicted	Actual
Dyslexia	4	4	56	52	44	40

ment on the Aphasia Screening Test, and this prediction was confirmed. We predicted that reading difficulty would actually be more common among the children with learning disabilities than among the brain-damaged children, respecting the fact that each child in the learning-disability group had been identified by the classroom teacher as having specific academic deficits which needed evaluation and remediation. Thus, we predicted that 56% of the children in this group would manifest positive findings on the Aphasia Screening Test, and the actual outcome was 52%. Of course, reading difficulties are not uncommon among children with cerebral lesions, and we predicted that 44% of these children would have such evidence. The actual outcome was 40%. Again, the correspondence between predicted and actual values was extremely close.

Table 7-4 presents the predicted and actual results for right-left confusion and spelling dyspraxia, two types of deficits that are fairly common even among control subjects in the 9- through 14-year age range. Therefore, we predicted that 24% of the control children would manifest right-left confusion and spelling dyspraxia. Our predictions for these variables were rather deviant from the outcome; more children than expected actually showed evidence of right-left confusion, and less children than expected demonstrated spelling dyspraxia.

TABLE 7-4

Predicted and actual incidence of "common" symptoms.

	Control %		LD %		BD %	
Deficit	Predicted	Actual	Predicted	Actual	Predicted	Actual
Right-Left Confusion	24	36	48	48	48	28
Spelling Dyspraxia	24	12	76	76	68	68

Our predictions of the frequency of these deficits among the children with learning disabilities turned out to be exactly in accordance with the actual outcome. As we had predicted, children with brain damage also frequently manifest evidence of spelling dyspraxia. However, in this brain-damaged sample, the incidence of right-left confusion was strikingly low, not only deviating from our predicted frequency, but actually being lower than the frequency for the control sample in this study.

The final variable we evaluated was constructional dyspraxia. We expected this deficit to be more common among brain-damaged children than among the subjects with learning disability, and to occur rarely with control children. As shown by the values in Table 7-5, these predictions were essentially confirmed.

TABLE 7-5
Predicted and actual incidence of constructional dyspraxia.

	Control %		LD %		BD %	
Deficit	Predicted	Actual	Predicted	Actual	Predicted	Actual
Constructional Dyspraxia	4	8	32	32	48	52

After we made predictions about the frequency of each deficit for each group, we were able to compute mean scores for the predictions as well as for the actual outcome results. As seen in Table 7-6, the controls had a predicted mean of 0.64 and an actual outcome of 0.80. This means that the average performance of the control children was nearly perfect on the Aphasia Screening Test, since any type of deficit would have contributed a minimum score of *1*. Predictions for the learning-disabled group yielded a mean of 5.88 points; the actual outcome was 5.72 points. The brain-damaged group performed just a little worse than the children with learning disabilities, earning a predicted mean of 6.24 points (which agreed exactly with the actual outcome).

TABLE 7-6
Predicted and actual mean scores (based upon ratings from 0 to 3 for each variable) for control children, learning-disabled children, and brain-damaged children.

	Control	**LD**	**BD**
Precicted Outcome	.64	5.88	6.24
Actual Outcome	.80	5.72	6.24

It is apparent from these summarical findings that basic and simple aspects of language abilities are substantially impaired in groups with learning disability or brain damage, but that performances are essentially normal for control children. This observation led us to tally the number of children in each of several categories to determine differences in the distributions for the three groups. These results are shown in Table 7-7.

TABLE 7-7
Performance of groups on the Aphasia Screening Test and classification of subjects based on aphasic deficits.

	Total Deficit Score			
Groups	**0**	**1**	**2 or more**	**Correct Classification**
Control	12	11	2	92%
Learning-Disabled	2	4	19	76%
Brain-Damaged	2	2	21	84%

In total, 23 of the 25 control children (92%) had total scores of *0* or *1*. More specifically, 12 of the control children made no errors at all on the entire Aphasia Screening Test. Eleven children demonstrated either spelling dyspraxia or right-left confusion, and 2 of the 25 children had difficulties which extended beyond this level.

Children with learning disability or brain damage were rarely perfect in their performances, and usually accumulated a substantial number of points reflecting their deficits. In fact, 19 of the children with learning disability (76%) and 21 of the brain-damaged children (84%) had scores of 2 or more points. These results suggest that the Aphasia Screening Test can be a very valuable screening procedure for identifying children with learning disabilities or brain damage. In addition, the results demonstrate that the Aphasia Screening Test is useful in identifying impairment in the ability to use language and verbal symbols for communicational purposes.

Concerning the varying positions reviewed at the beginning of this section about the nature of developmental dysphasia and its relationship to the biological condition of the brain, our results strongly confirm the position of Gaddes (1980), who felt that brain-damaged subjects would perform significantly worse than controls and that learning disability, at least in most cases, resulted from a more subtle type of cerebral impairment. In turn, these empirical findings argue strongly that (1) a condition such as developmental dysphasia can be identified using even simple techniques and procedures of examination, (2) the deficits manifested by children with developmental dysphasia are related to cerebral damage, and (3) clinical evaluation using the Aphasia Screening Test can provide very useful information not only among children with definite cerebral damage but among children with learning disabilities as well.

Comparisons of Performances of Brain-Damaged and Non-Brain-Damaged Children on the Neuropsychological Deficit Scale

The Neuropsychological Deficit Scale (NDS) provides extensive information about the performances of individual children:

1. Raw-scores for each of the 45 variables composing the NDS can be converted to clinically significant categories. These categories are numbered *0* (perfectly normal performances), *1* (normal but not excellent performances), *2* (performances that fall in the range of mild to moderate neuropsychological impairment), and *3* (raw scores that are definitely deviant and impaired). These normative ranges provide a basis for evaluating the results of the individual child on each of the 45 variables.

2. There are 45 variables which contribute to the Total NDS score. These variables, in turn, have been organized into three methods of inference categories: Level of Performance, Dysphasia and Related Variables, and Right/Left Comparisons.

The Level of Performance category is composed of six subcategories: (1) Motor Functions, (2) Sensory-perceptual Functions, (3) Visual-spatial Skills, (4) Attention and Concentration, (5) Immediate Memory and Recapitulation of Past Experiences, and (6) Abstraction, Reasoning, and Logical Analysis Skills. The items contributing to the Dysphasia and Related Variables category are taken from the Reitan-Indiana Aphasia Screening Test. The Right/Left Comparisons category is subdivided into two categories: (1) Motor Functions, and (2) Sensory-perceptual functions.

Except for the last category, Right/Left Comparisons, the various areas of function can be used to evaluate results for the individual child in the principal categories of function that are included in the Reitan-Wolfson neuro-psychological model. Thus, determining the individual child's mean score in each of these categories and sub-categories results in a profile of abilities and identification of areas of deficit or of special abilities (weaknesses and strengths in terms of neuropsychological functioning). The child's Total NDS Score can be compared to mean performances of brain-damaged children and non-brain-damaged control children.

3. Cut-off points and estimated errors in classification at these points of both control and brain-damaged children are provided for the total scores that summarize the 25 variables that contribute to Level of Performance, the 8 variables that compose the section on Right/Left Comparisons, and the 12 variables that make up the section on Dysphasia and Related Variables. In addition, a cut-off point is suggested for the Total NDS Score together with estimated misclassifications in groups of both brain-damaged and non-brain-damaged children.

In summary, the information based upon the NDS permits (1) characterization of the adequacy of each score earned by the child, (2) determination of patterns representing strengths and weaknesses in neuropsychological performance, (3) an estimate of the overall adequacy of the child's neuropsychological abilities, and (4) a basis for inferring the presence of significant neuropsychological deficit. This information, in turn, has proved to be very helpful in developing a therapeutic rehabilitation program for the individual child.

Our preliminary research results on the NDS were developed by comparing a group of 35 brain-damaged children and 35 controls who were matched for gender and were closely similar in chronological age. The average age was 141.23 months for control subjects and 141.26 months for brain-damaged children. The severity of impairment in the brain-damaged children ranged from very minimal brain damage to definite and serious deficits. Every child had unequivocal independent neurological evidence of damage to the brain tissue or significant neurological evidence of cerebral disease. This group was deliberately quite variable in the types of cerebral damage in order to achieve a more representative status. The non-brain-damaged control children were volunteers from one small-town school and one suburban school. None of the controls had any history or evidence of brain damage or dysfunction, and each child was functioning normally without any special academic problems or complaints.

Table 7-8 presents means and standard deviations for the scores representing each of the sections of the NDS (Level of Performance, Dysphasia and Related Variables, and Right/Left Comparisons) and for the Total NDS Score. It is apparent that the mean values for the brain-damaged children were generally twice as large as the means for the controls, indicating significant impairment in the former group. These differences were highly significant statistically in every comparison of pairs of means. Table 7-8 includes cut-off points for each of the sections as well as for the Total NDS Score. Estimated misclassifications of subjects, using these cut-off points, are also provided.

The reader will note that the cut-off point of 43/44 for the Total NDS Score is well above the mean score for the control children and well below the mean score for the brain-damaged children, thus providing a relatively conservative basis of differential classification. Of course, it is possible to be conservative in this respect, considering the extremely large difference between the means for the two groups.

The most striking difference between the two groups was shown on the mean scores for Dysphasia and Related Variables. This result occurred because control subjects demonstrate relatively few errors on the Aphasia Screening Test. This phenomenon is further documented by the fact

TABLE 7-8

Means and standard deviations for brain-damaged and control groups on various sections of the Neuropsychological Deficit Scale (NDS) and for the Total NDS.

Neuropsychological Deficit Scale (NDS)

Group		Motor Functions	Sensory-perceptual Functions	Visual-Spatial Skills	Attention and Concentration	Immediate Memory	Abstraction, Reasoning, and Logical Analysis	Total Level of Performance
Controls	M	6.29	5.15	4.06	1.91	2.23	2.63	22.27
	SD	3.28	3.40	2.66	1.59	2.19	2.04	10.40
Brain-Damaged	M	14.05	10.77	7.69	3.78	3.31	6.03	45.63
	SD	4.69	5.81	2.97	1.84	2.19	2.37	16.03
Learning-Disabled	M	9.61	7.00	4.61	4.26	2.43	4.65	32.56
	SD	3.95	4.12	2.48	1.80	1.84	2.24	9.97

TABLE 7-8 (continued)

Total NDS

Group		Level of Performance	Right-Left Differences	Dysphasia and Related Deficits	Total NDS
Controls	M	22.27	6.79	1.37	30.43
	SD	10.40	2.80	1.42	12.97
Brain-Damaged	M	45.63	13.74	7.97	67.34
	SD	16.03	5.03	6.98	24.32
Learning-Disabled	M	32.56	8.35	7.04	47.95
	SD	9.77	2.71	4.07	11.23
Cut-off Point for Controls vs. Brain-Damaged		33/34	9/10	3/4	43/44
Estimated Misclassification					
Controls		14%	14%	9%	14%
Brain-Damaged		23%	23%	37%	17%

217

that the estimated misclassification of control subjects is very low for these variables, whereas it tends to be somewhat high for the brain-damaged children. Although control subjects make very few errors on this test, a number of brain-damaged children are also capable of performing these relatively simple tasks essentially without error.

As is well recognized, the data derived from the Aphasia Screening Test is reflected by a dichotomous distribution, and whenever a pathognomonic sign approach is used there is a tendency to generate a considerable number of false negatives. Evaluation of results using the Aphasia Screening Test simulates the procedure generally applied and used in the field of behavioral neurology, but the HRB complements this approach with evaluations of adequacy of performance and quantitative comparisons of performances on the two sides of the body.

Table 7-9 provides means for each of the 45 variables that constitute the NDS as well as means for the total score reflecting performance in each of the areas of function. Each variable (or test) numbered 1 through 45 is identified in Chapter IX.

These values can be used as guidelines for assessing the performance of the individual child on each of the 45 variables comprising the NDS and determining deficits in any particular area. As mentioned above, Tables 7-8 and 7-9 provide an opportunity to construct a profile of neuropsychological abilities for the individual child. It would be possible to plot the results for each area of function for each child to represent graphically areas of strength and weakness. However, before recommending the use of such a graphic profile, we would prefer to develop results on larger and perhaps more representative samples. This may be particularly necessary, since certain areas of function are based upon considerably more variables than others.

TABLE 7-9

Means and standard deviations for control and brain-damaged children aged 9 through 14 years on each variable of the Neuropsychological Deficit Scale.

Level of Performance — Variables 1–25

Motor Functions (1-7)

	N		Age (Mo.)	1	2	3	4	5	6	7	Total
Controls	35	Mean	141.23	.94	.83	1.03	.80	.66	.83	1.20	6.29
		SD	18.39	.92	.84	.97	.86	.75	.74	1.01	
Brain-Damaged	35	Mean	141.26	1.86	2.11	1.91	2.09	2.17	2.20	1.71	14.05
		SD	20.65	1.10	1.06	1.20	1.02	.97	1.01	1.23	

Sensory-perceptual Functions (8-14)

		8	9	10	11	12	13	14	Total
Controls	Mean	.77	.86	.66	.94	1.03	.60	.29	5.15
	SD	1.02	.93	1.07	1.04	.97	.96	.70	
Brain-Damaged	Mean	1.43	2.00	1.91	1.77	1.66	1.20	.80	10.77
	SD	1.34	1.12	1.18	1.27	1.29	1.35	1.28	

Visual-Spatial Skills (15-18)

		15	16	17	18	Total
Controls	Mean	1.23	1.09	1.00	.74	4.06
	SD	1.10	1.11	1.07	.81	
Brain-Damaged	Mean	1.80	1.80	1.86	2.23	7.69
	SD	1.28	1.06	1.20	.96	

Attention and Concentration (19-20)

		19	20	Total
Controls	Mean	.91	1.00	1.91
	SD	1.00	.96	
Brain-Damaged	Mean	1.89	1.89	3.78
	SD	1.09	1.12	

219

TABLE 7-9 (continued)

		Immediate Memory and Recapitulation (21-22)			Abstraction, Reasoning, and Logical Analysis (23-25)				Total Level of Performance
		21	22	Total	23	24	25	Total	Total
Controls	Mean	1.17	1.06	2.23	1.06	.83	.74	2.63	22.27
	SD	1.13	1.17		1.04	.77	.84		10.40
Brain-Damaged	Mean	1.80	1.51	3.31	2.06	2.14	1.83	6.03	45.63
	SD	1.12	1.27		.93	1.02	1.13		16.03

Right/Left Differences (26–33)

		26	27	28	29	30	31	32	33	Total
Controls	Mean	1.09	1.06	1.09	.46	1.00	.66	1.03	.40	6.79
	SD	1.13	.92	1.00	.81	1.20	.86	.94	.55	2.80
Brain-Damaged	Mean	2.09	1.94	2.17	2.26	1.31	1.43	1.71	.83	13.74
	SD	1.08	1.22	1.16	1.10	1.39	1.02	1.11	1.16	5.03

Dysphasia and Related Deficits (34–45)

		34	35	36	37	38	39	40	41	42
Controls	Mean	.17	.00	.34	.00	.17	.00	.09	.17	.00
	SD	.70	.00	.47	.00	.56	.00	.50	.56	.00
Brain-Damaged	Mean	.66	1.14	.71	.74	.86	.69	.60	.80	.60
	SD	1.14	.99	.45	.97	.99	1.26	1.20	.98	1.20

		43	44	45	Total	Total NDS Score (1-45)
Controls	Mean	.06	.37	.00	1.37	30.43
	SD	.33	.48	.00	1.42	12.97
Brain-Damaged	Mean	.74	.43	.00	7.97	67.34
	SD	.97	.49	.00	6.98	24.32

The reader is referred to Chapter IX for specific instructions and tables used in converting raw scores to NDS scores for each of the 45 variables, computing means for each of the areas of function, and for determining the Total NDS Score.

The results of Tables 7-8 and 7-9 make it quite clear that the NDS is extremely sensitive to the effects of cerebral damage and dysfunction and provides significant information about analysis of neuropsychological deficit for the individual child.

Research Comparisons of Brain-Damaged, Learning Disabled and Control Groups Using the NDS

A recent study (Reitan & Wolfson, 1988c) used NDS scores to characterize and compare normal, learning-disabled, and brain-damaged children. The same 35 children with brain damage and 35 children with normal brain functions presented above were used for this study, and 23 children with learning disabilities were also included. Age differences between the groups did not approach statistical significance.

Although none of the children with learning disabilities showed any evidence of abnormalities on the physical neurological examination, each child demonstrated significant problems in school. In every case these problems had been formally noted in the classroom and the child was referred for evaluation because of learning deficits. These children also demonstrated retardation of one year or more in reading and/or spelling on the Wide Range Achievement Test. However, none of the learning-disabled children had a WISC-R Full Scale IQ below 80.

Raw scores were converted to NDS scores and means were computed for each of the three groups in the following subcategories: (1) Motor Functions, (2) Sensory-perceptual Functions, (3) Visual-spatial Skills, (4) Attention, Concentration, and Immediate Memory, and (5) Abstraction,

Reasoning, and Logical Analysis. A Total Level of Performance score was also obtained by adding the subtotals of these five subcategories. The results for the three groups are depicted in Figure 7-1.

Multivariate analysis of variance yielded highly significant differences between the three groups, with the control children having the best mean scores in every subcategory as well as the best Total NDS Score. The children with learning disability had intermediate scores in every area except for Attention and Concentration. On this section their scores were significantly worse than even the brain-damaged group.

In each of the other subcategories the brain-damaged group performed most poorly. Comparisons of paired groups for the Total NDS Score were highly significant in each instance, clearly indicating that when the neuropsychological variables were considered in total, the controls performed best, the group with learning disabilities was intermediate, and the brain-damaged group performed most poorly.

The results of this study clearly demonstrated that differential levels of performance characterized the neuropsychological functions of control children, learning-disabled children, and brain-damaged children. This finding was not particularly surprising, although the quantitative results help to provide guidelines for clinical interpretation of the protocols of individual subjects.

The striking finding in this study was the severe degree of deficit shown by children with learning disabilities in the area of Attention and Concentration. This result would appear to have definite implications for remedial approaches. Prior research has indicated that impairment in abstraction, reasoning, and logical analysis has constituted a significant problem for children with learning disabilities (Reitan, 1985; Selz & Reitan, 1979a), but the great difficulty that

LEVEL OF PERFORMANCE

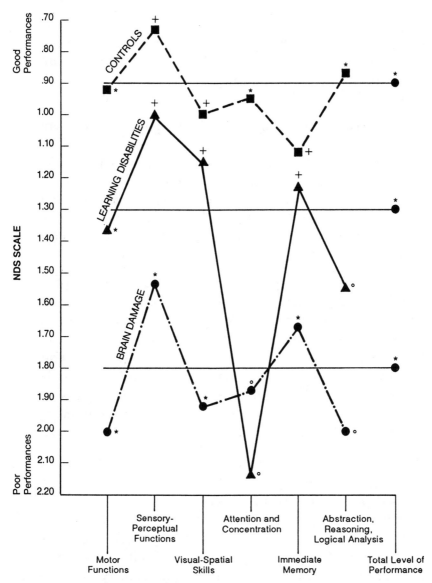

*Significantly different from both other groups
+Significantly different only from the brain-damaged group
°Significantly different only from controls

Fig. 7-1. Comparative performance in various neuropsychological areas of normal children, children with learning disabilities, and brain-damaged children in the 9- through 14-year age range.

these children have with relation to other areas of neuro-psychological functioning is in the area of Attention and Concentration, indicating that they need structured help focused on developing primary attentional capabilities.

It appears, therefore, that in addition to abstraction and reasoning deficits, children with learning disability have great difficulty at the first level of central processing, which is concerned with registration of incoming material to the brain and maintenance of continued attention or concentration. If a child is limited in the ability to register information per unit of time, it is obvious that additional aspects of central processing will suffer.

The comparative performances of the three groups of children used in this study — and the strikingly deviant pattern of the learning-disabled group — would have been much more difficult to discern without the type of scoring provided by the Neuropsychological Deficit Scale for Older Children. It would therefore appear that the NDS may be particularly advantageous as a basis for grouping test results in research analyses as well as in the clinical interpretation of results for individual children.

Emotional Problems of Adjustment Associated with Brain Damage

The interaction of cognitive, conative, and emotional aspects of behavior, either in persons with brain damage or in normal subjects, tends to be underestimated. While some forms of behavior may emphasize one or another of these aspects, it must be recognized that almost all human behavior, regardless of when and where it occurs, involves elements of all three types. Evaluating and understanding the behavior of a particular individual therefore requires a focus oriented toward integration of intellectual and cognitive functions, conative factors, and emotional responses.

Nevertheless, standard practice tends to segregate and differentiate these various kinds of behavior, with clinical descriptions frequently separating them as if they were independent entities within the behavior of the individual subject. However, a meaningful understanding of the behavior of the individual depends upon an integrated comprehension of the interaction (rather than differentiation) of these aspects in producing the behavioral end result. In fact, the brain-injured child may appear to have limited motivation and an impaired ability to initiate appropriate action, but these limitations may be largely determined by intellectual and cognitive impairments.

In turn, there is no question that behavior described as an "emotional response" may be determined in part by cognitive deficits. The interaction of problems deriving from these three areas has been recognized historically in the writings of many investigators, as clearly illustrated by Goldstein's (1942a) description of the catastrophic reaction (or extreme behavior responses), resulting essentially from an interaction of frustration with environmental circumstances and impairment of the "abstract attitude." Although attributing catastrophic responses to frustrating circumstances in everyday living resulting from impairment of the "abstract attitude" appears to be an oversimplification, there is no doubt that such interactions exist. In fact, apparently for purposes of convenience in communication (regardless of the extent to which fractionalization tends to retard understanding the total end-product of behavior), we still find many examples of this kind.

In a book that is undoubtedly valuable for understanding the behavior of persons with brain injury, Rosenthal, Griffith, Bond, and Miller (1983) give essentially separate attention to areas of communication disorders, cognitive deficits, disorders of memory, and behavioral sequelae, not to mention a subclassification of the types of physical impairments that may result from brain injury. Their chapter on behavioral sequelae, for example, cites types and examples of behavioral disturbances that are almost certainly related to intellectual and cognitive impairment, but cognitive impairment as a determining factor is at best only alluded to; variables cited as being of influence in determining behavioral dysfunction included premorbid factors, site of brain lesion, and environmental factors.

Apparently, this omission of intellectual and cognitive problems resulted from the fact that cognitive deficits were previously considered in the volume by other authors in a separate chapter. Even the category of "personality changes" following brain disease or damage is probably, in many cases, principally a matter of behavioral change that results from impairment of basic cognitive abilities (Reitan & Wolfson, 1988b and this volume). It is clear that additional attention needs to be directed to the interaction of cognitive, conative, and emotional responses to brain damage in attempting to understand the integrative influences on end-result behavior of persons with cerebral damage.

Much the same type of problem exists in identifying etiological factors in the individual case that predispose a person toward deviant or impaired behavior. In many instances, brain damage is definitely and unequivocally established through neurological diagnostic procedures, observations and measurements at the time of brain surgery, or at autopsy. In many other cases, however, more subtle damage (or damage of a different type) has undoubtedly occurred in many children in whom a definitive neurological diagnosis has not been established (Kennedy & Ramirez, 1964). Neuropsychological testing for purposes of identifying neurological factors obviously is not of importance in cases where the diagnosis has already been established by unequivocal neurological findings. However, even in such cases, it is important to recognize that the behavioral consequences of cerebral damage represent quite another domain of evidence as contrasted with the type of evidence (contrast studies, etc.) on which the neurological diagnosis is based.

In many children who do not have definitive neurological evidence of brain damage but nevertheless still show
the presence of deviant and impaired behavior, it becomes
particularly important to have developed neuropsychological diagnostic methods that can identify the impairment as
brain-related rather than due to other causes. While some
writers (e.g., Ross, 1967) have denied the necessity of en-
cumbering the clinical situation with inferences about etiology, stating that observation of the defective or impaired
behavior is sufficient as a basis for devising intervention
strategies and procedures, careful reflection has made it
clear that the more that can be understood about the child
and the circumstances that have given rise to the impaired
behavior, the more likely it is that the clinician will be able
to devise an appropriate and effective program of treatment
or intervention.

A number of neuropsychological problems and circumstances may predispose a child to experience extremely
stressful situations. These nearly always derive from a
faulty understanding of the neuropsychology of the child,
coupled with the imposition of unrealistic demands or pressures to achieve. To illustrate this point, we will discuss the
case of a 10-year-old boy with unrecognized neuropsychological deficits, principally involving the left cerebral hemisphere.

Harry: A Child with a Problem of Academic and Social Interaction

Harry was referred to a child guidance center because he
was blocked in his learning, withdrawn, feeling defeated,
and crying easily. Harry's father had been trying to make
him compete with his peers in the areas of sports and
academics, and had come to believe that his son's failures
resulted from an "ornery attitude." The parents also reported that Harry had a "spastic muscle condition" in his
right leg that caused a slight limp. At the age of six Harry

had had measles with a high temperature. His developmental history was normal.

Conventional testing by the clinic psychologist led to the impression that Harry tended to be passive and dependent, but felt punished every time he wanted to relax into dependency. Right-left confusion and difficulty organizing verbal responses were also noted.

The clinic referred Harry for neuropsychological testing to determine whether there was any cerebral damage and, if so, to investigate its possible interaction with the child's emotional problems. More specifically, did Harry respond to excessive parental pressure by wanting to be passively dependent and angrily resistive to demands? Or had some form of brain damage left him with inadequate intellectual resources to meet parental and academic demands (even though these demands would not be excessive for most children)? The answer to these questions would influence the counseling approach toward the parents and determine which educational procedures to apply.

The WISC-R showed a 21-point disparity between Harry's Verbal IQ and Performance IQ values. The Verbal decrement was consistently shown on each of the subtests. All of the Performance subtest scores, with the exception of Coding and Mazes, exceeded the highest Verbal subtest scores. Harry's Wide Range Achievement Test scores indicated that his academic progress was even more limited than one might expect in consideration of his relatively low Verbal IQ.

Neuropsychological tests indicated a level of performance consistent with that obtained on the Performance subtests of the WISC-R. However, certain of the findings quite definitely indicated mild impairment of brain functions. Despite the fact that Harry was strongly right-handed, on the Tactual Performance Test he was somewhat slow with his right hand as compared with his left hand. Furthermore, his grip strength was 17 kg in his right hand as compared to

18 kg in his left (nonpreferred) hand, and he showed a very mild tendency to fail to respond to a tactile stimulus applied to the right hand when a competing stimulus was applied to the left face. He also demonstrated mild difficulties in tactile finger recognition, but on this test he made more errors on the left hand than on the right hand.

The above results indicated that there was mild, chronic damage, principally to the left cerebral hemisphere, and certain suggestions of minimal involvement of the right cerebral hemisphere as well. Further, the findings that implicated dysfunction of the left cerebral hemisphere were perfectly compatible with the low Verbal IQ and inadequate academic achievement.

The Aphasia Screening Test also indicated that Harry had some difficulty in interpreting the symbolic significance of letters. These results suggested that the left hemisphere dysfunction provided the basis for his difficulty in the appreciation of letters and words, both in understanding what was said to him and in his own verbal expression. He performed fairly well on complex concept formation tasks, as long as the stimulus material did not relate to language. The restriction of his weaknesses to the language area, rather than a much more general area of deficit, probably was a favorable prognosis for academic progress and emotional adjustment.

Harry experienced with painful sensitivity the discrepancy between his limited verbal abilities and his much higher nonverbal skills. Pushing him to perform better in school probably accentuated his defeatist attitude and only exaggerated the negative elements in his interaction with his parents. There was a serious risk that Harry would avoid areas of behavior that require verbal communication, such as learning fundamental school subjects, verbal interaction with other people, and the ability to express feelings through language. He required a remedial approach directed towards repeated positive reinforcements for verbal activity, geared to his developing ability level. When Harry seemed ornery and willful, he was reacting to the frustrations imposed by the limitations of his verbal abilities that resulted, at least in part, from mild left hemisphere dysfunction.

Next, we will present the case of a child with a somewhat different problem.

Charles: A Child with Superior Intelligence and Academic Difficulties

Charles was a 9-year-old boy in the fourth grade. He was referred to a child guidance clinic because he acted younger than his age, did not get along well with other children, and was failing in school despite several previous examinations indicating that he had superior intelligence. His birth and development were normal, and the medical history was noncontributory.

Projective tests suggested that Charles was conflicted between giving in to the dependency needs his mother encouraged and becoming assertive (at the risk of displeasing his mother). His father was described as "coolly intellectual."

Although emotional problems stemming from the personal interactions in the family might have been responsible for the disparity between the reports of measured intelligence and academic achievement, there was a question about cerebral dysfunction. The parents reported that Charles was ambidextrous and had poor motor co-ordination. Conventional psychological testing showed that Charles had some difficulty in changing set and achieving accuracy of responses. He also experienced trouble in copying geometric figures and in reading.

The present neuropsychological testing confirmed Charles's problems of academic progress that were unexpected in view of his superior intelligence. Although he was well along in the fourth grade, his academic achievement levels were in the third grade level. Neuropsychological examination indicated that his basic adaptive abilities were in the normal range. Even though he performed adequately on the Category Test, the Tactual Performance Test, and the Trail Making Test, certain of the test results strongly suggested the presence of mild damage involving principally the left hemisphere.

Although Charles tended to be ambidextrous, he wrote with his right hand and probably was more right-handed than left-handed. Nevertheless, his finger tapping speed was not as fast with the right hand as with the left hand. The Tactile Form Recognition Test and the Finger-tip Number Writing Test results suggested slightly more difficulty with the right hand than with the left. Disparities in lateralized functions therefore included both motor and sensory-perceptual functions.

Despite the high level of abilities shown by this child, these lateralizing signs indicated some mild cerebral dysfunction, primarily involving the left hemisphere. Since language functions are generally subserved by the left hemisphere, some of Charles's difficulty in academic achievement was probably attributable to cerebral damage. In view of his high level of general intelligence and adaptive abilities, with the help of tutoring his prognosis seemed favorable for overcoming his present academic difficulties.

Psychotherapy for Charles and his family appeared to be indicated to resolve the personality problems that centered around dependency on his mother and a sense of distance from his father. In this case neuropsychological examination provided evidence suggesting a basis for inadequate school progress and the need for special, individualized attention for developing academic skills.

The knowledge gained from interrelating psychological and neurological data emphasizes the inadequacy of the old procedures of applying counseling techniques to children whose problems are diagnosed as psychogenic, and academic training procedures for children diagnosed as brain-damaged. Such facile distinctions can be made only at the risk of overlooking some of the needs of the individual child. Brain-damaged children frequently require intensive counseling as well as academic training, and the child with a psychogenic learning disturbance is often helped by specialized tutoring in conjunction with psychotherapy.

We could recount many instances of gross or obvious impairment of neuropsychological functions which resulted in deviant responses within the context of social expectations. However, it is important to recognize that there are a great number of additional instances in which the emotional trauma may be even greater among children who experience severe emotional stress resulting directly from unrecognized neuropsychological problems. Without neuropsychological evaluation these children, many of whom have average intelligence levels and demonstrate the presence of psychological disorders on interview, projective tests, and other clinical psychological evaluation procedures, will not be differentiated from children whose emotional problems of adjustment are not complicated by impaired brain functions.

Qualitative versus Quantitative Neuropsychological Changes as a Result of Cerebral Damage

A review of the history of clinical neuropsychology reveals a recurring question about the extent to which neuropsychological deficits following brain damage are represented by quantitative or qualitative changes, or possibly an interaction of both. Quantitative deficits would obviously be reflected by numerical scores resulting from scaled measurements. Thus, changes of this type, which have been emphasized in the tradition of quantitative measurement in

American psychology, would be manifested by brain-damaged children obtaining lower scores than normal children. The quantitative approach would also be reflected by comparative differences in level of performance on various measures, since quantitative assessment would still serve as the basis for demonstration of such differences.

Qualitative deficits have also been proposed, and impairment of this type would not necessarily be reflected by the quantitative score obtained, but instead by the manner in which the problem was approached. In fact, certain investigators (e.g., Goldstein, 1942a, 1942b) have argued that the quantitative score one earns has little significance, because exactly the same score might be earned by a brain-damaged child and a normal child, even though the neuropsychological functions used by the brain-damaged child reflected impairment. Goldstein contended that brain damage resulted in impairment of the abstract attitude and the exclusive use of concrete approaches in problem-solving. As a result, he considered it to be necessary to observe the performances of the brain-damaged subject to determine the method used to accomplish the task in order to understand whether limitations had been imposed by brain damage.

Luria (personal communication, 1967) had a very similar orientation toward this question. He felt that little, if anything, could be gained by attempting to translate neuropsychological deficits into quantitative values, and believed that it was necessary to observe the performance style of the brain-damaged individual in order to understand that person's limitations. More recent considerations along this same line are implicit in Kaplan's "process-oriented" approach.

Many neuropsychologists would believe that both quantitative results and observations of performance deficits are relevant to clinical assessments. In other words, a quantitative score might validly reflect the limitations of the brain-damaged individual, but an experienced clinician might gain additional insights by observing the types of deficits manifested by the subject attempting to solve the task. Thus, quantitative deficits (limitations in degree) and qualitative deficits (limitations in the type of process used) might both be significant in the assessment process.

However, other neuropsychologists, while accepting the above contention, would cite the criterion of replicability as a hallmark of scientific methodology which should be observed. Quantitative expression of performances by the subject in a structured and standardized testing procedure constitutes a set of circumstances deliberately designed to produce replicability (reliability) of results. This occurs because a complete description of testing circumstances, procedures, and materials can be specified, resulting in an exact replication for each subject. This argument goes on to point out that unless reliability of measurement is achieved, at least to a substantial degree, there would be only limited validity of the measurements with resulting limitations of scientific meaning.

The scientific hallmark of replicability (reliability) may also be considered with regard to identification of qualitative deficits in performance. In this instance the individual neuropsychologist observes the test-taking performances of the subject and reaches conclusions based upon an impressionistic description (which is inescapably personalized) of how the subject approached and performed the task. There is no doubt that some observers (such as Luria), who had a great deal of personal experience in studying brain-damaged persons individually, could offer insightful descriptions of behavior.

It must also be recognized, however, that in clinical practice such observations are made only by the examiner, and there is every reason to believe that substantial differences in both the description of the subject's behavior as well as conclusions about the behavior would differ from one examiner to another. A degree of reliability in examiner-observations could possibly be achieved through extensive training, but the great variability in the processes used both by normal and brain-damaged subjects would make this difficult. In fact, assessment and evaluation based upon clinical observations might well be considered more of an art than a science, with the required artistic skill varying greatly from one observer to another.

Considerations of this kind led Halstead and Reitan to emphasize standardized procedures which produced quantitative results as the basic methodological procedure underlying the Halstead-Reitan Batteries. The aim was to achieve replicability in measured results among the broad range of practitioners as contrasted with the variable artistic clinical skill of those who tested brain-damaged subjects. This policy decision about general procedure, however, is intended in no way to demean the clinical skill that can be achieved by individual clinicians.

It should also be noted that use of a standardized and replicable procedure in data collection in no way obviates or even interferes with the use of artistic clinical observation by those neuropsychologists who feel that they are skilled in this area. At the same time, it should be stated that clinical observation (as contrasted with quantitative measurement of performances) should not be proposed (as Goldstein and Luria have done) as the *only* valid method to identify the deficits of brain-injured persons.

It has been possible to investigate the question of validity of quantitative approaches to assessment of neuropsychological deficits resulting from brain lesions. The rationale underlying these investigations was that if the same neuropsychological functions were used by both normal and brain-damaged subjects in performing an extensive battery of neuropsychological tasks, the interrelationships between these tests, as expressed in correlational matrices, would be essentially the same for both groups. If, however, the neuropsychological functions used by brain-damaged persons were different from those used by control subjects, the tests in an extensive battery would not represent the same kinds of tasks for both groups and, as a result, the intercorrelations between tests would differ.

If the first of these hypotheses was confirmed, the results would constitute a strong argument that essentially the same abilities had been used by normal and brain-damaged subjects. If the correlational matrices between the two groups were dissimilar, a less powerful argument for qualitative differences in types of neuropsychological functions used would be supported, because additional factors could have contributed to the differences obtained.

As an initial step in investigating the general consequences of cerebral damage in adults, Reitan (1956) reported intercorrelations between a battery of tests composed of procedures developed by Halstead and Reitan and the Wechsler-Bellevue Scale. An extensive matrix of 300 coefficients of correlation was produced separately for control (non-brain-damaged) subjects and brain-damaged subjects among these variables.

The next step in this procedure was to compute a coefficient of correlation between the two matrices themselves in order to learn whether the magnitude of the coefficients was essentially similar in the two groups. The coefficient between the two matrices was 0.79, leading Reitan (1958a) to conclude that ". . . the interrelationships between various tests are remarkably similar for our groups with and without brain damage" (p. 344).

The results of this study provided a strong basis for concluding that the intellectual and cognitive functions used by brain-damaged and control subjects in performing an extensive number of tests was essentially the same for both groups. Observational differences of test-taking procedures and reactions might well have varied for the two groups, but from the results of the study it did not appear that the brain-damaged subjects used neuropsychological functions that were different from those used by the control subjects.

Goldstein (1942a, 1942b) has been particularly emphatic in stating that brain damage causes impairment of the abstract attitude. In fact, he contended that brain damage invariably causes a change in this behavioral dimension which results in a difference in kind (as compared with degree) of neuropsychological impairment. He said that there was no overlap among brain-damaged and control subjects in this respect, and that persons with normal brains solve problems through appropriate use of the abstract attitude whereas persons with brain damage were limited to a concrete approach. More specifically, Goldstein (1942a) said, "Even in its simplest form, however, abstraction is separate in principle from concrete behavior. There is no gradual transition from one to the other."

Because of the importance Goldstein attributed to the abstract attitude in problem-solving as a basis for his argument that neuropsychological deficits were qualitative in nature and not subject to quantitative measurement in a valid manner, Reitan (1959c) devised an experiment to provide additional information. In this study the Category Test was administered to a group of brain-damaged subjects and a comparable group of controls without cerebral damage. The Category Test obviously involves abstraction and reasoning abilities, and it has been demonstrated consistently that brain-damaged subjects make more errors on this test than do control subjects (Halstead, 1947; Reitan, 1955b, 1960). In fact, to our knowledge, there has never been a study comparing adult subjects who have cerebral damage with persons who do not have such damage which has failed to show a significant degree of impairment in the brain-damaged group. Thus, the quantitative deficit (number of errors) that brain-damaged subjects make on the Category Test is well established.

The design and composition of the Category Test allowed us to evaluate the validity of Goldstein's claim that
brain damage, in its effect on the abstract attitude, makes it
impossible for the subject to improve in his/her performance. The 5th and 6th subtests of the Category Test are based
upon the same principle. Persons without brain damage,
who are presumably able to assume the abstract attitude,
show a significant degree of improvement on the 6th subtest
after having been given the 5th subtest. If impairment of the
abstract attitude would, in fact, make it impossible for
brain-damaged subjects to improve, one would expect the
results to be essentially the same for both subtests. However, Reitan (1959c) found that among both groups the
degree of improvement from subtest 5 to subtest 6 was
essentially the same, either in absolute or proportional
terms. Therefore, although brain-damaged subjects performed more poorly (quantitative deficits) than did the
control subjects on both subtests, their comparative performances and degree of improvement from one subtest to
the next were essentially identical, reflecting no evidence
for qualitative changes or differences in the types of neuropsychological functions that were used.

This review of investigations of quantitative and qualitative neuropsychological deficits among adult subjects lays
the groundwork for similar investigations with children.
Child neuropsychology and adult neuropsychology are
strikingly different, particularly concerning the interaction
between cerebral damage and age-related development of
neuropsychological functions.

As we have previously observed, in adult neuropsychology the major emphasis has centered on impairment of
previously developed neuropsychological functions. In
child neuropsychology, impairment of brain functions occurs during the developmental years, and a major additional factor involves the limiting effect of brain damage on
the potential for normal development of brain-behavior relationships. Adult brain-damaged subjects appeared to

demonstrate essentially similar neuropsychological functions as did control subjects, even though the brain-damaged subjects were impaired in terms of level of performances.

The types of neuropsychological functions among brain-damaged children, and the relationships between abilities, might well be different from those of brain-damaged adults. Certainly the types of deficits that were most prominent among children were different from the deficits seen in adults. As noted earlier in this chapter, brain-damaged children demonstrated major limitations in development of IQ values as well as verbally-oriented intellectual and cognitive skills. Among adults, on the other hand, it is not at all uncommon to find relatively unimpaired measures of verbal intelligence among brain-damaged subjects. In fact, such measures, which represent stored information developed over a period of years, tend to be resistive to the effects of cerebral damage. Considering the evidence which clearly indicates that the structure of neuropsychological functions in brain-damaged children is generally different from the structure of such functions in brain-damaged adults, it might be quite reasonable to postulate that brain-damaged children and normal control children have a differential organization of inter-relationships among abilities.

Boll and Reitan (1972a) investigated this question using essentially the same research design that had been used with adults. A group of 27 children with documented brain damage and a group of 27 children without past or present evidence of neurological disease or damage were matched in pairs on the basis of age, race, and gender. The mean age was 146.59 months (SD, 19.2) for the brain-damaged group and 143.20 months (SD, 18.9) for the controls. The mean difference in age between the two groups did not approach statistical significance.

Each group was composed of 11 females and 16 males. The brain-damaged subjects were diversified with respect to type of brain injury as well as the inter-related variables of age at which brain damage was sustained and duration of brain damage. Neurological diagnosis was based on evidence entirely independent of neuropsychological test results. Although history information indicated that many of the brain-damaged children had difficulty in making normal academic progress, the referrals were made for medical reasons rather than because of learning and academic deficits.

Each child was given an extensive battery of neuropsychological tests, administered by carefully trained technicians who were not familiar with the hypotheses or purposes of the study. The tests included the Halstead-Reitan Neuropsychological Test Battery for Older Children and the Wechsler-Bellevue Scale. A total of 31 scores was obtained for each subject, which yielded a matrix composed of 465 coefficients of correlation for each group. The coefficients were converted to Fisher's z values, the standard error of the difference for z was computed, and the pairs of coefficients (brain-damaged vs. controls) were compared for statistically significant differences.

The results in this study were considerably different from previous findings among adult subjects. A total of 465 coefficients of correlation composed the entire matrix (the full range of Wechsler and Halstead-Reitan variables) for each group. For the brain-damaged group, 268 (58%) of the coefficients were significant at the .05 level or beyond and for the control group 206 (44%) were significant at comparable levels. Comparison of the coefficients between pairs of tests for the two groups yielded 79 (17%) that showed significant differences, over four times as many as would be expected on a chance basis. The brain-damaged group tended to have the larger coefficients when significant differences between the two groups were found. Of the 79 significant differences, 52 (66%) occurred in instances in which the coefficient was higher for the brain-damaged group than the control group. In the remaining 27 instances (34%), the magnitude of the coefficient in the control group exceeded that for the brain-damaged group.

These results indicated that a considerable number of variables used in this study were significantly inter-correlated (58% for the brain-damaged group and 44% for the controls). Thus, despite the fact that clinical observation might suggest that different functions were being measured, there obviously is a considerable overlap in the variance represented by distributions of the individual tests.

Of greater interest to the above discussion, however, was the fact that many more significant differences between intercorrelations of the control and brain-damaged groups were found than would be expected on the basis of chance. This finding emphasizes the importance of differences in child as compared with adult neuropsychology. Apparently the ability structure of brain-damaged children tends to be different from that of children with normal brain functions, presumably because of the influence of brain damage sustained during the maturational years on the eventual development of various abilities.

Boll and Reitan (1972b) reported an extension of this study, which determined and compared intercorrelations on the Trail Making Test and the Wechsler-Bellevue Scale. The same groups of 27 brain-damaged and control subjects were used. The total possible number of coefficients of correlation for each group was 34. These coefficients were computed, transformed to Fisher's z scores, and the two groups were compared for significant differences in the coefficients of correlation.

The coefficients were generally significant at or beyond the .05 level for the brain-damaged group, with 31 of the 34 coefficients reaching this level. However, for the control subjects, only 3 of the 34 coefficients reached the .05 level of significance. This finding suggests that for brain-damaged children there is a close relationship between results on the Trail Making Test and the Wechsler Scale, but that the results on sets of data for these two tests are much less closely linked for control subjects. In fact, the absolute magnitude of coefficients of correlation was larger for brain-damaged children than for control children between the Wechsler variables and Part A of the Trail Making Test in 16 of 17 instances (94%) and in 17 of 17 instances (100%) for Part B of the Trail Making Test.

Comparisons of the paired coefficients (brain-damaged group vs. the controls) yielded nine differences that were significant beyond the .05 level, or four times as many as expected by chance. In each of these nine significant differences the brain-damaged group had a larger correlation than did the controls. The results of this study reinforce those reported earlier (Boll & Reitan, 1972a), suggesting that the ability structure of brain-damaged children is different (at least in certain respects) from the ability structure of normal children, and this finding stands in distinct contrast to results of similar studies among adult subjects.

Age-Related Changes in Neuropsychological Performances

There is no question that as children grow older there is a general trend for performances on neuropsychological tests to improve. Our clinical evidence suggests that on the average these developmental changes reach an asymptotic level at about 15 or 16 years of age. In some cases, obviously, age-related improvement continues beyond this age but, in general, by 15 years of age neuropsychological functions have developed to the point that the Halstead-Reitan Neuropsychological Test Battery for Adults is appropriate.

In clinical interpretation it must be recognized that in the 9- through 14-year age range younger children generally do not perform as well as older children. Although distributions for each test will eventually be developed at each chronological age-year (or perhaps for each six-month interval), we have not considered this to be a priority issue for two major reasons.

The first of these reasons is that in interpretation of neuropsychological data it is imperative to use the various methods of inference in a complementary manner in order to understand brain-behavior relationships for the individual child. An approach oriented toward age-related normative data focuses specifically on level of performance and does not integrate the performance of the individual child with the occurrence of specific deficits that may suggest impaired brain functions, patterns and relationships among the test results, and, especially, comparisons of performances on the two sides of the body.

Methods of data analysis which are based only on interindividual comparisons and totally neglect intraindividual considerations cannot possibly reflect the uniqueness of brain functions for the individual child. Thus, while it is important to bear in mind the fact that as they grow older children generally improve in their test performances, it is also important to remember that a great deal of variability occurs at any given age, and to a large extent this variability is to be expected among normal subjects as well as among brain-damaged subjects.

The second major point that constitutes a problem with clinical use of age-related changes in test scores concerns the relationship between group data and data based on the individual subject. Neuropsychologists often show an uncritical tendency to use descriptive statistics (such as means and standard deviations) based upon groups of subjects for establishing expectations for the performances of individuals.

Even a brief reflection on the statistical meaning of measures of central tendency and variability make it quite clear that such practices are hazardous. The best method to predict scores for individual subjects in a single group, based only upon knowledge of the mean and standard deviation for the distribution, would be to apply the mean to every subject in the group. However, this procedure would result in a variability estimate of zero and would obviously be in error for individuals who did not fall at the mean. Thus, if one were to observe the mean and standard deviation for children aged 10 years, and expect the individual child to match the mean in terms of his/her performance, there would be a substantial error in most instances.

For purposes of clinical interpretation, it is dangerous to proceed from data based on individuals to data based upon a group of individuals and then attempt to use the group data to go back to individual clinical interpretation. The conclusion to be drawn is that group data can be used only as a general guide in clinical interpretation, and should not be used by itself to establish specific expectations of performances for the individual subject.

The use of group data for clinical purposes can be improved, to a degree, by consideration of a series of test results for the individual subject. If the individual subject falls below the mean level for a known group, and does so consistently on a number of the tests, it probably is safe to assume that the individual has abilities which do not measure up to expectation. In addition, the standard deviation for the group can provide additional information about the degree of deficit shown by the individual. However, even this type of procedure neglects the additional methods of inference which must necessarily be used to evaluate brain-behavior relationships for the individual child.

These considerations led us to recommend that the clinician obtain a general idea of the scale of measurements used for any test and learn how that scale relates to age-related performances, but use this information only as a general guide in his/her clinical evaluation of individual subjects. In fact, this kind of information is readily absorbed as the clinician develops experience with individual cases of various ages. We recommend that the neuropsychologist develop skill in clinical interpretation of individual test protocols, learning to recognize (1) the variability among an extensive series of performances (*patterns and relationships*), (2) the specific deficits which occur almost exclusively among brain-damaged children (*pathognomonic signs*), (3) comparative results obtained in testing the same function on the two sides of the body (*right/left differences*), and (4) how well the subject performs compared with normative samples (*level of performance*).

In order to emphasize the fact that a child's level of performance generally improves between 9 and 15 years, we will review a study on the Trail Making Test (Reitan, 1971c). In this study two samples were composed: 51 normal boys and 47 normal girls ranging in age from 109 months to 170 months. These children were volunteers who responded to a request sent to parents for children to participate in a psychological testing study. These subjects were not compensated for their participation and were told in advance that they would not be informed of the test results. Their participation was merely to assist us in collection of data.

The mean ages were 151.65 months (SD, 17.41) for boys and 151.02 months (SD, 19.51) for girls. The mean difference in age between the boys and the girls did not approach statistical significance (t ratio of 0.17; p<.90). Computing educational levels on the basis of the last grade completed, the mean level of education was 6.07 years (SD, 1.27) for the boys and 6.04 years (SD,1.54) for the girls. These differences did not reach statistical significance. Obviously, the boys and girls were essentially similar in age and education.

The subjects were given the Trail Making Test by technicians who were well trained and experienced in administration of the test. They followed standard procedures and had been given no information about the specific research uses for which the test results were intended.

As a total group, the boys completed Part A in a mean of 15.04 seconds (SD, 4.76) and the girls required a mean time of 14.85 seconds (SD, 6.82). Comparison of the difference between these means did not approach statistical significance (p<.90). On Part B the boys required 32.98 seconds (SD, 12.05) and the girls needed 31.51 seconds (SD, 14.57). These distributions also were very similar and did not approach statistical significance (p<.60). From these results it would appear that normal boys and girls are very similar in their performances of the Trail Making Test and that there are no gender differences for level of performance.

The next step in data analysis was to plot the performances of boys and girls on both Parts A and B and to compute coefficients of correlation between test performances and age. These results are depicted in Figure 7-2.

The data suggests that 9- and 10-year-old children are somewhat slower on Part A than older children, but that minor differences were found for children aged 11 through 14 years. The rather simple task represented by Part A appears to reach essentially an asymptotic level by the time children are 11 years of age. However, for both boys and girls across the 9 through 14 year-age range, a significant correlation was found between test performance and age. The Pearson Product-moment coefficient of .33 for boys reached only the .05 level of significance, whereas for the girls a slightly higher coefficient of .43 was significant beyond the .01 level.

Part B of the Trail Making Test is obviously somewhat more difficult than Part A, and this factor probably was responsible for the more orderly improvement of performances across the 9- through 14-year age range. The progression of improved performances with advancing age was particularly pronounced for girls, who demonstrated a correlation coefficient of .60 between age and test performances. Among boys, however, the age-related improvement

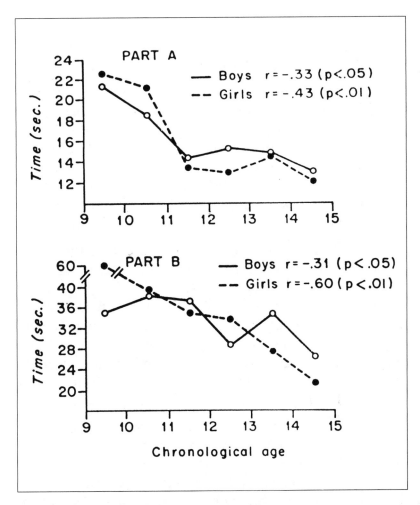

Fig. 7-2. Relationships between Trail Making Test performances and chronological age for normal boys and girls.

in performances was nowhere nearly as clear, and their coefficient between age and test scores was only .31.

We tested these coefficients for a significant difference by converting the coefficients to Fisher's z values, determining the standard error of z and computing a t ratio. We obtained a t ratio of 1.78, which corresponded with a probability level of less than .10. Thus, the data in this particular

study did not reach an adequate level of statistical significance in terms of the correlations between boys and girls on
Part B, but there appeared to be a trend.

We should note that very large differences between
coefficients of correlation are required when both coefficients fall toward the center of the range rather than representing extremely high or extremely low values. In addition,
group size is a factor in determining the statistical significance of the result obtained; these same coefficients, based
on distributions with similar characteristics, would have
been significant if the groups had been substantially larger.

It would appear safe to suggest that on Part B the results
point toward a less orderly relationship between age and
test performance for boys than for girls. In fact, if there is a
less orderly relationship between neuropsychological test
performance and age for boys as compared with girls more
generally, the inconsistency and variability among performances across a range of abilities for the individual boy might
well be a factor in determining the much greater frequency
of academic difficulties among boys as compared with girls.

More specifically, this particular result suggests the
possibility that boys have an uneven development of neuropsychological functions at any given age, with some abilities well developed and others being relatively deficient. If
this actually is true, one would expect that tasks that required a combination of abilities for successful performance
might be less well performed by boys than girls because
certain of the essential abilities necessary for completion of
the complex task were inadequate. Obviously, this is a question that cannot be answered by the limited data based on
Part B of the Trail Making Test. However, it would appear
that additional attention should be directed to this question,
using correlational techniques to establish general differences between boys and girls, followed by clinical evaluation of individual children who showed the most striking

inconsistencies as compared with those who had a more consistent development of various abilities and a more orderly ability structure.

This same investigation on the Trail Making Test included a study of control subjects and children with cerebral lesions. Thirty-five subjects with documented brain damage were matched for age and gender with 35 controls who had no past or present evidence of neurological disease or damage. The mean age was 141.26 months (SD, 20.65) for the brain-damaged group and 141.23 months (SD, 18.39) for the control group. Because academic progress (at least in many cases) is a dependent variable with respect to brain damage, no attempt was made to match the groups for education. Evaluation of the age difference between the groups did not approach statistical significance.

The brain-damaged children were heterogeneous for neurological diagnoses, and had the following conditions: traumatic brain injury, 12; tumor, 7; congenital vascular anomaly, 5; inflammatory damage, 5; perinatal lesions, 5; and cerebral abscess, 1. The testing was done by carefully trained technicians who had no knowledge of the specific research purposes of the resulting data.

TABLE 7-10

Means, standard deviations, and t ratios for matched groups with and without cerebral lesions on Parts A and B of the Trail Making Test.

		Brain-Damaged	Control	t	p	t	p
Part A	Mean	37.06	16.74	3.75*	<.001	5.15**	<.001
	SD	29.79	8.12				
Part B	Mean	110.19	35.03	4.48*	<.001	5.06**	<.001
	SD	85.91	15.76				

* Computations based on raw-score distributions (sec).
**Computations based on normalized T-score distributions.

Differences between the groups were very striking on both Parts A and B. The control subjects required a mean of 16.74 seconds (SD, 8.12) to complete Part A and the brain-damaged subjects needed more than twice as much time, requiring a mean of 37.06 seconds (SD, 29.79). The difference between the two means was highly significant statistically (p<.001).

Differences between the two groups were even more striking on Part B. The control subjects had a mean of 35.03 seconds (SD, 15.76), whereas the brain-damaged group had a mean of 110.19 seconds (SD, 85.91). This difference also was highly significant (p<.001). While the means for the control subjects on both Parts A and B were similar to the means recorded above for the normal boys and girls, the brain-damaged children performed much worse.

As is commonly seen in nearly all studies of control and brain-damaged groups, the standard deviations were much larger for the brain-damaged group. This finding reflects the fact that brain damage may have a devastating effect on some children and a relatively lesser effect on others. However, with mean values more than two or three times larger than the mean for control subjects, it was not difficult to identify most of the brain-damaged children by their level of performance. Even the youngest control children had means that were far better than the average performances for the brain-damaged group. This finding makes it clear that in the 9- through 14-year range, chronological age is far less potent than is brain damage as a determiner of results on Parts A and B of the Trail Making Test, confirming our previously reported findings of profound neuropsychological impairment in children with definite cerebral disease or damage.

We must mention again that some children have relatively mild cerebral damage which may be associated with performances that approach or fall within the normal range. It is therefore necessary to restate the obvious fact that no single test represents an adequate behavioral representation of brain functions. Even if a single test permitted perfect classification of children into normal and brain-damaged groups, relatively little would be achieved by such categorization. The purpose of neuropsychological evaluation is to provide a description and characterization of neuropsychological functions as they relate to the biological condition of the brain (a result that may have clinical implications in many relevant respects) rather than to achieve only a dichotomous diagnostic classification.

Finlayson and Reitan (1976a) investigated comparative abilities of younger children (aged 6, 7 and 8 years) and older children (12, 13, and 14 years) on tactile-perceptual and motor abilities with relation to handedness. Twenty normal children (10 boys and 10 girls) were tested at each of these six chronological years for a total of 120 subjects. At each age level the groups were matched for Wechsler Full Scale IQ and educational achievement. All children were volunteers and came from a generally similar socioeconomic setting. None of the children had significant medical, behavioral or academic difficulties and each child was right-handed as defined by a score of at least 6 out of 7 on the Reitan-Kløve Lateral Dominance Examination.

Each child was tested for finger-tapping speed and grip strength (motor measures) and for tactile finger localization and finger-tip symbol or number writing abilities (tactile-perceptual abilities). The results indicated that for both younger and older children age was a significant factor on the motor measures. Although an age effect for the tactile-perceptual measures was not observed within the younger or older age groups, on the tactile finger localization test a general reduction in errors occurred as children aged from 6 years to 14 years. Gender was significant only for grip strength.

The results were also analyzed for differences in performance between the right and left hands. Considering that all subjects were definitely right-handed, it may have been expected that right-handed performances would consistently be superior. However, the results showed that for both younger and older children the hand variable was a significant factor for motor functioning but not for tactile-perceptual functioning. The right hand was consistently superior to the left hand on motor speed and grip strength. The difference between the right and left hand did not approach statistical significance in any of the comparisons of tactile-perceptual functioning. In the present investigation the only gender difference found was that the performance of the boys exceeded that of the girls on the measure of grip strength. The evidence indicating no hand superiority for tactile-perceptual functioning was consistent with Reitan's (1971a) earlier findings.

Screening Devices for Identification of Cerebral Dysfunction in Children

Early in the modern history of clinical neuropsychology, there was a pervasive interest in devising a short test for "brain damage" that would effectively differentiate all subjects with cerebral dysfunction from the rest of the population. Gradually, however, as this quest continued, investigators in the field became aware of the multi-dimensional aspect of neuropsychological impairment, of the impossibility of finding a single short test that would be satisfactorily effective, and the idea that the problem should not be to discover a single, short test, but instead to describe brain-behavior relationships for the individual subject.

In fact, the approach in clinical neuropsychology should recognize that the meaningful task is to describe the behavioral correlates of brain functions in the individual subject, regardless of whether or not brain damage has been sustained. Persons without past or present evidence of cerebral damage demonstrate clinically meaningful variations in brain-behavior relationships, just as do persons who have sustained cerebral disease or damage. In the latter case there are often variations or deficits that extend beyond those found among normal subjects; nevertheless, the meaningful aim is to describe behavior as it relates to the brain for each person. If this rationale for neuropsychological assessment is accepted, the purpose behind finding a short, single test for "brain damage" becomes rather meaningless.

Essentially the same arguments might be proposed about development or identification of screening devices. The purpose of a screening device would be to develop a relatively short procedure which would validly indicate whether or not the individual subject had experienced significant impairment of brain functions. Use of a screening device, however, certainly would not rule out more extensive neuropsychological assessment and evaluation, if appropriate, either in cases with normal or impaired results. However, the implicit intent would be one of screening out the normal cases or screening in persons with evidence of neuropsychological deficit. In this sense, the use of screening devices would imply that it is unnecessary to evaluate the brain-behavior relationships among normal subjects.

In our investigations we have found that about one-third of children who are classified as normal (in the sense that they [1] have no past or present evidence of cerebral disease or damage based on history and neurological evaluation, and [2] have been making normal progress in academic development) nevertheless show significant evidence of mild neuropsychological impairment. In these cases the neuropsychological assessment with the Halstead-Reitan Battery nearly invariably produces information which provides additional understanding of the ability structure of the child as it relates to brain function and identifies cognitive and intellectual areas of function that require special attention and remediation.

Even among the remaining two-thirds of normal children (who show no clinically significant evidence of neuropsychological impairment), the test results are generally valuable in presenting an assessment of comparative abilities across a broad array of neuropsychological functions. Against considerations of this kind, one wonders why screening devices would be used. Why would the clinical neuropsychologist "screen" brain-behavior relationships, when the obvious need is to understand them?

Attention should be given to differentiation between screening devices and measures of general aspects of brain functions. The general aim in using a screening instrument is to obtain a preliminary indication of possible impairment of brain functions using a minimum amount of testing time. Although in recent years great emphasis has been placed upon "left brain" versus "right brain" considerations (which in fact represent the specialized neuropsychological functions of the brain), the general neuropsychological functions, which are represented throughout the cerebral cortex, constitute very significant aspects of ability structure.

As we have described in the Reitan-Wolfson neuropsychological model of brain functions, areas such as attention, concentration, memory, reasoning, logical analysis, and planning abilities appear to permeate the entire cerebral cortex, including tissue that subserves primary motor and sensory functions. The fact that nature has distributed these abilities throughout the cerebral cortex, including the areas that subserve specialized higher-level abilities as well as input and output functions, may well be documentation of their importance. Every clinical neuropsychological assessment should include evaluation of general as well as specific indicators of neuropsychological functions (Goodglass & Kaplan, 1979; Reitan & Wolfson, this volume).

Because general indicators are diffusely distributed throughout the cerebral cortex, they frequently reveal impairment regardless of the location of a specific lesion and, as a result, are sometimes thought of as screening procedures. While there may be some validity to this notion, it is more important to recognize that such tests measure the general neuropsychological functions of the brain and thus constitute only part of an adequate neuropsychological evaluation. In some cases, of course, general neuropsychological functions are less impaired than specific functions, although in most instances the general functions are clearly compromised even by focal lesions. There certainly is more validity in using general neuropsychological tests as screening devices than using specific neuropsychological tests, but the principal orientation in conducting a comprehensive neuropsychological evaluation probably should be directed toward the integrated evaluation of general, specialized, and specific neuropsychological measures.

Summary indices, based upon a number of neuropsychological tests, have also been used as general indicators of the overall adequacy of cerebral functions, and the demonstrated validity of procedures such as the Impairment Index and the Neuropsychological Deficit Scale bear out the clinical significance of such approaches. These additive or summarical indices, however, achieve generality of significance by including a series of measures rather than measurement of functions which are diffusely distributed in the cerebral cortex. Of course, there is some question regarding the unity of such functions as abstraction, reasoning, logical analysis, and planning abilities. Conceivably such areas of function achieve their generality of representation in the cerebral cortex through a subtle combination of a range of more specific abilities, and thus represent a combination of functions in a single score.

The basic aim of a screening device is to provide a general assessment, even though in preliminary form, about brain-behavior relationships through the use of a limited number of tests which can be administered in a short time. The limitation of a screening device is that it is likely to provide an inadequate assessment of brain-behavior relationships because it is, by definition, a screening approach.

Next, it must be recognized that screening devices are obviously intended to screen for one or more identified conditions. The more specific the condition, the more likely it is that the screening device will be successful. The more general the condition and the greater number of variables involved, the less likely it is that the screening device will be useful.

In clinical neuropsychology the purpose of a screening instrument is to screen for "brain damage." Brain damage, in turn, has been identified as such a broad and inclusive term that it has hardly any specific meaning whatsoever (Reitan & Wolfson, 1992a). In other words, the neuropsychological manifestations of impaired brain functions are so diversified that it would be difficult to devise brief testing procedures that would be likely to identify the effects of impairment in one case after another.

When the question becomes, "Screening for what?", the complexity and diversity of the consequences of brain damage overwhelm the prospect of developing a valid screening instrument. The complexity of the question, coupled with the desired simplicity of the answer, tends to create an impossible situation. Nevertheless, as we will describe later in this section, it is possible to make some limited progress in devising a screening instrument by deliberately selecting a series of brief tests to cover a broad range of neuropsychological functions subserved by the brain.

Another way of viewing the development of screening devices is to recognize that neuropsychological tests must be given in a sequence, regardless of whether the sequence is deliberately planned or not. It would be possible to plan the sequence of test administration in such a manner that clinical information about the subject was gradually unfolded. Presumably it would be possible to produce information progressively and to discontinue the testing in the

individual case when enough information had been produced to answer any clinical questions that might be present. Following such an approach, in some instances the
screening procedure might be adequately accomplished by
giving only a few tests, and with other persons the screening
procedure would continue to the point of completing a comprehensive neuropsychological evaluation.

Although an approach of this kind seems reasonable in
clinical application, there is still the problem of the screening questions to be asked and the sequence of test administration necessary to provide the answer. In fact, we have
attempted to explore this framework for developing screening procedures, but in the individual case we have found
that variability in the test results and the complexity of
questions concerning the behavioral manifestations of
cerebral impairment are so diversified that different sequences of tests are required for different subjects.

It is apparent that development of a screening procedure is an immensely complex issue, precisely because of
the complexity of brain-behavior relationships, and there
appears to be little prospect of solving the problem adequately. Just as we recognized many years ago that we
should abandon the idea of developing a short, simple test
of brain damage that would divide the population into two
camps (brain-damaged and normals), perhaps we should
now forego the desire to simplify the issue of brain-behavior
relationships by attempting to develop a screening battery.

We have followed two approaches in attempting to develop summary indices for the general characterizations of
neuropsychological performances of children with and
without cerebral damage (Reitan, 1984b; Reitan & Wolfson,
this volume). The first of these approaches was to develop
an Impairment Index of brain functions in children. The
Halstead Impairment Index for Adults had proved to be of
great clinical value in neuropsychological assessment in the
entire adult battery and had consistently been shown to be

the single most sensitive measure of the biological adequacy of brain functions (Reitan, 1955a, 1966; Wheeler, Burke, & Reitan, 1963; Wheeler & Reitan, 1963).

For a number of years we had considered developing a comparable Impairment Index for children, but were dissuaded by both clinical and experimental observations of the developmental changes in neuropsychological functions which corresponded with advancing chronological age (Reitan, 1971c). These observations suggested that among both control and brain-damaged children across the 9- through 14-year age range, the development of neuropsychological abilities was so variable that one could hardly expect to use a single index to differentiate younger from older children. In fact, an inspection of age-based curves suggested that normative and comparative data might be needed in six-month age increments.

It is well known that a normative (level of performance) approach represents only one of the methods of analysis and interpretation of clinical results on the Halstead-Reitan Battery, and that a comprehensive clinical assessment involves additional approaches, including the occurrence of pathognomonic signs, relationships among the test results, and assessment of differences in performances on the same tasks on the two sides of the body. In fact, the Halstead-Reitan Batteries have been deliberately composed to include evaluation of both *inter*individual and *intra*individual comparative data.

Selz and Reitan (1979a, 1979b) devised a system of rating results from the Halstead-Reitan Battery for Older Children that considered these various methods of data evaluation and, in addition, transformed each score or test result for each child into a scoring system that reflected four categories of performance ranging from perfectly normal scores to scores that were definitely abnormal and indicative of significant deficit. This conversion procedure, which was similar to the method used with the Neuropsychological Deficit Scale, was a transformation of raw-score data into scores that represented clinically significant categories of performance. These categories, in turn, created an effective method for comparing the effects of brain damage with no brain damage and minimized developmental influences on the test scores. Using this transformation of test data it appeared to be possible to develop an Impairment Index for older children that could be used clinically in much the same manner that the Halstead Impairment Index was used for adults.

We recognize that a summary index makes no pretense of identifying differentially various areas of impairment that might be shown by the individual child. However, an overall indication of adequacy of neuropsychological performance does serve as a very valuable initial characterization of performances, within which the details of the testing can be evaluated. Although some authors have criticized the general and additive nature of summary indices because they do not reflect performances in specific areas of intellectual and cognitive functions, they seem to have failed to realize that there is nothing about having a summary index that prevents the clinician from proceeding with more specific interpretations. A composite index has the advantage of reliability and generality of assessment, and in this sense often turns out to be a more sensitive and valid variable than scores which represent abilities in selective areas of function. As we have emphasized previously, a summary index does not, in any sense, obviate or preclude the importance of a more detailed evaluation of brain-behavior relationships.

We have previously described a study by Selz and Reitan (1979a, 1979b) that compared three groups of 25 children who were classified into categories of brain-damaged, learning-disabled, and normal controls. Raw scores were converted to ranked scores representing the following categories: (1) perfectly normal performances, (2) adequate performances still in the normal range, (3) impaired performances of a mild to moderate nature, and (4) definitely impaired and abnormal performances indicative of significant deficit. This procedure yielded a possible score range for the entire Battery from 0-102 points. The children's Impairment Index was computed by dividing the total score for each child by the maximum total of 102 points, thereby producing a proportion which reflected the severity of deficit shown by each child. For example, if a child earned a total sum of 10 points, the Impairment Index would be .098.

Using this computational procedure, the subjects earned the following mean Impairment Indices: controls, 0.11 (SD, .02), learning-disabled, 0.23 (SD, .08), and brain-damaged, 0.38 (SD, .18). Analysis of variance yielded a F ratio indicating that the groups differed at a significant probability level. Post-hoc testing of pairs of groups indicated that each possible pair showed highly significant differences. Distributions of the Impairment Indices for each group were inspected in order to determine cut-off points. Using 0.17 as a cut-off point yielded correct classifications for 76% of the control subjects and 80% of the brain-damaged subjects.

The children with learning disabilities tended to resemble the brain-damaged group much more than the control group; only 28% of the children in this group had Impairment Indices of 0.17 or less and 72% scored above 0.18. This finding is not surprising, considering the fact that Selz and Reitan (1979a) found that about 80% of the children with a learning disability showed evidence of neuropsychological deficits on the Halstead-Reitan Battery for Older Children.

This investigation was promising for development of a valid Impairment Index of the general adequacy of neuropsychological functions for children. We have now developed the Neuropsychological Deficit Scale (NDS) for Older Children, and this measure replaces the Impairment Index described in 1984. The Neuropsychological Deficit Scale is basically similar to the Impairment Index, but we have developed much more complete guides for scoring particular performances, especially those involved in the Aphasia Screening Test.

In spite of the limitations and possible criticisms of screening devices, Reitan and Herring (1985) explored the development of a screening index. These researchers performed an initial investigation followed by a cross-validational study. In the first study, groups of 25 brain-damaged subjects and 25 neurologically normal subjects, aged 9-14 years, were composed for investigation. The brain-damaged subjects were heterogeneous with respect to types of cerebral damage and the controls had no past or present evidence of cerebral disease or damage. The tests were administered by carefully trained technicians who had no knowledge of the specific research purposes for the data.

The mean age was 141.58 months (SD, 16.54) for the control subjects and 140.02 months (SD, 18.75) for the brain-damaged subjects. The two groups were drawn from similar urban and rural locations, and very few of the brain-damaged subjects or the controls were dependent upon public funds for medical expenses. Thus, we believe that there were no systematic differences in socioeconomic status. The entire Halstead-Reitan Neuropsychological Test Battery for Older Children and the Wechsler Intelligence Scale for Children were administered to all of the subjects. Using the Selz-Reitan rules system, the raw-scores were transformed to scaled scores and the converted scores were used in all subsequent analyses.

The first step in evaluation of the data and development of the screening index was based upon determination of the statistical significance of differences between the two groups on the variables employed. Using a criterion of a probability value of less than .001, 12 of the original 37 variables were retained for possible use. A discriminant analysis comparing the two groups using these 12 variables yielded an overall classification accuracy of 96%.

We then proceeded to choose a number of tests for the screening battery, observing (1) a criterion of relatively short time for administration, (2) representation of the various inferential strategies that we have found to be important in clinical assessment, and (3) representation of a range of measures. The variables selected were: (1) Part A of the Trail Making Test for Children, (2) Part B of the Trail Making Test for Children, (3) name-writing time with the preferred hand, (4) difference in name-writing time between the preferred and nonpreferred hand, (5) difference between the two hands in grip strength, (6) finger tapping speed of the nonpreferred hand, (7) difference in finger tapping speed between the two hands, and (8) results on the Reitan-Indiana Aphasia Screening Test. These tests can be administered in less than one hour. Discriminant analysis of results for the two groups using these eight variables yielded an overall hit rate of 94% (controls, 100%; brain-damaged subjects, 88%).

The next step in the development of a screening index was to weight the results for the eight measures. The ranked score for each variable is multiplied by a given factor, determined on the basis both of inspection of discriminant function coefficients as well as experience with the clinical utility and sensitivity of each of the eight measures. Details of this scoring procedure are given in the original publication (Reitan & Herring, 1985).

The weighted screening index, based on the eight measures, had an accuracy rate of 92% in differentiating the initial groups of 25 brain-injured and 25 control subjects. Additional groups of 25 children were composed according to the same selection criteria and the original scoring system was used to determine the accuracy in cross-validation. The second groups of 25 brain-damaged and 25 normal children were differentiated with an 86% accuracy rate, indicating that the initial scoring system did not reflect the chance characteristics of the original group but applied quite well to the second samples that were selected.

These results indicated that it was possible to devise a screening index that was quite effective in differentiating between children with cerebral damage and controls. However, we noted in the original discussion of these results that perhaps relatively little had been achieved merely by identifying a child as brain-damaged, even when the classification was correct. Obviously, it is necessary to identify the specific types of impairment and to achieve an overall evaluation that determines the unique ability structure, including both strengths and weaknesses, of the individual child. The screening device may be helpful as an initial characterization of neuropsychological findings, but it certainly could never serve as a substitute for complete neuropsychological evaluation nor as a basis for developing a program of cognitive brain training, both of which can be achieved with administration of the complete battery.

Differences in Verbal and Performance IQ Scores with Relation to Lateralized Cerebral Lesions

One of the most striking disparities in neuropsychological research on adults as compared with children concerns investigation of verbal and performance intelligence differences with relation to left or right cerebral lesions. This question has been investigated extensively in adults, but for children there are few reports on this subject in the literature.

In one study, Reitan (1955a) administered the Wechsler-Bellevue Scale to groups of adult subjects with left, right, and generalized cerebral lesions. While the groups with lateralized cerebral lesions were equivalent for types of focal lesions, the group with generalized damage had diffuse conditions. The results were quite decisive in showing that left cerebral lesions were associated with lower Verbal IQ than Performance IQ values (13 of 14 cases). Right cerebral lesions demonstrated the reverse relationship, with Performance IQ lower than Verbal IQ in 15 of 17 cases. Subjects with generalized cerebral involvement were essentially evenly distributed. This finding provided strong evidence that verbal intelligence was principally represented in the left cerebral hemisphere and performance intelligence was dependent upon the right cerebral hemisphere.

An extensive series of additional studies using adult subjects was performed in order to pursue this relationship from various approaches. Kløve (1959) used subjects from Reitan's laboratory to investigate electroencephalographic criteria. He composed four groups of subjects with the following characteristics: (1) EEG abnormalities of the left cerebral hemisphere, (2) comparable EEG abnormalities of the right cerebral hemisphere, (3) generalized and non-lateralized EEG abnormalities, and (4) definite evidence of cerebral damage but normal EEG results.

The findings were quite distinct with respect to differences in the groups. The group with left EEG disturbances was substantially lower on Verbal IQ than Performance IQ, and the group with right EEG disturbances was lower on Performance IQ than Verbal IQ. The group with generalized and nonlateralized EEG disturbances showed little difference in Verbal IQ and Performance IQ values. Despite the fact that they had definite brain damage, the group with normal EEGs performed a little better than the other groups, but showed no differences between Verbal and Performance IQ levels.

Kløve and Reitan (1958) investigated this same question with relation to behavioral deficits that have been identified as having lateralizing significance. In this study they composed three groups of subjects: (1) persons with definite evidence of dysphasia (implying evidence of left cerebral damage), (2) subjects with definite constructional dyspraxia (as manifested by clear deficits in copying the square, cross, triangle, and key from the Reitan-Indiana Aphasia Screening Test), and (3) subjects who demonstrated both of these difficulties.

As might well be expected, the group with dysphasia was substantially lower on Verbal IQ than Performance IQ. The group with constructional dyspraxia reversed this relationship, and was consistently lower on the Performance subtests than the Verbal subtests. The third group of subjects, in whom both kinds of deficits were present, performed very poorly on the Verbal as well as the Performance subtests.

In another study, Doehring, Reitan, and Kløve (1961) studied the organizing influence of homonymous visual field defects on the comparative relationships of Verbal IQ and Performance IQ levels. These authors composed four groups of subjects: (1) subjects with left homonymous visual field defects (which would imply right cerebral damage), (2) subjects with right homonymous visual field defects (which would imply left cerebral damage), (3) persons with definite evidence of cerebral damage but without visual field defects (which would tend to permit cerebral damage to involve both hemispheres without a systematic basis for differences in frequency), and (4) non-brain-damaged control subjects.

The results indicated that a homonymous visual field defect was sufficiently strong as a variable to organize Verbal and Performance levels quite systematically. The subjects in the group with left homonymous visual field defects were low on Performance IQ as compared with their own Verbal IQ, and the reverse relationship was obtained from the group with right homonymous visual field defects. The brain-damaged group without visual field defects showed no differences. The control subjects performed better than the brain-damaged groups, but again showed no differences between Verbal IQ and Performance IQ.

We had begun to feel that a powerful effect had been discovered which was substantiated in one study after another using different but related criteria. The dependence of verbal intelligence on the left cerebral hemisphere and performance intelligence on the right cerebral hemisphere had been borne out regardless of whether we used criteria relating to lateralized structural damage, electroencephalographic abnormalities, behavioral deficits, or neuroophthalmological results. However, in our clinical evaluations we noticed individual cases in which independent neurological findings that implicated one of the cerebral hemispheres did not correspond with the expected relationship between Verbal IQ and Performance IQ values. These observations were facilitated by our standard practice of the sequence in which we performed our work (i.e., to review the neuropsychological test results initially before referring to the neurological findings).

In observing these cases, it seemed likely that the significant factors associated with lack of correspondence between expected Verbal IQ and Performance IQ relationships and lateralization of cerebral damage related to chronicity of the lesion and the age at which the lesion was sustained. Chronic, long-standing lateralized lesions did not seem to have a predictable effect on verbal and performance intelligence levels, regardless of which cerebral hemisphere was involved. In addition, in our observation and study of children with lateralized cerebral lesions, the interaction between the lesion and the developmental process tended to obscure any lateralized effect.

In order to explore these hypotheses in more detail, Fitzhugh, Fitzhugh, and Reitan (1962) composed groups of adult subjects with lateralized and diffuse cerebral damage. These persons had chronic, long-standing lesions that in nearly every instance dated back to childhood. In a companion study, these authors used groups of adult subjects who had developed normally but had sustained recent lateralized or diffuse damage. The latter groups confirmed the earlier findings quite distinctly. Left cerebral damage was associated with verbal intelligence deficits, right cerebral damage was correlated with performance intelligence impairment, and diffuse cerebral damage showed no essential differences between verbal and performance intelligence levels. However, the comparable groups with chronic, long-standing cerebral damage showed no evidence of significant differences between verbal and performance intelligence levels regardless of whether the damage was left, right, or generalized in nature.

As noted above, there have been few direct studies of verbal and performance intelligence levels in children with lateralized cerebral damage. Pennington, Galliani and Voegele (1965) studied groups of children with electroencephalographic abnormalities that implicated one cerebral hemisphere or the other, but found no differences in WISC Verbal and Performance IQ values with relation to EEG lateralization.

Reed and Reitan (1969) composed a group of 35 children with right hemiplegia or hemiparesis and another group of 25 children with left hemiplegia or hemiparesis and compared their scores on the Reading (word recognition) component of the Wide Range Achievement Test (WRAT) as well as the WISC. Lateralization of motor deficit would imply that the cerebral hemisphere contralateral to the side of motor impairment would be more seriously involved and, if the results simulated those obtained with adult subjects, performance intelligence would be impaired in cases of left-sided motor deficit and the reverse relationship would exist in the group with right-sided motor impairment. However, the results of the study showed no differences between the two groups. Reading scores on the WRAT were equivalent, and there were no significant differences between Verbal and Performance IQ values. Thus, no evidence was found to suggest an association between lateralized cerebral damage in children and differential impairment of Verbal IQ as compared with Performance IQ.

A question can be raised about whether the lateralized intellectual abilities that eventually emerge in adult subjects have become established in children, whether the effects of cerebral damage in children interfere with the normal development of lateralization of intellectual functions, or even whether there may be an instrumental effect in comparison of the adult tests with those used for children. This latter possibility is accentuated by the procedure used with the WISC for age adjustment of scaled scores, whereas with the WAIS the score achieved by any subject represents his/her actual performance and the age adjustment is made upon obtaining the IQ values. In addition, the availability of children with lateralized cerebral lesions seems to be considerably less than with adults, and it has been difficult for investigators to compose groups of children with lesions of the left or right cerebral hemisphere. It therefore seems possible that a number of factors have been significant in limiting the development of knowledge about Verbal and Performance IQ values, as related to lateralization of cerebral damage in children.

As we noted in Chapter II, a basic difference between neuropsychological studies of adults and children relates to the fact that the assessment procedure with most adults concerns evaluation of loss of previously acquired abilities. With children, however, the situation is frequently one not only of loss of limited previous acquisitions, but of the impairing effect of the brain lesion on acquisition of neuropsychological functions. Both of these circumstances that affect children would tend to minimize the resulting differences between verbal and performance intelligence levels in children. If the child had not developed these abilities to a very substantial extent, the potential for differences between the abilities would be at least somewhat minimized. Therefore, a loss of previously developed abilities might not be as great among children as among adults.

Secondly, if the cerebral lesion had been present for some time (regardless of whether it involved the left or right cerebral hemisphere), it seems likely that the development of further intellectual functions with an impaired and compromised brain would affect abilities rather generally, regardless of whether the abilities were principally of a verbal or performance nature. Therefore, a lateralized brain lesion, which had existed for a period of time and had adversely affected the acquisition of abilities, would have a generally impairing effect.

These various reasons converge to determine the fact that, insofar as we know, in the literature there is no study based on children which indicates that left cerebral lesions are reliably associated with selective impairment of verbal intelligence and that right cerebral lesions have a specific adverse effect on performance intelligence. Nevertheless, in older children who have developed the types of abilities measured by verbal and performance intelligence tests, and who have recently sustained lateralized cerebral damage, it is entirely likely that assessment would reveal a selective and specific deficit. In other words, the closer one comes to simulating the conditions met in the adult studies, the more likely it is that the results will imitate the pattern seen with adults. However, in children with lateralized cerebral lesions sustained perinatally or in infancy, the consequences are likely to (1) be quite generalized, (2) impair both verbal and performance intelligence, and (3) show no differential pattern associated with the cerebral hemisphere involved.

Conceptual and Practical Problems in Classification and Diagnosis of Children with Cerebral Damage or Dysfunction

Historically, many terms have been used to refer to children with brain damage (or impairment resulting from brain damage), including labels such as *the perceptually handicapped child, the hyperactive child, the developmentally dysphasic child, the developmentally handicapped child,* etc. Some of the terms used (including those just cited) tended to focus on behavioral deficits, whereas others, such as *the cerebral palsied child* or *the brain-injured child*, had more direct reference to brain pathology. Still another term, *minimal brain dysfunction (MBD)*, seemed to have biological implications (which were never identified), although the criteria for classification or diagnosis were based on behavioral disorders (Clements, 1966).

Many psychologists were loathe to use terms that had neuropathological significance (especially if they carried a direct connotation of brain damage), because of the general view of the importance of the brain and the permanence of deficits resulting from brain damage. (Parents have actually pleaded with us to change our diagnostic conclusions from impairment due to brain damage to impairment due to childhood schizophrenia or any condition other than brain damage.) This feeling of fear (or respect) for the brain was partly responsible for the tendency to use behaviorally-oriented terms to classify the brain-damaged child.

Another set of influences also was of significance in predisposing psychologists to avoid the use of terms that had neuropathological significance: In the cases of many of these children there was no objective evidence of damage or pathological dysfunction of the brain. Examinations by pediatric neurologists were often completely normal, even when the child demonstrated many behavioral disorders that were thought to reflect altered brain functions. Respect for the findings based on neurological examination influenced psychologists even more to use descriptive terms that were based on the behavioral deficits; one would not want to call a child brain-damaged when there was no neurological evidence of brain damage. However, these children showed ample evidence of behavioral deficits and disturbances, and thus they could readily be classified (labeled) on the basis of these behavioral disorders.

There were two problems associated with this type of reasoning, both related to the validity of diagnostic conclusions. First, among adults as well as children, the neurological examination frequently yields completely normal results, even among persons who are known unequivocally to have sustained cerebral damage. The fact that evidence of brain damage was not elicited by the neurological examination does not mean that there was no brain damage. The limitation of the clinical neurological examination in producing false negatives has become better known, and there is presently less of a tendency to presume that brain structure and/or function are normal merely because results of the neurological examination were within normal limits.

The second problem related to the inadequacies of classification (diagnosis) on the basis of behavioral evidence. In most instances the diagnostic category (e.g., *developmentally dysphasic, hyperactive child, minimal brain dysfunction*) had little specific meaning, was superficial and only descriptive, and most seriously, emphasized obvious behavioral deviations and neglected the more subtle (and perhaps more basic) aspects of neuropsychological impairment. Thus, the problem, which is still with us to a considerable degree, was represented by an absence of biological (neuropathological) evidence to use as a basis for diagnosis, and the inadequacies of behavioral observations as a method for meaningful classification.

As an example of our current status, the term *attention deficit disorder (ADD)*, either with or without hyperactivity, has largely replaced the term *hyperactive child*. The "improvement" is that the focus is now directed toward impairment of attention, and this deficit may exist with or without hyperactivity. However, upon careful and detailed neuropsychological examination, children with ADD show a host of deficits, and an exclusive focus on attentional deficits tends to obscure the basic, complex neuropsychological problems that characterize the condition.

Diagnostic categories based on behavioral descriptions invariably seem grossly to oversimplify the condition in question regardless of the term used. For example, the classification *mental retardation* includes children with and without conventional evidence of brain damage (biological criteria), and a great number of children classified as mentally retarded have many types of neuropsychological deficits beyond limited intelligence as measured by conventional intelligence tests.

Children with learning disabilities usually have no positive neurological findings, but upon complete examination demonstrate neuropsychological deficits that extend far beyond academic learning problems. Some professionals believe that children with developmental dysphasia have brain-related pathology, while other researchers claim that these children have essentially normal brains (see Reitan, 1985 and our discussion earlier in this chapter). These children are customarily diagnosed and treated for their speech and language problems alone, and their extensive neuropsychological deficits (which extend beyond the language area) are usually unidentified and essentially neglected.

The inadequacy of the behavioral diagnosis (such as ADD) stems essentially from the fact that it emphasizes a selected and obvious facet of a very complex range of deficits and tends to ignore the full extent of the child's problem. As a result, behavioral diagnoses tend to be strongly overlapping, with individual children in each diagnostic category having similar neuropsychological deficits across many areas and being subject to differential identification only in accordance with a selected and obvious behavioral characteristic.

From this point of view, it is clear that behavioral diagnoses almost invariably oversimplify a complex range of neuropsychological deficits and lead to a situation in which rehabilitation attempts are oriented toward changing or modifying a limited and circumscribed behavior. This problem can be remediated by administering a comprehensive examination, such as the Halstead-Reitan Battery, which has been devised to measure the full range of neuropsychological functions, in order to obtain a basis for both interindividual (normative) comparisons as well as intraindividual (personal strengths and weaknesses) assessments.

Comparative Areas of Neuropsychological Deficit

Based on the study of children with known cerebral lesions, Reitan and his colleagues adopted an approach aimed toward clarifying the behavioral manifestations of cerebral damage. Their belief was that the problem of impaired brain functions in children with essentially normal neurological findings (despite learning, behavioral, and intellectual impairment), could never be understood without first discovering the basic and characteristic neuropsychological deficits of children with definite brain lesions. If the problem was one of discerning brain-behavior relationships, there was little point, at least initially, in investigating only one side of the equation.

The initial step in this process would require evaluation of children with definitely established cerebral damage (and therefore known to be different from normal children in neuropathological terms) across an extensive range of neuropsychological measures and to compare the results in the two groups. Results of these studies, which provided a general characterization of the neuropsychological effects of cerebral damage as well as validation of individual tests, were reported in the first part of this chapter.

Following this approach, the second step was to investigate areas of neuropsychological function to determine whether brain-damaged children demonstrated greater deficits of one kind or another than normal children. In other words, was there any validity, across the full range of brain damage, that would support general appellations such as the *perceptually handicapped child, the conceptually handicapped child, the developmentally dysphasic child,* etc.? More important, were there any areas of function that were especially vulnerable to impairment as a result of brain damage?

Obviously, an answer to this question might have significant implications, not only for understanding the neuropsychological consequences of brain damage, but for questions, which logically follow, about approaches to rehabilitation and remediation. It is important to note, however, that generalizations to brain-damaged children as a group about vulnerable areas or patterns of neuropsychological deficits would not preclude the clinical necessity of finding significant patterns, perhaps of unique importance, in individual children. While research results relate to group findings and support categorical generalizations, clinical evaluations concern the individual and have implications for the child as a unique person.

Differentiation of neuropsychological functions into higher and lower level abilities has long been recognized (Chapman & Wolff, 1959; Halstead, 1945). Lower-level brain functions, in turn, have been differentiated both theoretically (Halstead, 1947; Luria, 1970; Reitan & Wolfson, 1988b) and in assessment procedures (Reitan & Wolfson, 1985 and this volume) into motor (output, expressive) and sensory (input, receptive) functions. In terms of lower-level neuropsychological functions, then, it seemed reasonable to inquire whether any aspect of sensorimotor functions was more significantly impaired in brain-damaged children.

Comparisons of Sensory-perceptual · and Motor Functions

Tests of tactile functions, specifically including tactile finger localization, had previously been studied in mentally retarded subjects (Benton, 1959a, 1959b) and in normal children (Reed, 1967a), but there had been scarcely any studies of sensory-perceptual skills evaluating abilities in comparable groups of brain-damaged and normal children. Among adult brain-damaged subjects, however, several studies of sensory-perceptual deficiencies had been reported (Carmon & Benton, 1969; Reitan, 1970; Semmes, Weinstein, Ghent, & Teuber, 1960). These studies had dealt in considerable detail with various techniques for examining sensory-perceptual deficits, and the results indicated that limitations in this receptive avenue to the brain had striking implications for the general adequacy of cerebral functions and for a wide range of psychological performances. While these findings indicating the importance of sensory-input to the brain were well demonstrated in adults, they had not been studied in brain-damaged as compared with normal children, even though many studies had indicated the importance of motor (output) functions in both adults and children.

Boll and Reitan (1972c) investigated this question by comparing sensory and motor functions in groups of 35 brain-damaged children and 35 control children. Each of the groups consisted of 23 males and 12 females. The mean ages were 141.26 months (SD, 20.65) for the brain-damaged children and 141.23 months (SD, 18.39) for the control children. The difference in age between the groups did not approach statistical significance. The brain-damaged children had the following etiologies: traumatic injury, 12; tumors, 7; congenital vascular anomalies, 5; inflammatory damage resulting from viral infection, 5; perinatal lesions, 5; and abscess, 1. The control children were volunteer subjects from local school systems. In terms of socioeconomic status, nearly all of the brain-damaged children were private patients and, considering the nature of the referral system, we had no reason to believe that there were any striking differences between the two groups.

The dependent variables included two measures that were strictly dependent on motor functions (Finger Tapping and Grip Strength), three measures that required essentially no motor function but demanded tactile-perceptual abilities (Tactile Finger Localization, Finger-tip Number Writing Perception, and Tactile Form Recognition), and another test that was complex in nature, requiring tactile-perceptual skills, proprioceptive abilities, motor functions, and complex problem-solving skills (Tactual Performance Test). All tests were administered individually to the subjects by technicians who were thoroughly trained in administration and scoring procedures. These technicians had no knowledge of either the neurological findings for any subject or the purposes of the research study.

An overall analysis of variance indicated that the brain-damaged group performed significantly more poorly than the controls ($p < .001$). Five of the six measures showed significant differences on individual comparisons. The two motor tests yielded significant differences as follows: Finger Tapping ($p < .01$) and Grip Strength ($p < .05$). The tactile-perceptual tests were significant in two instances: Tactile Finger Localization ($p < .01$) and Finger-tip Number Writing Perception ($p < .05$). The tests based on tactile form recognition did not show a significant difference between the two groups. Finally, the complex test that depended upon both input and output abilities as well as problem-solving skills (Tactual Performance Test) demonstrated a significant difference between the two groups ($p < .01$).

The results for the two groups were also analyzed with relation to performances by the dominant and nondominant hands. The findings indicated that the control group performed better than the brain-damaged group with the dominant hand (p<.01) as well as with the nondominant hand (p<.05). Although members of each group did not show evidence of differential abilities within tactile or motor functions on each hand considered separately, they consistently performed more poorly on both tactile-perceptual and motor tasks when comparisons were made between the dominant hand and the nondominant hand.

In summary, the results of this study indicated that both motor (output) and tactile-perceptual (input) abilities were significantly impaired in children with cerebral damage. Obviously, there must be a limitation in the ability of the individual with regard to central processing functions if input of material from the environment is altered or diminished. In turn, since most nonverbal responses are manifested through motor functions, the executive functions of the brain concerned with analysis of problem-situations must be limited when response capabilities are diminished.

It is therefore important to evaluate both sensory-perceptual and motor functions in any attempt to reach an overall understanding of the behavioral and neuropsychological consequences of cerebral damage. While the results of this study indicated that motor impairment was somewhat more pronounced than sensory-perceptual losses, the more significant finding concerned the prominent deficits among brain-damaged children, as compared with controls, in both areas.

Sensorimotor Functions Compared with Higher-Level Functions

Reitan (1970) investigated the relationship between sensorimotor functions and intelligence, cognition, and emotional status in adult subjects with cerebral lesions. A group of 31 brain-damaged subjects was identified who showed evidence of relatively serious impairment of sensorimotor functions, based upon the fact that they fell in the lowest one-third of a total of 197 brain-damaged subjects. Five tests were used to provide a combined score for bilateral performances: Finger Tapping, Grip Strength, Tactile Finger Recognition, Finger-tip Number Writing Perception, and sensory imperception phenomena using tests of bilateral simultaneous stimulation through the tactile, auditory, and visual avenues. The same total sample of 197 brain-damaged subjects was used to select a group of subjects who fell in the upper one-third with respect to the combined score based on these sensorimotor variables. These two groups' performances were then compared on intellectual, cognitive, and emotional measures.

The results showed that the groups were strikingly different in terms of Verbal IQ, Performance IQ, and Full Scale IQ results. Additional cognitive measures included the Category Test, the Speech-sounds Perception Test, the Seashore Rhythm Test, and Parts A and B of the Trail Making Test. Again, the groups were strikingly different on each of these measures, and the subjects who had impaired sensorimotor skills performed much more poorly.

The emotional status of the two groups was evaluated with the Minnesota Multiphasic Personality Inventory (MMPI). The group with impaired sensorimotor functions consistently had higher mean values on each of the Clinical scales, although in a number of instances the differences between the two groups did not reach statistically significant levels. In total, however, impairment of sensorimotor functions corresponded very closely with impairment of intellectual and cognitive abilities and, to a lesser extent, with indications of emotional disturbances.

Raw scores were converted to McCall T-scores in order to provide information about the comparative deficits. The two groups had mean T-scores that were nearly as different on the intellectual and cognitive measures as they were on the criterion measures that expressed sensorimotor deficits. In other words, there was scarcely any collapse of differences between the two groups, indicating that differences in

sensorimotor functions have a profound influence on intellectual and cognitive function and a lesser influence on
measures of emotional adjustment. In conclusion, the results indicated that impairment of sensorimotor functions of
adult subjects was closely related to a broad range of higher-
level neuropsychological performances.

Reitan (1971a) compared sensorimotor functions of a
group of 29 brain-damaged young children (aged 5-8 years)
with a group of comparably aged normal control children.
In this study dependent variables included finger tapping
speed, grip strength, motor co-ordination as measured by
the Marching Test, and psychomotor problem-solving abilities as reflected by the Tactual Performance Test.

The results of the study yielded statistically significant
differences between the two groups, indicating that both
motor functions and tactile-perceptual functions, ranging
from relatively simple to quite complex procedures, were
impaired in the brain-damaged group of children. Some
variability in sensitivity to brain damage was present for
individual tests, but the data obtained from the sensorimotor measures permitted classification of 70%-80% of the
subjects to their appropriate groups, using the median of
combined distributions as the cut-off point. This finding
made it quite clear that generally considered, brain damage
had a profound effect on adequacy of sensorimotor functions among young children.

Finlayson and Reitan (1976b) investigated the relationship of tactile-perceptual functioning with relation to intellectual, cognitive, and reading skills in both normal older
children (12-14 years of age) and younger children (6-8
years of age). Available data from larger samples permitted
composition of 24 older children who fell within the lower
quartile on sensorimotor performances and these were compared with 24 older children who fell within the upper
quartile.

The same procedure was used to compare younger children who were impaired on tactile-perceptual tasks with children who were less impaired on such tasks. There were no differences in groups with higher and lower ability levels within the older and younger groups in terms of chronological age or education. Dependent variables included the Verbal IQ, Performance IQ, and Full Scale IQ values from the Wechsler Intelligence Scale for Children, the Category Test, and the Reading section of the Wide Range Achievement Test.

The results indicated that the two groups of older children showed significant differences on all of these tests except for the Performance IQ value, with the children who had the poor tactile-perceptual skills earning the lower scores. A definite trend toward this same result was obtained with the younger children, with the mean score on every variable being less adequate for the group with poor tactile-perceptual skills. However, statistically significant differences were found only on the Verbal IQ and Full Scale IQ measures. These results were consistent with other reports (Reed, 1967a; Rourke, 1975) in terms of the differential findings for older as compared with younger children. Older children appear to have a more consistent organization of brain-behavior relationships than younger children, probably because various abilities, related to the condition of the brain, are more completely developed and the results are not as much affected by differing levels of performance in accordance with the early phases of the developmental process.

Boll (1972) pursued the question of differential degrees of performance among brain-damaged children by comparing results obtained on tests considered to measure perceptual deficits, conceptual deficits, and motor impairment. In his study he compared 27 brain-damaged children to 27 controls who fell in the 9- through 14-year age range and were comparable in their age distributions.

Boll applied a method developed by Reitan (1959a) that permitted a comparison of the adequacy of each measure's ability to differentiate between the two groups. Perceptual skills were evaluated using visual, auditory, and tactile measures, including the Block Design from the Wechsler Intelligence Scale for Children, the Seashore Rhythm Test, and the Tactile Form Recognition Test. Conceptual abilities were evaluated with the Category Test. Primary motor skill was measured by the finger tapping speed of each child. Boll was interested in whether the term "perceptual disability" was more appropriate than the term "conceptual disability" in describing brain-damaged children or whether their major deficit actually was in primary motor functions.

The results of this investigation are presented in Table 7-11.

TABLE 7-11
Comparative sensitivity of various conceptual, perceptual, and motor measures to cerebral damage in older children (see text).

Probability levels in the table below refer to the results found in comparing the sensitivity of one test against another. For example, the Category Test (#1) was more sensitive to brain damage than the Block Design Test (#2) at a significance level of p<.006, more sensitive than the Seashore Rhythm Test (#3) at p <.006, more sensitive than the Finger Tapping Test (#4) at p<.001, more sensitive than the Tactile Form Recognition Test (#5) at p<.001, etc. The WISC Block Design subtest (#2) showed no difference in sensitivity as compared with the Seashore Rhythm Test (#3), but was significantly more sensitive than the Finger Tapping Test (#4) and the Tactile Form Recognition Test (#5), both at a level of p<.001.

Test of Measure	1	2	3	4	5
1. Category Test	—				
2. WISC Block Design Subtest	.006	—			
3. Seashore Rhythm Test	.006	NS	—		
4. Finger Tapping Test	.001	.001	NS	—	
5. Tactile Form Recognition Test	.006	.001	.001	.004	—

In comparing the results of matched pairs of control and brain-damaged children, the findings indicated that conceptual deficits were more sensitive to cerebral damage than any of the other tests used. These results were highly significant. Perceptual deficits measured using the visual modality (Block Design) were more sensitive than motor performances (finger tapping speed) or tactile recognition (Tactile Form Recognition Test). Perceptual function measured through the auditory avenue (Seashore Rhythm Test) was more sensitive than tactile perception (Tactile Form Recognition Test), but was either less sensitive or showed no significant differences with other comparisons. Motor performance, represented by impaired finger tapping speed, was more sensitive than tactile perception, but was poorer or failed to show a significant difference in comparison with other measures. Tactile perceptual abilities, represented by results on the Tactile Form Recognition Test, were significantly less sensitive than any of the other measures used.

In summarizing these results, one would conclude that (1) conceptual losses are by far the most consistent in differentiating between brain-damaged and normal groups of children, (2) visual-perceptual tasks occupy a secondary position, followed by an auditory perceptual task and a task measuring primary motor functions, and (3) a tactile perceptual task was least effective in differentiating the groups. Obviously, however, a study of this type would be limited by the adequacy of each of the tests included as a neuropsychological measure. For example, certain visual perceptive tasks might be more sensitive than others, and the results of this study were based upon selected measures. In general, though, the results of this study do suggest that conceptual, abstraction, and reasoning deficits are extremely prominent in brain-damaged children as compared with normal children, and that abilities on other types of measures involving perceptual and motor functions are not as consistently impaired.

Among brain-damaged children it is difficult to determine the degree to which various abilities are impaired because of the possibility that individual tests, representing one area or another, may have a differential degree of sensitivity to brain pathology. Nevertheless, as we have noted, Reitan (1956) had found that adults who had developed normal brain-behavior relationships and then sustained cerebral damage had general ability structures similar to normal adults. The similarity in relationships of various abilities among children, however, deviated from these findings (Boll & Reitan, 1972a, 1972b) inasmuch as the pattern of test intercorrelations differed beyond chance levels. These findings, indicating that children with brain damage may have an organization of brain-behavior relationships that is considerably different from either adults with brain damage or normal adults, suggest the importance of developmental factors. The growing interest in brain retraining in both adults and children (Reitan & Sena, 1983; Reitan & Wolfson, 1988b; Rourke, Bakker, Fisk, & Strang, 1983) constitutes another critical reason for detailed exploration of this problem.

As reviewed above, Boll (1972) had found that conceptual skills were the most impaired and that motor speed was more impaired than one of three perceptual measures. However, he had relied on single tests to represent certain areas of function and, as noted, his results may have been influenced by the differential sensitivity of these tests.

Nici and Reitan (1987) explored this question further, using at least four separate measures for evaluation of each category (motor abilities, sensory abilities, general neuropsychological abilities, and verbal/academic skills). These investigators hypothesized that brain-diseased or brain-damaged children would demonstrate relatively more impairment than control children on tasks requiring higher-level brain functions (categories of general neuropsychological and verbal/academic skills) than on tasks requiring lower-level abilities (sensory-perceptual and motor functions).

The study was pursued by composing a brain-damaged group and a normal control group, each consisting of 10 girls and 15 boys. The mean ages were 133.80 months (SD, 17.31) for the brain-damaged group and 138.16 months (SD, 13.08) for the control group. The mean education grade level was 4.08 years (SD, 1.41) for the brain-impaired group and 4.92 years (SD, 1.04) for the control group. The difference in the age distributions of the two groups was not statistically significant, but the difference in grade level reached the .02 level, a finding that was not unexpected, since brain-damaged children are often less successful in school than control subjects.

Sensory skills were evaluated on each hand with the following tests: Tactile Form Recognition, Tactile Finger Recognition, and Finger-tip Number Writing Perception. Motor skills were assessed using four measurements: Finger Tapping for each hand and Grip Strength for each hand. Tests falling in the category of general neuropsychological abilities were selected to reflect substantial problem-solving requirements and included Parts A and B of the Trail Making Test, the Category Test, and the Total Time, Memory, and Localization components of the Tactual Performance Test. The area of verbal/academic skills was assessed by using Wechsler's subtests of Arithmetic, Vocabulary, Similarities, and Comprehension and the Reading and Spelling sections of the Wide Range Achievement Test.

For each group each distribution of scores was transformed into normalized T-scores and a score for each subject, representing each area of function, was obtained by averaging T-scores. A multivariate analysis of variance demonstrated highly significant differences between the brain-damaged group and the control group, indicating the appropriate use of a post-hoc univariate analysis of variance for each category of ability. These analyses indicated that the two groups were significantly different in each of the four areas of function.

Impairment of general neuropsychological abilities and motor abilities showed the greatest differences between the two groups. The sensory-perceptual measures demonstrated the least difference, and the verbal/academic measures fell in-between. Differences between the brain-impaired and control groups were essentially similar for each of the four motor measures, with the differences reaching highly significant levels. However, differences of essentially the same magnitude were obtained with each of the measures of general neuropsychological abilities, regardless of whether these tests required motor performances (Tactual Performance Test) or had limited requirements in this respect (Category Test).

The discriminant analysis using summary scores from each of the four categories of ability resulted in correct classification of 84% of the subjects (three brain-damaged subjects were classified as controls and five control subjects were classified as brain-damaged). As expected on the basis of the rest of the data analysis, the motor and general neuropsychological summary scores contributed most heavily to this discriminant function, with the sensory-perceptual and verbal/academic summary scores contributing far less. The coefficients used in this discriminant function were as follows: sensory-perceptual, −0.19; motor, +0.67; general neuropsychological, +0.56; and verbal/academic, +0.17.

Nici and Reitan had postulated that general academic abilities and verbal/academic skills would differentiate the groups better than lower-level brain functions (motor abilities and sensory-perceptual skills). The results of this study only partially supported this hypothesis. The deviations from expectation involved the evidence of striking impairment on motor tests and the lesser impairment on the verbal/academic measures of brain-damaged subjects.

This result could possibly have come about, at least in part, because of the early recognition of brain disease or damage and the emphasis placed on academic progress in our culture. In other words, it is entirely possible that the brain-damaged children had received special and focused help in developing academic skills, which resulted in a higher level of performance in this area than in the other areas evaluated. It should also be recognized that motor impairment is frequently identified through neurological examination and that rehabilitation programs often devote systematic attention to physical therapy.

Although Nici and Reitan had no documentation of the amount of attention to remediation and rehabilitation that had been offered in the four areas evaluated, it seems likely that most effort had probably been directed to the areas of academic skills and motor functions. Sensory-perceptual skills were not generally compromised as severely as the other abilities. This consideration leaves the area of general neuropsychological functions, which was considerably impaired, standing fairly much alone. The results of this study indicate that (1) higher-level abilities (such as abstract thinking, logical analysis, flexibility of thought, speed in comprehending and analyzing complex situations, and memory) suffer significant impairment following brain damage, (2) these higher-level deficits are often relatively neglected when determining areas for focused remediation, and (3) brain-retraining efforts, within a neuropsychological framework, need to be directed to these deficits.

Reitan and Wolfson (1988c) investigated this problem in further detail using tests which covered six areas of neuropsychological functions and were represented by transformation of raw scores to Neuropsychological Deficit Scale scores in order to reflect clinically significant performances and to minimize chance variations in test scores. (A detailed description of this study was presented earlier in this chapter in the section on validity studies of the Neuropsychological Deficit Scale.)

The results of this study are of interest with regard to comparative areas of neuropsychological deficit and will be reviewed briefly in this context at this point. The findings clearly demonstrated that differential levels of neuropsychological performance characterized the functions of control children and children with learning disabilities or brain damage. It was not surprising that children with actual structural cerebral damage or significant cerebral disease performed more poorly than controls. This finding merely confirmed the observations of our previous studies. The fact that children with learning disabilities occupied an intermediate position also was only to be expected in accordance with our previous research.

The most striking finding of this study was represented by the severe degree of deficit shown by children with learning disabilities in the area of alertness and concentration. These children have great difficulty in paying attention to specific stimulus material and registering incoming information in a way that would make it possible for the brain to deal with it in terms of central processing.

In summary, the results indicate that brain-damaged subjects are generally impaired in various areas of neuropsychological functioning, tending to do somewhat better on sensory-perceptual measures than on other types of tasks. In fact, in terms of raw-score means, the results for sensory-perceptual measures were actually a little better for each of the groups than their results in other areas. Compared to the children with documented evidence of brain disease or damage, control children were much better in every area of function.

It is especially important to note that children with learning disabilities have a very special and serious problem in the area of alertness and concentration in much the same way as children diagnosed as having Attention Deficit Disorder (ADD), even though this problem represents only one aspect of the total picture of neuropsychological deficits in each condition: they appear to be impaired in their ability to relay information to the brain through sensory avenues. Obviously, if the brain is not able to obtain the necessary information initially, there is no chance that higher-level brain functions can serve adequately to analyze the incoming information and to deliver an appropriate response. Thus, even though children with learning disabilities appear to be only mildly impaired in various aspects of central processing, they face a most serious problem with respect to initial registration by the brain of incoming information.

The area of abstraction, reasoning, and logical analysis, however, must also be noted as an area of relative weakness for children with learning disabilities which, in turn, would limit the pertinence and relevance of any response based on analysis of incoming information. The results of this study indicate quite clearly that for children with learning disabilities, remediation efforts must be directed initially to the problem of registering incoming information. The next step in the remediation process is to train the child to analyze this information in a meaningful way as a basis for an appropriate and meaningful response.

Investigations of Mental Retardation Using the HRB

The HRB has been used quite extensively for research purposes, and particularly in clinical evaluation within the area of mental retardation. In order to gain clinical insight regarding results obtained with the HRB, Reitan initially reviewed test results obtained with the Battery and did clinical interpretations of the findings for hundreds of mentally retarded subjects.

Definitions of mental retardation, as well as diagnostic and classification systems that have been proposed, have been subject to many practical difficulties and criticisms (Hays, 1962; Sanders, 1970; Zigler, 1967). While categories of mental retardation — such as cultural, familial, brain-damaged, undifferentiated, and undifferentiated accompanied by psychosis or personality disorder — have been proposed, the problem lies essentially in the fact that the individual mentally retarded subject almost invariably has been influenced by a complex array of disadvantageous circumstances regarding the development of intellectual and cognitive skills.

There is nothing mutually exclusive about adverse environmental influences and brain pathology. In fact, it is likely that there actually is some degree of positive correlation between the occurrence of one kind of disadvantageous circumstance and others. Thus, as frequently is true of classification systems, the individual subject does not fall neatly into one category or another but, instead, has developed mental retardation as a result of the interaction of many etiological factors.

A second significant limitation regarding the area of mental retardation is that in practical terms classification of the individual subject frequently relies very heavily (if not exclusively) on results obtained with standard intelligence tests. Even the best of these tests falls far short of providing a comprehensive evaluation of the full range of intellectual and cognitive abilities and, in general, the results are probably more influenced by cultural and educational opportunities than by cerebral damage. Anyone who has worked extensively among persons classified as mentally retarded has encountered instances of persons with quite limited verbal intelligence and academic abilities who, as a result, have been classified as mentally retarded even though further examination reveals evidence of perfectly normal or even quite competent neuropsychological capabilities. A question then exists about whether evaluation with the HRB might contribute valuable clinical understanding of individual subjects who have been classified as mentally retarded.

It is clear that an approach to psychological assessment that is characterized exclusively by determining level of performance is scarcely adequate to draw inferences about brain damage or dysfunction as a basis for ability limitations. Nevertheless, the major method of classification of individuals as mentally retarded, using IQ measures, does exactly this. A more comprehensive type of assessment, which is based on both interindividual and intraindividual methods of evaluation, obviously is necessary, and is provided by the HRB.

In our examination of hundreds of subjects classified as mentally retarded, we routinely found evidence of impairment in terms of level of performance and even on specific tasks (such as those used to elicit pathognomonic signs) among the more usual brain-damaged populations. The results indicated that performances based upon interindividual comparisons (the subject's performance with relation to normative samples) were inadequate in determining whether impaired brain functions were a factor contributing to a person's behavior. The use of intraindividual inferential methods was required, so that deviations among the individual's performances could be assessed (as contrasted with comparison of the level of performance with normative data).

The HRB includes two types of intraindividual evaluations. The first of these methods is directed toward evaluation of patterns or relationships between levels of cognitive performances. This method is based on the presumption that good performances in one area may reflect adequacy of certain brain functions, whereas poor performances in another area may reflect brain damage or dysfunction. However, because their performances consistently are in the lower part of the distribution, it is difficult to generate meaningful patterns or relationships among test results for mentally retarded subjects. Intraindividual variability due to chance variations is difficult to differentiate from systematic influences on various abilities when the potential for overall variability is quite limited. These circumstances are responsible for the difficulties that have been encountered in various attempts to identify intellectual and cognitive patterns that might characterize mentally retarded subjects as contrasted with those in other groups or categories than mental retardation (Matthews, 1974).

The second method for evaluating intraindividual differences compares the same types of performance (which presumably are related to homologous areas within the cerebral cortex of the two hemispheres) on the two sides of the body. In this approach the individual essentially serves as his/her own control. For example, if the subject has definite difficulty in tactile finger recognition on his/her right hand, but performs this task relatively adequately with the left hand, it is difficult to escape the conclusion that there is a biological basis for the finding.

In our analysis of HRB protocols for hundreds of mentally retarded subjects, we were particularly dependent upon this method for drawing inferences about impairment of brain functions. The limitation of an inferential basis, using the other three methods of evaluation that are customarily employed, may well have limited the prospect of identifying biologically-based correlates of defective performances. Nevertheless, it was not at all uncommon to discover convincing evidence of distinct deviations from normal expectancy in performances on the two sides of the body. We were able to use standards for clinical interpretation derived from study of thousands of normal persons as well as people with documented cerebral lesions of either a focal or generalized nature.

It should be noted that most persons with cerebral damage, even though identified as diffuse or generalized in terms of neurological evaluation, show deviations in performances on the two sides of the body that go beyond expected limits. Thus, although there was little if any reason to suspect the presence of specific, focal lesions in these mentally retarded subjects, it was likely that definite differences would appear even if there was diffuse or generalized cerebral dysfunction.

Despite the fact that we were essentially using only one of the four methods of inference (and therefore possibly underestimating the frequency of cerebral damage), it was not at all uncommon for us to discover distinct deviations from normality in terms of right-sided and left-sided performances. These lateralized deficits frequently involved both motor and sensory-perceptual functions, although they usually did not involve one side of the body as exclusively as we found in many patients with focal cerebral lesions. Nevertheless, using this method of inference, we would estimate that cerebral impairment was present in up to 50% of the cases diagnosed as mentally retarded.

These observations suggest that evidence of cerebral damage is encountered much more commonly using the HRB than one would postulate on the basis of findings from physical neurological examination or electroencephalography. Our observations are consistent with the review by Masland, Sarason, and Gladwin (1958) of the pre-, peri-, and post-natal biological factors that may cause mental deficiency and that contribute to brain damage in a substantial proportion of retarded persons. These authors stated, " . . . the factor of brain injury can operate throughout the whole range of intelligence, and, in fact, the minor degrees of injury are far more common than are the severe and grossly evident ones. Pathological studies of the brains of mildly retarded persons show minor developmental anomalies in a large proportion of cases" (p. 11), a conclusion supported by Benda (1944). Evidence suggesting that biological impairment of the brain may be a significant factor in many mentally retarded subjects serves to emphasize the potential importance of evaluating these subjects with a comprehensive neuropsychological battery.

We have conducted a number of specific research investigations to study the neuropsychological characteristics of mentally retarded persons. Although there may be some value in determining whether impairment of brain functions has contributed to the mental retardation of a particular individual, a further delineation and definition of the neuropsychological characteristics may be especially significant in developing treatment and rehabilitation plans. Using a test of general intelligence to determine whether an individual is mentally retarded is hardly adequate and definitely cannot be considered a complete neuropsychological evaluation, regardless of the level of the individual's intelligence.

Abstract thinking ability has frequently been identified as a fundamental and essential characteristic of intelligence, but subtests from the WISC-R (even those often interpreted as relating to abstract thinking) have no better correlation with a test such as the Category Test than do subtests which are not thought to measure abstraction. Thus, a serious question exists about the extent to which abstraction and logical analysis skills are actually measured by the subtests of the WISC-R. Considering the fact that most definitions of intelligence have assigned a certain primacy to abstraction ability as an attribute of intelligent behavior, this may be a serious omission in the Wechsler Scales. Terman (1921) stated that, "An individual is intelligent in proportion as he is able to carry on abstract thinking" (p. 128).

While ability in abstraction and logical analysis has been considered to be an important intellectual and cognitive function, many criticisms have been directed against conventional psychological tests in the area of mental retardation (Sarason & Gladwin, 1958). These criticisms have frequently charged that to a marked degree intelligence tests measure educational opportunity and attainment, and that the range of problem-solving behavior sampled in the majority of psychometric studies of the retarded is too narrow to justify the generalization and predictive burdens which have been placed upon these measures. In order to learn more about the importance of abstraction ability among the mentally retarded, Matthews and Reitan carried out a number of studies.

In the first of these studies, Matthews and Reitan (1961) composed a group of 20 adult subjects who had recently sustained cerebral damage and 20 adult mentally retarded subjects. A review of case histories for the retarded subjects suggested that each had developmental or learning deficits that were present before the age of three years. The two groups were matched according to Wechsler Full Scale IQ scores, with each pair of subjects falling within two points of each other. The purpose of this study was to determine whether subjects who had the advantage of normal development up until sustaining recent brain damage in adulthood had abstraction skills which were better or worse than mentally retarded subjects who had been impaired most of their lives.

The results indicated that Category Test scores were much worse in the subjects with mental retardation than in the subjects who had recently sustained brain damage. Thus, the findings strongly suggested that long-standing impairment, of the type seen in mental retardation, has a very serious limiting effect upon abstraction, reasoning, and logical analysis and that abilities in this area are less compromised among persons who have the advantage of normal neuropsychological development and then sustain an acute insult to the brain.

Another feature of the data analysis resulted in a finding that was quite the opposite, showing that in one aspect the mentally retarded subjects performed better than the recently brain-damaged group. This result was concerned with the learning potential demonstrated on continued exposure to the problem. Subtests 5 and 6 of the Category Test are based upon the same principal, although the subject is not informed of this. Intraindividual changes, or improvement from performances on subtest 5 to subtest 6 were computed for each subject. The mentally retarded subjects showed much better improvement, at highly significant statistical levels, than the subjects with recent cerebral damage.

These findings suggest that the mentally retarded subjects were strikingly handicapped in their initial ability to grasp the abstraction principle involved in the test, indicating significant impairment in abstract learning as well as in the ability to shift between abstraction principles. However, the significantly better improvement rate upon additional exposure to stimulus material almost certainly indicates a greater ability among MR subjects to profit from experience when the problem solving task depends upon application of a continuing principle. This finding may have important implications for rehabilitation as well as eventual mastery of a task. In other words, the potential for significant improvement with continued training and exposure to the problem may bode well for the potential of mentally retarded subjects to eventually master an appointed task.

Matthews and Reitan (1962) used essentially the same design to compare 15 adult subjects with cerebral damage and 15 mentally retarded subjects matched in pairs within two Wechsler Full Scale IQ points.

In this study the groups were compared on the Tactual Performance Test. Prior investigations, including the normative data reported by Matthews (1974), suggests that mentally retarded subjects tend to perform much better on the Tactual Performance Test than on the Category Test, indicating that they have considerably better psychomotor capabilities (as compared with reference groups) than abstraction abilities. In this study no differences in performances were found between the two groups either on the first trial (preferred hand), second trial (nonpreferred hand), or third trial (both hands). The total time required to complete the three trials was nearly identical in the two groups. Thus, on this task no differences were found between subjects with recent cerebral damage (and the advantage of normal neuropsychological development) and mentally retarded subjects (who had evidence of developmental or learning deficits that were present before the age of three years), as long as the groups were equivalent for Full Scale IQ.

The Tactual Performance Test also provides an opportunity to evaluate improvement with continued exposure to the task through comparison of the time required on each of the three trials. The groups did not differ in the amount of improvement (practice-effect) from the first trial (dominant hand) to the second trial (nondominant hand), but there was a statistically significant difference between the groups in the improvement from the second trial (nondominant hand) to the third trial (both hands). Again, the greater improvement was shown by the mentally retarded subjects.

These results stand in direct contrast to the highly significant differences which were found in comparing abstraction and reasoning abilities as measured by the Category Test. As demonstrated by the results on the Tactual Performance Test, the mentally retarded subjects had better motor-manipulative abilities than abstraction and reasoning skills. Thus, even though the mentally retarded subjects were especially impaired in their initial ability in concept formation, they also showed greater improvement on successive trials, particularly in concept formation but also in psychomotor tasks.

Matthews and Reitan (1963) performed another study to investigate the significance of differential abstraction levels among mentally retarded older adolescents. Based on Category Test performances, two groups of mentally retarded subjects were composed to reflect relatively adequate and relatively poor abstraction ability levels. A large normative data group of institutionalized mentally retarded persons had been examined, and one group of 15 subjects was selected from those who were at least one standard deviation above the mean and another group from those subjects who were at least one standard deviation below the mean. Thus, comparisons were made between two groups of retarded subjects; one group was relatively "good" in abstraction ability and the other group relatively "poor." The groups were matched for chronological age, gender, and mean Wechsler Full Scale IQ. However, in accordance with the selection process, the groups had strikingly different scores on the Category Test.

The two groups were compared on an extensive number of variables, drawn principally from the HRB. For purposes of data analysis, these tests were subdivided into two groups: tests most dependent upon immediate problem-solving capabilities and tests most dependent upon stored information and background knowledge. Three neuropsychologists who had detailed familiarity with the HRB ranked the test's characteristics to place them in one of the two categories. The purpose of the study, therefore, was to determine the significance of retarded subjects' abstraction abilities on measures of immediate problem-solving versus stored information.

The results showed that on tests that were included in the problem-solving procedures, the group with good abstraction ability performed significantly better than the group with poor abstraction ability. This finding, considered by itself, would hardly be surprising; IQ was held constant (and therefore presumably had no influence on the results) and ability in abstraction and reasoning would be expected to produce better scores on tests that required immediate problem-solving skills. However, on measures that depended principally upon stored information and background experience, the group with relatively poor abstraction abilities performed better than the group with relatively good abstraction skills.

Since the group with poor abstraction ability performed better on tests that reflect stored information, one might wonder whether ability in abstraction and reasoning might, in fact, detract from acquisition of stored information.

Perhaps among retarded subjects there is an advantage in rote memorization of information if the subject is not distracted by any inclination to engage in analysis or reasoning. However, further analysis of these groups shows that the group with good abstraction ability was significantly higher on Performance IQ and the group with impaired abstraction ability was significantly higher on Verbal IQ. These IQ differences may well have been of significance in producing the results of this study, but in that case another question would be raised: Is there any systematic relationship between disparities in verbal and performance intelligence among the mentally retarded in accordance with differential abilities in abstraction and reasoning?

It is apparent from a review of these individual studies that there are interesting and potentially significant relationships in ability among retarded subjects compared with other groups in the area of clinical neuropsychology as well as within retarded groups themselves. Matthews (1963) found that there were certain differences among diagnostic categories of retarded subjects (cultural-familial, brain-damaged, undifferentiated, and undifferentiated accompanied by psychosis or personality disorder) when evaluating results on the HRB in accordance with the categories of immediate-problem-solving and stored information as described above.

The results indicated that on tests in the problem-solving section the familial group performed significantly better than the other three groups, but performed significantly worse than the other three groups on measures of stored information. Thus, even categories of mental retardation, composed according to etiology in spite of the criticisms and difficulties in doing this validly for the individual subject, appear to have some neuropsychological significance. The neuropsychology of mental retardation obviously has not been studied in comprehensive detail, but the results cited above clearly indicate that further investigations in this area should be pursued.

■

CHAPTER VIII

Description of Tests in the Halstead-Reitan Neuropsychological Test Battery for Older Children

The individual neuropsychological tests included in the Halstead-Reitan Neuropsychological Test Battery for Older Children have long and varied histories. The tests originated from many sources: several of the tests were adapted from instruments originally developed by Halstead; Wechsler's Scale (the WISC-R) has long been used for measurement of general intelligence (1974); and a number of the tests were adapted or developed by Reitan and Kløve.

This chapter will give a brief description of the various tests in the HRB for Older Children. Detailed and specific instructions for administration and scoring of the tests are presented in Chapter IX. Instructions for administering the WISC-R can be found in a separate publication (Wechsler, 1974).

Wechsler's Scale

The Scales developed by Wechsler are generally recognized as the most widely used individual tests for evaluating general intelligence. Since Wechsler's tests are well known and have been described in detail by others (Kaufman, 1990; Matarazzo, 1972; Wechsler, 1955, 1974), in this chapter we will provide only brief descriptions of this instrument.

The Scales are divided into groups of six Verbal subtests and five Performance subtests. The Verbal subtests include Information (questions involving general factual information on subjects such as history, geography, and current events); Comprehension (questions concerning the proper course of action in a variety of situations that have some judgmental or social significance); Arithmetic (arithmetic problems of increasing difficulty performed without the use of paper or pencil); Digit Span (repetition in forward and reverse of a sequence of increasingly longer series of digits); Similarities (stating the most common characteristic of word pairs); and Vocabulary (giving the definition of individual words).

In order to respond correctly to the questions or instructions of the examiner, most of the Wechsler tests require previously acquired skill or knowledge. Immediate or direct problem-solving skills are only minimally required on the Verbal subtests. In the case of the Arithmetic subtest it is necessary for the subject to solve the particular problems presented, but the ability to do so is obviously dependent upon having previously developed these arithmetical skills.

Even the Similarities subtest probably depends largely upon vocabulary skills (or a full understanding of the meaning of each of the words in the pair) as a basis for correct performance. Although among adult subjects the Similarities subtest has been proposed to measure abstraction abilities, Reitan (1956) did not find that the Similarities subtest had any higher correlation with the Category Test than did subtests such as Information and Vocabulary. We therefore suspect that the Similarities subtest is more closely related to vocabulary skills than abstraction ability.

In contrast to the Verbal subtests, the Performance subtests of the Wechsler Scale do require immediate problem-solving capabilities. The Performance subtests include Picture Arrangement (sequential arrangement of picture cards to tell the most meaningful story); Picture Completion (identification of the missing part in each of a series of pictures); Block Design (arrangement of colored blocks in a spatial relationship that reproduces a design depicted on a card); Object Assembly (arrangement of variously shaped pieces to complete a whole figure in the format of a jigsaw puzzle); Coding (reproduction of different symbols corresponding to numbers given in a conversion code); and (optionally) Mazes (solving mazes of increasing difficulty).

More detailed information about the Wechsler Intelligence Scale for Children-Revised (Wechsler, 1974) is given in Chapter IV.

Reitan-Kløve Lateral Dominance Examination

The Lateral Dominance Examination consists of a series of questions used to determine an individual's preference for using (1) the left or right hand on a unimanual task, and (2) the left or right foot on a unipedal task. Originally, this test also evaluated eyedness, but preference for the right or left eye has not been shown to have relevance.

Lateral dominance can be evaluated either in terms of the side the subject prefers to use to perform a task or the subject's comparative skill when performing the same task on each side of the body. Although both types of evaluations relate to lateral dominance, the two methods should not be confused. For example, when the subject performs a uni-manual task (such as throwing a ball), he/she demonstrates which hand is preferred for performing this task. Alternatively, the subject's finger tapping speed can be measured for each hand, and the results relate much more to the function of the cerebral hemisphere contralateral to the hand being examined.

Therefore, if the examiner wishes to determine hand or foot (i.e., peripheral) preference, tasks that can be performed with only one hand or one foot at a time should be used. These would typically be well-practiced tasks for which an individual's preference has been established. Conversely, to assess brain functions the examiner should compare the subject's performances on relatively nonpracticed tasks on each side of the body. The tasks may range in difficulty from simple to complex.

In the HRB the procedures for determining lateral dominance (or preference) utilize tasks for which one side of the body would be preferred. Other tests in the Battery — such as the Finger Tapping Test, Grip Strength, the Tactual Performance Test, and measures of sensory-perceptual functions — provide information about the comparative functional efficiency of motor and sensory-perceptual performances as they relate to brain functions.

Hand preference is determined by having the subject perform a series of simple unimanual tasks. First, the individual is asked to write his/her name in the usual manner. The hand used and the time required is recorded. Then the subject is asked to write his/her name using the other hand. The time required to complete the task is again recorded.

The subject is next requested to perform six other unimanual tasks: throwing a ball, hammering a nail, cutting with a knife, turning a door knob, using a pair of scissors, and using an eraser. The examiner records which hand the subject uses to perform each task.

For tests in the HRB, the hand used by the subject for writing his/her name is considered to be the preferred or dominant hand, regardless of how many of the tasks are performed with the other hand. As an extreme example, consider a child who writes his name with his left hand but uses his right hand to perform all six of the other tasks in the Lateral Dominance Examination. For purposes of testing, we would consider this child to be left-hand dominant, and would therefore have the child use his left hand on the first trial of the TPT. However, when doing a clinical interpretation of this child's test results, we would take into account the fact that he demonstrated ambidexterity. The clinical implications of ambidexterity are discussed more fully in the case interpretations.

Footedness is briefly evaluated by having the subject demonstrate how he/she would (1) kick a football, and (2) step on an imaginary bug on the floor. The examiner records which foot is used to perform each task.

Reitan-Indiana Aphasia Screening Test

This test represents Reitan's modification of the Halstead-Wepman Aphasia Screening Test (Halstead & Wepman, 1949). A comprehensive review of aphasia and illustrations of the interpretation of this test have previously been published (Reitan, 1984a, 1985).

The Aphasia Screening Test (AST) was not devised to provide continuous distributions that reflect a range of responses on the individual items, but instead to identify failures of performance and specific deficits. Therefore, we do not score the results; we evaluate them for any indications of brain-related deficiencies or abnormalities in performance. This procedure is in accordance with an approach intended to identify pathognomonic signs.

Although only a few procedures are used to evaluate each kind of ability, the Reitan-Indiana Aphasia Screening Test provides an extensive survey of aphasic and related deficits. In fact, research using adult subjects has shown that the performances on this test are strongly correlated to the status of each cerebral hemisphere and actually appear to contain almost as much neurologic diagnostic information as the tests in the rest of the HRB (Wheeler & Reitan, 1962, 1963). This latter conclusion is based on discriminant function analyses of the Aphasia Screening Test and Sensory-perceptual Examination, which permitted classification of normal subjects and persons with right, left and generalized cerebral lesions into their appropriate groups with essentially the same degree of accuracy as achieved using the rest of the Battery (Wheeler, Burke, & Reitan, 1963).

One must remember, however, that the major purpose of a neuropsychological examination is to provide an adequate set of psychological measures that correlate with brain functions rather than to generate neurological diagnoses. The rest of the Battery yields much more neuropsychological information than the Aphasia Screening Test, and this additional information is necessary for understanding the neuropsychology of the individual subject.

The tasks involved in the Aphasia Screening Test are simple, and the presumption is that it should be possible for any normal adult with an elementary eduction to perform the items satisfactorily. Among children care must be taken to determine whether the child has had the basic academic training to ensure satisfactory performances. If this is the case, adequate responses are expected and deficient performances assume definite significance.

A test strategy of this type, intended to elicit specific pathognomonic signs of brain damage, necessarily produces many cases of "false negatives" (persons with cerebral lesions who do not show deficits). Therefore, the examiner is usually able to draw meaningful conclusions about brain impairment only when deficits in performance occur. Such a strategy places a special burden on the person who interprets the results; the neuropsychologist must be able to (1) identify a defective performance, and (2) judge whether it is the type of deficit characteristic of persons with cerebral damage.

The strength of this testing strategy, and the factor that makes it such a valuable complement to test-data scaled on a continuous distribution, is that specific deficits of known cerebral significance may be discerned. The weakness of this format is that without provision of guidelines and examples of scoring, the neuropsychologist doing the interpretation must have considerable experience and competence in order to be able to judge whether the performances represent brain-related deficits. Because of the need for further instructional material of this kind, Reitan (1985) has published a volume providing detailed illustrations of brain-related deficits on the Aphasia Screening Test. In addition, the instructions for scoring of the Aphasia Screening Test (Chapter IX) provides specific examples of adequate, borderline, and inadequate responses and performances.

The Aphasia Screening Test requires the subject to perform a series of tasks: name common objects; spell simple words; identify individual numbers and letters; read, write, enunciate, and understand spoken language; identify body parts; calculate simple arithmetic problems; differentiate between right and left; and copy simple geometric shapes. The Aphasia Screening Test is so organized that these various performances are examined, to some extent, in terms of the particular sensory modalities through which the stimuli are perceived. The receptive and expressive components of the test (as differentially required by various items) provide an opportunity to judge whether the limiting deficit for a particular subject is principally receptive or expressive in character.

Finger Tapping Test

This test is a measure of finger-tapping speed using a specially adapted manual tapper. Precise characteristics of this apparatus (tension of the arm, angle of the arm, position of the board, etc.) have been maintained to ensure comparability of data between subjects and between various investigators.

Measurements are made first with the subject using the index finger of the preferred hand. Next, a comparable set of measurements is obtained with the nonpreferred hand. Five consecutive 10-second trials within five taps of each other are given to each hand with the hand held in a constant position in order to require movements of only the finger rather than the whole hand and arm. Every effort is made to encourage the subject to tap as fast as possible. This test would appear to be rather purely dependent upon motor speed.

Grip Strength

The subject's grip strength of each upper extremity is measured twice, in an alternating sequence beginning with the preferred hand. To obtain standard results, the subject extends his/her arm with the dynamometer pointed toward the floor as the handle of the dynamometer is squeezed as hard as possible. Normally, the grip strength of the preferred hand is about 10% greater than the nonpreferred hand. Obviously, motor strength complements the finger tapping measure (motor speed) included among Halstead's tests.

Sensory-perceptual Examination

Tests for Perception of Bilateral Sensory Stimulation

These procedures attempt to determine how accurately the subject can perceive bilateral simultaneous sensory stimulation after it has been established that perception of unilateral stimulation of each side is essentially intact.

To examine tactile function, each of the subject's hands is first touched separately to determine whether the subject is able to respond correctly to unilateral stimulation. Next, unilateral stimulation is interspersed with bilateral simultaneous stimulation. The normal subject is able to accurately recognize stimulation of the right hand, left hand, and both hands simultaneously.

Subjects with lateralized cerebral lesions are often able to identify unilateral stimulation correctly, but sometimes fail to respond correctly to bilateral simultaneous stimulation; the stimulus to the hand contralateral to the damaged hemisphere is often not perceived. Contralateral face-hand combinations are also used with unilateral and bilateral simultaneous tactile stimulation as part of the standard procedure.

In testing for auditory perception the subject is required to identify the side of the body on which an auditory stimulus is heard. The examiner administers the stimulus by rubbing the thumb and index fingers together lightly, very quickly and sharply, next to the subject's ear.

A similar procedure is used in the visual examination. The examiner executes discrete movements of the fingers while the subject focuses on the examiner's nose. The standard procedure is to use as minimal a stimulus as necessary to achieve consistently correct responses to unilateral stimulation.

A test for perception of bilateral simultaneous stimulation is, of course, precluded if the subject has a serious lateralized tactile, auditory or visual loss and is not able to respond correctly to unilateral stimulation on the affected side. Such unilateral impairment is rarely encountered in the tactile modality, although unilateral deafness (at least to a degree) occasionally occurs. Deficits are not infrequently seen among persons with certain types of lesions which affect the visual modality (homonymous hemianopia). Lateralized deficiencies may, of course, have significant implications for nervous system disorders even though they obviate use of a test for perception of bilateral stimuli. The score for each modality is recorded as the number of errors made on bilateral simultaneous stimulation.

Valuable historical background information regarding sensory-perceptual losses in persons with cerebral lesions is given in Bender's 1951 book, *Disorders of Perception* and Critchley's 1953 book, *The Parietal Lobes*. The neurological model being investigated with such tests is relatively simple: even a damaged hemisphere can adequately subserve perception of a simple stimulus when there is no functional involvement of other brain areas. Therefore, if the left hand is lightly touched, the stimulus is perceived by the right cerebral hemisphere; perception can occur even if the right cerebral hemisphere is damaged. However, when the left cerebral hemisphere is required to perform exactly the same task simultaneously, the damaged right cerebral hemisphere sometimes is no longer able to perceive the stimulus. A damaged hemisphere is not able to perform its function as well when the homologous area of the other cerebral hemisphere is processing information at the same time.

We have experimented informally with alterations of the input (stimulus) characteristics to give the damaged hemisphere a better competitive status when functioning simultaneously with the unimpaired cerebral hemisphere. This can be done by administering a more intense stimulus on the side contralateral to the damaged hemisphere. When stimulus intensity is increased, it is often possible for the subject to recognize that both sides were touched.

Birch, Belmont, and Karp (1967) performed this type of experiment by altering the temporal relationships of the stimuli rather than the intensity of the stimuli. They found that is was possible to elicit recognition that both sides were touched when the stimulus was given slightly sooner to the side across from the damaged cerebral hemisphere.

In other words, if the damaged cerebral hemisphere is given an advantage (a stronger stimulus or a stimulus that occurs slightly before the competing input from the other side), it is able to be competitive with the intact cerebral hemisphere. Obviously, this kind of information is of great importance concerning administration of the tests: under normal testing conditions, it is necessary to maintain approximate equivalence of the intensity and the timing of the stimuli to the two sides of the body.

Although we have not done research specifically examining areas of the cerebral cortex that are involved in subserving perception of the stimuli used in testing for sensory perception, our impressions are that (1) tactile perception is a function of the parietal cortex, (2) auditory perception is subserved by the temporal cortex, and (3) visual perception is a function of the more posterior parts of the cerebral hemispheres. However, it must be recognized that many (if not most) lesions associated with pathological developments (as contrasted with surgical resection) are not restricted to a single lobe.

Tactile Finger Recognition

This procedure tests the subject's ability to identify the individual fingers on each hand following tactile stimulation. Before the examination begins, the examiner must work out a system with the subject for reporting which finger was touched. Most subjects customarily will report by number, but some subjects prefer to identify their fingers in other verbal terms. Although the test itself is given without the subject's use of vision for identification, it is sometimes necessary to give the subject brief practice with his/her eyes open to ensure that a reliable verbal report can be obtained. The subject is given a total of twenty trials on each hand. The score is recorded as the number of errors for each hand.

This test is relatively easy for most normal subjects and few errors are expected. Although normal subjects occasionally will find their attention wandering on one or two trials and not be quite sure which finger was touched, we generally expect a nearly perfect score on tactile finger recognition. Parietal lobe lesions, contralateral to the hand on which defective responses are found, definitely impair the performance on this test. Of course, many lesions are sufficiently large to involve more than just the parietal lobe and, in general, posterior cerebral lesions are principally responsible for defective responses in tactile finger recognition.

Finger-tip Number Writing Perception

This procedure requires the subject to report numbers written on the fingertips of each hand without the use of vision. The stimulus numbers (3, 4, 5, and 6) are written on the fingertips in a standard sequence with a total of four trials for each finger. The score represents the number of errors for each hand.

Some practice is required for the examiner to develop skill in writing numbers on the fingertips with constant and steady pressure. The numbers are written slowly and carefully and are sufficiently large to cover most of the pad at the end of the finger.

Errors in finger-tip number writing perception are more common than errors in tactile finger recognition; apparently finger-tip number writing perception requires more concentrated attention. Research has shown that finger-tip number writing perception is more closely correlated with IQ than tactile finger recognition (Fitzhugh, Fitzhugh, & Reitan, 1962), and a number of mistakes in finger-tip number writing perception is usually expected in persons of lower general intelligence.

The primary information gained from this test is based upon differences in performance on the two sides of the body. Inferences regarding contralateral parietal lobe damage or dysfunction can be drawn when the performance on one hand is definitely deficient compared to the other hand.

Tactile Form Recognition Test

In this evaluation of tactile form recognition ability the subject is asked to identify flat, plastic shapes (cross, square, triangle, and circle) as they are individually placed in one of the subject's hands as it is held out of his/her range of vision. The subject feels the plastic shape and, with the other hand, points to one of the four plastic shapes mounted on a board corresponding to the shape in his/her hand. The response element of this task is deliberately minimized and the input sensory (afferent) aspect, together with central processing, predominates. This test has been found to be suitable for use with subjects five years of age and older.

Response time measurements are made for each trial and the total time required for the four trials for each hand is determined. The total number of errors for each hand is recorded as a separate score.

Rhythm Test

The Rhythm Test is a subtest of the Seashore Measures of Musical Talent. In this test the subject is required to differentiate between thirty pairs of rhythmic beats. The stimuli are presented to the subject from a standardized tape recording. After listening to a pair of stimuli the subject writes "S" on the answer sheet if the two stimuli sound the same, "D" if they sound different. This test requires alertness to nonverbal auditory stimuli, sustained attention to the task, and the ability to perceive and compare different rhythmic sequences.

It is interesting to note that many psychologists presume that the Rhythm Test is dependent upon the integrity of the right cerebral hemisphere. This presumption stems from the observation that the test is nonverbal in nature. We have analyzed results on the Rhythm Test in groups of subjects with left and right cerebral damage (Reitan & Wolfson, 1989) and found that both groups were significantly impaired when compared with a control group. However, since the brain-damaged groups showed no differences between themselves, the Rhythm Test seems to be an indicator of the general adequacy of cerebral functioning and has no lateralizing significance.

In the presence of serious generalized impairment, a good score on the Rhythm Test may be an indication of a relatively stabilized (as contrasted with progressive) condition of brain damage. This point will be illustrated later in this book when individual cases are presented.

Speech-sounds Perception Test

The Speech-sounds Perception Test (SSPT) consists of sixty spoken nonsense words which are variants of the *ee* sound. The stimuli are played from a tape recording with the volume adjusted to the subject's preference. The subject responds by underlining one of the three alternatives printed for each item on the test form.

For example, on the answer form in front of the subject, the following appears:

1. theets   theeks   zeets

The voice on the tape player says, "The first word is theets." The subject must listen closely and underline the alternative he/she thinks is correct. This test requires the subject to (1) maintain attention through sixty items, (2) perceive the spoken stimulus sound through hearing, and (3) relate the perception through vision to the correct configuration of letters on the test form.

As might be expected, research results (Reitan & Wolfson, 1990) show that some persons with left cerebral lesions are considerably more impaired on this test than persons with right cerebral lesions, but usually no striking lateralization effects are found. Adult brain-damaged subjects average about fourteen errors on the Speech-sounds Perception Test, whereas control subjects average only about seven errors (Reitan, 1955b). The SSPT therefore serves as a good indicator of the general integrity of cerebral cortical functions.

Although we have not demonstrated precise localization of the brain area involved in processing the visual and auditory information required by the SSPT, we would postulate that the most important area is in the posterior part of the left cerebral hemisphere, especially involving the left posterior temporal-parietal area. Precise localization is difficult to demonstrate, because this test is a good general indicator (apparently relating to the requirement of alertness and concentration) as well as a reflection of the adequacy of receptive language functions through the auditory and visual avenues.

Trail Making Test

The Trail Making Test is composed of two parts, A and B. Part A consists of fifteen circles printed on a white sheet of paper. Each circle contains a number from 1 to 15. The subject is required to connect the circles with a pencil line as quickly as possible, beginning with the number 1 and proceeding in a numerical sequence. Part B also consists of fifteen circles. The circles are numbered from 1 to 8 and lettered from A to G. The subject is required to connect the circles, in sequence, alternating between numbers and letters. The scores represent the number of seconds required to finish each part.

This test requires immediate recognition of the symbolic significance of numbers and letters, ability to scan the page continuously to identify the next number or letter in sequence, flexibility in integrating the numerical and alphabetical series, and completion of these requirements under the pressure of time. It seems likely that the ability to deal with the numerical and language symbols (numbers and letters) is sustained by the left cerebral hemisphere, the visual scanning task necessary to perceive the spatial distribution of the stimulus material is represented by the right cerebral hemisphere, and speed and efficiency of performance may be a general characteristic of adequate brain functions. It is therefore not surprising that the Trail Making Test is one of the best measures of general brain functions (Reitan, 1955c, 1958b).

Tactual Performance Test

The Tactual Performance Test (TPT) utilizes a modification of the Sequin-Goddard formboard. The subject is blindfolded before the test begins and is not permitted to see the formboard or blocks at any time. The first task is to fit the blocks into their proper spaces on the board using only the dominant (preferred) hand.

After completing this task (and without having been given prior warning), the subject is asked to perform the same task using only the nondominant (nonpreferred) hand. Finally, and again without prior warning, the subject is asked to do the task a third time using both hands.

The amount of time required to perform each of the three trials is recorded. This provides a comparison of the efficiency of performance of the two hands. The total time score for the TPT is the amount of time needed to complete all three trials.

After the subject has completed the third trial, the board and blocks are removed from the testing room (or at least from the subject's field of vision) and the subject is then allowed to remove the blindfold. The subject is next asked to draw a diagram of the board with the blocks in their proper places. The Memory score is the number of shapes correctly remembered. The Localization score is the number of blocks correctly identified by both shape and position on the board.

The Tactual Performance Test is undoubtedly a complex task in terms of its requirements. Ability to correctly place the variously shaped blocks on the board depends upon tactile form discrimination, kinesthesis, co-ordination of movement of the upper extremities, manual dexterity, and an understanding of the relationship between the spatial configuration of the shapes and their location on the board.

Halstead had observed that many adults with biologically compromised cerebral functions were deficient in performing relatively simple tasks, especially if required to perform the task in an unusual way or under unusual circumstances. Placing the blocks in their proper spaces is a relatively simple task; the novel aspect is requiring the subject to use only haptic sensitivity. At no time during the test is the subject allowed to use vision, the usual sensory avenue.

Halstead postulated that this task would be much more difficult for the brain-damaged adult than for the normal person when performance under unusual conditions was required. Halstead hypothesized that the person with brain damage, suffering from a general impairment of adaptive capabilities, would not be able to adapt to these more difficult circumstances as efficiently as persons with normal brain functions.

Halstead also believed that persons with brain lesions would not be able to reproduce as much of the content as persons with normal brain functions. In other words, he postulated that both control subjects and brain-damaged subjects could complete the task, but that the brain-damaged subject would learn less from the experience than the control subject — even though the brain-damaged subject has usually been exposed to the stimulus material about twice as long.

In order to test this hypothesis, Halstead decided to have the subject draw a picture of the board and blocks after the three trials had been completed. Of course, since subjects are never allowed to actually see the test, they are dependent upon the information gained through standard exposure to the task.

Halstead's postulate was confirmed by the experimental results. The mean number of remembered shapes and the mean number of properly localized shapes was strikingly less for brain-damaged than control groups. The results therefore indicate that the Tactual Performance Test has very definite meaning in describing the nature of psychological impairment in persons with brain lesions.

Another important aspect of the design and procedure used in this test relates to the neurological model. The design of the TPT allows comparison of the functional efficiency of the two cerebral hemispheres (right hand versus left hand) and supplies information about the general efficiency of brain functions (total time for three trials). During the first trial, when the subject uses the dominant hand, information is being transmitted from the preferred hand to the contralateral cerebral hemisphere (usually from the right hand to the left cerebral hemisphere). The time required to complete the task indicates the efficiency of brain functioning under these circumstances.

Of course, because of the connections between the two cerebral hemispheres through the anterior and the posterior commissures and the corpus callosum, the information sent to the left cerebral hemisphere is not restricted to that hemisphere. Therefore, although information is first delivered to the left cerebral hemisphere, the whole brain receives the information that is being brought in through sensory channels.

If the left cerebral hemisphere were damaged, it is likely that the information would not be registered very well initially and the rest of the brain would be impaired in its ability to contribute to the solution of the task. More specifically, the input area of the cerebral cortex for this task is probably mainly the parietal area, and distinct impairment in performance might well be principally related to the parietal lobe if the deficit were a function of input limitations.

It is possible that motor or expressive aspects of the task also limit the performance on a trial of the TPT, but motor measures which are not strongly influenced by sensory input (such as finger tapping and grip strength) can provide comparative information about motor function.

In the second trial of the TPT, the subject is required to perform the task using only the nondominant (usually left) hand, and the information is sent to the right cerebral hemisphere. The efficiency of performance is measured by the time required to complete the task. If the right cerebral hemisphere (particularly the parietal area) has been damaged, the performance on the second trial would be deficient.

One additional aspect of the neurological model must be considered. Obviously, there would be positive practice-effect (or bilateral transfer) from the first to the second trial. Therefore, for a right-handed subject, we would expect the left hand to perform the task better than the right hand, because the entire brain has had the advantage of experiencing solution of the problem when the right hand was performing during the first trial.

The neurological basis for bilateral transfer is represented by the commissures between the two cerebral hemispheres. Although the concept of bilateral transfer is discussed in nearly every introductory psychology textbook, its neurological basis is rarely considered. Developing a conceptual understanding of bilateral transfer, as manifested in the procedure in the Tactual Performance Test, was a relatively simple matter. The test had to be administered to a large number of control subjects to determine the magnitude of bilateral transfer among persons with normal brain functions.

The data indicated a rather consistent relationship: the second trial usually requires about two-thirds of the time required for the first trial and the third trial (using both hands) usually requires about two-thirds of the time of the second trial. In other words, the expected pattern and relationship among the results for the three trials is that the time required for a particular trial is reduced by about one-third in each ensuing trial.

By considering this pattern as the normal set of relationships, it is possible to compare the functional efficiency of the two cerebral hemispheres. For example, it would not be unusual to find the following pattern in a right-hand dominant person with a right cerebral lesion: right hand, 7.0 minutes; left hand, 10.0 minutes; both hands, 5.0 minutes. Such a pattern would suggest impaired functioning of the second trial (left hand), and provide a basis for inferring right cerebral hemisphere dysfunction.

Category Test

This test uses a projector to present the subject with a series of 168 stimulus figures on a 10" × 8" screen. An answer panel, containing four levers numbered from 1 to 4, is attached to the test apparatus at a convenient level below the screen. Subjects are told that they will be asked to inspect each stimulus figure when it appears on the screen and depress the lever corresponding to the answer they think is correct. Depressing a lever will cause either a bell (if the answer is correct) or a buzzer (if the answer is incorrect) to sound. The subject is allowed to make only one response for each stimulus item.

Before the test begins, the subject is told that the test is divided into subtests of items and that a single principle or theme runs through each entire subtest from beginning to end. The subject is instructed to try to figure out the principle for each subtest. As the subject responds to each item by depressing one of the four levers on the answer panel, the bell or buzzer indicates whether the choice was correct or incorrect. In this way the test procedure permits the subject to test one possible principle after another; a correct hypothesis is positively reinforced by the bell. Regardless of the difficulty, the subject is never told the principle for any subtest.

The first and second subtests are nearly always easily performed, even by persons with serious brain lesions. The first subtest requires matching Arabic numerals above each of the answer levers with individual Roman numerals shown on the screen.

In the second subtest the subject must learn to press the lever corresponding to the number of items appearing on the screen. For example, the answer would be 2 if two squares appeared, 4 if four letters of the alphabet were displayed, etc.

The examiner announces the end of each subtest group as it occurs. At the beginning of each new subtest the examiner tells the subject that the principle might be the same as it has been or it might be different. The subject's task is to discern the principle of each subtest.

The principle of Subtest III is based on the concept of uniqueness. Each stimulus item is composed of four figures, and the subject must learn to depress the lever corresponding with the figure which is most different from the others. Although this subtest begins rather simply, it progresses to items in which one figure may differ from the others in three or more respects (such as size, shape, color, or solidness of figure) while the rest of the figures differ from each other in only two respects.

For example, a stimulus item appearing in the beginning of the subtest may be made up of a row of four equilateral triangles; the first, second and fourth triangles are the same size and the third triangle is about 50% larger. In this case the correct answer would be 3, with size being the determinant of uniqueness. On a later item, all four figures, differing in shape and color, are the same size. The first figure is solid and the other three figures are formed only by an outline. In this instance, uniqueness could not be determined by shape, color, or size, since these determinants were entirely variable or entirely constant. The answer would be 1, since the first figure was the only one that was solid.

The fourth subtest is organized according to a principle based on the proportion of the figure that is composed of solid (versus dotted) lines. If one-quarter of the figure is solid, the answer is 1, progressing to an answer of 4 for a completely solid figure. The principle remains constant throughout the subtest even though various types of stimulus figures are used. As with other subtests, the examiner announces when the end of the subtest occurs and states that the next subtest may be based upon the same principle or it may use a new principle.

Subtest V is based on the same principle as Subtest IV. This is the only instance in the test in which use of the same principle is repeated in an ensuing subtest.

Subtest VI is not based on any single principle; it is a review group that uses items and principles which have previously been shown to the subject. The subject is told this information and instructed to try to remember the correct answer for each item.

The Category Test has several characteristics that make it different from many tests. It is a relatively complex concept formation test which requires ability to (1) note recurring similarities and differences in stimulus material, (2) postulate reasonable hypotheses about these similarities and differences, (3) test these hypotheses by receiving positive or negative reinforcement (bell or buzzer), and (4) adapt hypotheses based on the reinforcement following each response.

The Category Test is not particularly difficult for most normal subjects, but since the subject is required to postulate possible solutions in a structured (rather than permissive) context, it appears to require special competence in abstraction ability. In effect, the test presents each subject with a learning experiment in concept formation. This is in contrast to the usual situation in psychological testing, which requires solution of an integral problem situation.

The essential purpose of the Category Test is to determine the subject's ability to use both negative and positive experiences as a basis for altering his/her performance. The precise pattern and sequence of negative and positive reinforcement in the Category Test is probably never exactly the same for any two subjects (or for the same subject upon repetition of the test). Since it can be presumed that every item in the test affects the subject's response to ensuing items, the usual approaches toward determination of reliability indices may be confounded. Nevertheless, the essential nature of the test, as an experiment in concept formation, is fairly clear.

The Neuropsychological Deficit Scale (NDS) for Older Children

The NDS for Older Children, a summary score for the HRB for Older Children, was described in Chapter VII and research results were summarized which demonstrated its striking effectiveness in evaluation of brain-damaged and learning-disabled children. Specific instructions for scoring the NDS are given in Chapter IX.

A sample of computerized scoring of the NDS for Older Children is given in the Appendix.

■

Instructions for Administering and Scoring the Halstead-Reitan Neuropsychological Test Battery for Older Children

This section includes instructions for administering and scoring the following tests:

1. Lateral Dominance Examination
2. Reitan-Indiana Aphasia Screening Test
3. Finger Tapping Test
4. Grip Strength
5. Sensory-perceptual Examination
   A. Bilateral Simultaneous Sensory Perception
   B. Tactile Finger Recognition Test
   C. Finger-tip Number Writing Perception Test

6. Tactile Form Recognition Test
7. Speech-sounds Perception Test
8. Seashore Rhythm Test
9. Trail Making Test
10. Tactual Performance Test
11. Category Test

The HRB for Older Children also routinely includes the Wechsler Intelligence Scale for Children-Revised (WISC-R) and frequently utilizes tests of academic achievement. These tests are administered and scored according to published instructions.

Although the examiner should elicit the best performance of which the subject is capable, no actual help with the tasks should ever be given. No comments that would give the subject even procedural help are permitted (e.g., *Why don't you try another block?* or *Have you noticed the position of the figure that is different?*). Every effort is made to encourage subjects to perform as well as their brains will permit (e.g., during the demonstration the examiner may say, *I think you can tap faster than that — here, let me show you*).

Examiners may gain competence in administration of the Battery by practice and experience in testing a large number of subjects as well as by direct supervision and training by highly-skilled examiners. The entire HRB for Older Children, including the WISC-R, can be completed in about four hours by an experienced examiner who knows the instructions and procedures thoroughly. The instructions should be memorized and given in the exact form presented on the following pages.

Finally, we should warn the reader that many altered and abbreviated versions of the tests in the HRB are being sold by numerous individuals and firms. Anyone using these versions should be aware that they have usually NOT been adequately validated, either through experimental studies or in clinical practice. (The Booklet Category Test is an example.) Such validation is absolutely necessary to provide reliable and meaningful data for interpretation. Interpretations of brain functions, based on these altered or abbreviated versions of the tests, may well be questioned, considering the limited evidence for their validity.

Over the years we have made a determined effort to maintain standardization of each test, down to the last detail, so that the published research results and clinical interpretations may serve validly. We feel that this point must be emphasized, because the clinical responsibility implicit in drawing conclusions about a subject's brain is of a different order than many of the more typical evaluations done by psychologists. The only authorized version of the HRB for Older Children is the one that duplicates the tests exactly as they were when the validation studies were done. A number of modifications and alterations of tests in the HRB have been produced and are available for purchase. Limitations and requirements for revalidation after having made modifications and changes of content (including computer-assisted presentation of the test material) have been discussed previously (Reitan & Wolfson, 1988b).

The tests composing the HRB for Older Children have never been given in a rigid or perfectly standard sequence. We realized at the beginning of our work that testing might have to be done in multiple sessions, using the periods of time that were available (particularly for hospitalized patients), and that it would be a great advantage to be able to select tests that could be completed in the time available.

Testing is routinely begun with the Lateral Dominance Examination because it is necessary to know the child's handedness for administration of certain of the tests. We begin the Battery with tests that are relatively easy, nonthreatening and nondemanding, such as the Aphasia Screening Test, Finger Tapping, and Grip Strength. The Sensory-perceptual Examination and Tactile Form Recognition Test are often given next, before proceeding with the

Category Test, Speech-sounds Perception Test, Seashore Rhythm Test, Trail Making Test, and the Tactual Performance Test.

Background Information

Reitan developed the Battery for Older Children from 1951 to 1953, essentially adapting the Adult Battery for use with children aged 9 through 14 years. The Adult Battery had already been found to be valid for use with persons 15 years of age and older.

The first step in developing the Battery for Older Children was to administer the Adult Battery to a sample of normal children below the age of 15 years in order to determine the types of changes that needed to be made for children. From testing this sample of children it appeared that the tests required only relatively minor changes. These modifications were made, and a new group of children was then tested to evaluate the changes in actual practice.

The modifications of the tests represented simplification rather than any basic change in content or procedure. It was found that essentially the same instructions used for adults could also be used for older children.

The next developmental step was to administer the modified Adult Battery to children 14 years of age and younger to determine the lower age limit at which the tests could validly be interpreted. The results indicated that the tests could consistently be given to 9-year-old children. However, the complexity level of certain tests was too great for a number of children younger than nine years.

Since completion of the developmental research in 1954, the Halstead-Reitan Battery for Older Children has been in standard use and has been evaluated in formal research studies and tested in clinical practice far more extensively that any other neuropsychological battery for children (see Chapter VII).

Modifications in the adult version of the tests were necessary only for the Category Test, the Tactual Performance Test, the Speech-sounds Perception Test, and the Trail Making Test.

Changes in the Category Test included reorganization of some of the items in order to achieve a more orderly evolution of the principles in various subtests. In addition, Subtest IV (which in the adult version is based on identification of a particular quadrant) was completely eliminated from the Older Children's Category Test, because it was found that even normal children tended to have difficulty with this concept. Omission of this group of 40 items reduced the length of the test from 208 items to 168 items. As with the adult version, the final subtest was not based on any particular principle, but rather represented items that had been presented previously in the test.

The Tactual Performance Test was changed from the adult form by eliminating four of the ten figures. These four figures — the star, circle, triangle, and the elongated six-sided figure — were located at the top, bottom, and the two sides of the TPT board. The modification was effected merely by omitting these figures from the board, leaving the six remaining figures in the same place as they are located on the adult form of the test. The size of the blocks and spaces, the stand, and the outside dimensions of the board remained the same. In administration of the test, the board is placed in the same orientation as with the adult version, with the cross in the upper right-hand corner.

The Speech-sounds Perception Test remained the same in terms of the stimuli on the tape recording, but the answer form was modified. This modification was achieved by reducing the number of alternatives for each item from four to three. The alternative that was eliminated was the one that had both beginning and ending consonants that were incorrect in comparison with the stimulus. Thus, the alternative eliminated was the one that was most obviously incorrect.

In this way the difficulty level of the test was largely retained in terms of the discriminations required, but the test was simplified by reducing from four to three the number of alternatives that had to be considered in each of the sixty items.

Finally, the Trail Making Test was altered simply by shortening the test from twenty-five stimuli to fifteen stimuli in both Part A and Part B. This was done by omitting the last ten stimuli in each part of the test. Thus, Part A extends from numbers 1 through 15 and Part B, in which both numbers and letters are used, intersperses numbers 1 through 8 and letters A through G.

It is apparent that these modifications did not alter the essential requirements of the tests. The changes clearly represented only simplifications or abbreviations of the tests as they existed in the adult form, and the instructions are essentially the same as those given for adults (Reitan & Wolfson, 1985).

As with adult subjects, it has been our practice to attempt to communicate the requirements of the testing situation to the subject by giving the instructions in such a way that every subject has a complete understanding of what he/she is being asked to do. In trying to achieve this aim, it becomes clear that *understanding the instructions is not part of the tests in the Halstead-Reitan Batteries.*

It is of particular interest that it was not necessary to change the content of tests of brain functions in order to evaluate older children; it was necessary only to reduce the complexity (number of elements requiring simultaneous attention) in some instances.

Specific Suggestions for Testing Older Children

In general, children are probably easier to examine than adults, but certain differences in response patterns and capabilities should be noted.

First, we wish to caution examiners about the tendency sometimes seen in psychological testing to "find what one expects to find." Research has indicated that poor performances are more frequent when the examiner is influenced to expect poor performances; better performances are associated with higher expectations. The general approach in using the Halstead-Reitan Battery is to elicit the best possible performance of every subject; many children, even those who have brain damage or learning disabilities, are able to do a number of the tests satisfactorily, and a surprising degree of intraindividual variability occurs.

Several points can be made that will assist the examiner in eliciting the best performance of which a child is capable:

1. Always communicate to the child exactly what is expected from him/her for each particular test. Be sure that the child listens carefully to the specific instructions and understands exactly what is being requested before the task is begun. If it appears necessary, do not hesitate to repeat, restate, or amplify the instructions. Always try to avoid impulsive or premature responses. Remember that the goal is to elicit the best response of which the child is capable, *on the first attempt.*

2. More prompting is usually necessary with children than with adults. However, whenever possible, permit the child to respond without prompting. Prompting is permitted with either adults or children when it becomes clear that no response would otherwise be elicited. For example, a child may have spelling difficulties and be embarrassed by this fact. If the child is completely unwilling to attempt to spell a word (such as cross or triangle), the examiner might ask the subject to guess at the first letter or even to suggest

the first letter for the subject's consideration. In such instances the purpose is to find out how much the subject knows, rather that merely to record "No response" or "Does not know" for the item.

3. Children will often say, "I don't know how to do that," especially on items of an academic nature. Every attempt should be made to elicit a positive effort in order demonstrate just how much the child is able to do. A negative response or no response merely eliminates the item from the test for that child.

4. Children frequently want to correct their writing or drawing performances by scratching out, crossing out, or erasing. By doing so they can delete information that may have important diagnostic significance. We therefore recommend that these types of alterations not be permitted. Using pencils without erasers is often helpful, but the examiner must also be alert to stop a child from crossing out a performance he/she does not like. On the Aphasia Examination the child is told to complete the first attempt, and is then given a second or even third chance to perform the task (as indicated in the instructions).

5. Some 9- and 10-year-old children have not developed cursive writing skills very well and prefer to print. Although we allow the child to print on an initial performance, we request repetition of the item in cursive writing. The reason for this is that certain brain-related deficits are more easily noted in cursive writing than printing (which may be more primitive in style).

6. Finally, it is necessary to stimulate a desire on the child's part to put forth the best possible effort. As with any behavioral or psychological test, the examiner must play a major role in eliciting the subject's interest and motivation. A friendly approach is important, and the examiner must show flexibility and adaptability in encouraging the child to demonstrate his/her talents, even when they may be quite limited.

Certain specific suggestions may be given for administering the Sensory-perceptual Examination, and these recommendations are relevant to other tests as well. The purpose of this examination is to elicit evidence of sensory-perceptual disorders in children — not disorders of attention, concentration, or response capabilities. If valid evidence of sensory-perceptual deficits is to be obtained, it is incumbent on the examiner to be sure that incorrect responses are not due to failures of attention or response capabilities.

The most common causes of invalid responses on the tests in the Sensory-perceptual Examination stem from procedural errors in administering stimuli to a child who is disinterested in the tests, not paying attention, or perceives the stimulus correctly but responds incorrectly. The examiner should obtain experience practicing on normal adults and children in order to develop skill in eliciting normal sensory-perceptual responses in persons with intact brains. This type of experience gives examiners confidence in their examining technique and also contributes to their ability to recognize valid sensory-perceptual deficits.

Several steps can be recommended to aid in valid test administration:

1. The examiner should interact with the child and be actively involved in the testing procedure. To achieve this, various techniques may be used. For example, when delivering certain tactile stimuli, a very light stimulus is used. The examiner can use this requirement to motivate the child to pay close attention, challenging the child to see if it is possible for the examiner to touch the child without him/her noticing the touch and responding. An approach of this type is especially effective in stimulating attention and motivation when doing tests of unilateral and bilateral simultaneous sensory stimulation.

2. The examiner should not administer the sensory stimuli used in this set of tests unless it has been determined that

the child is paying attention. The sensory stimuli are of momentary (brief) duration, and children are sometimes difficult to examine because their attention strays. It is the responsibility of the examiner to determine whether the subject is alert and ready for the stimulus when it is delivered.

3. When a child's attention is wandering, the standard practice is to use a direct verbal instruction such as, *All right now — I am going to write another number (touch another finger, show you another picture). Pay close attention.*

4. Some children tend to become confused when they are required to respond to one test after another. In such instances it may be important to slow down the pace of the examination (limit the amount of sensory input per unit of time). Children can often deal with exactly the same types of problems as adults, but require a little more time to process and comprehend the material presented.

5. Behavioral notes, written by the examiner to explain errors or failures of the child, are especially important. Because errors might occur as a result of failure in attention or other bases for incorrectly responding, and the examiner is the only observer in the testing situation, behavioral notes may be of critical importance in contributing to valid interpretation of the results.

6. When administering the sensory-perceptual tests, the examiner must create a situation that minimizes the response requirements and reflects the intended requirements of the test. For example, complex verbal and/or movement responses should not be allowed to be the limiting factor and thereby cause errors or poor performances. An example would be a child's failure to observe bilateral visual stimuli when his/her eyes were both deviated in one direction. Children frequently look toward a stimulus when it is delivered, but the procedure calls for the child to be looking directly at the examiner with both eyes when a stimulus is given.

In one instance (when the tests for children were being introduced to Halstead's laboratory), an examiner-in-training permitted an active child to leave his chair and, between items on the Category Test, to dash under a table. Obviously, such behavior should never be permitted. If a test cannot be administered in the standard manner, we feel it is better to not give the test at all. In most cases, however, it is quite possible to elicit the child's co-operation if a firm manner and a no-nonsense attitude is employed. It is the responsibility of the examiner to be sure that proper testing conditions are met.

7. As noted earlier, children need specific and clear structure in administration of behavioral tests. They respond better, sustain interest longer, and are more co-operative when they understand exactly what is expected from them. The examiner must be sensitive to these needs of the individual and give elaboration and repetition of instructions when necessary.

We wish again to reiterate that testing of children in the 9- through 14-year age range is essentially similar to testing adult subjects. Although the same instructions and testing procedures are used, certain tests have been somewhat simplified. Normative data based on children is required, as reflected in the score ranges used for the Neuropsychological Deficit Scale for Older Children.

The subject's performances are recorded on the individual form for each test and on the Summary Sheet for Older Children (Fig. 9-1).

The Halstead-Reitan Neuropsychological Test Battery for Older Children

Name _____ Age _____

Gender _____ Education _____ Handedness: RH ____ LH ____

Neuropsychological Deficit Scale (NDS) Summary

Level of Performance	Subject's score	Mean for controls	Mean for brain-damaged	Cut-off score
Motor Functions	____	6.29	14.05	
Sensory-perceptual Functions	____	5.15	10.77	
Attention and Concentration	____	1.91	3.78	
Immediate Memory and Recapitulation	____	2.23	3.31	
Visual-spatial Skills	____	4.06	7.69	
Abstraction, Reasoning, Logical Analysis	____	2.63	6.03	
Level of Performance–Total	____	22.27	45.63	33/34
Dysphasia and Related Variables	____	1.37	7.97	3/4
Right / Left Differences	____	6.79	13.74	9/10
Total NDS Score	____	30.43	67.34	43/44

WISC-R

VIQ _____
PIQ _____
FS IQ _____

Verbal Subtests		Performance Subtests	
Information	_____	Picture Completion	_____
Similarities	_____	Picture Arrangement	_____
Arithmetic	_____	Block Design	_____
Vocabulary	_____	Object Assembly	_____
Comprehension	_____	Coding	_____
(Digit Span)	(_____)	(Mazes)	(_____)

WRAT

	Grade Equivalent
Reading	_____
Arithmetic	_____
Spelling	_____

Strength of Grip

Dominant hand ( ) _____ kg
Non-dominant hand ( ) _____ kg

Name Writing

Dominant hand ( ) _____ sec
Non-dominant hand ( ) _____ sec

Category Test

Number of errors _____

Tactual Performance Test

Dominant hand ( ) _____
Non-dominant hand ( ) _____
Both hands _____   Total Time _____
   Memory _____
   Localization _____

Seashore Rhythm Test

Number correct _____   _____

Speech-sounds Perception Test

Number of errors _____

Finger Tapping Test

Dominant hand ( ) _____   _____
Non-dominant hand ( ) _____

Trail Making Test

Part A _____ sec _____ error(s)
Part B _____ sec _____ error(s)

Bilateral Simultaneous Sensory Stimulation

RH ____ LH ____   Both: RH ____ LH ____
RH ____ LF ____   Both: RH ____ LF ____
LH ____ RF ____   Both: LH ____ RF ____

RE ____ LE ____   Both: RE ____ LE ____

RV ____ LV ____   Both: RV ____ LV ____
____ ____   ____ ____
____ ____   ____ ____

Tactile Finger Recognition

RH 1 ___ 2 ___ 3 ___ 4 ___ 5 ___   RH ___ / ___
LH 1 ___ 2 ___ 3 ___ 4 ___ 5 ___   LH ___ / ___

Finger-Tip Number Writing

RH 1 ___ 2 ___ 3 ___ 4 ___ 5 ___   RH ___ / ___
LH 1 ___ 2 ___ 3 ___ 4 ___ 5 ___   LH ___ / ___

Tactile Form Recognition Test

Dominant hand ( ) _____ sec _____ error(s)
Non-dominant hand ( ) _____ sec _____ error(s)

Fig. 9-1. Summary Sheet for Older Children.

Lateral Dominance Examination

Materials   recording form
blank sheet of paper
stopwatch
pencils (at least one with an eraser)
small ball
toy hammer
toy knife
small pair of scissors

General Instructions

The Lateral Dominance Examination is given to obtain information about the subject's handedness and footedness. There has been a great deal of interest about the relationships of these variables to cerebral dominance, or the extent to which the left and right cerebral hemispheres subserve specific and differential functions.

Lateral dominance can be approached in two different ways: (1) determination of the preferred side in performance of tasks that can be done using only one side or the other (lateral preference), and (2) comparison of the level of performance on one side versus the other in evaluating the efficiency or adequacy of performance on the two sides (lateral skill). The lateral dominance examination to be described here relates to the first type of criterion. Several other tests in the Battery (such as the Finger Tapping Test, the Strength of Grip Test, and the Tactual Performance Test) provide information about the comparative functional capability of the upper extremities.

One element of the lateral dominance examination determines which hand is used by the subject for writing. This information serves as the criterion for the hand used for the first trial on the Tactual Performance Test, the Finger Tapping Test, and Grip Strength Test. Therefore, the information concerning the hand used for writing should be obtained before any of these tests are administered. Generally, the Lateral Dominance Examination is the first measure given in the administration of the HRB. The subject's performances are recorded on the form shown in Fig. 9-2.

LATERAL DOMINANCE EXAMINATION

Name _____

Date _____ Examiner _____

1. Show me your:
    A. Right hand   _____
    B. Left ear   _____
    C. Right eye   _____

2. Write your full name:
    A. Preferred hand   ( )   _____ sec.
    B. Nonpreferred hand   ( )   _____ sec.

3. Show me how you:

	Right	Left
A. Throw a ball	_____	_____
B. Hammer a nail	_____	_____
C. Cut with a knife	_____	_____
D. Turn a door knob	_____	_____
E. Use scissors	_____	_____
F. Use an eraser	_____	_____
G. Write your name	_____	_____

4. Show me how you:
    A. Kick a football   _____   _____
    B. Step on a bug   _____   _____

Fig. 9-2. Recording form for the Lateral Dominance Examination.

Specific Instructions

1. The first item in this test is included principally to determine whether the subject is sufficiently intact to be able to understand the instructions that follow for additional items.

The subject and the examiner should be seated comfortably at a table.

Say to the subject:

> Show me your right hand.
>
> (Record the subject's response.)
>
> Show me your left ear.
>
> (Record the subject's response.)
>
> Show me your right eye.
>
> (Record the subject's response.)

2. This item provides a comparison of the time required for the subject to write his/her full name using each hand. The subject is *not* told to write quickly; instead, the examiner asks the subject to write his/her full name, first with the preferred hand, and then in the same manner (printing or cursive) with the nonpreferred hand, using his/her usual manner (normal speed or tempo). In each instance, the time required in seconds is recorded.

The examiner places a blank sheet of paper and a pencil in front of the subject and says:

> Now I want you to write your full name on the paper.
>
> (Record the hand used and time.)

Note the hand used by the subject but give no further direction concerning the hand that is used. The hand used spontaneously by the subject is considered to be the preferred hand.

> Now I want you to write your name in the same way, using your other hand.
>
> (Record the time.)

Again, no mention should be made to write quickly or in any other way alter the subject's conventional manner of writing his/her name. The difference in time required provides an additional indication of hand preference for this task.

3. This item requires the subject to perform a number of unimanual tasks. Do not try to influence the subject to use one hand or the other; present the stimulus material so that it is equally available to either hand. Except for writing, the tasks have been selected in such a way that they probably are not heavily influenced by social pressures. Items used in this measure include a small ball, a toy hammer, a toy knife, a small pair of scissors, and a pencil with an eraser (Fig 9-3).

Fig. 9-3. The Lateral Dominance Examination Kit, which contains the materials used to determine a subject's handedness.

Place the ball on the table in front of the subject and say:

Show me how you would throw a ball.

(Record the hand used.)

Be sure that the ball is presented so that it is equidistant and equally available to both hands. Essentially the same instructions should be used with the remaining items (see Fig. 9-4).

Fig. 9-4. Administration of the Lateral Dominance Examination.

Show me how you would hammer a nail.

(Record the hand used.)

Show me how you would cut with a knife.

(Record the hand used.)

Next, take the subject to a door, stand him/her directly before the knob, and say:

Show me how you would turn a door knob.

(Record the hand used.)

Return to the table and proceed with the next item, saying:

Show me how you would use scissors.

(Record the hand used.)

Show me how you would use the eraser on your pencil.

(Record the hand used.)

Also record which hand the subject initially used when asked to write his/her name.

The results obtained on this item are summarized by indicating the number of times the right hand and the left hand were used in performing the seven tasks.

4. Information regarding footedness is obtained by asking the subject to perform two tasks. In each of the next two items, it is necessary to have the subject stand when the instructions are given. Subjects in a wheelchair who are unable to stand should be asked to demonstrate which foot they would use if they were able to do the task.

First ask the subject:

> **Show me how you would kick a football.**
>
> (Record which foot is used.)

An actual football is not used for this item, because of the possibility that kicking it would cause some type of damage.

Next, say:

> **Pretend that there is a bug on the floor and show me how you would step on it.**
>
> (Record which foot is used.)

In the past we have used the Miles ABC Test of Ocular Dominance to obtain information about eyedness. However, we were never able to relate the results to cerebral damage or dysfunction. In addition, these test materials are no longer readily available for purchase.

Scoring

The subject's responses are noted on the Lateral Dominance form (Fig. 9-2). No formal scoring is done.

The results are also recorded on the top of the Summary Sheet for Older Children (Fig. 9-1). The examiner circles the hand the subject used for writing, and records the number of times the subject used each hand to perform a task.

Example: On the Lateral Dominance Examination the subject used his left hand to turn a door knob and used his right hand to perform the other six tasks (Fig. 9-5). On the Summary Sheet the examiner circles RH (to indicate that the subject wrote his name with his right hand), recorded a "6" on the line next to RH, and a "1" next to LH (Fig. 9-6).

---

3. Show me how you:

		Right	Left
A.	Throw a ball	✓	
B.	Hammer a nail	✓	
C.	Cut with a knife	✓	
D.	Turn a door knob		✓
E.	Use scissors	✓	
F.	Use an eraser	✓	
G.	Write your name	✓	

Fig. 9-5. Example of examiner's recording of a subject's performances on the Lateral Dominance Examination.

Name *Smith, John*   Age *9-11*

Gender *M* Education *3* Handedness: (RH) *6* LH *1*

Fig. 9-6. Examiner's recording on the Summary Sheet of subject's performances shown in Fig. 9-5.

Aphasia Screening Test

Materials Aphasia Test Booklet
recording sheet
blank, unlined paper
pencils (one without an eraser)

General Instructions

Although the Aphasia Screening Test is simple to administer, it is important for the examiner to follow the instructions explicitly. Because of the nature and purpose of the
test — to identify abnormal performances — the examiner
should repeat items or amplify instructions whenever necessary in order to elicit the subject's best performances.

Although the examiner should carefully avoid giving actual
help with any item, the instructions can be elaborated upon
if necessary, after they have been given in the standard
manner, to be sure the subject understands exactly what
each task requires. Sometimes it is difficult to communicate
the instructions because a subject demonstrates a receptive
language abnormality and impaired ability to understand
the instructions (auditory verbal dysgnosia). Such problems
should be noted and considered part of the test results.

Brief instructions for each item are given on the back of the
flipcards in the Aphasia Test Booklet, and can be seen by the
examiner at the same time the corresponding stimulus (on
the front of the card) is seen by the subject.

The very brief instructions on the back of the flipcards are
intended to be only a cue to the examiner, not a substitute
for the actual instructions used in administering the test.
(The cross-hatched instructions indicate that these items
have no accompanying visual stimulus.) The examiner
should have the instructions thoroughly memorized and
follow the recording form (Fig. 9-7) rather than depend on
the abbreviated instructions on the back of the stimulus cards.

Reitan-Indiana	Name _____ Age _____		
Aphasia Screening Test	Date _____ Examiner _____		
Form for Adults and Older Children			

Copy SQUARE	Repeat TRIANGLE
Name SQUARE	Repeat MASSACHUSETTS
Spell SQUARE	Repeat METHODIST EPISCOPAL
Copy CROSS	Write SQUARE
Name CROSS	Read SEVEN
Spell CROSS	Repeat SEVEN
Copy TRIANGLE	Repeat/Explain HE SHOUTED THE WARNING.
Name TRIANGLE	Write HE SHOUTED THE WARNING.
Spell TRIANGLE	Compute 85 − 27 =
Name BABY	Compute 17 x 3 =
Write CLOCK	Name KEY
Name FORK	Demonstrate use of KEY
Read 7 SIX 2	Draw KEY
Read MGW	Read PLACE LEFT HAND TO RIGHT EAR.
Reading I	Place LEFT HAND TO RIGHT EAR
Reading II	Place LEFT HAND TO LEFT ELBOW

Fig. 9-7. Recording form for the Reitan-Indiana Aphasia Screening Test.

The most likely type of deficit associated with a defective performance on each item is also noted on the back of the stimulus card. The psychologist should be aware, however, that a deficit may be receptive, expressive, or a combination of the two types. For example, a subject may not be able to name an object because of an expressive naming difficulty (dysnomia) or alternatively, because of a deficit such as visual form dysgnosia.

There is no absolute way to determine whether a deficit is expressive or receptive. Even the most simple type of response requires input, central processing, and output in order for the cycle to be completed. The subject's limitation may occur on the input or receptive side (dysgnosia) or on the output or expressive side (dyspraxia). Sometimes the subject's responses may make the nature of the deficit (receptive or expressive) quite obvious. In other instances, the neuropsychologist interpreting the subject's performances may need to consider recurring difficulties on individual items of the test to gain additional insight. A confident judgment regarding a preponderance of expressive or receptive aphasic problems can often be made by reviewing similar types of difficulties on various items of the test.

Before beginning with instructions for administering the test itself, we will review some general information concerning the procedure that should be followed. As with all of the neuropsychological testing procedures in the Halstead-Reitan Battery, the examiner should make every effort to elicit the best performance of which the subject is capable. (Note that this is in contrast to recommendations for some testing procedures, including parts of the Wechsler Scale.)

Since we are interested in learning how well the subject's brain is able to perform, the instructions should be given so that the subject understands that a formal test is being administered and that he/she is expected to do as well as possible. This approach may cause a certain amount of stress in some brain-damaged persons. The examiner should be aware, however, that the neuropsychological testing is intended to stress the subject's brain in order to find out the limits of what it can and cannot do, although emotional stress should be minimized when possible. If the subject obviously feels anxious, it is permissible to offer general support and verbal reassurance, but the examiner may neither give the subject any specific information about how to perform an individual task nor do the task for the subject.

The examiner should give the subject the best opportunity to perform correctly on the first attempt. Although additional trials may be given for the same item, consecutive trials permit some positive practice-effect which is often difficult to evaluate. Therefore, the examiner should be sure that the subject does not perform carelessly on the first trial. If the subject has difficulty on a task (such as drawing the square, cross, or triangle), standard practice requires that at least one additional trial be given to determine whether the subject is able to show improvement or, as sometimes occurs, demonstrates even more serious difficulties. Although it is rarely necessary, the examiner may give three (or more) trials if there seems to be significant variability in the performances.

When the subject has difficulty on an item, it is important that the examiner provide an opportunity to correct this difficulty. The examiner should make neutral requests such as, *Would you try that again?* or *Are you sure that is right?*. More specific verbal suggestions may be given later, but only after the subject has had an opportunity to correct the error.

The fact that an error occurred initially is not "excused" by a correct performance on the second trial. Since the tasks on the Aphasia Screening Test are quite simple, most children who make a serious attempt to do well are able to perform adequately. In most instances, if the subject was able to perform correctly on the second trial, the mistake should not have occurred initially. Since the material is relatively simple and the examiner is required to use careful and deliberate testing techniques, frequently a correct response on the second trial documents the fact that the subject can actually perform the task, but that some degree of brain dysfunction was manifested on the first trial.

It is important that the examiner record the actual responses made by the subject for each individual item on which deficits occur. If the responses are without error, the corresponding space on the recording form is customarily left blank. However, if the subject hesitates, appears confused, or has some difficulty in responding, this should be noted even if the response itself is correct. Self-corrections, whether spontaneous or prompted, should also be noted. Sometimes a verbatim response is difficult to record, but the examiner should attempt to record exactly what was said so that full details are available for interpretation.

For example, when the subject is asked to repeat *Methodist Episcopal*, it is not satisfactory for the examiner to merely write down that the subject had difficulty. The examiner should listen very carefully to the exact sounds produced by the subject and write the subject's response phonetically.

It is also important for the examiner to encourage the subject to attempt to perform each task. The examiner should not unquestioningly accept responses such as, "I don't know," since such responses do not yield any significant information. Because the Aphasia Screening Test depends upon the "sign" approach, it is important to determine whether the subject demonstrates the particular sign or deficit. Every effort must therefore be made to induce the subject to make an actual attempt on each task, or the examiner in effect has deleted some of the items from the test. Under such circumstances it may be difficult to interpret the results and determine, in terms of the overall pattern of responses, whether the deficit is expressive, receptive, or a combination of both.

In reaching a judgment about this problem, it is often important for the examiner to have made notes about the subject's ability to understand the instructions. A subject who is continually confused about the instructions demonstrates an important manifestation of auditory receptive difficulties in the language area.

It is imperative that the subject *never* be permitted to cross out or erase a performance. Persons who have difficulty with the tasks frequently want to delete their incorrect performance. Obviously, this may destroy the evidence of cerebral disease or damage.

Finally, we should state that it is not uncommon for inexperienced examiners to fail to observe errors in performances. The examiner must make a particularly careful effort to listen closely to all responses given by the subject. In our training programs we have found that novice examiners frequently accept spellings such as "t-r-a-i-n-g-l-e" as correct until they have learned to listen closely and carefully to the subject's response.

Specific Instructions

The subject and examiner should be seated at a table (see Fig. 9-8).

Place a piece of unlined, white paper and a pencil without an eraser in front of the subject and say:

> **I have a number of things that I want to ask you to do. Some of them are very simple, but even if they are easy for you, I want you to do them carefully and be sure to do your best.**

Fig. 9-8. Administration of the Aphasia Screening Test.

If the subject has obvious difficulty drawing any of the figures in the test, encourage him/her to proceed until it is clear that no further progress can be made. If the child has not accomplished the task reasonably well on the first trial, ask him/her to try again, and instruct the child to be particularly careful to do it as well as possible. Refer to Fig. 9-9 for the stimulus figures for the Aphasia Screening Test.

Open the Aphasia Screening Test booklet to the stimulus figure of the square. Place the booklet on the table so that the stimulus figure can easily be seen by the subject.

1. (Square)   First, draw this (point to the square) on your paper. I want you to do it without lifting your pencil from the paper. Make it about this same size (point to the square).

The purpose of asking the subject to avoid lifting the pencil is to prevent skipping around in the drawing. The task is to make steady progress in drawing the figure until it is finally completed at the original starting point. Although subjects are allowed to begin the drawing at whatever point they wish, the requirement of a continuous line brings about some standardization of the problem of "closing" the drawing.

If the subject is concerned about making a heavy or double line, point out that a double line is not necessary, and that only a reproduction (outline) of the shape is required.

2. (Square)   What is that shape called? Or, What is the name for that figure?

3. (Square)   Would you spell that word for me?

If the subject has not been able to name the figure, tell him/her that the name of the figure is a square, so that the subject can attempt to spell the correct name.

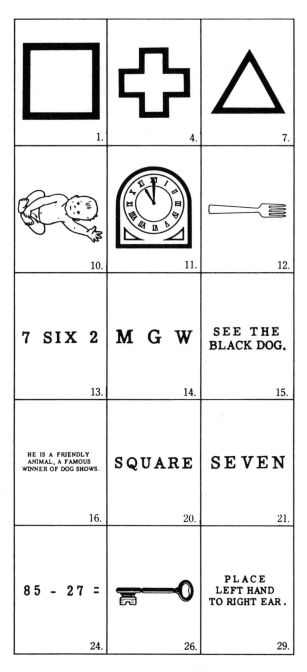

Fig. 9-9. Stimulus figures for the Aphasia Screening Test. The number in the lower right corner of each card corresponds with the instructions for administration in this chapter.

4. (Cross)   Draw this (point to the cross) on your
               paper. Go around the outside like this
               (quickly draw a finger-line around the
               edge of the stimulus figure) until you
               get back to where you started. Make it
               about this same size (point to the cross).

Additional instructions, if necessary, should be similar to
those used with the square.

5. (Cross)   What is that shape called?

6. (Cross)   Would you spell the name of it?

If the subject cannot name the figure or gives an incorrect
name, say:

Some people call this a cross. Would you spell
"cross" for me?

7. (Triangle) Now I want you to draw this figure.
              (Point to the triangle.)

8. (Triangle) What would you call that figure?

9. (Triangle) Would you spell that for me?

10. (Baby)   What is this?

The stimulus figure of the baby is deliberately presented in
a sideways position in order to make the problem of visual
form perception slightly more difficult.

11. (Clock)   Now I am going to show you another
              picture, but do not tell me the name
              of it. I don't want you to say anything
              out loud. Just write the name of the
              picture on your paper.

If the subject prints, allow him/her to finish and then request that the response be given in cursive writing.

12. (Fork)   What is this?

13. (7 SIX 2)   I want you to read this.

If the subject has difficulty, attempt to determine whether he/she can read any part of the stimulus figure.

14. (M G W)   Read this.

15. (See the black dog.) Now I want you to read this.

16. (He is a friendly animal, a famous winner of dog shows.) Can you read this?

Listen carefully for omissions, additions, transposition, or mispronunciations when the child repeats the words in items 17, 18, and 19.

17. Now I am going to say some words. I want you to listen carefully, and say them after me as carefully as you can.

    Say this word: Triangle.

18. The next one is a little harder, but do your best.

    Say this word: Massachusetts.

19. Now repeat this one: Methodist Episcopal.

20. (Square)   Don't say this word out loud. (Point to the stimulus word "square.") Just write it on your paper.

If the subject prints the word, allow him/her to finish and then request that the response be given in cursive writing.

21. (Seven)   Would you read this word?

21A. Remove the stimulus card and say:

    Now, I want you to say this after me: Seven.

22. I am going to say something and I want you to say it after me, so listen carefully: HE SHOUTED THE WARNING.

    Now you say it.

After subject responds, say:

Tell me in your own words what that means.

Sometimes it is necessary to amplify the instructions by asking about the kind of situation to which the sentence might refer. An adequate understanding brings the concept of impending danger into the explanation or illustration.

23. Now I want you to write that sentence on the paper.

Sometimes it is necessary to repeat the sentence (*He shouted the warning*) so the subject understands clearly what is supposed to be written.

24. (85 – 27 =) Here is an arithmetic problem. Copy it down on your paper any way you like and try to work it out.

If the subject does not perform subtraction, ask him/her to do the problem again, and to be very careful to do it right. If the subject still does not recognize the meaning of the minus sign, ask questions to determine the degree of the subject's confusion.

25. (17 × 3) Now do this one in your head. Write down only the answer. What is 17×3?

If the subject has difficulty with these problems, use some other simple problems in addition, subtraction, and multiplication. The purpose is not to see if the subject has developed skill in dealing with complex arithmetic problems, but to determine whether or not there are specific losses in understanding arithmetical processes. The drawback in using extremely simple problems is that the subject may respond correctly through rote memory rather than through immediate use of arithmetical processes, but some subjects have such limited formal training in arithmetic that it is necessary to use very simple problems.

26. (Key)   What is this?

27. (Key)   If you had one of these in your hand, show me how you would use it.

28. (Key)   Now I want you to draw a picture that looks just like this. Try to make your key look enough like this one (pointing to the key) so that I would know it was the same key from your drawing. Make it about the same size.

The examiner may tell the subject that lifting the pencil is allowed, but erasing is not permitted. If the subject makes a serious mistake, he/she may not want to continue. If this occurs, the examiner should encourage the subject to finish the drawing and tell him/her that another drawing may be done after the first one is completed. Erasing or crossing out the original error is never allowed, as it may be important for interpretation of the results.

It is not necessary for the subject to put the shading in the drawing; in fact, attempts to reproduce the shading some-times conceal errors that would be important to observe.

29. (Place left hand to right ear.) Would you read this?

30. (Place left hand to right ear.) Now, would you do what it said?

Be sure to note any false starts or even mild expressions of confusion.

31. Now I want you to put your left hand to your left elbow.

Confusion on this item often reveals minimal or subtle dif-ficulties in right/left orientation, even though the subject does not make mistakes in responding to direct requests that are within the realm of possibility.

Sometimes this item elicits evidence of a very serious prob-lem — confusion of body parts (body agnosia). For example, this may be manifested by confusion between the shoulder and the elbow, and may be evident even though right/left confusion was not demonstrated.

Scoring

Despite the tendency (and even published directions) of some investigators to score each item as pass/fail and then total the failures, we do not recommend that the Aphasia Screening Test be scored in this manner. It is more impor-tant to interpret the failures and use this test as intended, i.e., to identify specific deficits on simple tasks that should be performed satisfactorily by persons with normal brain functions.

The Aphasia Screening Test evaluates basic aspects of the use of language symbols for communicational purposes, and the information derived from the subject's responses can be used to determine the presence of dysphasic deficits (such as dysnomia, dysgraphia, spelling dyspraxia, dys-calculia, etc.) as recorded in scoring the Neuropsychological Deficit Scale.

Specific examples of adequate, barely adequate, and defec-tive responses are presented in the following section as well as in the case illustrations. These illustrations can be used as guides when scoring the Neuropsychological Deficit Scale for Older Children.

Evaluation of Performances of Children Aged 9 through 14 Years on the Reitan-Indiana Aphasia Screening Test and Scoring of the Neuropsychological Deficit Scale

When adult subjects demonstrate defective performances on the relatively simple tasks in the Reitan-Indiana Aphasia Screening Test, these performances usually represent losses, due to cerebral damage, of previously acquired abilities. Cerebral damage is usually also a significant factor in producing defective performances among children; however, a child's limited skills are sometimes due to brain-related limitations in the acquisition of abilities, loss of previously acquired abilities (among previously normal children who have sustained recent brain damage or disorders), or a combination of both impaired acquisitional aptitude and losses of pre-existing skills.

Thus, the task of interpreting children's performances is somewhat more complicated than interpreting adult performances. Specific guidelines for evaluating children's performances are presented below. Interpretation is oriented toward types of deficits and is grouped according to the items that contribute to identifying each type of deficit. The recommended procedure is first to determine if the deficit is present and then to assign the appropriate score.

The reader may wish to peruse the Aphasia NDS guidelines for adults (Reitan & Wolfson, 1992c) in order to review additional examples of deficits. The examples of adequate and defective responses are basically similar for adults and older children, but in a few instances the requirements for adults are a little more stringent.

Dysnomia

A deficit, due to brain impairment, in the ability to name common objects.

Contributing items:

Name pictures of a SQUARE
CROSS
TRIANGLE
BABY
FORK
KEY

■ **Name the SQUARE**

0 = "Square"

3 = Any obviously incorrect response

Examples of a score of 3:
"A square is a triangle."
"Window – window pane."
"Box – carry food in it." Examiner ? S cannot think
of another name.

■ **Name the CROSS**

0 = "Cross"
"Red Cross"
"Red Cross signal" acceptable, but examiner
should question S further.
"Plus" *if* there are no other naming deficits.

3 = Any obviously incorrect response

Examples of a score of 3:
"Plus" Examiner ? "X." Examiner ?
S could not give another name.
"An 'X' " Examiner ? "A 'T' "

■ **Name the TRIANGLE**

0 = "Triangle"
"Triang-gel"
"Trianger"

3 = Any obviously incorrect response

Examples of a score of 3:
   "Angle" Examiner ? "Square"
   "Rectangle" corrected to "Triangle"

■ **Name the BABY**

   0 = "Baby"
   "Baby boy"

   3 = Any obviously incorrect response

   Examples of a score of 3:
   "A man"
   "Boy"
   "Boy – I mean, baby"

■ **Name the FORK**

   0 = "Fork"

   3 = Any obviously incorrect response

   Examples of a score of 3:
   "Spoon"
   "Rectangle"

■ **Name the KEY**

   0 = "Key"

   3 = Any obviously incorrect response

Spelling Dyspraxia

A deficit, due to cerebral impairment, in the ability to spell words.

Contributing items:

Verbally spell SQUARE
         CROSS
         TRIANGLE

   Write CLOCK
      SQUARE
      HE SHOUTED THE WARNING

■ **Spell SQUARE**

0 = Square
Squar

1 = Any incorrect response (besides "squar")

Examples of a score of 1:
Suar
Squara
Sqware
Skare
Squre
Sqrae
Sqoeir
Crar

■ **Spell CROSS**

0 = Cross
Cu-Cross

1 = Any incorrect response

Examples of a score of 1:
Cars
Corss
Cros
Coss
Carase
Choar

■ **Spell TRIANGLE**

0 = Triangle
Trangle
Trinagle
Traingle
Triangl

1 = Any incorrect response (except those listed above)

Examples of a score of 1:
Tringel
Tragli
Triang . . . (S could not complete)
Triancle
Triango
Tryangli
Tringal

■ **Write CLOCK**

0 = Clock

1 = Any incorrect response

Examples of a score of 1:
Clook
Clok
Colk

■ **Write SQUARE**

0 = Square

1 = Any incorrect response (but not poor letter formation if the response is legible)

Example of a score of 1:
Sqare

■ **Write HE SHOUTED THE WARNING**

0 = He shouted the warning.
He shouted the warming.

Example of spelling dyspraxia:

Example of spelling dyspraxia and dysgraphia:

C /ø K

Example of spelling dyspraxia but not dysgraphia:

He showed the

woreind.

Example of spelling dyspraxia but not dysgraphia:

he showed the wrne

Constructional Dyspraxia

A deficit, due to cerebral impairment, in the ability to deal with spatial relationships in either a two- or three-dimensional framework.

Contributing items:

Drawings of the SQUARE
                   CROSS
                   TRIANGLE
                   KEY

0 = No significant evidence of constructional dyspraxia

Examples of adequate and barely adequate drawings:

Squares are generally drawn adequately in the 9- through 14-year age group.

Examples of adequate to barely adequate drawings:

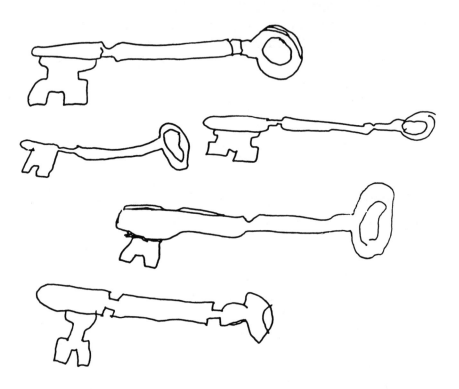

2 = Evidence of constructional dyspraxia

Examples of inadequate drawings:

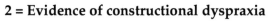

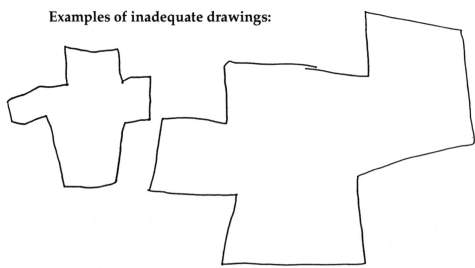

2 = Evidence of constructional dyspraxia

Examples of inadequate drawings:

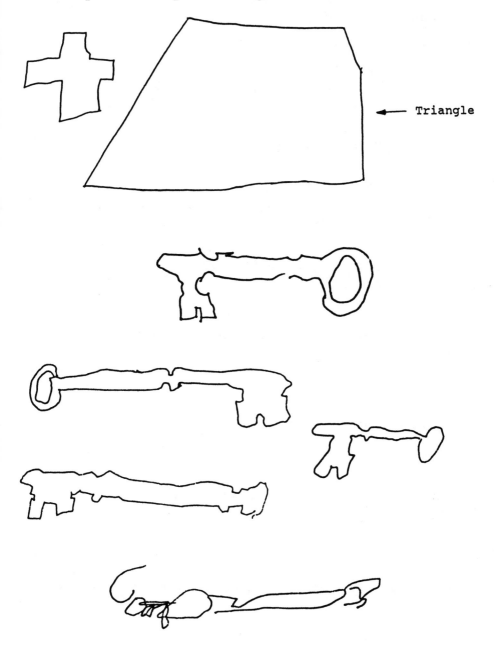

← Triangle

Dysgraphia

A deficit, due to brain impairment, in the ability to form letters when writing.

Contributing items:

Writing CLOCK (from a picture)
SQUARE (from a printed sample)
HE SHOUTED THE WARNING (from dictation)

0 = Adequate performances

Clock *clock* *square*

He shouted the warning.

He shouted the warning

2 = Inadequate performances

Square *he sqttled the worning*

He shoted the warnezing.

Dyslexia

A deficit, due to brain impairment, in the ability to read and understand the symbolic significance of words.

Contributing items:

Read 7 SIX 2
SEE THE BLACK DOG.
HE IS A FRIENDLY ANIMAL, A FAMOUS
WINNER OF DOG SHOWS.
SEVEN
PLACE LEFT HAND TO RIGHT EAR.

■ **Read 7 SIX 2**

0 = Correct response
"Six – 7 six 2"
"Seven hundred sixty-two" Examiner ?
S corrects answer without help.

2 = If S is unable to read one or more items.
If S gives an irrelevant verbal response.
"Letters."
"It says something."
"6-7-7"
"Seven hundred sixty-two" Examiner ? "7 S-I-X 2."

■ **Read SEE THE BLACK DOG.**

0 = "See the black dog."

2 = If S is unable to read one or more words.
If S gives an irrelevant verbal response.
"Letters."
"It says something."
"See the clock go."

■ **Read HE IS A FRIENDLY ANIMAL, A FAMOUS
WINNER OF DOG SHOWS.**

0 = "He is a friendly animal, a famous winner of
dog shows."

"He is a friendly animal, a famous winner of
show dogs – dog shows."
"He is a friendly animal, a famous winner
dog shows."
"He is a friendly animal, a _____ winner of
dog shows." (*In a child with limited training in
reading.*)

2 = If S is unable to read one or more words.
If S gives an irrelevant verbal response.
"Letters."
"It says something."
"He is a friend – friendly – a – nice of dog show."
"He is a friendly aminal – an-imal – a framous winner
of dog sh-shows."
"He is a friendly animal and a farmer's winner from
dog watching."
"He is a friendly animal and harmless winter of
dog show."
"He is a friendly animal and a famous weener dog
of shows."
"He is a beautiful animal, a famous _____
of dog shows."

■ **Read SEVEN**

0 = "Seven"

2 = If S is unable to read.
If S gives an irrelevant verbal response.
"Letters."
"It says something."

■ **Read PLACE LEFT HAND TO RIGHT EAR**

0 = "Place left hand to right ear."
"Please place left hand to right ear."
"Place left hand on right ear."

2 = If S is unable to read one or more words.
If S gives an irrelevant verbal response.

"Letters."
"It says something."
"Please left your hand to right ear."
"Please feet hand to right ear."
"Plack left hand to left lear."
"Please let hand to right ear."

Central Dysarthria

A deficit, due to brain impairment, in the ability to enunciate words; characterized by an omission, addition, or transposition of syllables.

Contributing items:

Say after me, TRIANGLE
                MASSACHUSETTS
                METHODIST EPISCOPAL

■ **Say after me, TRIANGLE**

0 = Triangle
    Triango

2 = Any incorrect response (except "triango")

Example of a score of 2:
    Trangle

■ **Say after me, MASSACHUSETTS**

0 = Massachusetts
    Massachusess
    Massachuchess
    Massatuchess

2 = Any incorrect response (besides those listed above)

Examples of a score of 2:
    Mass-sa-chu-sass
    Massa-chu-chess

■ **Say after me, METHODIST EPISCOPAL**

  0 = Methodist episcopal
     Methodist epistopal
     Methodist epistical
     Methodist epixipal
     Methodist episable
     Methodiss apiscabol
     Methodiss episticul
     Messadiss episs-si-pal

  2 = Any incorrect response (besides those listed above)
  Examples of a score of 2:
     Methodiss eppipal
     Methodist epistcal
     Meddist pisibal
     Methodiss apocal
     Messodis epick-kobal
     Methodiss episol
     Methodist pissocapal
     Methodist epistocopal
     Methodist mekiscobal

Dyscalculia

A deficit, due to cerebral impairment, in the ability to appreciate the symbolic significance of numbers and the nature of arithmetical processes.

  Contributing items:

  Compute $85 - 27 =$
           17×3
           and if necessary, simpler problems chosen
             by the examiner

  0 = No significant evidence of dyscalculia

Examples of acceptable answers:

$$\begin{array}{r} 85 \\ -27 \\ \hline 68 \end{array} \qquad \begin{array}{r} {}^{7}8\llap{/}5\llap{/} \\ -27 \\ \hline 59 \end{array}$$

If the subject is unable to do the problem because of limited arithmetical training, the examiner should give easier problems to determine if there is confusion about the symbolic significance of numbers in quantitative relationships (as contrasted with rote memory of given problems).

2 = Evidence of dyscalculia

Examples of inadequate responses:
    If the subject does not know the meaning of the
        minus sign ("What is it – divide?")
    "231"
    "Can't be done."

$$\begin{array}{r} 85 \\ -27 \\ \hline 62 \end{array} \qquad \begin{array}{r} 85 \\ \overline{2}7 \\ \hline 02 \end{array}$$

$$\begin{array}{r} 85 \\ -27 \\ \hline 62 \end{array} \quad -27 =$$

$$\begin{array}{r} 16 \\ -4 \\ \hline 10 \end{array}$$ (Problem written by examiner)

Right-Left Confusion

Confusion of the right and left sides of one's own body or of other persons or objects.

Contributing items:

PLACE LEFT HAND TO RIGHT EAR

PLACE LEFT HAND TO LEFT ELBOW

0 = No significant evidence of right-left confusion

Examples of a score of 0:

S responds correctly.

S tries repeatedly to place left hand to left elbow. (Following this response, some children try spontaneously to place their right hand to their right elbow. This is not an example of left-right confusion.)

1 = Evidence of right-left confusion

Note: A response is counted as an error even if the S makes a spontaneous correction.

Examples of a score of 1:

S uses his/her hand to identify the ear or elbow, but is confused about left and right, and makes an error such as placing:

Right hand to right ear

Right hand to left ear

Right finger to left elbow

Left hand to right elbow

Right hand to right elbow (as an initial response)

When a subject has obvious impairment of motor functions or limited mobility on the left side, the examiner should change the instructions to make a correct response possible. The following are examples of instructions given to a subject with left-sided hemiplegia:

Examiner asked the subject to PLACE RIGHT HAND TO LEFT EAR.

Examiner asked the subject to PLACE RIGHT HAND TO RIGHT ELBOW.

Body Dysgnosia

A deficit, due to cerebral impairment, in the ability to identify body parts.

Contributing items:

PLACE LEFT HAND TO RIGHT EAR

PLACE LEFT HAND TO LEFT ELBOW

0 = Correct identification of body parts
(Right-left confusion is not considered as a sign of body dysgnosia)

Examples of a score of 0:

S responds correctly with respect to use of hand and identification of ear or elbow.

3 = Evidence of body dysgnosia

Examples of a score of 3:

S identifies a body part incorrectly and makes an error such as placing his/her hand to the face, hand to eyebrow, hand to shoulder, etc., or demonstrates obvious confusion regarding body parts even though the final performance is correct.

Visual Number Dysgnosia

A deficit, due to brain impairment, in the ability to recognize the symbolic significance of numbers through visual perception.

(See examples under Visual Letter Dysgnosia.)

Visual Letter Dysgnosia

A deficit, due to brain impairment, in the ability to recognize the symbolic significance of letters of the alphabet through visual perception.

> *Contributing items:* Read 7 SIX 2
> MGW
> Perform 85 – 27 =
> Write SQUARE

0 = No significant evidence of visual number dysgnosia or visual letter dysgnosia
3 = Evidence visual number dysgnosia
3 = Evidence of visual letter dysgnosia

■ **Read 7 SIX 2**

"Six" (S does not know the numbers 7 and 2)
– *Visual number dysgnosia*

"7 – 2" (S does not know letters)
– *Visual letter dysgnosia*

"S-I-X-2." Examiner ? "2-X-I-S."
– *Visual number* and *letter dysgnosia*

"7-6-7" then S self-corrects answer
– *Visual number dysgnosia*

■ **Read MGW**

"A-G-W"
– *Visual letter dysgnosia*

"M – is that a word?"
– *Visual letter dysgnosia*

"M-G-Y" then S self-corrects answer
– *Visual letter dysgnosia*

"M-G-M"
– *Visual letter dysgnosia*

■ **Perform 85 − 27 =**

Any error that reveals a failure to understand the symbolic significance of the numbers, in contrast to arithmetical procedures or quantitative relationships
– *Visual number dysgnosia.*

Auditory Verbal Dysgnosia

A deficit, due to brain impairment, in the ability to understand the symbolic significance of verbal communication through the auditory avenue (loss of auditory verbal comprehension).

Contributing items:

■ **Repeat   HE SHOUTED THE WARNING**
■ **Explain   HE SHOUTED THE WARNING**

and examiner's observations throughout the testing situation when giving the subject instructions for the various tests.

The above items test for immediate registration of verbal communications through the auditory avenue as judged by the ability to repeat the information, and comprehension of the information as well as by the ability to explain its possible meaning. Registration and understanding of meaning are both required for auditory verbal comprehension. Competence in this area is also judged by the subject's ability to comprehend instructions for each item as the test is given. Notations regarding apparent deficits are recorded.

The subject's repetition of HE SHOUTED THE WARNING is recorded verbatim or, if necessary, phonetically. Usually the sentence can be repeated correctly, although enunciatory and registration problems may be shown as follows: "He touted da warming" and "He shall the warning." These responses qualify as defective. Poor explanations more often serve as a basis for scoring the presence of auditory verbal dysgnosia. Adequate responses include a recognition of impending danger.

0 = No significant evidence of auditory verbal dysgnosia

Examples of adequate responses:
"The house got on fire."
"He yelled a warning. Somebody in trouble."
   (The second sentence makes the response
   adequate.)
"He told him to stop shooting."
"Told them the warning or shouted at them."
   Examiner ? Then the S mentioned the concept
   of danger.
"Not to get away from home."
   (Marginally acceptable response.)
"He was afraid." Examiner ? "Of something."
   (Marginally acceptable.)

3 = Evidence of auditory verbal dysgnosia

Examples of inadequate responses:
   If the subject does not understand the sentence
   and can offer no explanation of its meaning.
"Someone was coming."
"Someone hollered at someone else."
   Examiner ? S could not explain any further.

Additional Examples of Auditory Verbal Dysgnosia

Spell TRIANGLE
S had difficulty understanding what to do, but finally
   responded correctly.

Write CLOCK
S could not understand what the examiner was asking
   him to do.

Repeat MASSACHUSETTS
S could not understand the instructions; did not know
   what he was supposed to do.

Demonstrate use of a KEY

S took a pencil and was about to draw the key.
Examiner repeated the instructions.
S withdrew his hand, seemed confused.

PLACE LEFT HAND TO RIGHT EAR.

S was slow to understand. Examiner had to repeat
instructions often.

PLACE LEFT HAND TO LEFT ELBOW.

S could not understand the instructions.
S crossed his arms at the wrists and said, "It just won't
stay there."
S had difficulty understanding the instructions, but
finally responded correctly.

Finger Tapping Test

Materials   Finger Tapping Test
stopwatch
recording sheet
pencil

General Instructions

The purpose of this test is to measure the maximal tapping speed of the index finger of each hand. The standard test procedure calls for five consecutive trials *within a five-point range* with each hand. This procedure is used in order to avoid single deviant scores from unduly influencing the total performance.

Clinically, it sometimes is very difficult to achieve this criterion for certain subjects, because their finger may slip off the lever or invalidate the trial in some other way and thus not represent the subject's maximal performance. These invalid trials may be deleted and therefore do not interrupt a "consecutive series" of trials, provided that the examiner is conservative in his/her interpretation, and deletes only trials in which some obvious factor has occurred that prevented the attempt from representing the subject's best performance.

Fatigue may definitely be a factor in limiting the performance on this test, and a brief rest period should be given after each trial. The examiner should be alert to the development of fatigue (such as obvious slowing toward the end of a trial), and require that the subject take rest periods as often as necessary in order to give him/her a full chance to do his/her best. A mandatory rest period of one to two minutes is required after the third trial, even when no sign of fatigue is apparent. A practice period is given before the test begins, so that the subject may get accustomed to the apparatus. However, the subject should not be allowed to practice to the point of becoming fatigued.

The heel of the subject's hand should rest firmly on the board during each trial. An attempt is made in this test to record isolated movement of the index finger. Although some accompanying movement of other fingers may occur, do not permit movement of the whole hand or arm.

Some subjects will aim for the score achieved on a preceding trial, slowing down or even stopping when that score is reached. In such instances the examiner may elect to cover the dial so that the subject will not see the score. In other cases, the subject may make such an effort to exceed a previous score that the arm (in addition to just the finger) will begin to move. If the dial seems to be distracting to the subject, it should be covered, and the examiner should comment that it is better for the subject only to try to do his/her absolute best on each trial and not pay attention to the score obtained.

It is important that exactly ten seconds be given for each trial. Some subjects do not start immediately when told to begin. Do not begin timing until the subject begins tapping. The examiner should say "Stop!" to coincide with the end of the ten-second period. Some subjects do not stop tapping immediately, and the examiner should deduct any extra taps that occur after the ten-second period. Practice is usually necessary for an examiner to develop skill in identifying the number of extra taps that have occurred.

The physical arrangement should be optimal regarding chair and table height in relation to body size; although no special arrangements are usually needed for adults, the examiner should be especially alert to this requirement when testing children.

During the practice period the examiner should be sure that the subject is in a comfortable position for his/her hand and arm with relation to the tapping apparatus. The subject should be encouraged to move the position of the apparatus as necessary in order to achieve the best performance.

Never alternate hand trials. The dominant hand is tested first; then the nondominant hand is evaluated.

We cannot emphasize strongly enough that the finger tapping test is not a reaction-time test. The object of the test is to measure how many times an individual can tap each index finger in a ten-second time period. Therefore, the examiner must be sure to give the subject ten seconds of timing. In other words, do not begin timing until you hear the first "click" of the counter, and listen carefully for extra taps after the subject is told to stop.

Test energetically and vigorously. Convey to subjects both directly and indirectly that you want them to tap as fast as possible: demonstrate tapping as fast as you are able to tap, keep the stopwatch clearly in view, and give active verbal encouragement.

Specific Instructions

The subject and examiner should be seated comfortably at a table (see Fig. 9-10).

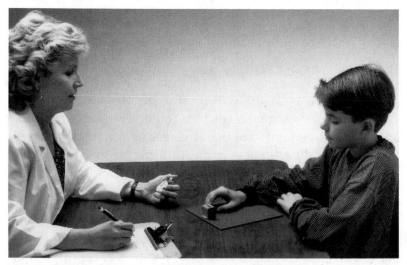

Fig. 9-10. Administration of the Finger Tapping Test.

Place the tapping apparatus in front of the subject and say,

> Now we are going to do a test to see how fast you can tap. We will use this little key here (indicate the lever to the subject) and I want you to tap just as fast as you can, using the forefinger (point to the subject's index finger) of your right (or left, if the subject is left-hand dominant) hand.

> When you tap, be sure to use a finger movement; do not move your whole hand or your arm. When you tap this key, you will have to remember to let the key come all the way up and click each time, or else the number on the dial won't change.

Demonstrate to the subject how the lever operates and how it should be allowed to "click" after each tap. Also demonstrate actual tapping for a five- or six-second period, going as fast as possible.

> Now you move the board to a comfortable position for your hand and try it for practice.

After a brief practice period, say:

> That was fine. Remember to tap as rapidly as you possibly can.

Be sure that the subject knows what to do and is properly challenged to tap as fast as possible. Then say,

> Do you have any questions? (Pause.) All right. Ready — Go!

Begin timing with the first tap. At the end of ten seconds, say, Stop!

The subject should be allowed to rest for one to two minutes after any trial, but always must take a mandatory rest period after the third trial for each hand.

After completing the test with the preferred hand, determine the finger tapping speed for the index finger of the non-preferred hand. *Never alternate between right and left hand trials.*

Scoring

The number of taps for each trial is noted on the recording form (Fig. 9-11). The score is the mean for five consecutive valid trials; i.e., five trials within a five-point range in which no obvious procedural disadvantage has occurred.

If five consecutive valid trials within a range of five points cannot be elicited, give no more than ten trials and determine the mean score for the total number of trials.

MANUAL FINGER TAPPING TEST

Name ______________________ Date ____________ Examiner ____________

Preferred Hand: Right ______ or Left ______

LEFT HAND	RIGHT HAND
1.	1.
2.	2.
3.	3.
4.	4.
5.	5.

Fig. 9-11. Recording form for the Finger Tapping Test.

Example: On the first five trials the subject obtains the following scores: 40, 41, 47, 48, 47 (see Fig. 9-12). Since the score on the third trial (47) is more than five taps greater than the score on the preceding trial (41), the examiner must administer additional trials until the subject has attained five trials within five taps of each other.

In this case, the examiner administered two additional trials, and the subject scored 44 and 46. Trials 3 through 7

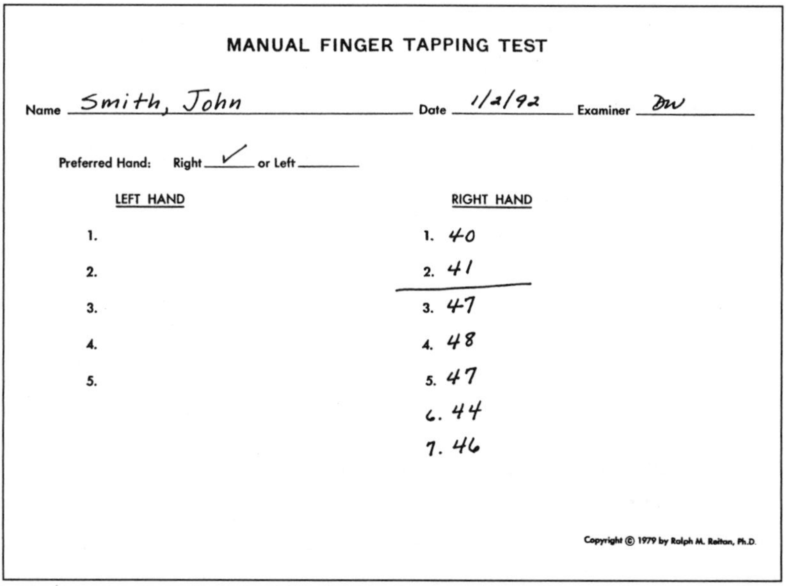

MANUAL FINGER TAPPING TEST

Name Smith, John Date 1/2/92 Examiner DW

Preferred Hand: Right ✓ or Left ____

LEFT HAND	RIGHT HAND
1.	1. 40
2.	2. 41
3.	3. 47
4.	4. 48
5.	5. 47
	6. 44
	7. 46

Copyright © 1979 by Ralph M. Reitan, Ph.D.

Fig. 9-12. Example of examiner's recording of a subject's performances on the Finger Tapping Test.

therefore produced five trials within five taps of each other, so no additional trials had to be given. The first two trials are discarded, and the subject's score is the mean of trials 3 through 7.

Grip Strength

Materials   dynamometer
recording sheet
pencil

General Instructions

This test measures the motor strength of each of the subject's upper extremities. In our laboratory we use a Smedley hand dynamometer for this purpose.

Because of the variability in hand sizes, the handle of the instrument is adjusted for each subject. We restrict the range to settings between 3 (small hand) and 5 (large hand) and attempt to find a comfortable position within that range for the individual subject. During the test it is important for the subject to keep his/her arm extended with the dynamometer pointed toward the floor (Fig. 9-13).

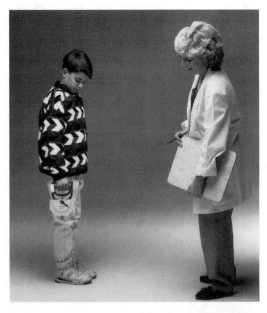

Fig. 9-13. Administration of the Grip Strength Test.

The standard procedure is to obtain two trials within five kilograms for each hand. The first trial is given to the dominant hand. The subject should be encouraged to take rest periods between the trials, and a mandatory rest period is given after each hand has been tested once.

If either an increase or decrease of more than five kilograms occurs on the second trial for either hand, the examiner should have the subject wait for a few minutes and then administer a third trial to that hand.

Specific Instructions

Ask the subject to stand, and say:

> Now I want to find out how strong you are. We will use this instrument (indicate the dynamometer) and have you grip it with your hand as hard as you possibly can.

> First, I'll show you how it works. Keep your arm straight and squeeze as hard as you can (demonstrate). This little lever (indicate) will move up as you squeeze and it will stay there until I reset it, so you just need to squeeze the handle as hard as you can and then let it go. The lever will record your strength.

Reset the dynamometer. Adjust the handle to the approximate size for the subject, and ask the subject to hold the dynamometer with his/her dominant hand. Then say:

> Before going ahead, I want to be sure that the instrument is adjusted so that it will be comfortable for you.

Increase or decrease the handle size of the dynamometer until it feels comfortable for the subject. With a little experience the examiner will be able to estimate the approximate position that will suit the subject, but in each case it should be checked with the subject to be sure that it feels comfortable.

Now, point the instrument toward the floor. Be sure to keep your arm straight, and squeeze as hard as you possibly can.

After recording the results for the first (preferred hand) trial, the same instructions are given for the next trial using the nonpreferred hand. Record the results for the non-dominant hand and give the subject a rest period of two to three minutes. Then administer a second trial to the dominant hand and record the results. Finally, administer a second trial to the nondominant hand and record the results.

If the second trial for either hand is *not* within five kilograms of the first trial, continue giving trials (with appropriate rest periods) until two trials within five kilograms are obtained.

Scoring

Measurements for each hand are noted on the recording form (Fig. 9-14). For each hand determine the mean value for the two trials within five kilograms.

GRIP STRENGTH TEST

Name:_____ Date: _____ Examiner:_____

Dominant Hand: Right ____   or Left ____

Left Hand   Right Hand

1. _____   1. _____
2. _____   2. _____

Total _____ kg   Total _____ kg

Mean _____ kg   Mean _____ kg

Fig. 9-14. Recording form for the Grip Strength Test.

The Sensory-perceptual Examination

A. Bilateral Simultaneous Sensory Stimulation

Materials   recording form
             pencil

General Instructions

The procedure for administering the Sensory-perceptual Examination is relatively simple, but requires practice on the part of the examiner and close attention to detail. With sufficient experience, many examiners are able to proceed quite quickly with the examination, mentally tabulating any errors made by the subject and recording them when a natural break occurs in the testing procedure. However, if the examiner has not had sufficient experience with administration of the test, it is necessary to record errors as they occur.

As with any standardized and formal testing procedure, it is important that the instructions be given to the subject in an exact and precise manner. In other words, the examiner must memorize (never read) the instructions. The instructions should be given in a standard form initially, but may be restated or elaborated upon whenever necessary so that the subject understands exactly what is expected from him/her.

If an examiner has never given these tests, it would be advisable for him/her to memorize the specific instructions, obtain "dry run" experience with practice subjects, and give the tests to an experienced and knowledgeable person who is familiar with the tests in order to be sure that all aspects of the procedure are followed correctly.

If the tests are routinely administered by an examiner who does not have background and experience in the area of human brain-behavior relationships, supervision should be provided by a person who is knowledgeable about the purpose of the tests and the neuroanatomical and neuropathological background for interpretation of the results.

In administering the tests for perception of bilateral simultaneous tactile stimulation, it is important that a minimal stimulus be given. The tactile stimulus is administered with the examiner's own finger, not a pencil or other object. The examiner should determine how minimal a stimulus will still elicit a correct response and should continue to use this degree of pressure when stimuli are given to both sides simultaneously (even in those instances in which one side may initially have been determined to require more pressure than the other).

The same general rule is followed with auditory stimulation. Use as minimal a sound as necessary to elicit correct responses to unilateral stimulation. A loud finger snap is not necessary. In fact, although the examiner is usually not even able to hear the stimulus, the subject is able to respond correctly.

A very minimal movement with only one finger is frequently sufficient to elicit correct unilateral responses with visual stimulation. It is not necessary to wave at the subject.

The Bilateral Simultaneous Sensory Stimulation Examination is concerned principally with evaluating the intactness of input (receptive) avenues to the brain rather than response (expressive) capabilities. Sometimes an individual has intact input avenues but has difficulty giving appropriate responses. This occurs particularly in persons with right-left confusion or serious impairment of the ability to pay attention. Therefore, the examiner must be alert to any general confusion or specific errors in identifying the right and left sides.

If a subject is confused by responding "right" or "left," a different response procedure should be used. In some instances, it is necessary to eliminate the verbal response and ask the subject to point to the side stimulated. With tactile stimulation it is not satisfactory to have the subject merely move the hand that was stimulated; more meaningful responses are obtained when the subject is instructed to point to the location of the stimulus, even though it may be necessary to point to both sides.

Homonymous visual field defects and lateralized instances of visual imperception generally have similar significance; however, the two findings may definitely be complementary and should not be considered to be identical manifestations. In some cases, a partial homonymous visual field defect does not preclude demonstration of visual imperception in the remaining part of the affected visual fields, even though in such instances it is not uncommon to find that routine examination of the visual fields has led to a conclusion of homonymous hemianopia.

Instances of unilateral impairment of tactile or auditory perception are important to note, but do not constitute a test for sensory imperception any more than does mapping of the visual fields. The principal purpose for giving unilateral stimulation initially is to determine (1) whether the individual has the capability to respond to stimulation on each side of the body, and (2) how light a stimulus can be used and still elicit a reliably correct response.

The term *imperception* refers to a failure to report a stimulus on one side of the body when in competition with a stimulus given to the other side. Thus, as defined by this test, bilateral simultaneous stimulation is necessary in order to elicit a manifestation of imperception.

Of course, unilateral impairment of tactile perception (hypesthesia) may be of definite significance for lateralization of a cerebral lesion. This may possibly be true of unilateral auditory impairment as well, although unilateral auditory deficiencies are more common (in association with peripheral rather than central hearing losses) than are deficits in tactile perception.

Specific Instructions

Sensory Imperception — Tactile

The examiner and subject should be seated across from each other at a table. Be sure that the subject is seated in a position which allows his/her arms to rest comfortably on the table. If necessary, a child's chair should be elevated on a platform to reach the table at a proper height.

Begin by saying:

> **Put your hands on the table like this** (demonstrate with palms down). **I am going to touch your right hand** (touch the subject's right hand) **or your left hand** (touch the subject's left hand). The place that should be touched is the back of the hand, just proximal to the middle knuckle (Fig. 9-15).

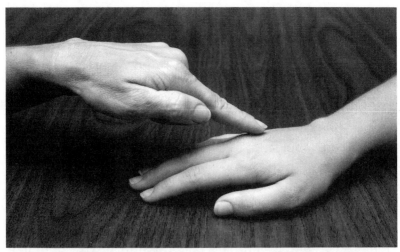

Fig. 9-15. Administration of tactile stimulus to the subject's hand.

The examiner should be careful to touch the back of the subject's hand with the pad of the finger and not the fingernail. In order to control the intensity of the stimulus, it is important that the examiner use his/her finger to administer the stimulus rather than some instrument, such as the eraser on a pencil.

> I want you to close your eyes, since I want you to
> depend only on your feeling to tell me which
> hand I touch. If I touch your right hand (touch the
> subject's right hand), you say, "right." That way I
> will know you felt it. If I touch your left hand
> (touch the subject's left hand) you say "left."
> Be sure you do not make a mistake in telling me
> which hand I touched. Do you have any questions?

Repeat or elaborate the instructions as necessary to be sure that the subject understands the procedure.

First, touch the subject's right hand or left hand in random sequence approximately four times each in order to determine the lightest pressure needed to obtain consistent and correct responses to unilateral stimulation (see Fig. 9-16). These responses are not recorded because they are not part of the test.

Then begin the test by touching the subject's right hand, left hand, or both hands simultaneously in random sequence until each has been tested at least four times. If the subject has more difficulty feeling the stimulus on one side or the other, this should be recorded.

The important aspect of this test is to determine whether the subject fails to respond to one side consistently during bilateral simultaneous stimulation (even if he/she responded correctly on the same side with unilateral stimulation).

Never warn the subject that both hands will be touched simultaneously on some trials. Never give bilateral stimuli on consecutive trials.

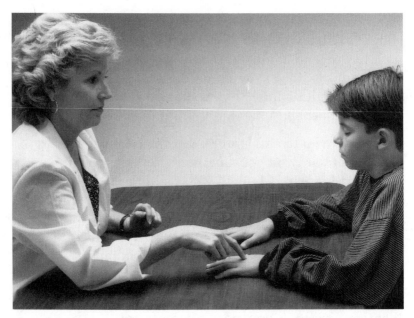

Fig. 9-16. Administration of tactile stimulus to subject's hand to determine whether subject can respond correctly to unilateral
stimulation.

Although it happens only rarely, some subjects have so
much difficulty keeping their eyes closed that it may be
necessary to use a blindfold. Be sure that the responses are
based upon tactile perception alone.

Note any instances of imperception on the recording form.

Using the above procedure as a model, proceed by saying:

> Now I'm going to touch either your hand or your
> face, and I want you to tell me which one I'm
> touching. You don't have to tell me "right" or
> "left." Just say "hand" or "face." All right, close
> your eyes.

Touch the subject's right hand, left face, and both hand and
face simultaneously in random sequence until each has been
done at least four times. Then repeat with left hand, right
face, and both (see Fig. 9-17).

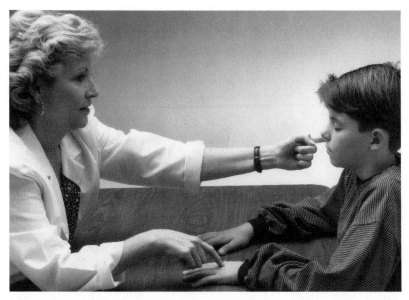

Fig. 9-17. Administration of tactile stimuli to hand and face during test of bilateral simultaneous stimulation.

The examiner should be careful to touch only the subject's face. If the subject's hair is close to the area where the stimulus is being administered, ask the subject to brush his/her hair away from that area of the face.

Sensory Imperception — Auditory

The subject should be seated comfortably with the examiner standing behind him/her. Begin by saying:

> **Now I'm going to stand behind you and make a noise like this** (demonstrate auditory stimulus).

Make a barely audible finger snap by rubbing two fingers (thumb and another finger) together lightly. Once should be sufficient. Be careful to avoid touching the subject's ear or hair when administering the stimulus (Fig. 9-18).

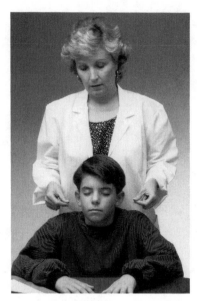

Fig. 9-18. Administration of auditory stimuli during test of bilateral simultaneous stimulation.

I want you to tell me if the sound is by this ear (touch the subject's right ear) or this ear (touch the subject's left ear). You can tell me which ear just by saying "right" or "left." Be sure to keep your eyes closed.

Use the instructions for tactile stimulation as a model for completing this test, interspersing unilateral with bilateral stimulation.

Sensory Imperception — Visual

The subject should be seated comfortably. The examiner should be sitting directly opposite the subject, approximately four feet away. The examiner and the subject are at equal eye level. If necessary, the subject's chair should be adjusted so that the subject and the examiner are at eye level.

Begin by saying:

> I'm going to sit in front of you and hold my hands
> out like this.

Extend your hands about two feet away to each side of your body, approximately twelve inches above eye level. Both the examiner and the subject should use binocular vision (both eyes open).

Tell the subject:

> I want you to look directly at my nose and tell me
> if I am moving this hand (move the index finger of
> your right hand obviously) or this hand (move the
> index finger of you left hand obviously). Tell me
> which hand I move by saying "right" if it is over
> to your right side, or by saying "left" if it is over
> to your left side. Be sure to look directly at my
> nose all the time — don't look at my hands.

Administer four unilateral stimuli to each side in random sequence in order to be sure that the subject understands the procedure and can respond correctly. Then, with your hands still above eye level, begin the test by administering random unilateral stimuli interspersed with four instances of bilateral stimuli. Record any errors.

Next, hold your hands at eye level, extended about two feet away from your body. Be sure that the subject is maintaining his/her vision on your nose.

Once again, administer four unilateral stimuli to each side in random sequence (see Fig. 9-19). Responses to these stimuli are not recorded. Next, with your hands still at eye level, administer random unilateral stimuli interspersed with four instances of bilateral stimuli. Record any errors.

Finally, hold your hands approximately twelve inches below eye level, extended about two feet away from your body. Remind the subject to maintain his/her gaze on your nose.

Fig. 9-19. Administration of visual stimulus.

Administer four unilateral stimuli to each side in random sequence. Responses to these stimuli are not recorded. Then, with your hands still below eye level, administer random unilateral stimuli interspersed with four instances of bilateral stimuli. Record any errors.

It is very difficult for some subjects to fixate their vision on one point. However, the test is invalidated if the subject's vision is not fixated in the center of his/her visual field (i.e., looking directly at the examiner's nose). The examiner must be alert to give the stimulus only when the subject's vision is properly fixated.

It must first be determined whether the subject can respond correctly to unilateral stimuli before failure to respond to one side of the body with bilateral simultaneous stimulation has any clinical significance.

If the examiner suspects a possible limitation of visual fields, gross confrontation procedures or more exact methods (perimetry or use of a tangent screen) may be used to map the visual fields. In the event of homonymous hemianopsia, bilateral simultaneous visual stimulation is meaningless, but the homonymous visual field loss may have given the lateralizing information sought.

Homonymous quadrantanopsia may not invalidate the test of bilateral simultaneous visual stimulation, provided that the intact quadrants are used for presenting the stimulus. The test may be given at eye level, but standard procedure is to give the test in the upper parts of the visual field, at eye level, and in the lower parts of the visual field in order to deal with partial homonymous visual field losses.

Scoring

The recording section for bilateral simultaneous sensory stimulation (Fig. 9-20) contains four sets of boxes in a row for each subtest (right hand/left hand, right hand/left face, etc.). Each box is divided into four smaller boxes. The first small box in each set corresponds to the first trial administered, the second small box corresponds to the second trial, etc.

REITAN-KLØVE SENSORY-PERCEPTUAL EXAMINATION
(Instance indicated where stimulus was not perceived or was incorrectly perceived.)

TACTILE:

Error Totals

Right Hand-Left Hand - RH ☐ LH ☐ Both: RH ☐ LH ☐ RH ___ LH ___

Right Hand-Left Face - RH ☐ LF ☐ Both: RH ☐ LF ☐ RH ___ LF ___

Left Hand-Right Face - LH ☐ RF ☐ Both: LH ☐ RF ☐ RF ___ LH ___

AUDITORY:

Right Ear-Left Ear - RE ☐ LE ☐ Both: RE ☐ LE ☐ RE ___ LE ___

VISUAL:

Above eye level
Eye level   RV ☐ LV ☐ Both: RV ☐ LV ☐ RV ___ LV ___
Below eye level

Fig. 9-20. Recording form for the tests of bilateral simultaneous sensory stimulation.

The first set of two larger boxes is used to record errors made on **unilateral** stimulation. The second set of two larger boxes is used to record errors made on **bilateral simulta-neous** stimulation. If the subject responds correctly to a trial the box is customarily left blank (see Fig. 9-21).

The examiner records an "X" in the appropriate box when-ever the subject fails to respond to a stimulus or reports the perception incorrectly.

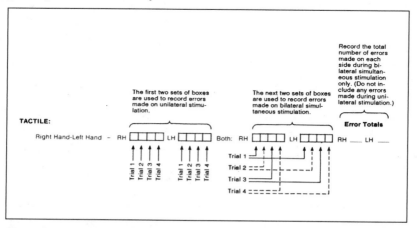

Fig. 9-21. Detail of recording form for tests of bilateral simultaneous stimulation.

Example: The examiner administered four unilateral stimuli to each hand in random sequence. The subject responded correctly and the examiner learned that it was possible to elicit consistent and correct responses even with a minimal stimulus.

The examiner was then ready to begin the formal examina-tion, which involved bilateral simultaneous stimulation in-terspersed with unilateral stimulation. The examiner first administered three unilateral stimuli: two to the subject's left hand and one to the right hand. The subject responded correctly to all trials. The examiner then administered a stimulus to each hand simultaneously, and the subject cor-rectly responded "both." A unilateral stimulus was then given to each hand and the subject responded correctly. Then the examiner again administered a stimulus to each hand simultaneously, and the subject responded "left." The examiner recorded an "X" in the second small box next to RH in the second series of four boxes next to RH, indicating that on the second trial of bilateral simultaneous stimulation the subject did not perceive the stimulus on the right hand (see Fig. 9-22).

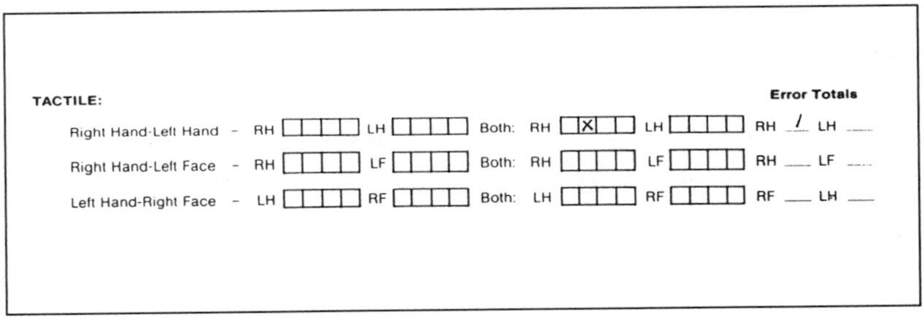

TACTILE:

						Error Totals
Right Hand-Left Hand	-	RH [ ][ ][ ][ ]	LH [ ][ ][ ][ ]	Both: RH [ ][X][ ][ ]	LH [ ][ ][ ][ ]	RH 1 LH ___
Right Hand-Left Face	-	RH [ ][ ][ ][ ]	LF [ ][ ][ ][ ]	Both: RH [ ][ ][ ][ ]	LF [ ][ ][ ][ ]	RH ___ LF ___
Left Hand-Right Face	-	LH [ ][ ][ ][ ]	RF [ ][ ][ ][ ]	Both: LH [ ][ ][ ][ ]	RF [ ][ ][ ][ ]	RF ___ LH ___

Fig. 9-22. Example of examiner's recording of a subject's performances on the test for bilateral simultaneous tactile stimulation.

The examiner proceeded to administer two more bilateral simultaneous stimulation trials interspersed with unilateral stimuli and the subject responded correctly to all trials. The examiner then recorded a "1" next to RH in the Error Totals column, indicating that the subject had a total of one error on the right hand on the right hand/left hand trials of the bilateral simultaneous stimulation examination. Note that the Error Totals column is used for recording only instances of imperception during bilateral simultaneous stimulation.

Errors on the auditory and visual subtests of the Bilateral Simultaneous Stimulation Examination are recorded in the same manner.

B. Tactile Finger Recognition Test

Materials   recording form
pencil

General Instructions

The Tactile Finger Recognition Test is an evaluation for finger dysgnosia (impairment of tactile finger localization).

In this test the least perceptible stimulus is used. Stimuli should be administered to the fingers in random order, but adjacent fingers should never be tested consecutively. The stimulus is applied to the fingers, just proximal to the nail bed, by giving a distinct, light touch (rather than a brushing or tapping motion).

The examiner should always be sure that both the examiner and the subject understand the reporting system that is going to be used. Any reporting system is satisfactory, provided that it is unambiguous. Remember that this is a test of tactile perception rather that a test of the subject's ability to report.

Specific Instructions

The subject should be seated comfortably at a table, with the examiner sitting directly across from the subject. Ask the subject to place his/her right hand palm down on the table, with the fingers extended and spread slightly apart. Ask the subject to close his/her eyes, or shield the subject's hand with a piece of paper.

Begin by saying:

> For this test I'm going to name (number) your fingers. We'll call this finger #1 (touch the subject's thumb), this one #2 (touch the subject's index finger), this one #3 (touch the subject's middle finger), this one #4 (touch the subject's

ring finger), and this one #5 (touch the subject's little finger).

Touch each finger with a distinct but light touch (using your own finger to control the intensity of the stimulus), just proximal to the nail bed of the subject's finger (Fig. 9-23).

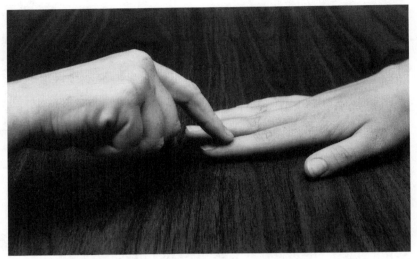

Fig. 9-23. Administration of stimulus during Tactile Finger Recognition Test.

Now, keep your eyes closed and tell me, by number, which finger I touched.

It is usually helpful initially to give a single trial to each of the subject's fingers in consecutive order. In this way the examiner ensures that the subject understands the reporting system and that the intensity of the stimulus (light touch) is sufficient.

The examiner should then administer a stimulus to the subject's fingers in a random sequence, touching each finger a total of four times (Fig. 9-24). Avoid delivering a stimulus to two adjacent fingers consecutively.

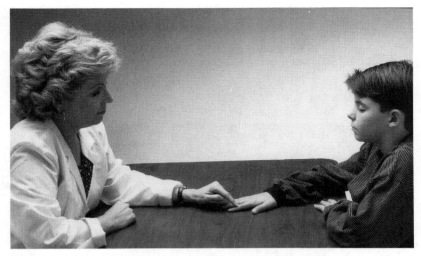

Fig. 9-24. Administration of Tactile Finger Recognition Test.

It is often necessary to remind the subject to pay close attention and tell the examiner exactly which finger was touched.

Most persons can understand and use this numbering/ reporting system, but it is sometimes necessary for the examiner to adapt to the limitations of individual subjects. For example, some persons prefer to name the thumb as "thumb" and then, beginning with the index finger, consecutively number the fingers 1 through 4.

Occasionally a subject will have difficulty keeping his/her eyes closed during this test. If it becomes a problem for the subject, the examiner may shield the subject's hand with a piece of paper or use the Tactile Form Recognition Test to prevent the subject from seeing the stimuli being administered. For this test the examiner should experiment with various methods and not resort to using a blindfold.

Scoring

Errors are noted on the recording form (Fig. 9-25). There is a separate score for the right hand and the left hand. The score is the number of errors which occurred on each hand.

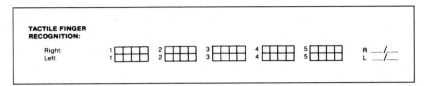

Fig. 9-25. Recording form for Tactile Finger Recognition Test.

On the recording form there are five sets of large boxes. Each large box is divided into eight smaller boxes. The top row of four small boxes is used to record errors on the right hand; the bottom row is for the left hand.

The first group of small boxes is used to record errors on the subject's thumb; the second group, the index finger; the third group, the middle finger, etc.

The first small box in each set corresponds to the first trial; the second box to the second trial, etc. (Fig. 9-26).

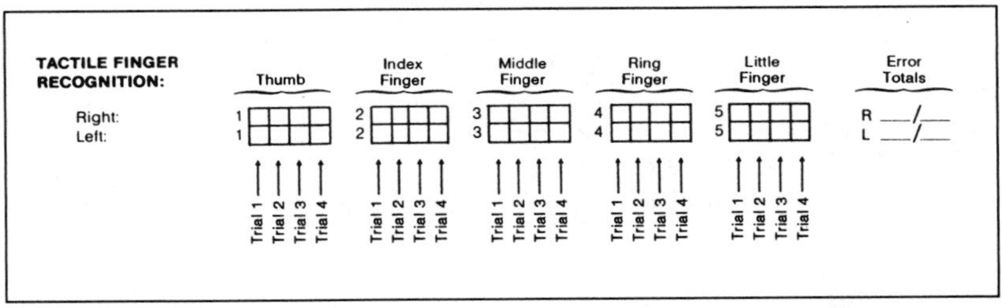

Fig. 9-26. Explanation of recording form for Tactile Finger Recognition Test.

Example: The examiner has randomly administered a stimulus to each of the subject's five fingers on his right hand and the subject has responded correctly. The first small box in each of the five sets of boxes has therefore been left blank.

The examiner then administered a stimulus to the subject's middle finger, and the subject responded "four." The examiner recorded an "X" in the second small box in the series of boxes next to the number 3, indicating that the subject made an error when responding to the second time a stimulus was given to his middle finger (see Fig. 9-27). Some examiners prefer to enter the number of the finger incorrectly named to record errors rather than an "X" in order to have a more exact record of the errors made.

The examiner proceeded to randomly administer stimuli and the subject responded correctly until the third time a stimulus was administered to his ring finger. His response was "three," and the examiner recorded an "X" in the third small box (for the third trial) in the set of boxes next to the number 4 (for the ring finger).

The subject made no additional errors in the examination of the right hand. The examiner recorded the score for the subject's right hand as 2/20, indicating that the subject made two errors out of twenty trials.

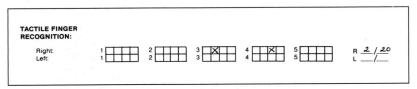

Fig. 9-27. Example of examiner's recording of a subject's performance on the right hand of the Tactile Finger Recognition Test.

C. Finger-tip Number Writing Perception Test

Materials   stylus
recording form
pencil

General Instructions

On the Finger-tip Number Writing Perception Test, the stimuli (numbers) are administered in the order indicated on the recording form (Fig. 9-28).

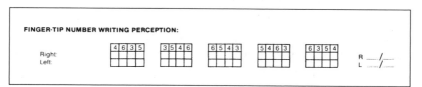

Fig. 9-28. Recording form for the Finger-tip Number Writing Perception Test.

The numbers should be written on the subject's palm for purposes of illustration, and on the distal part of the finger when performing the test.

To administer the stimuli, the examiner should use an instrument such as a stylus or ballpoint pen that has run out of ink. The numbers should be written clearly, slowly, and distinctly, in a form that might resemble "first grade" instruction (Fig. 9-29).

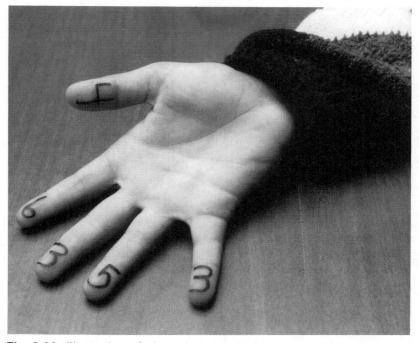

Fig. 9-29. Illustration of size, shape, and placement of stimuli for the Finger-tip Number Writing Perception Test. (Stimuli are written in ink for illustrative purposes only.)

Note that in this test the examiner does not use the least perceptible stimulus possible, but instead uses a steady pressure that is sufficient to leave a "trail of white" where the stylus has been.

Specific Instructions

The subject should be seated comfortably at a table, with the examiner sitting directly across from the subject. Begin by saying:

> For this test I am going to write some numbers on your fingertips. I want you to pay close attention so that you will be able to tell me the numbers that I write.

> First, I will show you how I will write the numbers. Ask the subject to close his/her eyes and place his/her right hand palm up on the table. The right hand is tested first, regardless of the subject's hand dominance. Then say:

> This is the way I will make a 3 (demonstrate on the subject's palm by using the stylus to write the number 3 on the subject's palm); this is the way I will make a 4 (demonstrate); this is the way I will make a 5 (demonstrate); and I will make a 6 like this (demonstrate) (Fig. 9-30).

If the subject gives any indication that he/she makes the numbers differently than the examiner, the examiner's method should be adapted to the subject's method for writing the numbers.

In some instances, it is worthwhile to have the subject write the numbers 3, 4, 5, and 6 on paper before the illustrations are given on the subject's palm, so that the numbers can be made in the way most familiar to the subject. However, this paper should then placed out of view so that it is not available for the subject to use as a guide during the test.

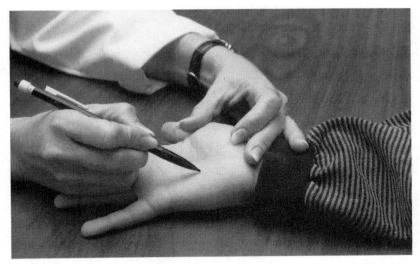

Fig. 9-30. Examiner administering a stimulus to subject's palm while giving instructions for the Finger-tip Number Writing Perception Test.

> Be sure to keep your eyes closed, and pay close attention so that you will be able to tell what numbers I write. Since I am facing you, remember that I will be writing the numbers upside down.

Shield the subject's finger as you write each number so that he/she will not be able to see what is written, even if the subject should open his/her eyes during the test (see Fig. 9-31).

The order in which the stimuli are administered are given on the recording sheet (see Fig. 9-28).

Begin by administering the stimulus number 4 to the subject's right thumb. Proceed by administering a 3 to the right index finger, a 6 to the right middle finger, a 5 to the right ring finger, and a 6 to the right little finger. Record any errors as they occur.

After each finger of the right hand has had one trial, begin the second series by administering the stimulus 6 to the

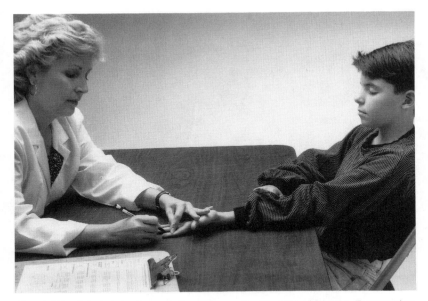

Fig. 9-31. Administration of the Finger-tip Number Writing Perception Test.

right thumb, a 5 to the right index finger, etc., following the stimuli given on the recording form.

After all twenty stimuli have been administered to the subject's right hand, repeat the procedure for the left hand. First, illustrate the numbers on the subject's left palm. Proceed to administer the stimuli to the fingertips in the prescribed order. Record any errors as they occur.

Remind the subject to pay close attention, keep his/her eyes closed, and remember that the numbers will be seem to be written upside-down.

Scoring

Errors are noted on the recording form (Fig. 9-28). There is a separate score for the right hand and the left hand. The score is the number of errors which occurred on each hand.

The recording technique for Finger-tip Number Writing is in many ways similar to the procedure for Tactile Finger Recognition.

On the recording sheet there are five sets of large boxes. Each large box is divided into twelve smaller boxes. The top row of boxes contain numbers, which are the stimuli in order of their presentation to the subject. The top row of empty boxes is used to record errors on the right hand; the bottom row is for the left hand.

The first group of small boxes are the stimulus numbers and recording spaces for the subject's thumb; the second group, the index finger; the third group, the middle finger, etc.

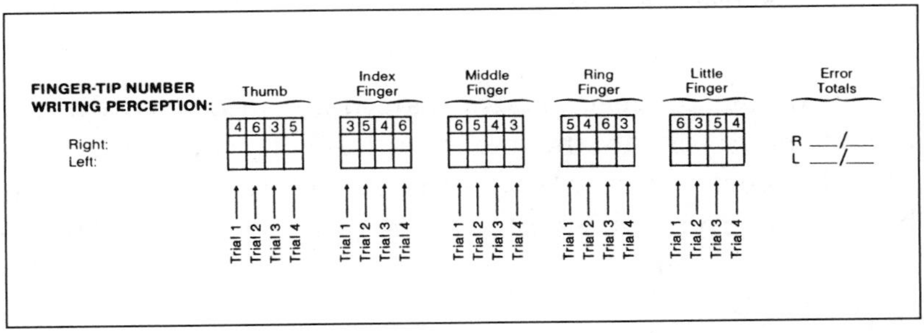

Fig. 9-32. Explanation of recording form for the Finger-tip Number Writing Perception Test.

The first small box in each set corresponds to the first trial; the second box to the second trial, etc.

For example, the number 4 is the stimulus which is administered on the first trial to the thumb. Any errors made by the subject on this trial are recorded in the boxes directly below, depending on which hand the error occurred.

Example: The examiner administered the first trial (the stimulus number 4) to the subject's thumb, and the subject responded correctly. The examiner then administered the next trial to the subject's index finger (the stimulus number 3) and the subject responded "eight." The examiner recorded the subject's incorrect response in the first small box in the second set of boxes (see Fig. 9-33), indicating that the subject made an error when responding to the first time a stimulus was administered to his index finger.

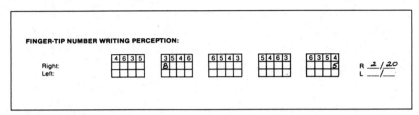

Fig. 9-33. Example of examiner's recording of the subject's performance on the right hand on the Finger-tip Number Writing Perception Test.

The examiner proceeded administering stimuli according to the order given on the recording sheet. The subject responded correctly until the fourth trial (the stimulus number 4) was given to his little finger. He responded "five," and the examiner noted his response in the fourth box of the fifth set of boxes.

The examiner recorded the subject's score for the right hand as 2/20, reflecting the fact that the subject made two errors in twenty trials.

Tactile Form Recognition Test

Materials Tactile Form Recognition Test
recording form
pencil

General Instructions

The Tactile Form Recognition (TFR) Test evaluates tactile form discrimination ability in each of the subject's hands. The right hand is tested first (regardless of the subject's handedness) using all four stimulus figures in sequence. Then the left hand is tested, followed by the right hand again, and finally the left hand again. It is important for the subject to understand that responses should be made as quickly as possible, but that he/she should be careful to avoid making errors.

The order of presentation of the figures (as indicated on the recording form, Fig. 9-34) is as follows:

Right hand: circle, square, triangle, cross
Left hand: triangle, cross, circle, square
Right hand: cross, circle, square, triangle
Left hand: square, triangle, cross, circle

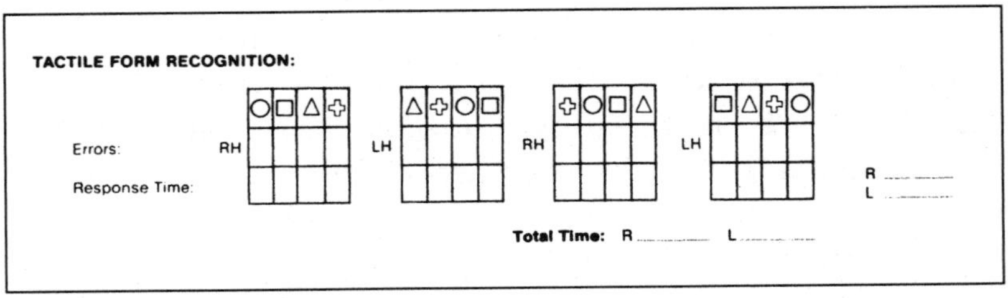

Fig. 9-34. Recording form for the Tactile Form Recognition Test.

To indicate his/her response, the subject points with the hand not being tested to one of the four figures displayed on the face of the TFR board (see Fig. 9-35).

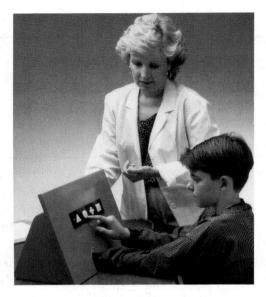

Fig. 9-35. Administration of the Tactile Form Recognition Test.

The subject is permitted to feel the figure as long as necessary in order to identify it, but is encouraged to respond as quickly as possible because each response is timed.

On the recording form the examiner notes the time required for each response and any errors that are made. In giving the test, do not allow the subject to remove the hand being tested from the board until all four trials have been completed. Be sure that the subject does not see the figure when it is being placed in his/her hand. The examiner should place the stimulus figure toward the subject's fingertips rather than in the middle of the palm.

Specific Instructions

The subject should be seated comfortably at a table with the Tactile Form Recognition Test placed directly in front of him/her. The examiner should be standing along side of the subject, positioned so that he/she can easily place the stimulus figures into the subject's hand and observe and time the subject's response.

Have the subject place his/her right hand through the hole in the board and say:

> I am going to place an object in your hand. Feel it carefully, then point with your left hand to the figure on the board (point to the row of figures on the front of the board) which is just like the one in your hand. Be sure to show me the right figure as quickly as you can.

The examiner should be sure that the subject realizes that he/she should respond as quickly as possible. Most normal subjects are able to respond almost instantaneously, and should be encouraged to respond quickly.

Place the first figure (circle) in the subject's right hand. After the subject responds, remove the figure from his/her hand and place the next figure (square) in the same hand. The sequence of administration of the stimulus figures is given on the recording sheet.

After each response, record the time in seconds required for the response. Do not attempt to fractionate seconds, but use the nearest whole number. If the subject's response is incorrect, also record the subject's response.

If the subject makes an incorrect response that is clearly due to carelessness, poor motor control, or other similar factor, it should not be counted as an error. However, even an immediate correction by the subject of a genuine error should not excuse the fact that the error occurred, and the examiner should make a note of the error as well as of the spontaneous correction. Verbal responses are permissible only if the subject is too handicapped to make the required motor response.

After completing the first series with the right hand, say:

> You may take that hand out now, and put in your
> left hand. We will do the same thing using your
> left hand. Feel the object with your left hand, and
> point to the correct figure with your right hand.
> Be sure to show me the correct figure as quickly
> as you can.

Place the first figure (triangle) in the subject's left hand and
proceed as above, following the sequence given on the recording sheet. After the left hand has completed the four
trials, the right hand and the left hand are each given
another series of four trials.

Scoring

Two scores are recorded for each hand:
1. total time required to complete all eight trials
2. total number of errors for all eight trials

Example: The examiner administered the first trial (the
circle) to the subject's right hand and the subject responded
correctly in one second. The examiner then placed the
square in the subject's hand. The subject first responded by
pointing to the triangle, said No, and then immediately
pointed to the square.

The examiner recorded the second trial response by (1) writing a "2" in the response time row (because the subject took
two seconds to respond), (2) drawing a triangle below the
square in the error row (to indicate the type of error), and (3)
writing "SC" above the column for that trial (to indicate that
the subject self-corrected his error) (see Fig. 9-36).

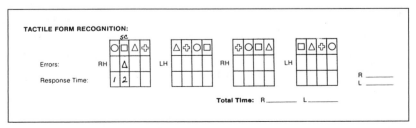

Fig. 9-36. Example of examiner's recording of a subject's response on
the Tactile Form Recognition Test.

Speech-sounds Perception Test

Materials   Speech-sounds Perception Test
(on cassette tape)
Speech-sounds Perception Test
answer sheet for older children
tape player
pencil

General Instructions

The Speech-sounds Perception Test (SSPT) measures the
subject's ability to match a spoken sound to the correct
alternative among a group of three similar printed sounds.
The double vowel *ee* is in the middle part of every syllable
spoken. A subject's performance is determined by his/her
ability to discriminate and match the consonant or combination of consonants at the beginning and end of each
syllable.

The subject should be seated comfortably at a table, with the
tape player placed directly in front of him/her, approximately four feet away (see Fig. 9-37). Make sure that the

Fig. 9-37. Administration of the Speech-sounds Perception Test.

subject faces the speaker and does not move his/her head excessively. This arrangement ensures that the sound comes equally to each of the subject's ears.

The first three items presented on the tape are samples. Instruct the subject to listen to each of the samples carefully, and point to the word he/she believes to be the correct response. Wrong answers are not corrected by the examiner. This procedure allows the examiner the opportunity to be certain that the subject understands the instructions.

If the subject does not understand the instructions, the sample can be replayed as many times as the examiner feels it is necessary. Once the test begins, however, no further help can be given. The only assistance the examiner can offer is to make sure that the subject is working in the correct column. Make certain the tape player's tone and volume are adjusted for the subject, and that the room is as free from distracting noises as possible.

Do not stop the tape player in the middle of any column. However, if the subject loses his/her place during any column, stop the test and repeat the instructions before beginning the next column.

Specific Instructions

Place the SSPT answer sheet for older children on the table directly in front of the subject and say:

> This is a hearing test. You are going to hear
> a man's voice saying, "The first word is (pause),"
> and then he will say one of the three nonsense
> words opposite number one on your answer sheet.
> Point to this place on the subject's answer sheet
> (Fig. 9-38).

Form for Older Children

Speech-sounds Perception Test

Name _____   Date _____

Examiner _____   Score _____

Directions: Underline the syllable which you hear.

Series A	Series B	Series C
1. theets theeks zeets	1. been peem peen	1. beel deeld deel
2. yeej weech weej	2. theerz theez feerz	2. weef weev heef
3. bleeng leeg leeng	3. sheez sheesh zeez	3. feer thee theer
4. teest peez peest	4. weeth veef veeth	4. meel neeld neel
5. freeb freep fleep	5. feeld theeld theel	5. zeet seed seet
6. preed pleed pleeb	6. peent peet beent	6. yeek yeeg heek
7. seek seech sheech	7. treep treeb teeb	7. neem meem meen
8. meenk neenk neek	8. speeks steets steeks	8. theerd theer teer
9. heesh wheech wheesh	9. beerd beert peerd	9. heev heez wheev
10. preet preekt peekt	10. zeend sheed sheend	10. neet neep teet

Series D	Series E	Series F
1. wheet heep heet	1. seen seeng sheen	1. heen yeem yeen
2. feem keev keem	2. geerd geer keer	2. leer leern theer
3. neeg neek meeg	3. keem keen geem	3. thees fees feeth
4. cheen cheem sheen	4. heeng heen ween	4. treek reeg reek
5. feet feep theet	5. teed teet peet	5. weet yeed yeet
6. weel heel heeld	6. keez keets teez	6. meep meet deet
7. teend deed deend	7. zeent theet theent	7. dees deez bees
8. teesh teez peez	8. peet beet beep	8. teel teeld peel
9. weef weev veef	9. peer tee teer	9. meer meel feer
10. heeng leeng leen	10. beeb beed deed	10. wheem weem ween

Fig. 9-38. Answer sheet for the Speech-sounds Perception Test for Older Children. Correct responses are underlined.

Then he will say, "The second word is (pause)," and say one of the three words listed opposite number two (indicate the correct place on the subject's answer sheet).

> We are going to start with a sample, so that you
> can see what the test will be like, and so that you
> can tell me how loud you want the recording to
> be. You just sit back and listen. Don't write
> anything yet. Tell me if this is loud enough or if it
> is too loud. During the sample do not write down
> any answers, but look at each word carefully and
> point to the word you think the man said.

Play the sample on the tape player. If the subject does not
point to one of the alternatives in line one after the first
sample, stop the tape player and say:

> That was the first sample. Look at your answer
> sheet here (indicate line 1) and point to the
> word you think he said.

After the subject has indicated his/her answer, say:

> That was fine. Now I'm going to play the next
> sample. Listen carefully and point to the word
> you hear. Continue with the second sample.

If the subject indicates a response for the next two samples,
continue with the test. If the subject is still having difficulty,
repeat the instructions and do the sample again.

After the subject has completed the sample, say:

> Now we are going to begin the test. The voice on
> the recording will say one of the three words each
> time, and you are to underline the word that you
> think he says. If you are not sure of what he says,
> then make a guess. Underline one word every
> time. If you make a mistake, don't bother to erase
> it. Just circle your mistake and underline the right
> answer.

> Work down column A from 1 to 10, then start
> column B over here (point to column B on the
> answer sheet), then column C. Then do columns D,
> E, and F down here. The examiner should be sure

that the subject realizes that column B is to the right of column A, not below it, as well as the overall sequence and location of columns.

The three samples you just heard will be repeated when the test starts. This time, underline your answer using the pencil. Then the test will go right on to number 4.

Be sure to pay close attention to each word. Do you have any questions?

After answering any questions, begin the test.

Scoring

The score is the number of errors or omissions among the sixty items. The answer sheet in Fig. 9-38 shows the correct answers underlined in blue. A template is available to facilitate scoring.

Seashore Rhythm Test

Materials   Rhythm Test (on cassette tape)
tape player
answer sheet
pencil

General Instructions

The Rhythm Test measures the ability to discriminate variations in rhythmical patterns. The test consists of thirty pairs of rhythmical patterns presented on a standardized tape recording. The subject is asked to determine whether the two stimuli in each pair are the same or different.

The first three items of the Rhythm Test are presented as a sample. After giving the instructions, these items should be played for the subject and the examiner should be alert to the following conditions:

a. that the volume is at the optimal level for the subject;

b. that the subject understands the meaning of S and D as a response (it is helpful to write "S = same" and "D = different" on the answer form when explaining the procedure to the subject);

c. that the subject understands that the items proceed down column A, then B, and then C; and

d. that the subject understands the silent interval which separates the two patterns of each item.

During the sample the examiner should have the subject verbally report his/her answer. The examiner should not comment upon the subject's answer or correct the subject if an incorrect response is given. In this way the examiner can determine whether the subject has understood the instructions.

The sample may be replayed as often as necessary for subjects having difficulty understanding the instructions. However, after the test has started there cannot be any interruption for further help.

Specific Instructions

The subject should be seated comfortably at a table, with the tape player placed directly in front of him/her, approximately four feet away (see Fig. 9-39). Make sure that the subject faces the speaker and does not move his/her head excessively. This is done so that the sound comes equally to each of the subject's ears.

Fig. 9-39. Administration of the Rhythm Test.

Tell the subject:

> You will hear two rhythmic patterns, one after the other. The second pattern is either the same as the first or different from it.

> Now I am going to play the sample. Listen closely and tell me whether the two patterns sound the same or different. Listen carefully so you will be sure to understand what to do.

Play the sample on the tape player. If the subject does not answer "same" or "different" after the first sample, stop the tape player and say:

> That was the first sample. Do you think they sounded the same or different?

After the subject has indicated his/her answer, say:

> That was fine. Now I'm going to play the next sample. Listen carefully and tell me whether the two patterns sound the same or different.
> Continue with the second sample.

If the subject gives an appropriate response for the next two samples, continue with the test. If the subject is still having difficulty, repeat the instructions and do the sample again.

When a subject has difficulty understanding the instructions, the nature of the difficulty usually relates to a failure to realize that the patterns are presented in "pairs." Some subjects do not appreciate the time intervals either between patterns or between pairs. Stopping the tape at appropriate times (during the sample only) is often all that is necessary to overcome these difficulties. However, some persons need additional instructions. This can often be accomplished by the examiner "tapping" out simple rhythmic patterns on the table and explaining the procedure to the subject.

Although it is permissible to stop the sample at any place, the test itself is never stopped during any column. If further instructions or encouragement are needed after the test has begun, the test can be stopped between columns. However, the examiner should make every effort to determine that the subject understands the task before the test is started so that stopping the tape will not be necessary. Part of the requirement of this task is maintaining immediate attention as well as discriminating auditory-nonverbal stimuli. The sample may be repeated as many times as necessary.

After presenting the sample, place the answer sheet and pencil in front of the subject and say:

> If the two patterns are the same, print S in the proper place on your test blank. If they are different, print D.

Write "S = same" and "D = different" on the side of the answer sheet, explaining that this shows the type of responses to be given.

> Remember, S if they are the same, and D if they are different. Put your first answer in the box opposite number 1 and go down column A (indicate to subject). Remember to listen for two patterns each time before putting down an answer. A voice will tell you when to start column B and column C, but he will not say any numbers to let you know what box you should be working in. The test moves rapidly, so be sure to put your answer down right away. Do you have any questions?

> You will hear the first three samples again. This time, write down your answer in the proper space. Then the test will go right on with the next item.

Begin the test.

If the subject has difficulty controlling a pencil, the subject may give an answer verbally and the examiner may write the response. However, in such cases the examiner can write an answer only when spoken by the subject.

If the subject becomes behind or ahead of the tape, the examiner is not permitted to give the subject any information. Standard procedure requires subjects to co-ordinate their responses with the speed of the tape without any assistance.

Scoring

The score is the number of correct answers among the thirty
items. The answer sheet in Fig. 9-40 shows the correct responses for the Rhythm Test. A template is available to
facilitate scoring.

		Column A	Column B	Column C
	SEASHORE RHYTHM TEST			
1.		S	S	D
2.		D	D	S
3.		S	S	S
4.		D	D	D
5.		S	D	S
6.		D	D	D
7.		S	S	S
8.		D	D	D
9.		D	S	D
10.		S	S	S

Name_____ Date_____ Examiner_____ Raw Score_____
Ranked Score_____

Fig. 9-40. Answer sheet for the Rhythm Test. Correct responses are
given in blue.

Trail Making Test

Materials   Trail Making Test for Older Children–Part A
Trail Making Test for Older Children–Part B
stopwatch
pencils

General Instructions

The subject should understand that when taking this test it is important to work as quickly as possible and try to avoid making mistakes. The most common examiner error in administering this test occurs when a subject makes a mistake. Correct administration procedure requires that the examiner stop the subject as soon as an error is made and return the subject to the last correct circle reached. This must be done quickly and efficiently, as the stopwatch is kept running during this time. The subject should not be penalized in his/her time score because of an examiner's lengthy verbalization or slowness in making corrections. Errors count against the subject's performance (by increasing the time score) because the stopwatch runs continuously until the test is completed (or discontinued).

Specific Instructions

The subject and examiner should be seated comfortably at a table. When ready to begin the test, place the sample side of Part A (Fig. 9-41) on the table directly in front of the subject. The bottom of the test sheet should be approximately six inches from the edge of the table.

Give the subject a pencil and say:

> On this page are some numbers (point). Begin at number 1 (point to 1) and draw a line from 1 to 2 (point to 2), 2 to 3 (point to 3), 3 to 4 (point to 4), and so on, in order, until you reach the end (point to the circle marked "end"). Draw the lines as fast as you can. Ready — Begin!

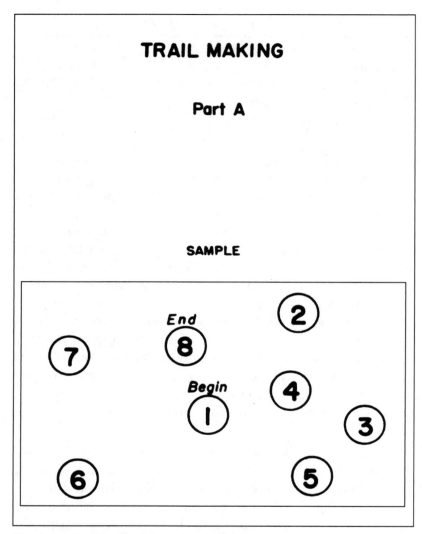

Fig. 9-41. Trail Making Test, Part A Sample.

If the subject completes the sample item correctly in a manner demonstrating that he/she understands what to do, say:

Good! Let's try the next one.

Turn the paper over and give Part A of the test (Fig. 9-42).

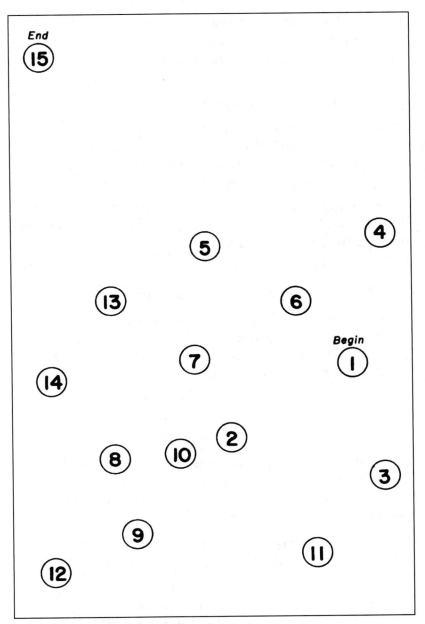

Fig. 9-42. Trail Making Test, Part A.

If the subject makes a mistake on the Sample for Part A, point out the error and explain it. The following explanations of mistakes serve as illustrations.

1. You started with the wrong circle. This is where you start (point to number 1).

2. You skipped this circle* (point to the circle the subject omitted). You should go from number 1 (point) to 2 (point), 2 to 3 (point to 3), and so on, until you reach the circle marked "end" (point).

If the subject cannot complete the Sample for Part A, take his/her hand and guide the pencil, using the eraser end, through the trail. Then say:

Now you try it.

Return the pencil to the subject with the point down and say:

Remember, begin at number 1 (point) and draw a line from 1 to 2 (point to 2), 2 to 3 (point to 3), 3 to 4 (point to 4) and so on, in order, until you reach the circle marked "end" (point).

Do not skip around, but go from one number to the next in the proper order. Remember to work as fast as you can. Ready — Begin!

If the subject succeeds this time, proceed to Part A. If the subject still has difficulty, repeat the above procedure until the task is completed successfully or it becomes evident that the subject cannot do the task.

After the subject has completed the Sample for Part A, turn the paper over to Part A (see Fig. 9-43) and say:

On this page are numbers from 1 to 15. Do this the same way. Begin at number 1 (point to 1) and draw a line from 1 to 2 (point to 2), 2 to 3 (point to 3),

---

*If it is clear that the subject intended to touch a circle but missed it, do not count it as on omission. Remind the subject, however, to be sure to touch each of the circles when drawing the connecting lines.

3 to 4 (point to 4), and so on, in order, until you reach the end (point). Remember to work as fast as you can. Ready — Begin!

Fig. 9-43. Administration of the Trail Making Test.

Start timing as soon as the instruction is given to begin. The examiner must watch the subject's performance closely in order to catch any errors as soon as they are made. If the subject makes an error, call it to his/her attention immediately, return the subject's pencil to the last correct circle, and continue the test from that point. Do not stop timing while correcting the subject's error.

After the subject completes Part A, take the test sheet and record the time in seconds. Remember that errors count only by increasing the total performance time.

Next, tell the subject:

That's fine. Now we'll try another one.

Place the sample side of Part B (Fig. 9-44) on the table in front of the subject, in the same position as the sheet for Part A was placed.

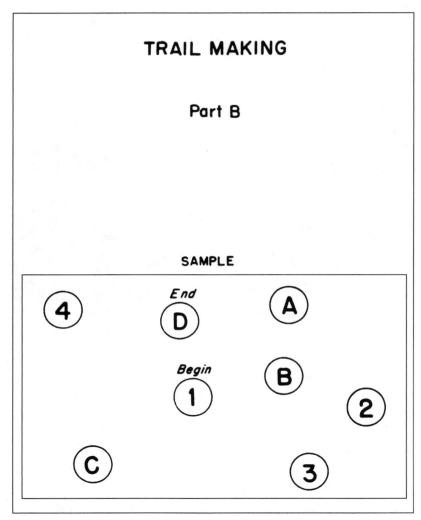

Fig. 9-44. Trail Making Test, Part B Sample.

Point to the sample and say:

> On this page are some numbers and letters. Begin
> at 1 (point) and draw a line from 1 to A (point to
> A), A to 2 (point to 2), 2 to B (point to B), B to 3
> (point to 3), 3 to C (point to C), and so on, in order,
> until you reach the end (point to the circle marked
> "end").

Remember, first you have a number (point to 1), then a letter (point to A), then a number (point to 2), then a letter (point to B), and so on. Draw the lines as fast as you can. Do you have any questions? Ready — Begin!

If the subject completes the Sample for Part B correctly, say:

Good. Let's try the next one.

Proceed immediately to Part B (Fig. 9-45).

If the subject makes a mistake on the Sample for Part B, point out the error and explain why it is incorrect. The following explanations of mistakes serve as illustrations:

1. You started with the wrong circle. This is where you start (point to number 1).

2. You skipped this circle* (point to the circle the subject omitted). You should go from 1 (point to 1) to A (point to A), A to 2 (point to 2), 2 to B (point to B), B to 3 (point to 3), and so on until you reach the circle marked "end" (point).

If the subject cannot complete the Sample for Part B, take his/her hand and guide the pencil, using the eraser end, through the circles. Then say:

Now you try it. Remember, you begin at number 1 (point) and draw a line from 1 to A (point to A), A to 2 (point to 2), 2 to B (point to B), B to 3 (point to 3), and so on until you reach the circle marked "end" (point). Ready — Begin!

If the subject succeeds this time, go on to Part B (Fig. 9-45). If not, repeat the procedure until the task is performed successfully or it becomes evident that the subject cannot do the task.

---

*If it is clear that the subject intended to touch a circle but missed it, do not count it as an omission. Remind the subject, however, to touch each of the circles.

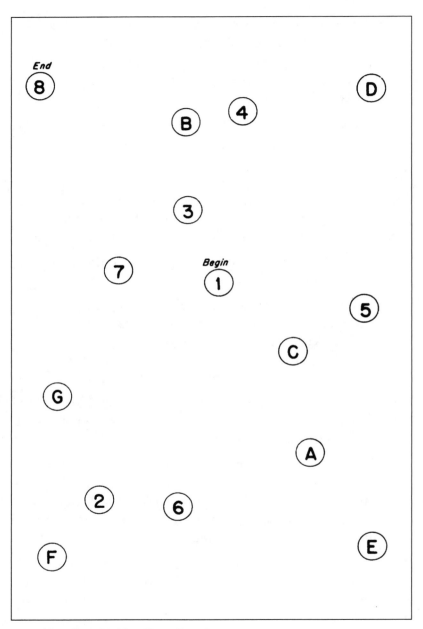

Fig. 9-45. Trail Making Test, Part B.

After the subject has completed the sample, turn the paper over to Part B (Fig. 9-45) and say:

> On this page are both numbers and letters. Do this the same way. Begin at number 1 (point to 1) and draw a line from 1 to A (point to A), A to 2 (point to 2), 2 to B (point to B), B to 3 (point to 3), 3 to C (point to C), and so on, in order, until you reach the end (point to the circle marked "end").
>
> Remember, first you have a number (point to 1), then a letter (point to A), then a number (point to 2), then a letter (point to B), and so on. Do not skip around, but go from one circle to the next in the proper order. Draw the lines as fast as you can. Do you have any questions? Ready — Begin!

Start timing as soon as the subject is told to begin. Remember to be alert for mistakes. If the subject makes an error, point it out immediately, return the subject to the last correct circle, and continue the test from that point. Do not stop timing.

After the subject completes Part B, take the test sheet and record the time in seconds. Errors count only by increasing the total performance time.

Scoring

Part A and Part B are scored separately. The score for each part is the number of seconds required to complete the task and the number of errors. The scores are recorded on the Summary Sheet for Older Children (Fig. 9-1).

Tactual Performance Test

Materials   Tactual Performance Test
          (stand, 6-hole board, 6 blocks)
       gauze eye pads
       blindfold
       stopwatch
       recording sheet
       pencil

General Instructions

The subject must never see the Tactual Performance Test (TPT) at any time before, during, or after the test. Adequate precautions must be taken to ensure that no other subject comes into the room while the test is being given.

The standard procedure is to have the subject do the test three times while blindfolded: first, using the dominant hand; second, using the nondominant hand; and third, using both hands. After the third trial, and before the subject is allowed to remove the blindfold, the examiner places the board and blocks out of the subject's field of vision. The subject is then allowed to remove the blindfold, and is asked to draw what he/she remembers of the board.

To take the test, the subject is seated squarely facing and close to a table. The child should be able to comfortably reach the top of the formboard from a sitting position. The child's chair may need to be elevated on a small platform or child-size furniture may need to be used.

A gauze pad is placed over each of the subject's eyes and a blindfold is placed over the gauze pads. Ask the subject if he/she can see, especially downwards. When you are certain the child cannot see, bring out the board.

Set up the board about six to eight inches in front of the subject and lay the blocks in a row between the board and the subject (Fig. 9-46). Although the blocks are put down essentially in random order, do not place blocks adjacent on the board next to each other on the table.

Fig. 9-46. Examiner arranging the blocks for the TPT.

Start the stopwatch when the subject first touches the board or blocks after you have given the signal "Begin." Stop timing as soon as the subject has correctly placed the last block of each trial. Record the time for each trial in minutes and seconds.

If the subject appears anxious or is having a difficult time, it is permissible for the examiner to offer encouragement and express praise when a subject places a block correctly, especially at the beginning of the test. Some subjects become apprehensive when blindfolded, and many find this task quite difficult. It is important for the examiner to offer encouragement if there is any sign that such verbal reinforcement is necessary to elicit the subject's best possible performance.

As the subject places blocks correctly, the examiner should move other blocks in front of the subject to keep a supply ready at hand.

As soon as the last block has been placed in the first trial, immediately warn the subject to not remove the blindfold, and suggest relaxing for a minute or two. Then, after laying out the blocks again in the same manner described above, proceed with the second trial.

After the second trial has been completed, the subject should be given a chance to rest for a moment, and then the third trial is started.

After the third trial is completed, remove the test from the subject's line of vision. Then remove the blindfold, and place a sheet of white, unlined paper and a pencil in front of the subject. Proceed with the instructions concerned with drawing a picture of the board.

Once a block has been properly placed by the subject, it is the responsibility of the examiner to keep it in place. If a block that had previously been placed correctly is accidentally knocked out, the examiner should immediately replace the block into its correct space, and inform the subject that this is being done.

Although it rarely happens, sometimes a subject forces a block into an incorrect space. If this occurs, the examiner should have the subject feel the block and space and explain that the block was not correctly placed and must be removed.

Some impaired subjects seem to forget the size of the board and tend to ignore the top row of spaces. If this occurs (generally after most of the other blocks have been placed), remind the subject to "feel the entire board." It may become necessary to run the subject's hand around the board again, the same way it was done at the beginning of the trial.

Occasionally subjects "wander" from the board to the stand or even to the table-top. Always tell the subject when he/she is working off the board. Some subjects would spend a great deal of time feeling the sections of the stand if the examiner did not intervene and redirect their attention to the board.

Some subjects could spend hours trying to complete this test. If the subject seems to be getting discouraged and is making very slow progress, it is permissible to discontinue each trial after fifteen minutes of working time. However, the trial should never be discontinued if the subject appears capable of completing it. If most of the blocks have been placed, the trial should continue until it is completed. In some very rare instances, the subject can tolerate only a five-minute or ten-minute trial. If this is the case, the second trial should not be discontinued until the same amount of time as used in the first trial has elapsed. This is also true with the third trial (unless, of course, the subject is able to place all the blocks before this time is reached).

An important part of the information derived from the TPT concerns the comparative performances of the two hands. The timing procedure described above permits collection of data relevant to such comparisons even if the test is not completed. Although we always try to obtain at least a fifteen-minute sample on each trial, it would be better to limit each trial to ten minutes rather than deplete the subject's emotional or physical resources on the first trial.

In cases in which the subject can use only one hand, all three trials should be done with the one functional arm. Such an instance would occur, for example, in subjects with a complete right or left hemiplegia. Examiners should be aware, though, that a subject with partial paralysis may be able to handle the blocks and feel the board well enough to do the task with each extremity. Even when a subject has some impairment of an upper extremity, it is advisable to have the person try to do the test using the standard testing procedure in order to get an actual comparison of the performances on the two sides of the body. If a subject has used only one extremity for the first two trials, only this same extremity should be used on the third trial.

Occasionally subjects may get extremely tired while working on this test and need rest periods. The stopwatch is stopped during these periods and the length of the rest period should be noted on the test form. Sometimes a subject (such as someone with intracranial hypertension) may become dizzy or nauseated during the test. If it becomes necessary to remove the blindfold, be sure that the board and blocks are first covered or put out of sight. The examiner should record the time elapsed, the length of the rest period, and the number of blocks in place up to that point.

After completing the part of the TPT that requires placement of the blocks, the subject is given a sheet of unlined, white paper and asked to draw a picture of the board, reproducing as many blocks in their correct positions as he/she can remember. This drawing is scored for the number of shapes remembered (Memory component) and the number of shapes correctly placed (Localization component).

Specific Instructions

Blindfold the subject as the first step in preparing to administer this test. Give the subject appropriate explanations of what is being done and reassurances as the eye pads and blindfold are being put on. While putting out the board and blocks, say:

> On the table in front of you I am putting out a
> board. The board is sitting on a stand so that it
> will be upright and will not fall over. On the
> board are spaces of various sizes and shapes. On
> the table I am putting out blocks of various sizes
> and shapes. The blocks will fit into the spaces on
> the board. There is a block for each space and a
> space for each block. You're going to try to place

the blocks into their proper spaces. When you have placed a block in its proper space, it will fit and will not fall out.

After the board and blocks are in position, say:

This is what the board feels like. While running the subject's preferred hand around board (Fig. 9-47) say: Here is one side, here is the top, and here is the other side. This is the stand that you feel out here at the sides. Guide subject's hand to the two sides of the stand.

As you run your hand over the board, you can feel the various spaces. Run the subject's hand quickly over the entire board, but do not permit the subject to explore and identify any particular shapes.

Fig. 9-47. Examiner guiding subject's hand over board of TPT.

Here are the blocks. Guide subject's hand over the
span of blocks.

Now using only your right hand (or left hand,
if the subject uses his/her left hand for writing),
I want you to fit the blocks into their proper
spaces on the board. Do you have any questions?
(Pause.) Remember to do it as quickly as you can.
All right — ready? Begin.

Start timing. Observe the subject's performance carefully
(Fig. 9-48). Occasionally a subject will forget that he/she is
allowed to use only one hand during the first two trials and
may start to use both hands to perform the task. The examiner must be alert and correct the subject quickly and efficiently.

After the subject has finished the task with the dominant
hand, say:

That was the last block that you just put in.
You can rest for a moment but you must leave
the blindfold on.

Fig. 9-48. Subject performing TPT during first trial with right
(dominant) hand.

> Now I would like you to do the same thing over
> again, but this time using only your left hand (or
> right hand, if the subject is left-handed for writing).

Before beginning the second trial, guide the subject's non-dominant hand quickly over the board and blocks, mentioning that it is the same board and the same blocks used during the first trial and that he/she is to do the same task again as quickly as possible while using only the left hand (or right hand, as the case may be).

After the subject has completed the task with the nondominant (usually left) hand, say:

> That was the last block you just put in. Now keep
> the blindfold on, because I want you to do this
> still another time. This time you get to use both
> hands. (Again, a short rest period is permissible,
> especially if the subject appears tired.)

When ready to begin the third trial, say:

> Now we are going to do this again, and you get to
> use both hands. Remember, put the blocks in their
> proper spaces as quickly as you can using both
> hands. Ready — begin!

After the third trial the examiner must be especially alert to be sure that the subject does not remove the blindfold before the blocks and board have been removed from view. After the test has been put out of sight, the blindfold may be removed. Allow the subject a few moments for his/her eyes to become adjusted to the light. Then place a blank sheet of paper and a pencil in front of the subject and say:

> Now I would like you to draw a picture of the
> board that you were just working with. Most
> people find it helpful first to draw an outline of
> the shape of the board and then fill the blocks in.

If the subject does not draw an outline of the board as the first step, encourage him/her to do so. In some cases, scoring the Localization component depends upon the subject's impression of the outer limits of the board.

Instruct the subject, if necessary, that the outline of the board should be large enough to permit him to draw the shapes within it. Children who start with a very small outline should be asked to start over again. If the child has drawn an outline of the board but is unable to include all the figures he/she remembers into the outlined space, allow the child to start over again and use the original drawing as a guide. If the subject is confused, it often helps to point out that the outside shape should represent the board but not the stand.

After the subject has drawn the outline of the board, say:

> Draw in as many of the blocks as you can
> remember and try to put them in their proper
> places as well as you can remember. If you
> remember a certain block but don't remember
> where it goes, put it in as best you can. Think
> carefully, and put down all of the blocks you
> can remember, and try to put them in their
> correct locations.

Sometimes subjects will ask how many blocks there were in the test. A simple answer such as, "That's part of what we want you figure out; draw as many of the shapes as you can remember" is usually sufficient to redirect the subject back to the task at hand.

When the subject has finished drawing the board and blocks, the examiner should inspect the drawing to determine whether any of the shapes need clarification. If one of the subject's drawings of a shape is not definitely recognizable, ask the subject to name the shape in the drawing and record the subject's response on that shape. If the subject names the shape correctly (even though the drawing is done inaccurately or poorly), credit is given. For example, if the subject has drawn a pointed type of figure and identifies it as a star, credit is given for a correct response.

When scoring the drawing later, it may not be obvious which direction the paper was placed when the subject was doing the drawing. Therefore, as soon as the subject has finished the drawing, mark "TOP" on the appropriate place on the paper.

Scoring

This test is scored by recording:

1. the time for each trial;
2. the total time for the three trials;
3. the number of blocks correctly reproduced in the drawing;
4. the number of blocks properly located in the drawing.

The time for the three trials and the total time score should be expressed to the nearest tenth of a minute (see Fig. 9-49 for a conversion table).

TPT Conversion Table		
Seconds	**=**	**10ths of Minute**
0-3	=	.0
4-9	=	.1
10-15	=	.2
16-21	=	.3
22-27	=	.4
28-33	=	.5
34-39	=	.6
40-45	=	.7
46-51	=	.8
52-57	=	.9
58-60	=	1.0

Fig. 9-49. Seconds expressed as 10ths of a minute.

In scoring the drawing for the number of blocks remembered (Memory score), usually it is necessary only to count those shapes which are fairly accurately drawn and indicate that the subject had a true concept of the block. A star of four or five points is accepted as correct. However, if you suspect that the subject had a correct shape in mind but could not draw it properly, be sure to question him/her about it. If the subject correctly identifies the shape verbally, give credit for remembering the shape.

The Localization score is obtained by counting the number of correctly drawn shapes located approximately in the right place in the drawing and in relation to the other blocks.

A useful procedure to follow in scoring localization is to divide the drawing into nine segments (Fig. 9-50). If the

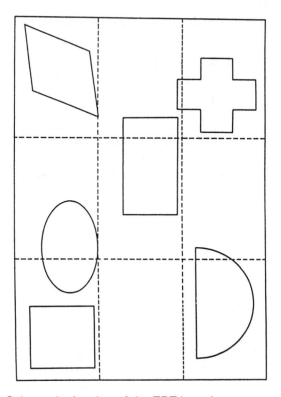

Fig. 9-50. Schematic drawing of the TPT board.

major portion of a block fits in its appropriate division, the block is given credit for localization. No localization credit is given unless memory credit for the block has already been given. Therefore, the Localization score must be equal to or less than (never greater than) the Memory score.

The subject's scores are noted on the examiner's recording sheet (Fig. 9-51).

If the subject is not able to complete the test and has worked for a standard time period (usually fifteen minutes) on each trial, both the time and the number of blocks successfully placed should be recorded.

The examiner should also record any other pertinent information, such as instances in which a trial was interrupted for the subject to take a rest break.

TACTUAL PERFORMANCE TEST

Name _____ Date _____ Examiner _____

Indicate form used:

_____ 10-figure board · Ages 15 years & older
_____ 6-figure board · vertical position · Ages 9 through 14 years
_____ 6-figure board · horizontal position · Ages 5 through 8 years

Trial	Hand	Circle	Time		
1	Dominant Hand	R L	' "	=	_____
2	Non-dominant Hand	R L	' "	=	_____
3	Both Hands		' "	=	_____

Total Time: _____

Memory: _____

Localization: _____

Comments:

USE REVERSE SIDE FOR DRAWING

Fig. 9-51. Recording form for the Tactual Performance Test.

The Category Test

Materials   Category Test
Category Test slides for Older Children
recording form
pencil

General Instructions

The purpose of the Category Test is to evaluate the subject's ability in abstraction and concept formation. To achieve this, it is necessary that the examiner elicit the subject's best possible performance. When giving the Category Test, we insist that the subject observe each item carefully before making a response. Subjects are usually very interested in this test and make a serious effort to answer correctly. Occasionally, a subject will answer apparently at random, and in such instances the examiner must attempt to get the subject to make a serious effort to solve the problems. If this is not possible (or the subject is too impaired to take the test), the examiner should discontinue the administration of the test and declare the test either invalid or beyond the abilities of the subject.

Since the purpose of the Category Test is to measure ability in concept formation (without the adverse influence of the subject's lack of interest, etc.), a variety of techniques may be used as necessary. Some subjects need to be told repeatedly to observe the items carefully (in some instances they must be asked to describe the figures before being permitted to answer), or to state the reason for selecting a particular response. If a subject admits to only "just guessing," he/she must be encouraged to try to figure out the principle and not answer randomly. As a general rule, any part of the instructions may be repeated or elaborated upon when the examiner believes it to be necessary. The examiner should strive to give the subject a clear and full understanding of the problem and the rules involved in its solution.

The principles themselves are never revealed to a subject. However, for subjects who are extremely impaired in their ability to form concepts, it may become necessary for the examiner to urge them to study each picture carefully, ask them to describe the stimulus material (followed by questions such as, *Does that give you any idea of what the right answer might be?*), encourage them to try to notice and remember how the pictures change (since this often provides clues to the underlying principle), and to try to think of a possible reason when a correct answer occurs.

In conversation such as that described above, it is possible that an unwary examiner may give unwarranted reinforcement to certain hypotheses voiced by the subject. The examiner should always remember that questions and advice should be pertinent and consistent with the aims of the formal instructions. The examiner should never provide any information relevant to the solution of the problems presented by the test; the only information of this kind comes from the bell or buzzer following each response.

Most subjects are able to take the Category Test with little additional information or direction other than that provided in the formal instructions. Although some impaired subjects sometimes find the test very trying and frustrating, others find the test to be very interesting and motivating. The examiner should always encourage the subject to continue working at the task, although any direct comment or response related to the underlying principle should never be made. If a subject shows no sign of making progress on any one of Subtests III through VI in the first twenty items and also shows extreme frustration with the task, it is better to discontinue the subtest after the first twenty items and prorate the error scores for each subtest (linear extrapolation) than to risk not being able to complete all of the subtests.

Some additional points should be mentioned briefly:

1. Although speed is not a factor in the Category Test and subjects should not be hurried, neither should they be permitted to sit and daydream or to take an unduly long time to respond. Some subjects would impair the continuity of the test if they were not encouraged to make reasonably prompt decisions. If excessive delays occur between items, some subjects might be placed at a disadvantage in remembering previous items and thereby in discerning the principle underlying the items in the group as a whole.

2. The examiner should always be alert to the slide on the screen, not only to monitor the subject's performance, but also to make sure the answer button on the examiner's panel is set appropriately.

3. Although it would be possible to automate the testing procedure and eliminate the need for the examiner to set the controls for the bell or buzzer for each item, we have always found that it is quite important for the examiner to be present, actively involved, alert to the test content and the subject's efforts at all times, and actually "giving" the test. In this way subjects are more readily motivated to pay attention and put forth their best effort (as contrasted with the possible reaction to an automated or impersonal situation).

4. The testing room should be somewhat darkened, but light enough for the examiner to see the recording sheet to set the answer button and record errors.

5. The subject should sit directly in front of the screen in order to maintain intersubject perceptual-constancy (some stimuli are difficult to see from an angle). The middle of the screen should be at approximately eye level. The examiner should be seated next to the subject, in such a position that the screen can be seen

easily but the subject cannot see the examiner's recording sheet (Fig. 9-52).

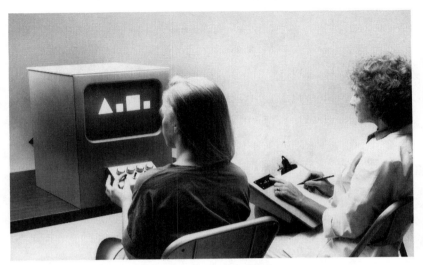

Fig. 9-52. Administration of the Category Test.

6. The examiner's panel (Fig. 9-53) is used to (1) set the
button to determine which lever on the Category Test
— 1, 2, 3, or 4 — will elicit the bell when it is pressed,
(2) change the slides to project the next stimulus figure on the screen, and (3) hold the recording sheet.

The examiner's panel contains five buttons. When the button outlined in red is depressed, the slide projector will
advance to the next slide. The remaining four buttons are
used to set the bell on one of the levers of the Category Test.
For example, when the first button on the examiner's panel
is depressed, a bell will be elicited when the lever corresponding to the number 1 on the Category Test is pressed
(and correspondingly, the levers for 2, 3, and 4 will elicit the
buzzer).

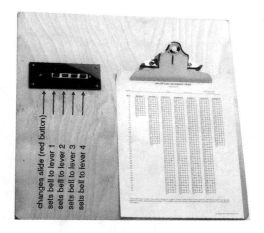

Fig. 9-53. Examiner's panel for the Category Test.

The recording sheet (Fig. 9-54) has two purposes: (1) it lists the correct responses for each of the 168 items in the Category Test, and (2) it provides a place for recording the subject's response to each item.

The examiner therefore will use the recording sheet to determine which button on the examiner panel should be depressed for each stimulus slide. For example, the correct answer to Subtest I, slide 1 is "1." The examiner will depress the first button on the panel so that the bell will be elicited when the lever corresponding to the number 1 is pressed. The correct answer to Subtest I, slide 2 is "3," so the examiner would depress the third button on the panel just before this slide is projected on the screen.

The recording sheet contains three blank boxes next to the box showing the correct response for that slide. If the subject responds to an item correctly, a check mark is customarily placed in the blank box furthest from the box containing the correct answer. If the subject responds incorrectly, the examiner records the number of the incorrect response in the

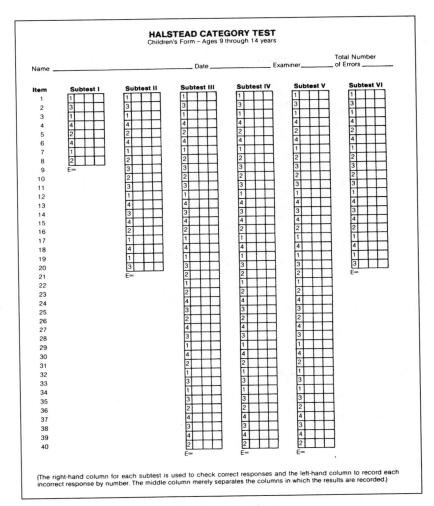

Fig. 9-54. Recording sheet for Category Test.

blank box next to the box containing the correct answer. The middle column of boxes is used merely to separate the two recording columns. Fig. 9-55 shows a sample recording of a subject's responses.

At the bottom of each subtest column the examiner records the number or errors made by the subject on that subtest. The examiner records the total number of errors at the top of the page after all 168 items have been administered.

HALSTEAD CATEGORY TEST
Children's Form – Ages 9 through 14 years

Name __Smith, John__   Date __1/2/92__   Examiner __DW__   Total Number of Errors ____

Item	Subtest I	Subtest II	Subtest III	Subtest IV	Subtest V	Subtest VI
1	1 ✓	1 ✓	1 *4*	1 *4*	1 *3*	1 *4*
2	3 ✓	3 ✓	3 ✓	3 ✓	3 ✓	3 ✓
3	1 ✓	1 ✓	1 *3*	1 ✓	1 *3*	1 ✓
4	4 ✓	4 ✓	4 *3*	4 ✓	4 *1*	4 *1*
5	2 ✓	2 ✓	2 ✓	2 ✓	2 ✓	2 *3*
6	4 ✓	4 ✓	4 *3*	4 ✓	4 *1*	4 ✓
7	1 ✓	1 ✓	1 ✓	1 ✓	1 ✓	1 ✓
8	2 ✓	2 ✓	2 ✓	2 ✓	2 ✓	2 ✓
9	E= 0	3 ✓	3 ✓	3 ✓	3 ✓	3 ✓
10		2 ✓	2 ✓	2 *3*	2 ✓	2 ✓
11		3 ✓	3 ✓	3 ✓	3 ✓	3 ✓
12		1 ✓	1 ✓	1 ✓	1 *4*	1 ✓
13		4 ✓	4 *3*	4 ✓	4 *2*	4 ✓
14		3 ✓	3 *1*	3 ✓	3 *2*	3 *2*
15		4 ✓	4 *3*	4 ✓	4 *2*	4 ✓
16		2 ✓	2 *3*	2 ✓	2 ✓	2 *4*
17		1 ✓	1 ✓	1 ✓	1 *2*	1 ✓
18		4 ✓	4 ✓	4 ✓	4 *2*	4 ✓
19		1 ✓	1 *2*	1 ✓	1 *3*	1 ✓
20		3 ✓	3 ✓	3 ✓	3 *2*	3 ✓
21		E= 0	2 ✓	2	2	E= 5
22			1 ✓	1	1	
23			2 ✓	2	2	

Fig. 9-55. Examiner's recording of a subject's responses on the Category Test.

Specific Instructions

With the subject seated comfortably in front of the Category Test, begin by saying:

> On this screen (indicate to subject) you are going to see different geometric figures and designs. Something about the pattern on the screen will remind you of a number between 1 and 4.

> On the keyboard in front of you (indicate to subject) the keys are numbered 1, 2, 3, and 4. You will first look at the screen, and then decide which number the picture suggests. When you figure it out, press down on the key that has that same number.

Depress the first answer button on the examiner's panel so that the bell will sound when the lever corresponding to 1 on the Category Test is pressed.

Project the first slide on the screen and say:

> For example, what number does this remind
> you of?

If the subject answers "one," ask which key should be pressed. After the subject has pressed the lever corresponding to the number 1, record the subject's response on the recording form and say:

> The bell you just heard tells you that you got
> the right answer. Every time you have the right
> answer you will hear the bell ring. Now try
> another key you know is wrong.

After the buzzer sounds, say:

> The buzzer is what you hear when you have the
> wrong answer. In this way you will know each
> time whether you are right or wrong. However,
> for each picture on the screen, you get only one
> choice. If you make a mistake, we just go right
> on to the next picture.

Depress the third button on the examiner's panel so that the bell will sound when the lever corresponding to 3 on the Category Test is pressed. Project the second slide by pressing the button outlined in red on the examiner's panel and say:

> Now, which key would you choose for this
> picture? Continue with the slides in Subtest I,
> recording the subject's response to each slide.

After the last slide in Subtest I, say:

> That was the end of the first subtest. This test is
> divided into six subtests. In each subtest there is
> one idea or principle that runs throughout the
> subtest. Once you have figured out what the idea
> or principle in the subtest is, by using this idea
> you will get the right answer each time.

Now we are going to begin the second subtest,
and the idea in it may be the same as the last one
or it may be different. We want you to figure it
out. Proceed with Subtest II.

When you reach the first slide in Subtest II that has circles
(slide #9), say:

You will notice that we first saw squares, then
lines, and now circles. Even though the patterns
change, you should continue to use the same idea
to get the right answer. Continue with the slides in
Subtest II.

After the last slide in Subtest II, say:

That was the end of the second subtest. As you
probably noticed, you don't necessarily have to
see a number to have a number suggested to you.
You saw squares, circles, and other figures. Also,
you probably noticed that there was only one idea
or principle which ran throughout each of these
subtests. Once you figured out the idea, you continued to apply it to get the right answer each time.

Now we are going to start the third subtest, and
the idea in it may be the same as the last one or it
may be different. I want to see if you can figure it
out and use it to get the right answer.

Remember, the idea remains the same throughout
the subtest. I will tell you when we complete one
subtest and are ready to begin a new one. Proceed
with Subtest III.

After Subtests III and IV, say:

That was the end of that subtest. Now we are
going to begin the next one. The idea in it may
be the same as the last one or it may be different.
We want you to figure it out. Proceed with the
next subtest.

After the last slide in Subtest V, say:

> In this last subtest there is no one idea or principle that runs throughout the group, because it is made up of items you have seen before. Try to remember what the right answer was the last time you saw the pattern, and give that same answer again. Proceed with Subtest VI.

Scoring

The score is the total number of errors on all six subtests.

In his/her notes the examiner should also describe any unusual behavior that occurred during the testing, note whether an excessive amount of instruction or prompting was given, or offer any other comments which would assist in clarifying the test performance.

Scoring the Neuropsychological Deficit Scale (NDS) for Older Children

In Chapter VII we presented research findings on the Neuropsychological Deficit Scale (NDS) for Older Children and evidence of its striking sensitivity to cerebral damage and dysfunction. In this section we will provide specific information about the NDS and instructions for scoring the NDS for the individual subject.

The NDS for Older Children is composed of 45 variables, derived from the HRB for Older Children, divided into three major groups (see Table 9-1). Each of these major groups represents one of the methods of neuropsychological inference used to evaluate children in the 9- through 14-year age range.

Variables 1 through 25 represent the *Level of Performance* measures, and are organized into six main areas of neuropsychological functioning: (1) Motor Functions (variables 1-7), (2) Sensory-perceptual Functions (variables 8-14), (3) Visual-Spatial Skills (variables 15-18), (4) Attention and Concentration (variables 19 and 20), (5) Immediate Memory and Recapitulation (variables 21 and 22), and (6) Abstraction, Reasoning, and Logical Analysis Skills (variables 23-25).

The section of the NDS concerned with differential performances on the two sides of the body, *Right-Left Differences*, is represented by variables 26 through 33. Because brain-impaired children generally differ from normal children in their ability to perform tasks efficiently on each side of their body, this method of inference therefore often provides the most convincing evidence of cerebral impairment in the individual child.

The *Dysphasia* and *Related Variables* section (variables 34 through 45) represents dysphasic pathognomonic signs, and is derived from the Reitan-Indiana Aphasia Screening Test.

TABLE 9-1

Scoring of the Neuropsychological Deficit Scale for Older Children Aged 9 through 14 Years.

I. LEVEL OF PERFORMANCE (1-25)	0	1	2	3	Estimated Rate of Misclassification BD	Controls
Motor Functions						
1. Finger Tapping – Dom	40 or more	36-39	31-35	30 or less*	34%	23%
2. Finger Tapping – NonDom	36 or more	32-35	27-31	26 or less*	29%	23%
3. Grip – Dom	23 or more	18.5-22.5	15-18	14.5 or less*	31%	31%
4. Grip – NonDom	20 or more	16-19.5	11.5-15.5	11 or less*	31%	29%
5. Name Writing – Dom	9 or less	10-12	13-19	20 or more*	23%	17%
6. Name Writing – NonDom	22 or less	23-27	28-53	54 or more*	20%	20%
7. TPT – Total Time	7.1 or less	7.2-9.9	10.0-17.5	17.6 or more*	46%	40%
Sensory — Perceptual Functions						
8. Bilateral Sensory Imperception (Total Errors)	0	1	2	3 or more	49%	20%
9. Finger Localization – Right (Errors)	0	1	2-3	4 or more	29%	20%
10. Finger Localization – Left (Errors)	0-1	2	3	4 or more	20%	23%
11. Finger-Tip # Writing – Right (Errors)	0-2	3	4-6	7 or more	37%	29%
12. Finger-Tip # Writing – Left (Errors)	0-2	3-4	5-7	8 or more	43%	26%
13. Tactile Form Recognition – Right (Errors)	0	–	1	2 or more	54%	29%
14. Tactile Form Recognition – Left (Errors)	0	–	1	2 or more	57%	14%

*or unable to do with one or both hands

TABLE 9-1 (continued)

	0	1	2	3	Estimated Rate of Misclassification	
					BD	Controls
Visual-Spatial Skills						
15. Picture Arrangement	10 or more	8-9	7	6 or less	43%	40%
16. Block Design	11 or more	9-10	7-8	6 or less	46%	37%
17. Object Assembly	11 or more	9-10	7-8	6 or less	40%	29%
18. Trail Making Test – Part A	13" or less	14"-18"	19"-26"	27" or more	20%	17%
Attention and Concentration						
19. Seashore Rhythm Test (# correct)	27 or more	24-26	21-23	20 or less	37%	23%
20. Speech-sounds Perception Test (Errors)	0-5	6-10	11-16	17 or more	37%	29%
Immediate Memory and Recapitulation						
21. TPT – Memory	6	5	4	0-3	40%	40%
22. TPT – Localization	6-4	3	2	0-1	49%	31%
Abstraction, Reasoning, Logical Analysis						
23. Category Test	31 or less	32-51	52-64	65 or more	29%	34%
24. Trail Making Test – Part B	27" or less	28"-37"	38"-69"	70" or more	23%	23%
25. Coding	9 or more	7-8	6	5 or less	46%	23%

457

TABLE 9-1 (continued)

II. RIGHT-LEFT DIFFERENCES (26-33)

	0	1	2	3	Estimated Rate of Misclassification	
					BD	Controls
For Variables 26-28: Divide the nondominant hand by the dominant hand and subtract from 1.00.						
26. Tapping	.07 to .14	.15 to .18 .06 to .03	.19 to .24 .02 to −.05	.25 or more* −.06 or less*	26%	40%
27. Grip	.07 to .15	.16 to .22 .06 to .03	.23 to .30 .02 to −.05	.31 or more* −.06 or less*	37%	29%
28. TPT	.19 to .53	.54 to .71 .18 to .07	.72 to .80 .06 to −.35	.81 or more* −.36 or less*	31%	37%
29. Name Writing (NonPref-Pref)	10"-16"	17"-21" 8"-9"	22"-30" 6"-7"	5" or less 31" or more*	23%	14%
For Variables 30-33: The score is the difference in the number of errors between the right side and the left side.						
30. Total Sensory Imperception	0	—	1	2 or more*	51%	43%
31. Tactile Finger Localization	0	1	2-3	4 or more*	57%	14%
32. Finger-Tip Number Writing	0	1	2-3	4 or more*	46%	29%
33. Tactile Form Recognition	0	1	2-3	4 or more*	85%	5%

*or unable to do with one or both hands

458

TABLE 9-1 (continued)

III. DYSPHASIA AND RELATED DEFICITS (34–45)

34. Dysnomia 3
35. Constructional dyspraxia 2
36. Spelling dyspraxia 1
37. Dysgraphia 2
38. Dyslexia 2
39. Visual number dysgnosia 3

40. Visual letter dysgnosia 3
41. Central dysarthria 2
42. Auditory verbal dysgnosia 3
43. Dyscalculia 2
44. Right-left confusion 1
45. Body dysgnosia 3

459

The procedure for scoring the NDS for Older Children is similar to the procedure for scoring the NDS for Adults (Reitan & Wolfson, 1988b) and the NDS for Young Children (Reitan & Wolfson, 1992).

Each variable in the *Level of Performance* and the *Left-Right Differences* sections is scored on a scale ranging from 0 to 3 points (see Table 9-1). A score of 0 corresponds with a perfectly normal performance. A score of 1 is still within the normal range, but represents a performance that was not quite as good as might ideally be expected.

A significant dividing point occurs between scores of 1 and 2; scores of 0 and 1 represent the normal range, and scores of 2 and 3 depict impaired performances. A score of 2 represents mild to moderate neuropsychological impairment, and a score of 3 indicates severe impairment.

Pathognomonic signs (variables 34 through 45 in the *Dysphasia and Related Variables* section) are scored differently than the other variables. Each of the pathognomonic signs is presumed to represent brain dysfunction (rather than a range of performances that extends from normal to impaired). In order to score the pathognomonic signs variables, it is advantageous to have experience and clinical competence with the Aphasia Screening Test, and explicit examples of scoring various performances on the Aphasia Screening Test can be found in this chapter and in an earlier publication (Reitan, 1985a).

Procedure for Scoring the NDS for Older Children

Level of Performance

Step 1.   On the Worksheet for the NDS for Older Children (Fig. 9-56), enter the raw score for variables 1 through 25. Refer to Table 9-2 for specific information about obtaining the raw score for each variable.

Fig. 9-56. Worksheet for Computing the Neuropsychological
Deficit Scale for Older Children – 9 through 14 Years

Name _____

Age_____ Gender_____ Educ_____ Handedness _____

LEVEL OF PERFORMANCE

	Raw Score	NDS Score
Motor Functions		
1. Finger Tapping – Dom Hand	_____	_____
2. Finger Tapping – NonDom Hand	_____	_____
3. Grip – Dom Hand	_____	_____
4. Grip – NonDom Hand	_____	_____
5. Name Writing – Dom Hand	_____	_____
6. Name Writing – NonDom Hand	_____	_____
7. TPT – Total Time	_____	_____
Score for Motor Functions section		_____
Sensory-Perceptual Functions		
8. Total Errors – Bilateral sensory imperception	_____	_____
9. Finger Localization – Right (Errors)	_____	_____
10. Finger Localization – Left (Errors)	_____	_____
11. Finger-Tip # Writing – Right (Errors)	_____	_____
12. Finger-Tip # Writing – Left (Errors)	_____	_____
13. Tactile Form Recognition – Left (Errors)	_____	_____
14. Tactile Form Recognition – Right (Errors)	_____	_____
Score for Sensory-perceptual Functions section		_____
Visual-Spatial Skills		
15. Picture Arrangement	_____	_____
16. Block Design	_____	_____
17. Object Assembly	_____	_____
18. Trail Making – Part A	_____	_____
Score for Visual-spatial Skills section		_____

Attention and Concentration

	Raw Score	NDS Score
19. Seashore Rhythm Test (# correct)	_____	_____
20. Speech-sounds Perception Test (# of errors)	_____	_____
Score for Attention and Concentration section		_____

Immediate Memory and Recapitulation

21. TPT – Memory	_____	_____
22. TPT – Localization	_____	_____
Score for Immediate Memory and Recapitulation section		_____

Abstraction, Reasoning, and Logical Analysis

23. Category Test	_____	_____
24. Trail Making Test – Part B	_____	_____
25. Coding	_____	_____
Score for Abstraction, Reasoning, and Logical Analysis section		_____
Total Score for Level of Performance section		_____

RIGHT-LEFT DIFFERENCES

26. Tapping	_____	_____
27. Grip	_____	_____
28. TPT	_____	_____
29. Name Writing (NonPref-Pref)	_____	_____
30. Total Sensory Imperception (# of errors)	_____	_____
31. Tactile Finger Localization (# of errors)	_____	_____
32. Finger-Tip # Writing (# of errors)	_____	_____
33. Tactile Form Recognition (# of errors)	_____	_____
Total Score for Right-Left Differences section		_____

DYSPHASIA AND RELATED VARIABLES

	If Present	NDS Score
34. Dysnomia	3	_____
35. Constructional dyspraxia	2	_____
36. Spelling dyspraxia	1	_____
37. Dysgraphia	2	_____
38. Dyslexia	2	_____
39. Visual number dysgnosia	3	_____
40. Visual letter dysgnosia	3	_____
41. Central dysarthria	2	_____
42. Auditory verbal dysgnosia	3	_____
43. Dyscalculia	2	_____
44. Right-left confusion	1	_____
45. Body dysgnosia	3	_____

Total Score for
Dysphasia and Related Variables section   _____

SUMMARY

Total Score for Level of Performance section   _____

Total Score for Right-Left Differences section   _____

Total Score for Dysphasia and Related
Variables section   _____

TOTAL NDS SCORE   _____

Step 2.   Using Table 9-1, convert each raw score to an NDS score of 0, 1, 2, or 3.

Step 3.   Add the NDS scores for variables 1 through 7 (Motor Functions), 8 through 14 (Sensory-perceptual Functions), 15 through 18 (Visual-Spatial Skills), 19 and 20 (Attention and Concentration), 21 and 22 (Immediate Memory and Recapitulation), and 23 through 25 (Abstraction, Reasoning, and Logical Analysis Skills).

Step 4.   Add the NDS scores for each of the subsections of variables 1 through 25 to obtain the NDS score for the *Level of Performance* section.

Right/Left Differences

Step 5.   Determine the raw score for variables 26 through 33 according to the instructions given in Table 9-2. Enter the raw score in the appropriate place on the Worksheet.

Step 6.   Using Table 9-1, convert each raw score to an NDS score of 0, 1, 2, or 3.

Step 7.   Add the NDS scores for variables 26 through 33 to obtain the total NDS score for the *Right/Left Differences* section.

Dysphasia and Related Variables

Step 8.   After reviewing the subject's performances on the Aphasia Screening Test, determine whether any deficits are present. Refer to the guidelines and examples presented earlier in this chapter for more specific information. If a particular deficit is judged to be present, enter the appropriate assigned NDS score on the Worksheet (variables 34 - 45).

Step 9. Add the assigned NDS scores for variables 34 through 45 to obtain the total NDS score for the *Dysphasia and Related Variables* section.

Summary

Step 10. On the last page of the Worksheet, enter the total NDS score for all of the *Level of Performance* variables (1 - 25).

Step 11. Enter the total NDS score for the *Left/Right Differences* variables (26 - 33).

Step 12. Enter the total NDS score for the *Dysphasia and Related Variables* (34 - 45).

Step 13. Add the scores from the *Level of Performance, Left/Right Differences,* and *Dysphasia and Related Variables* sections to obtain a Total NDS score the subject.

A sample of computerized scoring of the NDS for Older Children is given in the Appendix.

TABLE 9-2

Guidelines for Determining Raw Scores for the NDS for Older Children.

Variable	Raw Score

Level of Performance (1 - 25)

Motor Functions

1. Finger Tapping – Dom Hand — Average of 5 trials within 5 taps obtained by the dominant hand

2. Finger Tapping – NonDom Hand — Average of 5 trials within 5 taps obtained by the nondominant hand

3. Grip – Dom Hand — Average of 2 trials within 5 kg obtained by the dominant hand

4. Grip – NonDom Hand — Average of 2 trials within 5 kg obtained by the nondominant hand

5. Name Writing – Dom Hand — Time in seconds required to write name with the dominant hand

6. Name Writing – NonDom Hand — Time in seconds required to write name with the nondominant hand

7. TPT – Total Time — Sum of 3 trials on the TPT: Dominant hand, nondominant hand, and both hands

Sensory-perceptual Functions

8. Total Errors – Bilateral Sensory Imperception — Total number of errors made on both left and right sides on tactile, auditory, and visual stimulation during bilateral simultaneous stimulation

---

Example:

Bilateral Simultaneous Sensory Stimulation

Error totals

RH _/_ LH ____   Both: RH _2_ LH ____   RH _2_ LH ____
RH ____ LF ____   Both: RH _/_ LF ____   RH _/_ LF ____
LH ____ RF ____   Both: LH ____ RF ____   LH ____ RF ____

RE ____ LE ____   Both: RE ____ LE _2_   RE ____ LE _2_

RV ____ LV ____   Both: RV ____ LV ____   RV ____ LV ____
____ ____   _/_ ____   _/_ ____
____ ____   ____ ____   ____ ____

In this example, the raw score is 6.

466

9. Finger Localization – Right	Number of errors made with the right hand on the Tactile Finger Recognition Test
10. Finger Localization – Left	Number of errors made with the left hand on the Tactile Finger Recognition Test
11. Fingertip Number Writing – Right	Number of errors made with the right hand
12. Fingertip Number Writing – Left	Number of errors made with the left hand
13. Tactile Form Recognition – Right	Number of errors made on 8 trials with the right hand
14. Tactile Form Recognition – Left	Number of errors made on 8 trials with the left hand

Visual-Spatial Skills

15. Picture Arrangement	Scaled score obtained on the Picture Arrangement subtest of the WISC-R
16. Block Design	Scaled score obtained on the Block Design subtest of the WISC-R
17. Object Assembly	Scaled score obtained on the Object Assembly subtest of the WISC-R
18. Trail Making Test – Part A	Time in seconds required to complete Part A

Attention and Concentration

19. Seashore Rhythm Test	Number of correct responses on all 30 items
20. Speech-sounds Perception Test	Number of errors on all 60 items

Immediate Memory and Recapitulation

21. TPT – Memory	Number of shapes remembered correctly on TPT drawing
22. TPT – Localization	Number of shapes localized correctly on TPT drawing

Abstraction, Reasoning, Logical Analysis Skills

23. Category Test	Number of errors made on all six subtests
24. Trail Making Test – Part B	Time in seconds required to complete Part B
25. Coding	Scaled score obtained on the Coding subtest of the WISC-R

467

26. Tapping

    A. Divide the score obtained by the nondominant hand by the score obtained by the dominant hand

    B. Subtract the number obtained in Part A (above) from 1.00

Example:

Finger Tapping Test

Dominant hand   (*R*)   *45*

Non-dominant hand (*L*)   *40*

A. $40 \div 45 = .888$

B. $1.00 - .888 = .112 = .11$ (rounded)

In this example, the raw score is .11

---

27. Grip

    Procedure is the same as for # 26:

    A. Divide the score obtained by the nondominant hand by the score obtained by the dominant hand

    B. Subtract the number obtained in Part A (above) from 1.00

28. TPT

    Procedure is the same as for # 26:

    A. Divide the score obtained by the nondominant hand by the score obtained by the dominant hand

    B. Subtract the number obtained in Part A (above) from 1.00

29. Name Writing

    Subtract the time required by the dominant hand from the nondominant hand

30. Total Sensory Imperception

A. Determine the total number of errors made on the right side of the body on tactile, auditory, and visual stimulation during bilateral simultaneous stimulation

B. Determine the total number of errors made on the left side of the body on tactile, auditory, and visual stimulation during bilateral simultaneous stimulation

C. Subtract the smaller number from the larger number

Example:

Bilateral Simultaneous Sensory Stimulation

Error totals

RH _/_ LH ___   Both: RH _2_ LH ___   RH _2_ LH ___

RH ___ LF ___   Both: RH _/_ LF ___   RH _/_ LF ___

LH ___ RF ___   Both: LH ___ RF ___   LH ___ RF ___

RE ___ LE ___   Both: RE ___ LE _2_   RE ___ LE _2_

RV ___ LV ___   Both: RV ___ LV ___   RV ___ LV ___

___ ___   _/_ ___   _/_ ___

___ ___   ___ ___   ___ ___

A. Total # of errors on right side: $2 + 1 + 1 = 4$

B. Total # of errors on left side: 2

C. $4 - 2 = 2$

In this example, the raw score is 2.

31. Tactile Finger Localization   Difference in number of errors between the two hands

---

Example:

Tactile Finger Recognition

RH 1 ___ 2 _/_ 3 _/_ 4 ___ 5 ___   RH _2_ / _20_
LH 1 ___ 2 _/_ 3 _2_ 4 _2_ 5 ___   LH _5_ / _20_

5 – 2 = 3

In this example, the raw score is 3.

---

32 Fingertip Number Writing Perception   Difference in number of errors between the two hands

---

Example:

Finger-Tip Number Writing

RH 1 ___ 2 _2_ 3 _/_ 4 _/_ 5 ___   RH _4_ / _20_
LH 1 ___ 2 ___ 3 ___ 4 _/_ 5 ___   LH _/_ / _20_

4 – 1 = 3

In this example, the raw score is 3.

---

33 Tactile Form Recognition Test   Difference in number of errors between the two hands

---

Example:

Tactile Form Recognition Test

Dominant hand   (*R*)   _10_ sec   _0_ errors
Non-dominant hand (*L*)   _12_ sec   _1_ error

1 – 0 = 1

In this example, the raw score is 1.

Dysphasia and Related Variables (34 - 45)

If the pathognomonic sign is present, assign the value listed on the worksheet.

■

470

CHAPTER X

Principles and Illustrations of Individual Case Interpretations

As a method of demonstrating the processes involved in drawing clinical inferences from test data, in the latter part of this chapter we have selected cases which illustrate a wide range of etiologies, pathological conditions, learning disabilities, and behavioral disturbances. We have presented many examples of clinical interpretation, not only to show the range and interaction of neuropsychological deficits as they appear among individual subjects, but also to assist the reader to gain skill both in evaluation of test data and in report writing.

Every competent clinician knows that there is a great difference between knowledge of research results about neuropsychological tests and the application of those same tests in the evaluation of the individual subject (Reitan, 1988). Every competent neuropsychologist should also know that there is a significant difference between merely reporting the scores earned by a subject on a series of isolated tests and providing an integrated assessment of the tests as a battery (which reflects the uniqueness of an individual's brain-behavior relationships).

It is a simple matter merely to look up the percentile rank (or other indication of level of performance) for each test, offer a statement about how well the subject performed in the area of function presumed to be represented by that test, repeat this procedure for each test given, and present this series of statements as a neuropsychological report. However, this type of report often relates much more to *tests* than to the *subject*. Human abilities are not compartmentalized and completely separate. In fact, they are integrated in functional application even to simple problems in everyday life, as well as in more complex problems that may involve many elements and be distributed over time. Since practical applications of neuropsychological findings require a comprehensive and integrated assessment of brain-related abilities (as contrasted with a listing of level of performance on a series of tests), we have presented this integrated type of clinical interpretation for the reader to study.

We realize that a structured evaluation of the test findings may be helpful when initially gaining skills in clinical interpretation of results derived from the HRB for Older Children. In our case interpretations we will present step-by-step illustrations of the way in which the test data are transformed into clinically relevant conclusions.

Interpretation of Neuropsychological Deficit Scale Scores

The first step in our approach to clinical interpretation is to score the Neuropsychological Deficit Scale (NDS) for Older Children and to evaluate the results with regard to: (1) adequacy of brain functions (neurological inferences), and (2) adequacy of neuropsychological abilities, both on a general basis and in various areas of function (psychological inferences). The NDS provides an overall assessment of neuropsychological functions, with cut-off scores to use as a guide to compare a subject's performance with those of normal (non-brain-damaged) as well as brain-damaged children.

Next, the subject's NDS scores should be considered in relation to the mean scores and cut-off points for each major section of the NDS (Level of Performance, Right-Left Comparisons, and Dysphasia and Related Deficits) in order to determine whether the total number of points on the NDS was principally derived from one or two areas of function or reflected generalized impairment.

Finally, the subject's NDS scores should be compared with the mean performances of normal and brain-damaged children in each of the major areas of neuropsychological functioning: Motor Functions, Sensory-perceptual Functions, Attention and Concentration, Immediate Memory and Recapitulation, Visual-spatial Skills, Abstraction and Reasoning, and Dysphasia and Related Abilities.

This initial approach to the data provides a framework for the second step, a clinical evaluation of the entire set of results (including measures of verbal and performance intelligence and academic achievement).

Illustration using the Test Scores of Ted, Case #11

In order to illustrate the above guidelines, we will use one of the cases used for clinical illustration (Ted, #11). Ted's test scores and performances are presented first (Figures 10-1, 10-2, and 10-3). Figure 10-1 presents Ted's NDS scores, which provide the initial framework for interpretation of the findings. Next, we will comment on the organization of the data for clinical interpretation.

Ted's total NDS score was 58, a value that well exceeded the mean for control children (30.43) as well as the cut-off point of 43/44, and approached the mean for brain-damaged children (67.34).

The Halstead-Reitan Neuropsychological Test Battery for Older Children

Name **Ted** Age **12 – 1**
Gender **M** Education **6** Handedness: RH **0** LH **7**

Neuropsychological Deficit Scale (NDS) Summary

Level of Performance	Subject's score	Mean for controls	Mean for brain-damaged	Cut-off score
Motor Functions	14	6.29	14.05	
Sensory-perceptual Functions	11	5.15	10.77	
Attention and Concentration	4	1.91	3.78	
Immediate Memory and Recapitulation	0	2.23	3.31	
Visual-spatial Skills	2	4.06	7.69	
Abstraction, Reasoning, Logical Analysis	1	2.63	6.03	
Level of Performance–Total	32	22.27	45.63	33/34
Dysphasia and Related Variables	2	1.37	7.97	3/4
Right / Left Differences	24	6.79	13.74	9/10
Total NDS Score	58	30.43	67.34	43/44

WISC-R

VIQ **118**
PIQ **115**
FS IQ **119**

Verbal Subtests

Information	13
Similarities	13
Arithmetic	12
Vocabulary	13
Comprehension	14
(Digit Span)	(7)

Performance Subtests

Picture Completion	14
Picture Arrangement	11
Block Design	13
Object Assembly	14
Coding	9

WRAT

	Grade Equivalent
Reading	6.9
Arithmetic	5.6
Spelling	5.4

Strength of Grip

Dominant hand (L) **28.0** kg
Non-dominant hand (R) **3.5** kg

Name Writing

Dominant hand (L) **23** sec
Non-dominant hand (R) **93** sec

Category Test

Number of errors **30**

Tactual Performance Test

Dominant hand	(L)	2.4
Non-dominant hand	(L)	3.0
Both hands	(L)	1.8

Total Time	7.2
Memory	6
Localization	5

Seashore Rhythm Test

Number correct **20**   **10**

Speech-sounds Perception Test

Number of errors   **10**

Finger Tapping Test

Dominant hand (L) **38**   **38**
Non-dominant hand (R) **0**

Trail Making Test

Part A **22** sec **1** error(s)
Part B **26** sec **0** error(s)

Bilateral Simultaneous Sensory Stimulation

RH ___ LH ___		Both: RH ___ LH ___	
RH ___ LF ___		Both: RH **2** LF ___	
LH ___ RF ___		Both: LH ___ RF ___	
RE ___ LE ___		Both: RE ___ LE ___	
RV ___ LV ___		Both: RV ___ LV ___	
___ ___		___ ___	
___ ___		___ ___	

Tactile Finger Recognition

RH 1 **1** 2 **3** 3 **1** 4 **3** 5 **3**   RH **11** / 20
LH 1 ___ 2 **1** 3 ___ 4 ___ 5 ___   LH **1** / 20

Finger-Tip Number Writing

RH 1 **3** 2 **4** 3 **3** 4 **2** 5 **3**   RH **15** / 20
LH 1 ___ 2 ___ 3 ___ 4 ___ 5 ___   LH **0** / 20

Tactile Form Recognition Test

Dominant hand (L) **9** sec   **0** error(s)
Non-dominant hand (R) **14** sec   **5** error(s)

© 1991, Ralph M. Reitan, Ph.D. Reitan Neuropsychology Laboratory Tucson, Arizona

Fig. 10-1.

474

Reitan-Indiana Aphasia
Screening Test

Form for Adults and Older Children

Name __Ted__   Age __12 – 1__

Copy SQUARE	Repeat TRIANGLE
Name SQUARE	Repeat MASSACHUSETTS
Spell SQUARE S - Q - U - A - R - A *self-corrected to* S - Q - U - A - R - E	Repeat METHODIST EPISCOPAL Methodist Epistopal
Copy CROSS	Write SQUARE
Name CROSS Plus *Ex.?* Red Cross	Read SEVEN
Spell CROSS	Repeat SEVEN
Copy TRIANGLE	Repeat/Explain HE SHOUTED THE WARNING
Name TRIANGLE	Write HE SHOUTED THE WARNING
Spell TRIANGLE	Compute 85 − 27 =
Name BABY	Compute 17 x 3 =
Write CLOCK	Name KEY
Name FORK	Demonstrate use of KEY
Read 7 SIX 2	Draw KEY
Read MGW	Read PLACE LEFT HAND TO RIGHT EAR
Reading I	Place LEFT HAND TO RIGHT EAR
Reading II	Place LEFT HAND TO LEFT ELBOW

Fig. 10-2.

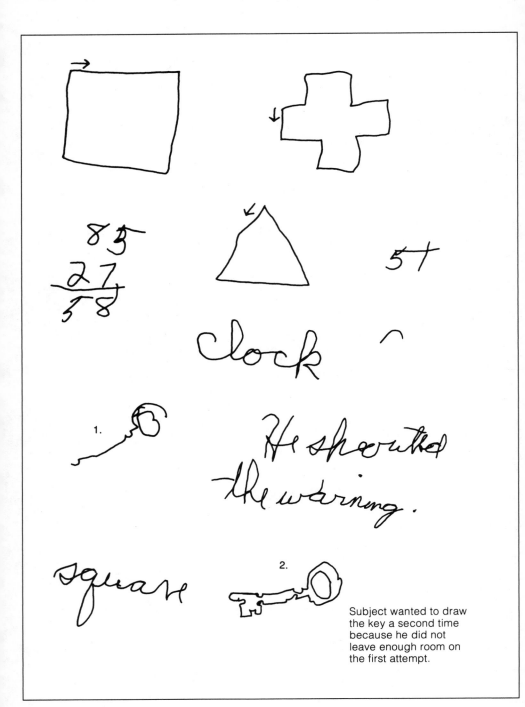

1.

2.

Subject wanted to draw
the key a second time
because he did not
leave enough room on
the first attempt.

Fig. 10-3.

This finding indicated that Ted's overall performance on the HRB was much more similar to the performances of brain-damaged children than normal control children, and suggested that he might well have some type of brain disease or damage. His score of 32 on the Level of Performance section of the NDS (which reflects the adequacy of his scores), was at a level intermediate to the mean score of normal children (22.27) and brain-damaged children (45.63), and did not quite reach the cut-off score of 33/34. This score, while possibly representing some impairment, certainly was better than expected in terms of the total NDS score.

On the Right-Left Differences section of the NDS Ted earned 24 points, a score which is strikingly elevated compared with the mean scores for both control children (6.79) and brain-damaged children (13.74). It well exceeded the cut-off score of 9/10, and emphasizes the importance of assessing and evaluating right-left comparisons in clinical neuropsychological assessment of the test results.

On the Dysphasia and Related Variables section Ted performed well, scoring only 2 points. Ted's performances on this section were much more similar to the mean of normal children (1.37) than brain-damaged children (7.97), and did not reach the cut-off of 3/4. However, the one deficit that was present, dysgraphia, might possibly have distinct implications in the context of the overall clinical analysis of the test results.

Finally, a more detailed evaluation of the adequacy of Ted's performances in various areas of functioning is required. He showed clear evidence of impairment of motor functions, earning a score of 14. On this section the means are 6.29 for control children and 14.05 for brain-damaged subjects. Ted earned a score of 11 on the section concerned with sensory-perceptual skills, surpassing the means of 5.15 for controls and 10.77 for brain-damaged subjects.

Impairment of both motor and sensory-perceptual abilities is more common when the responsible factor is a lesion at the cerebral level; selective impairment of motor functions may occur with spinal cord or peripheral disorders. In clinical interpretation it is also important to determine whether both types of impairment are present on the same side of the body, which may indicate the presence of a focal, lateralized cerebral lesion. In Ted's case the defective scores were predominantly on the right side of the body.

Ted performed somewhat poorly on tests of alertness and concentration, but this was due primarily to a poor score on the Seashore Rhythm Test (a finding which, when isolated, might be attributable either to cerebral damage or other causes). His fairly good score on the Speech-sounds Perception Test (10 errors) was sufficient to provide evidence that Ted did in fact have adequate ability to sustain concentrated attention over time. He performed very well on tasks that required immediate memory and recapitulation (TPT-Memory and Localization), earning an NDS score of 0 for each of these variables.

There were no findings to indicate that the specialized functions of the left cerebral hemisphere were grossly impaired. On the Dysphasia and Related Variables section Ted earned a score of 2, compared with means of 1.37 for control subjects and 7.97 for brain-damaged subjects. However, as mentioned above, the evidence of dysgraphia requires clinical evaluation with relation to the overall pattern of test results.

Ted performed relatively well on the measures evaluating visual-spatial skills, earning a score of 2. On this section the mean for control children is 4.06. Finally, the area of abstraction, reasoning, and logical analysis reflected no significant impairment. On this section Ted had a score of 1, compared with means of 2.63 for normals and 6.03 for brain-damaged subjects.

In summary, the NDS yielded evidence of significant neuropsychological impairment, derived principally from deficits of sensory-perceptual and motor functions (Level of Performance) on the right side of the body (Right-Left Differences).

The next step in clinical interpretation requires organization and evaluation of the test data. In this procedure we consider intelligence scores with relation to the full range of neuropsychological measures, evaluate general and more specific test indicators, identify and evaluate lateralizing findings, and formulate an overall basis for both neurological and psychological inferences regarding the individual child. The interpretations for each of the individual case examples illustrate this process.

Evaluation of the Wechsler Intelligence Scale for Children — Revised

On the WISC-R Ted earned a Verbal IQ of 118, a Performance IQ of 115, and Full Scale IQ of 119. These good scores add to the significance of the results shown on the NDS; the high IQ values serve as a basis for expecting Ted to demonstrate better-than-average neuropsychological performances, and his total NDS score of 58 was much worse than expected for normal children. However, there was no significant difference between the Verbal IQ and the Performance IQ values.

We do not intend to present a complete clinical interpretation at this point, since such an evaluation for this child is given in the section on case illustrations. However, it is important to note the types of findings that are listed as indicators of left or right cerebral dysfunction. These findings are usually represented by *signs* of cerebral damage or dysfunction: dysphasic symptoms (typically implicating the left cerebral hemisphere) and constructional dyspraxia (implicating the right cerebral hemisphere), lateralized motor deficits or sensory-perceptual losses on one side of the body (implicating the contralateral cerebral hemisphere), or striking deviations from normal or expected patterns and relationships among test scores that represent higher-level brain functions. We tend to list even quite minor deviations from normal findings (rather than only scores that contribute to the NDS score), realizing that consistencies may emerge among these minor deviations that have clinical significance and thereby permit the clinical interpretation to assume a degree of sensitivity that goes beyond the more formal scoring of the NDS.

Evaluation of Other Test Scores

In many instances the critically significant data is provided by a detailed clinical analysis of the remaining test scores. It is, of course, necessary to effect an integration of the overall findings. The NDS and clinical organization of the test data permit identification of brain-related neuropsychological findings, and these in turn have implications for both neurological and psychological inferences.

In interpreting Ted's test findings, the neuropsychologist must determine how the relatively high IQ values and good scores on measures such as the Category Test can be integrated with the strong indications of dysfunction on the right side of his body. Even though Ted's academic achievement scores do not meet expectation with relation to his IQ levels, they are not grossly below his grade level. Is there a type of brain lesion that could allow development of these higher-level neuropsychological functions and still selectively impair lower-level functions on the right side of the body? Perhaps the lesion is of recent origin, sustained only after general intelligence and other neuropsychological functions had developed, such as a traumatic lesion (head injury) of the left cerebral hemisphere.

But it is important to remember that the general indicators are usually sensitive to lateralized as well as generalized cerebral lesions, regardless of the side involved. In addition, considering the consequences of a strong force delivered from the external environment, traumatic injuries of the brain usually cause generalized deficits in addition to any lateralized indications (see Reitan & Wolfson, 1986, 1988b). Thus, if the brain damage was the result of an outside blow to the head, how could there be such profound left cerebral indicators and sparing of both the general neuropsychological functions and right cerebral hemisphere abilities? Would it not seem more reasonable that the lesion of the left hemisphere developed from inside the brain rather than being the result of a destructive force from the outside?

Even though intrinsic lesions may develop over a considerable period of time (and thus impair development of general neuropsychological functions), are there some types of relatively focal or lateralized lesions which may essentially be dormant (and permit normal acquisition of higher-level abilities) until they develop to the point at which they produce pathological clinical symptoms? Should such indications alert the neuropsychologist to the probability of a lesion that might require immediate medical attention?

Questions of this type test the acumen and clinical experience of the neuropsychologist in his/her attempt to understand an individual's brain-behavior relationships, and the reader should bear in mind such questions while reviewing the clinical interpretations which follow. In Ted's case we have emphasized questions concerned with neurological inferences, because that is the area to which the test findings led. However, in many other cases, the test findings imply a chronic-static neurological condition (for which medical evaluation would be nonproductive), and in which the indications of neuropsychological deficits dominate the picture in terms of understanding the problems of the child and in formulating plans to adapt to the situation through environmental adjustments, psychotherapeutic intervention, educational procedures, and the use of brain retraining procedures.

Sequential Organization of Illustrative Cases

The first two cases we will discuss represent normal control children who had no specific complaints; they had volunteered to be tested as part of a research study. They were selected to represent a rather typical child (Terry) and a child who performed among the poorest in this category (Ben).

Cody (Case #3) and Denise (Case #4) would also be considered control subjects in terms of their essentially negative neurological (medical) findings. However, in terms of their history and current complaints, both of these children had clinical problems. Cody had a long history of inadequate academic achievement, and Denise had problems of a neurological nature. These cases illustrate the importance of neuropsychological evaluation in developing an understanding of brain dysfunction even when the findings of the clinical neurological examination and objective neurological tests are within the normal range.

The clinical illustrations then proceed to include an extensive range of established neurological disorders, including brain tumors, a suspected brain tumor, and cerebral conditions of abscess, hemispherectomy, arteriovenous malformation, encephalitis, idiopathic epilepsy, and traumatic brain injury (cases 5 through 17). These cases will give the reader a degree of familiarity with the relationships between the test results and the instances of brain disease and damage represented among these children.

Finally, cases 18 through 22 turn again to children with essentially normal neurological findings who have serious learning and/or behavioral problems. After having been exposed to a series of cases with various types of brain disease or damage, it may be instructive to the reader to see how the same tests, and principles of interpretation, clarify the underlying brain dysfunction and lead to a basic understanding of the problems experienced by these children.

Throughout the case illustrations emphasis is placed not only on evaluation but also on approaches to remediation.

Neuropsychological Evaluation of Normal Children

In order to understand and appreciate the types of test results that fall within the normal range, it obviously is necessary to assess normal children. Nevertheless, many practicing neuropsychologists have had limited professional contact with normal children, gaining essentially their entire experience from clinical referrals. In fact, research has shown that nearly one-third of normally functioning children show significant (though not pathological) deviations of brain-behavior relationships.

The following points should be noted explicitly:

1. The physical (medical) neurological examination of children has been developed to identify pathology. As a result, children who do not have a definite brain lesion or disease will be classified as being essentially within normal limits. This situation leaves the entire range of "normal" children irrelevant in terms of brain functions which subserve behavior quite variably across the broad expanse of cognitive and intellectual abilities. It is apparent that a procedure which leads to a gross dichotomous classification of children into "brain-damaged" and "normal" categories is hardly adequate to describe the individual child. Nor is it surprising, as noted in point (2) below, that about one-third of "normal" children demonstrate evidence of mild neuropsychological impairment. This concept is documented more fully in Chapter VII.

2. Research studies using the Halstead-Reitan Battery have shown that about one-third of children classified as normal (based on the neurological history and examination and adequate academic progress) have at least mildly deviant neuropsychological findings. This finding helps to explain the problems these children often have, and provides a basis for prescribing training procedures over and beyond those customarily used in the regular or special education classroom.

Terry is representative of these "normal" children, whereas Ben was a normal volunteer who showed clear evidence of neuropsychological dysfunction. The two additional children in this introductory section were referred for clinical problems; Cody for learning difficulties and Denise because she had experienced a seizure. However, both children were normal in terms of results obtained on the medical (physical neurological) examination.

■

Case 1 — TERRY

Age:	13-2	**Gender:**	Male
Education:	5	**Handedness:**	Right

Background Information

Terry was a 13-year, 2-month-old boy who had nearly completed the sixth grade in school when we examined him. In terms of academic placement he was almost a year behind his age peers, because his sixth birthday occurred a few days past the deadline for starting school; he was therefore almost 7 years old when he entered the first grade.

Terry's teachers viewed him as being a rather typical, normal 13-year-old child, although they did feel that he did not apply himself as much as he might to his academic work. His grades as well as his evaluations by his teachers suggested that he was having somewhat more difficulty than most children in making academic progress.

Terry volunteered to take the Halstead-Reitan Battery for Older Children as a control subject, in the interest of contributing to a scientific research study. He received no compensation of any kind for participating in the study. During the examination he was friendly, interested in the tests, and appeared to make a sincere effort to perform well.

Neuropsychological Examination

Wechsler Intelligence Scale for Children — Revised

We administered the WISC-R to evaluate Terry's general level of intelligence. He earned a Verbal IQ of 94, a score that falls in the lower part of the Average range and exceeds approximately 34% of his age peers. His Performance IQ

The Halstead-Reitan Neuropsychological Test Battery for Older Children

Name __Terry__   Age __13 – 2__

Gender __M__ Education __5__   Handedness: RH __7__ LH __0__

Neuropsychological Deficit Scale (NDS) Summary

Level of Performance	Subject's score	Mean for controls	Mean for brain-damaged	Cut-off score
Motor Functions	0	6.29	14.05	
Sensory-perceptual Functions	4	5.15	10.77	
Attention and Concentration	1	1.91	3.78	
Immediate Memory and Recapitulation	0	2.23	3.31	
Visual-spatial Skills	1	4.06	7.69	
Abstraction, Reasoning, Logical Analysis	2	2.63	6.03	
Level of Performance–Total	8	22.27	45.63	33/34
Dysphasia and Related Variables	3	1.37	7.97	3/4
Right / Left Differences	8	6.79	13.74	9/10
Total NDS Score	19	30.43	67.34	43/44

WISC-R

VIQ __94__
PIQ __104__
FS IQ __98__

Verbal Subtests		*Performance Subtests*	
Information	9	Picture Completion	8
Similarities	11	Picture Arrangement	10
Arithmetic	10	Block Design	13
Vocabulary	7	Object Assembly	10
Comprehension	8	Coding	12
(Digit Span)	(8)	(Mazes)	(8)

WRAT

	Grade Equivalent
Reading	6.6
Arithmetic	6.3
Spelling	6.3

Strength of Grip

Dominant hand   (R) __24.0__ kg
Non-dominant hand (L) __20.5__ kg

Name Writing

Dominant hand   (R) __8__ sec
Non-dominant hand (L) __15__ sec

Category Test

Number of errors __38__

Tactual Performance Test

Dominant hand   (R) __2.3__
Non-dominant hand (L) __2.1__
Both hands __0.4__   Total Time __4.8__
   Memory __6__
   Localization __6__

Seashore Rhythm Test

Number correct _____   Not given _____

Speech-sounds Perception Test

Number of errors __7__

Finger Tapping Test

Dominant hand   (R) __41__   41
Non-dominant hand (L) __39__

Trail Making Test

Part A __11__ sec __0__ error(s)
Part B __30__ sec __0__ error(s)

Bilateral Simultaneous Sensory Stimulation

RH ___ LH ___   Both: RH ___ LH ___
RH ___ LF ___   Both: RH ___ LF ___
LH ___ RF ___   Both: LH ___ RF ___

RE ___ LE ___   Both: RE ___ LE ___

RV ___ LV ___   Both: RV ___ LV ___
___ ___   ___ ___
___ ___   ___ ___

Tactile Finger Recognition

RH 1 ___ 2 ___ 3 _1_ 4 _2_ 5 ___   RH _3_ / 20
LH 1 ___ 2 ___ 3 ___ 4 ___ 5 ___   LH _0_ / 20

Finger-Tip Number Writing

RH 1 _1_ 2 _1_ 3 ___ 4 ___ 5 _2_   RH _4_ / 20
LH 1 ___ 2 ___ 3 _1_ 4 _1_ 5 ___   LH _2_ / 20

Tactile Form Recognition Test

Dominant hand   (R) __6__ sec __0__ error(s)
Non-dominant hand (L) __7__ sec __0__ error(s)

Reitan-Indiana Aphasia Screening Test

Form for Adults and Older Children

Name <u>Terry</u>   Age <u>13 – 2</u>

Copy SQUARE	Repeat TRIANGLE
Name SQUARE	Repeat MASSACHUSETTS
Spell SQUARE	Repeat METHODIST EPISCOPAL
Copy CROSS	Write SQUARE
Name CROSS	Read SEVEN
Spell CROSS	Repeat SEVEN
Copy TRIANGLE	Repeat/Explain HE SHOUTED THE WARNING
Name TRIANGLE	Write HE SHOUTED THE WARNING
Spell TRIANGLE	Compute 85 − 27 =
Name BABY	Compute 17 x 3 = 210 --- No --- 93 --- 41
Write CLOCK	Name KEY
Name FORK	Demonstrate use of KEY
Read 7 SIX 2	Draw KEY
Read MGW	Read PLACE LEFT HAND TO RIGHT EAR
Reading I	Place LEFT HAND TO RIGHT EAR *S placed left hand to left ear. Ex.? Then S responded correctly.*
Reading II	Place LEFT HAND TO LEFT ELBOW

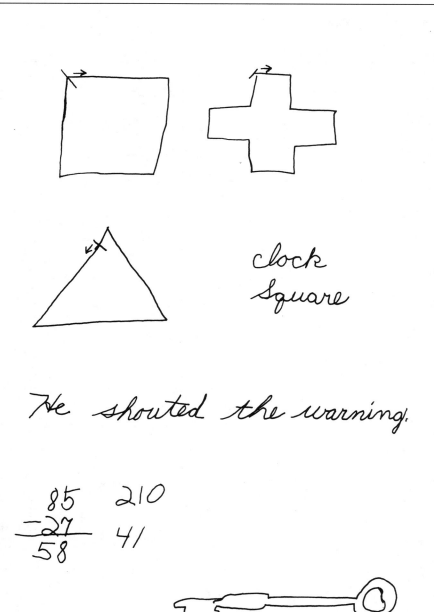

clock
Square

He shouted the warning.

$$\begin{array}{r} 85 \\ -27 \\ \hline 58 \end{array}$$

210

41

(104) was 10 points higher and exceeded 61%. These values yielded a Full Scale IQ of 98, a score that falls almost exactly at the average level (45th percentile).

The scaled scores for the Verbal subtests ranged from 7 (Vocabulary) to 11 (Similarities). Considering the fact that all of Terry's scores on the Verbal subtests fell essentially within the normal range (within one standard deviation on either side of the mean), specific comments about their variability may not be justified. However, it is possible that Terry's vocabulary is not quite as well developed as might be expected for a 13-year-old.

The Performance subtests had scores ranging from 8 (Picture Completion and Mazes) to 13 (Block Design). It should be noted that four of the six Performance subtests had scores of 10 or above, whereas only two of the six Verbal subtests fell in this range. This comparison suggests that the 10-point difference in favor of the Performance IQ may be a valid indication that Terry has somewhat better performance intelligence than verbal intelligence. Nevertheless, even though the IQ values were rather substantially different in terms of their percentile ranks, both the verbal and performance areas were within the normal range.

Wide Range Achievement Test

The WRAT, administered to obtain information about Terry's academic achievement, yielded the following grade equivalents: Reading (word recognition), 6.6; Spelling, 6.3; and Arithmetic, 6.3. Since Terry was now in the latter part of the sixth grade, these values fell just a little below average expectation. These findings are consistent with Terry's school grades and the evaluations by his teachers reporting that although he was making generally adequate progress, he was not doing quite as well as the average sixth-grade student.

Halstead-Reitan Battery for Older Children

Neuropsychological Deficit Scale. We recommend using the NDS for Older Children as an initial approach to evaluating the results of the Halstead-Reitan Battery, keeping in mind that younger children in the 9- through 14-year age range perform somewhat less proficiently than the older children in this group. Since Terry was 13 years, 2 months old when he was examined, we would expect that his NDS scores would be somewhat better than those of the average control child in this age group. However, it should be remembered that on neuropsychological tests brain-damaged children regularly perform much worse than control children, and research analyses of results on the NDS indicate that the presence of brain damage is a much more significant factor than chronological age in determining a child's performance.

Terry performed very well on the Level of Performance section of the NDS, earning a total of only 8 points. On this section the average score for control subjects is 22.27 points and the average for brain-damaged subjects is 45.63 points. For the Level of Performance section the recommended cut-off score is between 33 and 34 points.

Terry's scores on all seven variables in the section on Motor Functions were perfectly normal and earned an NDS score of 0. His scores on five of the seven variables in the Sensory-perceptual Functions section were perfectly normal, and two variables had scores in the mildly impaired range and earned NDS scores of 2 points each. All of his scores on the individual tests in the remaining sections (Visual-spatial Skills, Attention and Concentration, Immediate Memory and Recapitulation, and Abstraction, Reasoning, and Logical Analysis) were either perfectly normal (0) or normal (1). As noted, Terry's total score of 8 points for this section was considerably better than the score of 22.27 earned by the average control child.

Terry's scores on the measures concerned with dysphasia and related variables totaled 3 points. On this section the mean for control subjects is 1.37 points and the mean for brain-damaged subjects is 7.97 points. The recommended cut-off score, between 3 and 4 points, just includes Terry's score in the normal range. Although he was not grossly impaired on any items in this section, he did show mild but definite evidence of right-left confusion, and made a type of mistake that is rather characteristic of brain-damaged children: when asked to mentally multiply 17 × 3, his initial response was "210."

Terry also tended to do somewhat poorly on the Right-Left Differences section, earning a score of 8 points. On this section control children average 6.79 points and brain-damaged children average 13.74 points. The cut-off score between 9 and 10 points includes Terry's total score within the normal range.

In summary, we can see that although Terry did extremely well on the Level of Performance section, he closely approached the cut-off points in the Dysphasia and Related Variables and Right-Left Differences sections.

Terry's total NDS score of 19 points was well within the normal range, and was considerably better than the average score of 30.43 earned by control children. The recommended cut-off score (between 43 and 44 points) is substantially less than the average score of 67.34 points earned by children with documented brain damage. There seems to be no question that on the HRB Terry earned overall scores that were well within the normal range; however, as expected even with normal children, some of his scores suggested that certain aspects of his brain functions were a little less than optimal.

Clinical Evaluation of the Test Results. At this point in the analysis of the test results we will consider the specific tests for a more detailed consideration of their significance. It is apparent initially that overall Terry performed quite well. His ability to register incoming material was perfectly normal (as shown by his good score of 7 on the Speech-sounds Perception Test). Unfortunately, we were not able to complete the Seashore Rhythm Test because of an unexpected outside noise interruption.

Terry's ability to deal with visual-spatial tasks was generally within the normal range. His drawings of the key and the triangle showed mild deficiencies, but he had relatively adequate scores on the Performance subtests of the WISC-R and an excellent overall performance on the Tactual Performance Test. His good scores on the three trials of the TPT indicate excellent psychomotor skills, especially in the area of adapting to tasks that are difficult and unusual in their requirements. In addition, he demonstrated good ability to remember and recapitulate the shapes involved as well as their proper location.

It is especially important to recognize that Terry had adequate abilities in abstraction and reasoning skills and flexibility in thought processes (as indicated by normal scores on the Category Test, Trails B, and Coding). In our clinical experience, competence in these areas implies a good potential for future learning and psychological development.

Although his performances could probably be considered just within the range of normal variation, Terry did have some mild difficulties in dealing with simple spatial configurations. For example, his drawing of the triangle makes it quite clear that he failed to estimate the overall shape of the figure accurately, and it was necessary for him to effect a compensatory adjustment in closing the figure. His drawing of the key was also somewhat deviant, particularly the elongation of the stem, some loss of symmetry in dealing with the notches of the stem, and a mild disparity in symmetry of the teeth. We would not classify these drawings as definite evidence of constructional dyspraxia, but it must be observed that these figures do deviate mildly from the ability shown by most normal children. Terry's performances should be noted clinically to represent a mild problem in these aspects of visual-spatial functions.

Complementing these indications of right hemisphere deficits was evidence of a mild degree of impairment of the left upper extremity (20.5 kg) as compared with the right (24.0 kg) in grip strength. Terry also failed to show quite as much improvement as expected with the left hand (second trial) on the Tactual Performance Test, but one must note that his time for each hand was excellent, and there certainly would be no basis for serious implication of the structural integrity of the right cerebral hemisphere because of the performance with the left hand.

The test results up to this point describe Terry as a child who has (1) average general intelligence, (2) academic achievement levels within the range of normal variation, and (3) generally good neuropsychological test results.

Next, we will consider the findings implicating the left cerebral hemisphere. Although Terry's finger tapping speed was in the normal range in terms of level of performance, he was a little slow with the right hand (41) as compared with the left hand (39). On the Tactile Finger Localization (Finger Agnosia) Test, Terry had no difficulty whatsoever identifying fingers on his left hand, but made three mistakes on his right hand. This performance receives a score of 2 (mildly impaired) on the NDS.

On finger-tip number writing perception Terry also had a somewhat deficient score, making four mistakes on his right hand but only two mistakes on his left hand. As noted above, he demonstrated a degree of confusion when asked to mentally multiply 17×3. His first response was "210," an error that for some reason is quite typical of children with mild brain dysfunction. And finally, Terry demonstrated mild right-left confusion by placing his left hand to his left ear instead of to his right ear as instructed.

Summary and Recommendations

Although Terry's score of 8 on the Right-Left Differences section of the NDS was still just within the normal range, one must take into consideration the consistency of the findings on the neuropsychological examination. He demonstrated very mild indications of right cerebral dysfunction, and there were a number of variables which consistently implicated left hemisphere impairment. Even though the overall results are within the range of normal variation, the test findings make it quite clear that Terry has a mild degree of left cerebral dysfunction, which in turn is probably related to his apparent tendency to lag a little behind his peers in academic work.

As with many children who fall within the normal range, Terry's test results imply that certain training procedures still could be of definite benefit to him. Children who show signs of left hemisphere dysfunction on tests that compare performances on the two sides of the body nearly always have some degree of retardation in academic development. With findings of the type noted in Terry's case, it is not at all surprising that his WRAT scores were somewhat below average and that his teachers felt he was not expending enough effort toward his school studies.

When a student shows a discrepancy in performances, it is often mistakenly assumed that the child can do better and that the problem is merely one of convincing the child to "apply himself." In many cases (such as this one), we have found that in reality these "unmotivated" children demonstrate subtle though definite neuropsychological deficits. With the benefit of a cognitive rehabilitation program specifically designed to remediate these deficits, children often show remarkable progress in their academic subjects as well as in their attitude toward school and learning.

Ideally, when working with a child who has these types of problems, specific remediation efforts should be directed toward upgrading the basic functions of the left cerebral hemisphere. It would be advantageous for Terry to be enrolled in a training program using REHABIT and utilize many of the materials in Track A, which deals with developing expressive and receptive language skills. Considering his ability level, it is unlikely that Terry would need training with the most simple material; however, this is difficult to judge in the individual case, and the therapist should experiment with the specific items to determine which material would be most appropriate to use with this child. It is likely that certain aspects of phonics, especially relating to blends and digraphs, would be useful, and Terry very probably could profit from the word-building exercises which are included in a number of the training procedures.

Materials which encourage vocabulary development are clearly indicated in this case, especially using the material in REHABIT that is specifically geared for grade levels 5 through 8. We would also recommend using the training materials concerned with reading readiness to determine the extent to which Terry might need further assistance. Materials organized to promote reading skills should also be explored. Finally, considering the mild difficulties that Terry showed in dealing with simple spatial configurations, we would recommend giving him additional training with items from Tracks D and E in order to develop better abilities in dealing with simple and basic aspects of visual-spatial configurations.

Although the test results made it quite clear that Terry did not have brain damage in the conventional sense, they did demonstrate mild cognitive deficits, particularly concerning left cerebral functions. It is not at all surprising that the traditional approaches to education in the classroom usually fail to identify the special needs of children such as Terry. Educational principles and practices are organized according to an entirely different set of criteria than those which emanate from an approach oriented toward upgrading brain functions. As children like Terry demonstrate, there appears to be a definite need to infiltrate the practices of the classroom with principles and procedures which are derived from a neuropsychological approach, which explicitly values the brain as the organ of behavior. Until this is done, children like Terry will never receive either the comprehensive evaluations nor the remediation they need to help them reach their full neuropsychological potential.

■

Case 2 — BEN

Age:	11-4	**Gender:**	Male
Education:	5	**Handedness:**	Right

Background Information

Ben was a sixth-grader who volunteered to be examined without compensation as part of a research project. His medical history was entirely negative for any disease or traumatic incident which might have caused impairment of brain functions.

We included Ben's test results in this series of cases to illustrate a specific configuration: findings which show a number of indications of some degree of neuropsychological impairment, but not reaching the point at which one would postulate that any significant structural damage to the brain had occurred or that a neurological diagnosis of disease or damage would be found in the history information. Ben's set of neuropsychological test results are particularly instructive because they show about as much deviation from normality as one is likely to encounter in a control subject who has no symptoms or complaints.

Neuropsychological Evaluation

Wechsler Intelligence Scale for Children — Revised

Results on the WISC-R indicated that Ben had a Verbal IQ of 97, a score in the Average range exceeding about 42% of the normative distribution. His Performance IQ of 93 also fell within the Average range, exceeding about 32%. These values yielded a Full Scale IQ of 95 that exceeded 37%.

The Halstead-Reitan Neuropsychological Test Battery for Older Children

Name: Ben   Age: 11 – 4
Gender: M   Education: 5   Handedness: RH 7 LH 0

Neuropsychological Deficit Scale (NDS) Summary

Level of Performance	Subject's score	Mean for controls	Mean for brain-damaged	Cut-off score
Motor Functions	5	6.29	14.05	
Sensory-perceptual Functions	11	5.15	10.77	
Attention and Concentration	1	1.91	3.78	
Immediate Memory and Recapitulation	6	2.23	3.31	
Visual-spatial Skills	2	4.06	7.69	
Abstraction, Reasoning, Logical Analysis	3	2.63	6.03	
Level of Performance–Total	28	22.27	45.63	33/34
Dysphasia and Related Variables	0	1.37	7.97	3/4
Right/Left Differences	13	6.79	13.74	9/10
Total NDS Score	41	30.43	67.34	43/44

WISC-R

VIQ 97
PIQ 93
FS IQ 95

Verbal Subtests
Information 11
Similarities 10
Arithmetic 8
Vocabulary 10
Comprehension 9
(Digit Span) (5)

Performance Subtests
Picture Completion 4
Picture Arrangement 8
Block Design 13
Object Assembly 10
Coding 11

WRAT

	Grade Equivalent
Reading	7.1
Arithmetic	6.2
Spelling	6.2

Strength of Grip

Dominant hand (R) 20.0 kg
Non-dominant hand (L) 23.0 kg

Name Writing

Dominant hand (R) 9 sec
Non-dominant hand (L) 28 sec

Category Test

Number of errors   36

Tactual Performance Test

Dominant hand (R) 8.1
Non-dominant hand (L) 3.7
Both hands 3.2   Total Time 15.0
Memory 3
Localization 1

Seashore Rhythm Test

Number correct   25   6

Speech-sounds Perception Test

Number of errors   5

Finger Tapping Test

Dominant hand (R) 41   41
Non-dominant hand (L) 36

Trail Making Test

Part A   12 sec   0 error(s)
Part B   44 sec   2 error(s)

Bilateral Simultaneous Sensory Stimulation

RH___ LH___   Both: RH___ LH___
RH___ LF___   Both: RH_1_ LF___
LH___ RF___   Both: LH___ RF___

RE___ LE___   Both: RE___ LE___

RV___ LV___   Both: RV___ LV___

Tactile Finger Recognition

RH 1__ 2_1_ 3__ 4_1_ 5__   RH 1/20
LH 1__ 2_3_ 3_3_ 4_1_ 5__   LH 7/20

Finger-Tip Number Writing

RH 1_1_ 2_3_ 3_2_ 4_1_ 5_1_   RH 8/20
LH 1_3_ 2_2_ 3_2_ 4_3_ 5_2_   LH 12/20

Tactile Form Recognition Test

Dominant hand (R) 9 sec   0 error(s)
Non-dominant hand (L) 8 sec   0 error(s)

Reitan-Indiana Aphasia Screening Test

rm for Adults and Older Children

Name __Ben__   Age _11 – 4_

Copy SQUARE	Repeat TRIANGLE
Name SQUARE	Repeat MASSACHUSETTS
Spell SQUARE	Repeat METHODIST EPISCOPAL
Copy CROSS	Write SQUARE
Name CROSS	Read SEVEN
Spell CROSS	Repeat SEVEN
Copy TRIANGLE	Repeat/Explain HE SHOUTED THE WARNING
Name TRIANGLE	Write HE SHOUTED THE WARNING
Spell TRIANGLE	Compute 85 − 27 =
Name BABY	Compute 17 x 3 =
Write CLOCK *S started to print, then began again in cursive.*	Name KEY
Name FORK	Demonstrate use of KEY
Read 7 SIX 2	Draw KEY
Read MGW	Read PLACE LEFT HAND TO RIGHT EAR
Reading I	Place LEFT HAND TO RIGHT EAR
Reading II	Place LEFT HAND TO LEFT ELBOW

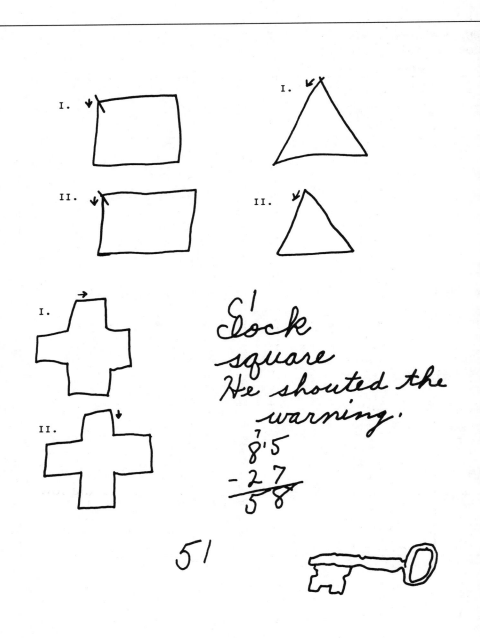

Ben showed a considerable degree of variability among scores on the individual subtests. The scaled scores on the Verbal subtests ranged from 5 (Digit Span) to 11 (Information), and the Performance subtests ranged from 4 (Picture Completion) to 13 (Block Design). Although one can postulate conclusions intended to have clinical significance on the basis of the low scores on the Digit Span and Picture Completion subtests, we have found that this procedure is open to question when based upon the Wechsler subtest scores alone. In any case, we can say that on an overall basis Ben's WISC-R scores suggest that he has both verbal and performance intelligence levels within the average range.

Wide Range Achievement Test

At the time of this neuropsychological examination, Ben was about one-third of the way through the sixth grade in school. On the WRAT he earned the following scores: Reading (word recognition), 7.1; Spelling, 6.2; and Arithmetic, 6.2. These results suggest that Ben's academic progress was within the range of expectation for a child with his IQ values.

Halstead-Reitan Battery for Older Children

Up to this point in the neuropsychological evaluation, one would conclude that Ben had essentially normal neuropsychological test findings (except perhaps for the low scores on the Digit Span and Picture Completion subtests). However, evaluation with the Halstead-Reitan Neuropsychological Test Battery for Older Children revealed a number of problems.

Neuropsychological Deficit Scale. On the NDS for Older Children, Ben's test results yielded a total NDS score of 41, a value which approaches the cut-off point of 43/44 and falls just within the normal range. On the Level of Performance section Ben's score of 28 points was greater than the mean of 22.27 earned by control children. The cut-off score for this section is 33/34 points.

Ben also performed poorly on the Right/Left Differences section, earning a score of 13 points (as compared with a mean of approximately 6.79 for control subjects) and exceeding the cut-off point of 9/10. However, Ben showed no evidence of deficits on the Dysphasia and Related Variables section, earning a score of 0 (as compared with a mean score of 1.37 for control children and a cut-off point of 3/4).

These results clearly indicate that in relation to his IQ values and level of academic achievement Ben performed poorly on brain sensitive measures, including tests that compared performances on the two sides of the body. At this point one could conclude that Ben had significant areas of deficits which were not prominent in the area of language and related abilities.

Examining Ben's scores in the areas of function represented under the Level of Performance section of the NDS, we see that he performed tasks measuring motor functions at about the average level for control subjects. However, he demonstrated significant deficits in the Sensory-perceptual Functions section, particularly in finger localization on the left hand (7) and finger-tip number writing perception on both hands (RH, 8; LH, 12). He also performed quite poorly compared to control subjects on measures of immediate memory and recapitulation (TPT-Memory, 3 and TPT-Localization, 1), indicating that he learned rather minimally from his experience of completing the Tactual Performance Test three times. On the individual tasks evaluating visual-spatial skills and alertness and concentration ability, Ben earned NDS scores of 0 (perfectly normal) and 1 (normal). Finally, on the Abstraction, Reasoning, and Logical Analysis section, Ben earned a total of 3 points, a little higher than the mean of 2.63 earned by the average control child.

These rather consistent indications of impairment on brain-sensitive tests, coupled with the striking differences in performances on the two sides of the body in grip strength, tactile finger localization, and finger-tip number writing perception, produced a total set of results that deviated from normality just enough to earn Ben a total

NDS score that was just below the cut-off point between normal and brain-damaged subjects.

Clinical Evaluation of the Test Results. Further analysis of the details of the test findings implicated each cerebral hemisphere. Although Ben was strongly right-handed, on the TPT he performed poorly with his right hand (8.1 min) as compared with his left hand (3.7 min). He also was somewhat weak with his right hand in grip strength. One might postulate peripheral involvement of the right upper extremity as an explanation for these deficient performances with the right hand, but the relatively poor scores on tests that are not limited by motor functions — together with the fact that Ben also showed striking deviations on the left side of the body — suggest that the etiology is central (cerebral) rather than peripheral.

In addition to the poor performances with the right hand on the TPT and grip strength, Ben had a tendency to fail to perceive a tactile stimulus to his right hand when it was given simultaneously with a stimulus to the left side of his face. However, he showed no evidence of specific aphasic deficits, and he performed very well on the Speech-sounds Perception Test (5 errors). These performances definitely argue against a recent or rapidly progressive focal lesion of the left cerebral hemisphere. In fact, as shown by his normal scores on the Speech-sounds Perception Test and the Seashore Rhythm Test (25 correct), it would appear that Ben has adequate ability to register incoming stimulus material (attention and concentration).

Findings implicating the right cerebral hemisphere included a very poor score on tactile finger localization on the left hand (7) as compared with the right hand (1) as well as significantly more errors on the left hand (12) than on the right hand (8) in finger-tip number writing perception (even though this latter task was done poorly on both sides). In addition, Ben's drawings on the Aphasia Screening Test demonstrate some of his difficulties with visual-spatial skills. (Note that the first drawing of the cross is barely adequate.)

Summary

Considering the overall test results, it would appear that Ben's performances deviate somewhat from normal expectancy. Some of the findings point toward involvement of the left cerebral hemisphere, other results indicate a degree of dysfunction of the right cerebral hemisphere, and still other scores suggest generalized impairment.

If a "blind" evaluation were being done, one might question whether Ben had at one time sustained some adverse insult to his brain that had caused a degree of generalized impairment. On the other hand, neuropsychological findings such as those shown by Ben are not uncommon in persons who do not have a specific neurological diagnosis, or in persons who fall within the normal range on neurological evaluation with only the history suggesting some possible etiology. In practical terms, it is likely that Ben will show a degree of inefficiency in his everyday problem-solving performances, and generally fail to measure up to the expectations people have of him based on his IQ values. In fact, Ben's relatively adequate academic achievement levels and IQ values may have resulted, at least in part, because of special concern and assistance from his family.

We specifically chose to present Ben as an example of a control subject because he met the criteria for this classification in spite of the fact that his test scores pointed toward impairment of brain functions. It is important for neuropsychologists to realize that many brains, even without evidence of prior disease or damage, are not perfectly normal. We presented Ben's case as an example of a child whose test scores came about as close to demonstrating impairment as one is likely to see in children who are classified as controls and have not been identified as needing any specific clinical help.

■

Case 3 — CODY

Age:	9-3	Gender:	Male
Education:	3	Handedness:	Right

Background Information

Cody is the son of a social worker and a physician specializing in internal medicine. When he was three years old, Cody experienced a series of ear infections and underwent a tonsillectomy. He recovered from these conditions uneventfully and had no history of any other significant medical illnesses.

Cody was classified as a control subject because he had a negative neurological history and examination and was making adequate progress in school. His parents, however, felt that their son did have some academic problems. They had noted a tendency toward "mirror writing," and believed that Cody sometimes showed a natural tendency to proceed from right to left when attempting to read.

The parents also admitted that Cody was not doing as well in school as they had hoped he would, and that during the last year particularly he had shown a loss of interest in studying and demonstrated some resistance even in going to school. They had no explanation for these difficulties, and were concerned that Cody might have some type of "perceptual problem" or emotional difficulties.

This case illustrates the overlap in children who might be classified as controls when judged according to certain criteria, but who nevertheless present problems that may have clinical neuropsychological significance.

Neuropsychological Examination

Wechsler Intelligence Scale for Children — Revised

On the WISC-R Cody earned IQ values that fell in the High Average range, with a Verbal IQ of 113 (exceeding 81% of his age peers), a Performance IQ of 111 (exceeding 77%), and a Full Scale IQ of 113 (exceeding 81%). Except for Digit Span (7), Information (10), Object Assembly (10), and Mazes (9), the scaled scores were consistently 11 or higher.

Whenever a series of tests is given, it must be expected that the child will earn some scores that will fall at the lower end of his/her own distribution. However, considering the fact that Cody's scores on Digit Span and Mazes were two or three points below the lowest of any of the other subtests, one might question whether Cody had some special difficulty on these two subtests. Despite this scatter, however, it is quite clear that one could not conclude from the results on the WISC-R that there was any significant impairment of brain functions.

Wide Range Achievement Test

Results on the WRAT confirmed the parents' impression that Cody was not doing as well in school as might be expected. On the WRAT Cody earned the following grade-equivalents: Reading (word recognition) 4.4; Spelling, 3.5; and Arithmetic, 3.0. Since Cody was just about to start the fourth grade in school, we would expect him to score 4.0. His score in Reading certainly was no greater than would be expected considering his IQ values, and he appeared to be lagging behind in both Spelling and Arithmetic.

As we will see when we review the results of the Aphasia Screening Test, Cody had the special kinds of problems in Spelling and Arithmetic which are often seen both in children with learning disabilities and children with brain

The Halstead-Reitan Neuropsychological Test Battery for Older Children

Name: Cody Age: 9 − 3
Gender: M Education: 3 Handedness: RH 7 LH 0

Neuropsychological Deficit Scale (NDS) Summary

Level of Performance	Subject's score	Mean for controls	Mean for brain-damaged	Cut-off score
Motor Functions	5	6.29	14.05	
Sensory-perceptual Functions	9	5.15	10.77	
Attention and Concentration	2	1.91	3.78	
Immediate Memory and Recapitulation	0	2.23	3.31	
Visual-spatial Skills	3	4.06	7.69	
Abstraction, Reasoning, Logical Analysis	3	2.63	6.03	
Level of Performance–Total	22	22.27	45.63	33/34
Dysphasia and Related Variables	4	1.37	7.97	3/4
Right/Left Differences	13	6.79	13.74	9/10
Total NDS Score	39	30.43	67.34	43/44

WISC-R

VIQ 113
PIQ 111
FS IQ 113

Verbal Subtests
Information	10
Similarities	12
Arithmetic	11
Vocabulary	15
Comprehension	13
(Digit Span)	(7)

Performance Subtests
Picture Completion	13
Picture Arrangement	12
Block Design	11
Object Assembly	10
Coding	12
(Mazes)	(9)

WRAT

Grade Equivalent
Reading 4.4
Arithmetic 3.0
Spelling 3.5

Strength of Grip
Dominant hand (R) 18.5 kg
Non-dominant hand (L) 17.5 kg

Name Writing
Dominant hand (R) 10 sec
Non-dominant hand (L) 19 sec

Category Test
Number of errors: 51

Tactual Performance Test
Dominant hand (R) 4.0
Non-dominant hand (L) 4.4
Both hands 1.2
Total Time 9.6
Memory 6
Localization 4

Seashore Rhythm Test
Number correct 26 — 5

Speech-sounds Perception Test
Number of errors 7

Finger Tapping Test
Dominant hand (R) 46 — 46
Non-dominant hand (L) 34

Trail Making Test
Part A 22 sec 0 error(s)
Part B 46 sec 1 error(s)

Bilateral Simultaneous Sensory Stimulation
RH___ LH___ Both: RH___ LH___
RH___ LF___ Both: RH___ LF___
LH___ RF___ Both: LH___ RF___
RE___ LE___ Both: RE___ LE 1
RV___ LV___ Both: RV___ LV___

Tactile Finger Recognition
RH 1__ 2__ 3 1 4__ 5__ RH 1/20
LH 1__ 2__ 3__ 4 3 5 2 LH 5/20

Finger-Tip Number Writing
RH 1 1 2 1 3 2 4 1 5__ RH 5/20
LH 1 2 2 1 3 2 4 1 5__ LH 6/20

Tactile Form Recognition Test
Dominant hand (R) 19 sec 0 error(s)
Non-dominant hand (L) 17 sec 0 error(s)

Reitan-Indiana Aphasia Screening Test

Form for Adults and Older Children

Name <u>Cody</u>   Age <u>9 – 3</u>

Copy SQUARE	Repeat TRIANGLE
Name SQUARE	Repeat MASSACHUSETTS

Spell SQUARE
    S - Q - U - E - R
	Repeat METHODIST EPISCOPAL
	          Methodist Episabal

Copy CROSS	Write SQUARE
Name CROSS Red cross	Read SEVEN
Spell CROSS	Repeat SEVEN
Copy TRIANGLE	Repeat/Explain HE SHOUTED THE WARNING
Name TRIANGLE	Write HE SHOUTED THE WARNING

Spell TRIANGLE
    T - R - A - E - G - I - R - L
	Compute $85 - 27 = 62$
	    $24 - 12 = 12$

Name BABY	Compute $17 \times 3 = 45$ $11 \times 4 = 45$
Write CLOCK	Name KEY
Name FORK	Demonstrate use of KEY
Read 7 SIX 2	Draw KEY
Read MGW	Read PLACE LEFT HAND TO RIGHT EAR Place your left hand to the right ear.
Reading I	Place LEFT HAND TO RIGHT EAR S put left hand on left ear. Ex.? S performed correctly.
Reading II . . . of the dog . . .	Place LEFT HAND TO LEFT ELBOW

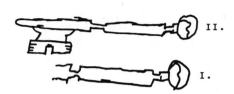

II.

I.

He shoulded the warning

45 (17X3) 45 (11X4)

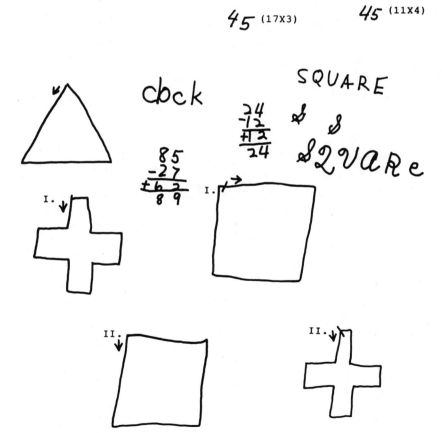

SQUARE

clock

$$\begin{array}{r} 74 \\ -12 \\ \hline 72 \\ \hline 24 \end{array}$$

$\mathscr{S}$ $\mathscr{S}$

$$\begin{array}{r} 85 \\ -27 \\ \hline 62 \\ \hline 89 \end{array}$$

S2VaRe

I.

II.

II.

damage. Neuropsychological findings of this kind clearly would call for further evaluation in order to determine the extent of any additional neuropsychological deficit and the degree to which impairment of brain functions might be present.

Halstead-Reitan Battery for Older Children

Neuropsychological Deficit Scale. Results of the NDS for Older Children are valuable in identifying not only the general level of performance, but also the areas of particular deficit. A review of Cody's scores indicates that he performed adequately in the areas of Motor Functions, Attention and Concentration, Memory and Recapitulation, Visual-spatial Skills, and Abstraction, Reasoning, and Logical Analysis. In these areas only Part A (22 sec) and Part B (46 sec) of the Trail Making Test had scores in the impaired range.

Although the overall results were relatively adequate, Cody clearly showed evidence of dysfunction in the sections concerned with Sensory-perceptual Functions, Right-Left Differences, and Dysphasia and Related Variables. His score of 22 points on the Level of Performance section compared closely with the mean of 22.27 points for control subjects and did not approach the cut-off of 33/34 points. However, his score of 13 points on the Right-Left Differences section well exceeded the mean of 6.79 points for control subjects, and the cut-off of 9/10, and approximated the mean of 13.74 points for brain-damaged subjects. Cody also made specific errors on the Dysphasia and Related Variables section, and his score of 4 points exceeded the mean of 1.37 for control subjects and deviated toward the mean of 7.97 for brain-damaged subjects. The cut-off for this section is 3/4 points.

These values yielded a total NDS score of 39, a value which falls above the mean of 30.43 points for control subjects but does not reach the cut-off of 43/44 points. Brain-damaged subjects had a mean total NDS score of 67.34

points, and Cody's scores clearly did not approximate this level. Nevertheless, considering his IQ values, he did not perform at a comparable level on brain-sensitive tests. His areas of deficiency were particularly evident on sensory-perceptual performances (including right-left differences) and on simple tasks in spelling, arithmetic, and right-left orientation. The reader will observe the general similarities between Cody's results and those customarily seen in children with definite learning deficits when results for children with identified learning disabilities are reviewed later in our analysis of individual cases.

Clinical Evaluation of the Test Results. A more detailed analysis of Cody's test findings emphasized the difficulties he had with simple performances in the academic area. On the Aphasia Screening Test he spelled SQUARE as S-Q-U-E-R. He was much more confused in his attempt to spell TRIANGLE, as can be noted in his response of T-R-A-E-G-I-R-L. In this instance Cody failed to establish a sequence of letters that even came close to the sounds involved in the word. When he was asked to look at a picture of a clock and write its name on the paper, he initially omitted the L and inserted it after he had finished the word. It is apparent from these performances that Cody is impaired in the ability to use letters for word-building purposes.

Cody also had significant difficulties in cursive writing. He had learned to print, and although he had not had a great deal of experience in cursive writing, his attempt to write the word SQUARE makes it quite clear that he had special problems in the ability to form letters.

Cody's ability to perform simple arithmetical computations were clearly deficient. In attempting to do $85 - 27 =$ he obviously became confused between addition and subtraction. He puzzled over the problem at length, finally wrote his solution, and then attempted to "prove" his answer. When this procedure did not work out he was unsure of what to do next, and admitted finally that he could not do the problem. He was able to perform a simpler problem (24 − 12) that did not require borrowing. It is likely that multiplication problems were too difficult for him, and he was not able to answer correctly any of the problems given by the examiner (17 × 3, 8 × 6, and 11 × 4). The confusion between addition and subtraction on 85 − 27 = was the principal basis for counting dyscalculia on the NDS.

Cody had other problems of the kind that frequently are seen in children with learning difficulties. For example, on the reading items he inserted words that were not on the stimulus card; when asked to read PLACE LEFT HAND TO RIGHT EAR, Cody read PLACE *YOUR* LEFT HAND TO *THE* RIGHT EAR. Children with normal reading abilities do not customarily add words that are not included in the stimulus material. Note, however, that although Cody's reading performance must be considered clinically, we did not feel that his difficulties were sufficiently severe to be considered dyslexia on the NDS.

Cody made an explicit mistake when asked to place his left hand to his right ear: he placed his left hand to his left ear. Even though Cody corrected his mistake when questioned by the examiner, in terms of NDS scoring criteria this error contributes one point toward right-left confusion.

When a right-handed child demonstrates the type of difficulties described above, it suggests the presence of some degree of left cerebral dysfunction. Although Cody showed definite right-left differences in his performances, he did not demonstrate many specific indications of dysfunction with the right upper extremity as compared with the left. His grip strength was just a little weak with the right hand (18.5 kg) as compared with the left hand (17.5 kg), but this finding by itself certainly is not sufficient to implicate the left cerebral hemisphere on the basis of comparative performances on the two sides of the body. It should be noted, however, that Cody performed poorly on each side in finger-tip number writing perception and was slow to respond on the Tactile Form Recognition Test. Thus, considered in total, the test results would suggest that there was some basis for inferring involvement of the left cerebral hemisphere in the context of diffuse cerebral dysfunction.

Lateralizing results implicating the right cerebral hemisphere were quite distinct. Although he performed within the normal range in terms of total scores on the Tactual Performance Test, Cody was clearly slow with his left hand (4.4 min) as compared with his right hand (4.0 min). On finger tapping his left hand (34) was also slower than expected compared to the right hand (46). Cody also showed definite sensory-perceptual deficits on the left side, in one instance failing to respond to an auditory stimulus to the left ear when stimuli were administered to both ears simultaneously. On tactile finger localization he had more difficulty on his left hand (5 errors) than on his right hand (1 error).

As might be expected with these rather pronounced lateralizing findings which implicate the right cerebral hemisphere, Cody had a little difficulty in copying simple spatial configurations (see his second attempt to copy the Greek cross and his drawings of the key). Although we did not consider these drawings to be sufficiently distorted to qualify as constructional dyspraxia on the NDS, they are undoubtedly difficulties which have to be recognized clinically.

Summary and Recommendations

Evaluation of the overall results on the Halstead-Reitan Battery indicated that Cody has many abilities which are in the normal range. Nevertheless, the findings in total definitely cannot be considered normal, even though summary scores (such as the total NDS score) did not fall in the brain-damaged range. Although Cody's results are not sufficiently poor to postulate the presence of brain damage that would be confirmed by neurological examination and diagnostic tests, his test scores do indicate the presence of brain-related neuropsychological deficits.

This illustrative case makes it quite clear that the sensitivity of neuropsychological measures exceeds the sensitivity of neurological criterion measures. In terms of findings with the Halstead-Reitan Battery, it is not uncommon to see evidence of disparities in performances on the two sides of the body which we have learned to recognize as warning signals of higher-level problems which center, especially with children, in the area of academic achievement. From a neuropsychological point of view, Cody clearly represents a mild case of learning disability, even though his IQ values are definitely above average and his academic achievement scores, though mildly impaired, are still within the normal range of variation.

In terms of remediation, the neuropsychological test results indicate that Cody needs special help in developing academic skills, particularly as they relate to verbal and numerical symbols. Cody's parents should be counseled to help them understand that the types of difficulties their son is experiencing do not represent a "developmental phase" that he will eventually grow out of spontaneously. Nor is it likely that Cody will receive the specialized remediation procedures he requires from his normal classroom instruction. In order for Cody to receive appropriate and pertinent rehabilitation, he should be given treatment by a neuropsychologist who understands his cognitive ability structure in terms of its strengths as well as its weaknesses.

Cody would be an excellent candidate for training using REHABIT, and we would recommend beginning with Track B in order to give him an opportunity to use his fairly adequate conceptual ability and apply it initially to verbal and language problems. However, Track B would be only an introduction to the training procedures, because the major concentration would necessarily focus on the materials included in Track A. Considering Cody's generally good abilities, special training of this type will probably be sufficient to help him overcome his current difficulties.

Immediate implementation of such a training plan would be important, especially since Cody has already shown signs of losing interest in school. Obviously, these manifestations of diminished interest in academic subjects must be viewed as an eminently reasonable response for this child, considering the difficulties he must be experiencing and the lack of understanding of his problems by his teachers and parents. Once Cody has had the opportunity to work with material specifically designed to remediate the particular deficits he demonstrates, it is quite likely that his interest in academic subjects will improve.

■

Case 4 — DENISE

Age:	9-10	**Gender:**	Female
Education:	4	**Handedness:**	Right

Background Information

Denise was a little girl who had just finished the fourth grade in school when we examined her. The only remarkable incident in her medical history was the fact that she had required a blood exchange transfusion shortly after birth because of an Rh-negative factor. However, she had appeared to be quite normal in her development and up to six days before we tested her, she would have been classified as a control subject.

On the morning six days before this neuropsychological examination, Denise's mother observed her experiencing a five-minute episode of jerking of her arms while she was apparently unconscious. After the seizures stopped Denise was unresponsive for approximately five minutes. She then regained consciousness but remained drowsy for an additional 15 minutes. Her parents reported that after that time she appeared to be entirely normal and did not seem to have any residual effects from the seizure.

The next day Denise had a similar episode, and her parents immediately took her to be examined by a child neurologist. Although an EEG showed generalized cerebral dysrhythmia, the physical neurological examination was entirely within normal limits. Denise was diagnosed as having major motor epilepsy of unknown etiology with cerebral dysrhythmia. The neurologist referred the child to our laboratory, and a comprehensive neuropsychological examination was performed six days after the initial episode.

Neuropsychological Examination

Wechsler Intelligence Scale for Children — Revised

Denise's results on the WISC-R were entirely within normal limits. She earned a Verbal IQ of 108, a value that falls in the upper part of the Average range and exceeds about 70% of her age peers. Her Performance IQ of 114 was in the High Average range, exceeding about 82%. These values yielded a Full Scale IQ of 112, a value that falls in the lower part of the High Average range and exceeds 79%.

The individual subtest scores ranged from 9 (Picture Arrangement) to 14 (Similarities and Coding), and all subtests (except for Picture Arrangement) had scores of 10 or higher. The results of the WISC-R correspond with Denise's school grades and her teacher's reports that she was making adequate progress in school.

Wide Range Achievement Test

On the WRAT Denise earned the following grade-equivalents: Reading (word recognition), 4.8; Spelling, 5.5; and Arithmetic, 4.7. Considering the fact that Denise had just completed the fourth grade, her scores on the WRAT were within normal limits.

Halstead-Reitan Battery for Older Children

Neuropsychological Deficit Scale. Despite these relatively average findings, Denise earned a total NDS score of 44, a value that is just beyond the cut-off point of 43/44 and falls into the brain-damaged range. The Level of Performance section contributed 30 points (cut-off: 33/34) and the Right-Left Differences section contributed 14 points (cut-off: 9/10). Denise performed fairly well on the Aphasia Screening Test, and did not earn any points on the Dysphasia and Related Deficits section of the NDS. These summary values

**The Halstead-Reitan
Neuropsychological Test Battery
for Older Children**

Name   Denise   Age 9 – 10

Gender   F   Education   4   Handedness: RH 7 LH 0

Neuropsychological Deficit Scale (NDS) Summary

Level of Performance	Subject's score	Mean for controls	Mean for brain-damaged	Cut-off score
Motor Functions	9	6.29	14.05	
Sensory-perceptual Functions	12	5.15	10.77	
Attention and Concentration	3	1.91	3.78	
Immediate Memory and Recapitulation	0	2.23	3.31	
Visual-spatial Skills	2	4.06	7.69	
Abstraction, Reasoning, Logical Analysis	4	2.63	6.03	
Level of Performance–Total	30	22.27	45.63	33/34
Dysphasia and Related Variables	0	1.37	7.97	3/4
Right / Left Differences	14	6.79	13.74	9/10
Total NDS Score	44	30.43	67.34	43/44

WISC-R

VIQ   108
PIQ   114
FS IQ 112

Verbal Subtests		*Performance Subtests*	
Information	10	Picture Completion	12
Similarities	14	Picture Arrangement	9
Arithmetic	11	Block Design	13
Vocabulary	12	Object Assembly	12
Comprehension	10	Coding	14
(Digit Span)	(10)	(Mazes)	(12)

WRAT

	Grade Equivalent
Reading	4.8
Arithmetic	4.7
Spelling	5.5

Strength of Grip

Dominant hand   (R)   11.5 kg
Non-dominant hand (L)   10.0 kg

Name Writing

Dominant hand   (R)   18 sec
Non-dominant hand (L)   25 sec

Category Test

Number of errors   46

Tactual Performance Test

Dominant hand   (R)   4.3
Non-dominant hand (L)   1.2
Both hands   0.6   Total Time   6.1
                                                    Memory   6
                                                    Localization 4

Seashore Rhythm Test

Number correct   23   9

Speech-sounds Perception Test

Number of errors   6

Finger Tapping Test

Dominant hand   (R)   43   43
Non-dominant hand (L)   38

Trail Making Test

Part A   18 sec   0 error(s)
Part B   80 sec   3 error(s)

Bilateral Simultaneous Sensory Stimulation

RH ___ LH ___	Both: RH ___ LH ___
RH ___ LF ___	Both: RH 2 LF ___
LH ___ RF ___	Both: LH ___ RF ___
RE ___ LE ___	Both: RE ___ LE ___
RV ___ LV ___	Both: RV ___ LV ___
___ ___	___ ___
___ ___	___ ___

Tactile Finger Recognition

RH 1 _1_ 2 ___ 3 _1_ 4 _2_ 5 ___   RH 4 / 20
LH 1 ___ 2 ___ 3 ___ 4 ___ 5 ___   LH 0 / 20

Finger-Tip Number Writing

RH 1 _1_ 2 _1_ 3 ___ 4 _2_ 5 ___   RH 4 / 20
LH 1 _2_ 2 _1_ 3 _2_ 4 ___ 5 _3_   LH 8 / 20

Tactile Form Recognition Test

Dominant hand   (R)   9 sec   1 error(s)
Non-dominant hand (L)   8 sec   0 error(s)

Reitan-Indiana Aphasia Screening Test

rm for Adults and Older Children

Name _Denise_   Age _9 – 10_

Copy SQUARE	Repeat TRIANGLE
Name SQUARE Picture frame *Ex.?* Box	Repeat MASSACHUSETTS
Spell SQUARE	Repeat METHODIST EPISCOPAL Methodist Epistopal
Copy CROSS	Write SQUARE
Name CROSS Red cross	Read SEVEN
Spell CROSS	Repeat SEVEN
Copy TRIANGLE	Repeat/Explain HE SHOUTED THE WARNING
Name TRIANGLE Triangular	Write HE SHOUTED THE WARNING
Spell TRIANGLE T - R - Y - A - N - G - L - E	Compute $85 - 27 =$
Name BABY	Compute $17 \times 3 =$
Write CLOCK	Name KEY
Name FORK	Demonstrate use of KEY
Read 7 SIX 2	Draw KEY
Read MGW	Read PLACE LEFT HAND TO RIGHT EAR
Reading I	Place LEFT HAND TO RIGHT EAR
Reading II	Place LEFT HAND TO LEFT ELBOW

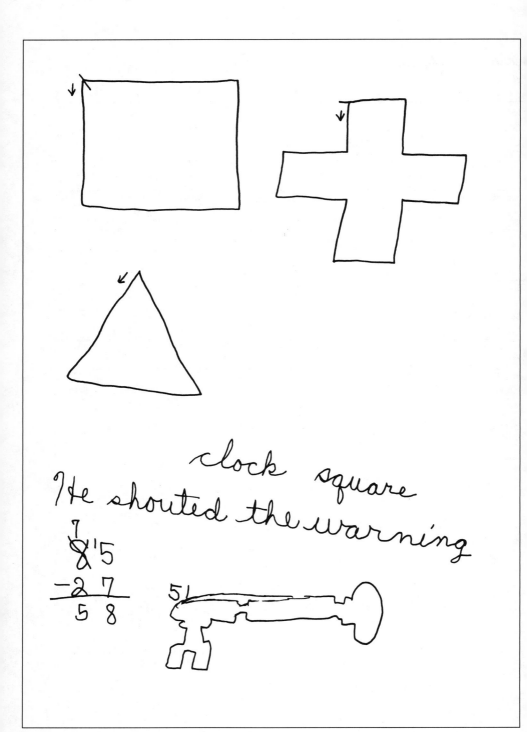

clock   square

He shouted the warning

$$\begin{array}{r} \overset{7}{\cancel{8}}{}^1 5 \\ -2\ 7 \\ \hline 5\ 8 \end{array}$$

indicate that Denise did not do particularly well on brain-related tests, and showed striking deviations from normal expectancy in terms of comparative performances on the two sides of the body. As we will describe below, the particular types of deficits Denise demonstrated are strongly suggestive of some type of neurologically significant impairment of brain functions.

Except for her performances on the Seashore Rhythm Test and Part B of the Trail Making Test, Denise's scores on all sections of the NDS representing higher-level brain functions — Attention and Concentration, Memory and Recapitulation, Visual-spatial Skills, and Abstraction, Reasoning and Logical Analysis — were within or close to the normal range. In addition, the complete absence of deficits on the Aphasia Screening Test and the results on the Verbal subtests of the WISC-R demonstrate her ability to use language functions and verbal symbols for communicational purposes.

On the Motor Functions section of the NDS Denise earned 9 points, a score intermediate to the means of 6.29 for control subjects and 14.05 for brain-damaged children. It is important to note that 6 of the 9 points she earned on this section were due to low scores on grip strength on each hand. Since Denise had a relatively small body size for her age, it is likely that these findings are not a reflection of neuropsychological impairment. This hypothesis is supported by the fact that her scores on grip strength were in the normal relationship, and she earned no points for grip strength on the Right-Left Differences section of the NDS.

Denise had definite difficulty with a number of tasks included in the Sensory-perceptual Functions section. Her scores were definitely deviant on finger localization on the right hand (4 errors) and on finger-tip number writing perception on the left hand (8 errors). Mild impairment was also shown by (1) the two errors on the right hand when stimuli were delivered simultaneously to the right hand and the left face, (2) four errors in finger-tip number writing perception on the right hand, and (3) one error with the right hand on the Tactile Form Recognition Test. However, it should be pointed out that on the TFR Test Denise confused the square and triangle, a mistake that sometimes occurs among normal children, especially when they hurry.

As we noted above, Denise's pattern of errors was of the type that has particular significance concerning neurological deficits. In children with neurological deficits it is common to find evidence of motor and sensory-perceptual deficits (lower-level aspects of brain functions) even though higher-level dysfunction is usually also prominent. When higher-level functions are relatively intact, as they were in this case, lower-level deficits still carry neurological significance. Thus, a child showing results of this kind is an appropriate candidate for referral for a comprehensive neurological evaluation if one has not already been performed.

A more detailed evaluation of the test results may be helpful in this respect. The tests which had scores that fell outside of the normal range (as summarized by NDS scores of 2 points) were as follows: name writing with the right (dominant) hand; total errors in bilateral sensory imperception; finger-tip number writing with the right hand; and tactile form recognition with the right hand. Several performances were even more poorly done, earning a converted score of 3 on the NDS: grip strength with the right hand; grip strength with the left hand; finger localization with the right hand; finger-tip number writing perception with the left hand; and Part B of the Trail Making Test. It is important to note that most of these variables related to sensory-perceptual deficits.

Clinical Evaluation of the Test Results. A clinical evaluation of Denise's performances indicated that her general level of performance was fairly adequate, although somewhat below the level of the average control child. Note, though, that there are several performances which implicated the left cerebral hemisphere. These included (1) a relatively poor performance with the right hand (4.3 min) as compared with the left hand (1.2 min) on the Tactual Performance Test, (2) clear deficiencies on the right side as compared with the left side on tactile tests of bilateral simultaneous stimulation, and (3) definite impairment in tactile finger localization on the right hand (4 errors) as compared with the left hand (0 errors). Denise also made one mistake with her right hand on the Tactile Form Recognition Test, but as we noted, this error was of equivocal significance.

On the Aphasia Screening Test Denise called a triangle a "triangular," but this mistake is not entirely uncommon among normal nine-year-olds. Denise also spelled TRIANGLE with a Y, but for a child this age, this mistake is of no particular significance, particularly since she used an appropriate phonetic spelling.

The neuropsychological findings implicating the right cerebral hemisphere were less prominent. Denise made a total of 8 mistakes on her left hand in finger-tip number writing, as contrasted with 4 mistakes on the right hand. Her drawing of a key was definitely deviant, particularly the failure to achieve symmetry in the notches. Although the drawings were not entirely within the normal range, we did not judge them to be sufficiently impaired to be given points for constructional dyspraxia on the NDS. However, her drawings must be considered clinically as indicating a deviation from the performances of normal children.

The significant indications of deficit based on higher-level tests of brain functions included only a relatively poor performance on Part B of the Trail Making Test (80 sec) and mild difficulty on the Seashore Rhythm Test (23 correct). Thus, we would not postulate that Denise would have manifestations of brain dysfunction severe enough to affect her academic performances to any significant degree. In addition, both her Verbal and Performance IQ values were well above average, falling in the upper part of the Average range to the middle part of the High Average range. Since this child's indications of brain dysfunction fall almost entirely among motor and sensory-perceptual tests, we would raise a question about the neurological significance of the findings. We would have referred this child for a neurological evaluation if she had not already been under the care of a neurologist.

Summary and Recommendations

In many respects Denise's neuropsychological test results were within the normal range, but considered as a whole, the findings certainly would raise the possibility of mild impairment of brain functions. On the NDS her Level of Performance score of 30 approaches the cut-off of 33/34. Her score of 14 on the Right-Left Differences section exceeds the cut-off score of 9/10 and is slightly higher than the mean of 13.74 earned by brain-damaged children. Although Denise did not show any difficulties on the Dysphasia and Related Variables section of the NDS, her total NDS score of 44 was past the cut-off of 43/44 and fell into the brain-damaged range. The overall results indicate that Denise had lower-level neuropsychological deficits that might well be associated with a condition such as major motor seizures. Her performances on tests of higher-level neuropsychological function were within the range of normal variation, and would probably be of limited significance concerning possible impairment of academic performances.

At this point we did not believe that any specific intervention with cognitive retraining was necessary. We advised Denise's parents to watch her academic progress closely and to contact us if it appeared that she was beginning to demonstrate any types of difficulties. This was particularly important, since Denise would be starting the fifth grade with a new teacher who was unfamiliar with her and her abilities. A conference was arranged to meet with Denise's new teacher and explain the situation to her.

Our recommendation was that Denise should be reevaluated neuropsychologically in six months, or sooner if she experienced any further acute medical problems or academic difficulties.

■

Neuropsychological Evaluation of Children with Neurological Conditions as well as Neuropsychological Problems

The following pages include brief neurological and neuro-pathological introductions to various diseases and clinical conditions. For a more complete discussion of the conditions and etiologies, as well as information concerning the neurological procedures used in their diagnosis, the reader is referred to *Neuroanatomy and Neuropathology: A Clinical Guide for Neuropsychologists* (Reitan & Wolfson, 1992a).

Neoplasms of the Brain

In this volume we cannot discuss or identify the neuropsychological consequences of the entire wide range of brain neoplasms that may develop in children. We therefore selected three children with tumors at various levels of the brain: (1) a tumor in the region of the fourth ventricle, (2) a thalamic tumor, and (3) a tumor at the cerebral level.

These children were selected to illustrate the following points: (1) tumors at lower levels of the brain, though often causing serious disruption of metabolic and life-sustaining functions, have relatively little effect on higher-level neuropsychological functions; (2) tumors of the thalamus begin to have certain deleterious effects on general neuropsychological functions, but in and of themselves do not usually cause specific higher-level deficits; and (3) tumors of the cerebral hemispheres, particularly when they clearly involve the cerebral cortex, cause serious impairment of both general and specific aspects of higher-level neuropsychological functions.

The above generalizations must be tempered by the realization that many additional factors may also influence the individual case. These factors include the specific location of the lesion; the type of tumor (which is also reflected in the degree of anaplasia or malignancy) (Hom & Reitan, 1984); the size of the lesion; associated secondary factors such as edema, adverse vascular effects, displacement of structures, increased intracranial pressure; and other variables.

An interaction therefore occurs between the level of the lesion in the brain and other factors which represent the full range of adverse influences caused by and associated with the neoplasm. However, our experience suggests that when these additional influences are minimal, the higher-level neuropsychological functions are only mildly (if at all) impaired in lesions that are located below the midbrain level. It must also be remembered that motor functions may be affected in various ways, depending upon involvement of particular structures and pathways, regardless of the level of the brain lesion.

Medulloblastoma

Definition

A medulloblastoma (sometimes referred to under the more general term of *primitive neuroectodermal tumor*) is a malignant tumor that occurs almost exclusively in persons below the age of 20 years. These tumors typically involve the cerebellar vermis, fill the cavity of the fourth ventricle, and infiltrate the floor of the fourth ventricle. The tumor grows rapidly and may metastasize to other parts of the brain and spinal cord.

Incidence

Approximately half of all childhood brain tumors arise in the posterior fossa, and approximately 30% of posterior fossa tumors are represented by medulloblastomas. Several hundred cases of medulloblastoma are diagnosed each year in the United States.

Symptoms

Medulloblastomas represent a growth of tissue into a rather limited subtentorial area, and thus impinge upon the normal structures in this region. The growth of the medulloblastoma results in brainstem or cerebellar dysfunction and is often associated with obstruction of the fourth ventricle and resulting hydrocephalus.

Children with these tumors often initially show symptoms of increased intracranial pressure, including vomiting, lethargy, and morning headache. In addition, the child may demonstrate motor unsteadiness, clumsy gait with frequent falls, and diplopia. If the tumor has metastasized, the child may demonstrate symptoms reflecting the location of the metastases.

Diagnosis

Any child with a relatively abrupt onset of the symptoms described above should be evaluated for the possibility of medulloblastoma. The diagnosis can be established with a high degree of certainty by CT scans and MRI.

Treatment

The treatment for medulloblastoma is surgical removal of the tumor followed by radiation therapy and chemotherapy. Relatively recently the prognosis was quite poor for children with medulloblastoma, even with the use of radiation therapy. However, more aggressive treatment of these malignancies, combining surgery, radiation treatment, and chemotherapy has yielded a remarkable improvement in results. Some researchers are reporting that over half of these children are surviving for five years after diagnosis, and some may possibly be cured of the disease (Packer, Atkins, Littman, et al., 1983). Long-term survival, however, is infrequent in children who do not receive postoperative radiotherapy or in children in whom radiotherapy is delivered only to the primary tumor site. (Radiation should be done to the entire neuraxis, even with children who have evidence only of disease in the primary tumor site.)

Prognosis

A number of risk factors have been identified that have a significant relationship to outcome. Children under three years of age who are diagnosed as having a medulloblastoma are at greater risk. Children whose primary tumor has metastasized also have a poorer prognosis than children who have only local involvement. Evidence also suggests that total surgical resection of the tumor yields better results than only a partial resection or only a biopsy of the tumor. The histological features of the tumor are also significant, with the more malignant tumors having a less favorable prognosis.

The aggressive treatment that is presently used to treat medulloblastomas clearly prolongs life and results in a significant improvement in symptoms. However, radiation therapy frequently causes long-term neuropsychological impairment (Danoff, Cowchock, Marquette, et al., 1982). These deficits may progress during the child's developmental years, and a complete neuropsychological assessment should be performed not only at the end of the initial treatment, but also on a regular basis thereafter, at least for several years.

Although a number of studies have shown an increased frequency of eventual learning disability, seizure disorder, and other kinds of conditions in children who have been exposed to radiotherapy of the head, more comprehensive neuropsychological studies of these children are needed.

Case 5 — ANN

Age:	11-5	**Gender:**	Female
Education:	5	**Handedness:**	Right

Background Information

Ann was a little girl who had developed normally, experiencing only the usual childhood illnesses, until the age of 10 years, 8 months. At that time she began having episodes of vomiting which occurred about once a week. Over a two-month period these episodes increased in frequency to the point that they occurred every morning.

A gastrointestinal evaluation was performed, but the findings were normal. Ann was treated with antacids and antispasmodics, which decreased the episodes of vomiting to once or twice per week. However, the episodes never stopped entirely, and a complete GI work-up was performed about eight months after the initial symptoms began. The GI results were within normal limits, but the general physical examination demonstrated a nystagmus on right lateral gaze and blurring of the margins of the optic discs of both eyes. This latter finding suggested increased intracranial pressure, and Ann was referred to a pediatric neurologist.

The neurologist found that Ann had a right lateral gaze nystagmus, a vertical nystagmus, gliotic changes of the optic discs, and blurring of the margins of the discs. Because of the likely possibility of increased intracranial pressure, Ann was hospitalized for further neurological evaluation.

X-rays of the skull were normal. However, an EEG demonstrated a generalized dysrhythmia, Grade II, with maximal involvement over the left parietal area. The EEG tracings were compatible with a deep-seated midline disturbance. A pneumoencephalogram was attempted on two occasions but it was not possible to achieve filling of the ventricles, apparently due to some type of obstruction. A ventriculogram demonstrated a marked hydrocephalus and a lesion of the fourth ventricle. A ventriculo-subgaleostomy tube was placed over the right temporal area to decompress the site.

Ann was taken to surgery four days later, and an exploration of the posterior fossa revealed a medulloblastoma projecting from the foramen of Magendie. The vermis of the cerebellum was incised and the neurosurgeon was able to resect a large amount of tumor, but thought that a small amount of tumor may have remained on the floor of the fourth ventricle. A Torkildsen procedure was performed to maintain the cerebrospinal fluid pathway. X-ray therapy to the posterior fossa and spine was instituted after this surgery.

Although Ann tolerated the operation well and recovered rapidly from the acute effects of the surgery, she had some residual ataxia and right lateral gaze nystagmus. By the time she had completed the course of x-ray treatments she was afebrile, eating well, and generally comfortable. Our neuropsychological examination was done almost exactly one month after surgical removal of the tumor. At this time Ann showed no evidence of ataxia, nystagmus, or increased intracranial pressure, and seemed to be making an excellent recovery.

Ann had follow-up neurological examinations for more than three years after her discharge from the hospital. During this period she was asymptomatic, doing well, and apparently developing normally, and the neurosurgeon reported that she saw no evidence of recurrence of the tumor. Ann did have a slight weakness of her left arm and hand, but in other respects the neurological examination was entirely within normal limits. Thus, it would appear that in this case surgical and radiological treatment were successful.

We have examined many children and adults with neoplasms. The range of lesions has varied from tumors that clearly and obviously involved the cerebral cortex to growths located in the lower part of the brainstem. The generalization suggested by our observations is that neuropsychological deficits — especially the specific types of impairment such as dysgnosia, dyspraxia, dysphasia, and constructional dyspraxia that occur in the context of serious impairment of general neuropsychological measures of brain functions — are most prominent with lesions clearly involving the cerebral cortex.

We have also seen many instances of gliomas located within a cerebral hemisphere in which the surgeon stated that the cerebral cortex appeared essentially normal. These persons, who apparently had less direct involvement of the cerebral cortex, frequently did not demonstrate the specific deficits commonly seen in persons with neoplasms that definitely involve the cerebral cortex. However, such specific deficits have occurred in individual cases, and on neuropsychological tests represented by continuous distributions, the indications of general neuropsychological impairment were frequently in the range of serious impairment.

Lesions involving the anterior brainstem or the thalamic area may show some selectivity for impairment of language (left hemisphere) or visual-spatial and manipulatory (right hemisphere) functions, depending upon the side of the thalamic area involved. However, in cases of early lesions (and especially when midline thalamic involvement is present), the patient shows few if any specific deficits, and only relatively mild impairment on general neuropsychological indicators. As the lesion grows, the deficits become more pronounced.

When the lesion has been as low in the neuraxis as the central aqueduct (aqueduct of Sylvius) or lower, our experience has been that the neuropsychological examination reveals little if any cognitive impairment.

Our observations over the years suggest that higher-level neuropsychological functions are represented by the rostral portion of the brain anterior to the midbrain level. Although in some instances tumors of the cerebellum may reflect a mild degree of impairment, these deficits often resemble a mild dysfunction of the temporal area contralateral to the cerebellar hemisphere that is involved.

Even though tumors involving the posterior fossa may be highly malignant, they rarely show significant neuropsychological deficits. Although these tumors usually progress and have a very high mortality rate, the individual's neuropsychological functions are rarely compromised to any significant extent (except as possibly affected by a general illness factor). Thus, in Ann's case we would not expect to see any of the serious types of neuropsychological deficits that often accompany a malignant tumor involving the cerebral hemispheres or cortex.

Neuropsychological Examination

Wechsler Intelligence Scale for Children — Revised

On the WISC-R Ann earned a Verbal IQ of 100, which falls exactly at the Average level and exceeds 50% of her age peers. Her Performance IQ of 112 was in the lower part of the High Average range, exceeding about 79%. These values yielded a Full Scale IQ of 105, which falls in the upper part of the Average range and exceeds about 63%. There was relatively little variability on the subtests, except that Ann did particularly well on Picture Arrangement (16).

In summary, Ann's performance on the Wechsler Scale failed to reveal any areas of selective deficit. The particularly good score on the Picture Arrangement subtest is not subject to ready explanation, but obviously it does not reflect impairment of brain functions. Ann had a Verbal IQ

The Halstead-Reitan Neuropsychological Test Battery for Older Children

Name __Ann__ Age __11 – 5__

Gender __F__ Education __5__ Handedness: RH __7__ LH __0__

Neuropsychological Deficit Scale (NDS) Summary

Level of Performance	Subject's score	Mean for controls	Mean for brain-damaged	Cut-off score
Motor Functions	16	6.29	14.05	
Sensory-perceptual Functions	4	5.15	10.77	
Attention and Concentration	3	1.91	3.78	
Immediate Memory and Recapitulation	2	2.23	3.31	
Visual-spatial Skills	3	4.06	7.69	
Abstraction, Reasoning, Logical Analysis	3	2.63	6.03	
Level of Performance–Total	31	22.27	45.63	33/34
Dysphasia and Related Variables	2	1.37	7.97	3/4
Right / Left Differences	7	6.79	13.74	9/10
Total NDS Score	40	30.43	67.34	43/44

WISC-R

VIQ __100__
PIQ __112__
FS IQ __105__

Verbal Subtests

Information	11
Similarities	11
Arithmetic	10
Vocabulary	10
Comprehension	8
(Digit Span)	(8)

Performance Subtests

Picture Completion	11
Picture Arrangement	16
Block Design	10
Object Assembly	11
Coding	11

WRAT

Grade Equivalent
Reading __6.5__
Arithmetic __6.2__
Spelling __5.6__

Strength of Grip

Dominant hand (R) __5.0__ kg
Non-dominant hand (L) __2.5__ kg

Name Writing

Dominant hand (R) __13__ sec
Non-dominant hand (L) __29__ sec

Category Test

Number of errors __50__

Tactual Performance Test

Dominant hand (R) __3.2__
Non-dominant hand (L) __2.3__
Both hands __1.7__ Total Time __7.2__
Memory __5__
Localization __3__

Seashore Rhythm Test

Number correct __23__ __9__

Speech-sounds Perception Test

Number of errors __7__

Finger Tapping Test

Dominant hand (R) __32__ __32__
Non-dominant hand (L) __26__

Trail Making Test

Part A __26__ sec __0__ error(s)
Part B __40__ sec __0__ error(s)

Bilateral Simultaneous Sensory Stimulation

RH ___ LH ___   Both: RH ___ LH ___
RH ___ LF ___   Both: RH ___ LF ___
LH ___ RF ___   Both: LH ___ RF ___

RE ___ LE ___   Both: RE ___ LE ___

RV ___ LV ___   Both: RV ___ LV ___

Tactile Finger Recognition

RH 1 ___ 2 ___ 3 ___ 4 _2_ 5 ___   RH __2__ / 20
LH 1 ___ 2 _1_ 3 _1_ 4 _1_ 5 ___   LH __3__ / 20

Finger-Tip Number Writing

RH 1 ___ 2 ___ 3 ___ 4 ___ 5 ___   RH __0__ / 20
LH 1 ___ 2 ___ 3 _1_ 4 ___ 5 ___   LH __1__ / 20

Tactile Form Recognition Test

Dominant hand (R) __9__ sec __0__ error(s)
Non-dominant hand (L) __8__ sec __0__ error(s)

Reitan-Indiana Aphasia Screening Test

Name Ann   Age 11 — 5

Form for Adults and Older Children

Copy SQUARE	Repeat TRIANGLE
Name SQUARE	Repeat MASSACHUSETTS
Spell SQUARE	Repeat METHODIST EPISCOPAL
Copy CROSS	Write SQUARE
Name CROSS	Read SEVEN
Spell CROSS	Repeat SEVEN
Copy TRIANGLE	Repeat/Explain HE SHOUTED THE WARNING
Name TRIANGLE	Write HE SHOUTED THE WARNING
Spell TRIANGLE T - R- A - N - G - L - E	Compute 85 − 27 =
Name BABY	Compute 17 x 3 =
Write CLOCK	Name KEY
Name FORK	Demonstrate use of KEY
Read 7 SIX 2	Draw KEY
Read MGW	Read PLACE LEFT HAND TO RIGHT EAR
Reading I	Place LEFT HAND TO RIGHT EAR
Reading II	Place LEFT HAND TO LEFT ELBOW

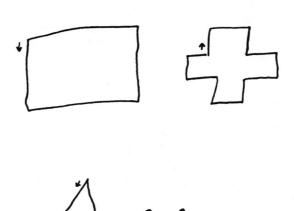

clock

square
He shouted the warning.

$$
\begin{array}{r}
8\,5 \\
-\,2\,7 \\
\hline
5\,8
\end{array}
$$

51

that was 12 points below her Performance IQ, but a difference of this magnitude occurs quite frequently among normal subjects (Silverstein, 1987). There was therefore nothing remarkable about the results on the Wechsler Scale that would suggest impairment of brain functions.

Wide Range Achievement Test

Ann had completed the fifth grade in school and was considered to be making normal progress. The WRAT yielded the following grade equivalents: Reading (word recognition), 6.5; Spelling, 5.6; and Arithmetic, 6.2. Since Ann had just completed the fifth grade, average scores for her would have been 6.0.

Halstead-Reitan Battery for Older Children

Neuropsychological Deficit Scale. The general adequacy of Ann's neuropsychological performances is shown by the NDS for Older Children. Her total NDS score was 40, which approaches the cut-off score of 43/44.

Ann performed quite poorly on the Motor Functions section. On six of the seven variables included in this section she earned scores in the range of mild to severe impairment. It is important to note that the only normal score in this section was on the Total Time for the Tactual Performance Test, a rather difficult procedure that clearly requires higher-level problem-solving skills. The finger tapping and name writing measures reflect motor speed, and Ann was comparatively slow on these measures. On this section Ann earned a score of 16, which exceeds the mean of 14.05 of brain-damaged children.

Grip strength obviously is a measure of primary motor strength, and Ann's score on this variable was very low. However, it is important to remember that as an absolute measure grip strength is easily affected by many factors besides impaired brain functions; body build, muscular development, and general physical condition all play a role in determining a person's performance. Data for adults indicates that women generally are not as strong as men, a finding that would be expected in terms of body build and muscular development (Dodrill, 1979). Although these considerations might be relevant in Ann's case, it should also be recalled that she had undergone major surgery one month before the testing and had been essentially bed-ridden since the surgery. Muscular inactivity, even for a relatively short period of time, can have a striking effect on muscular strength.

While motor speed (as measured by finger tapping and name writing) is not related to extraneous factors as clearly as is grip strength, it seems likely that a number of circumstances over and beyond brain damage may have been responsible for Ann's poor performances on the Motor Functions section.

Ann performed relatively well on measures included in the Sensory-perceptual Functions section, having some difficulty only on tactile finger localization.

Ann earned somewhat marginal scores on the Attention and Concentration section. However, the adequate score of 7 on the Speech-sounds Perception Test provides evidence that she is able to focus her attention over time to a task. Her scores on the Immediate Memory and Recapitulation and Abstraction, Reasoning, and Logical Analysis sections were essentially within the normal range. The only test on which she did not perform quite as well as may have been expected, Part B of the Trail Making Test, was another measure dependent upon speed of performance.

A summary of the results of the NDS indicates that in terms of level of performance Ann was not quite as fast as normal children on certain tasks (although she was quite quick and efficient on the TPT), and had relatively poor performances on a number of tests concerned with motor functions. There was no evidence, however, to indicate any significant or pervasive impairment of higher-level aspects of brain functions.

The remaining sections of the NDS had scores which were within normal limits. On finger tapping and grip strength Ann showed differences between her right-hand and left-hand performances that went beyond normal expectations, but in most respects comparative performances on the two sides of the body were well within normal limits. Her score of 7 for the Right-Left Differences section was just slightly above the mean of 6.79 for controls and below the cut-off of 9/10.

Ann also performed relatively well on the Dysphasia and Related Variables section. On the Aphasia Screening Test she showed no evidence at all of specific impairment in the use of language and related symbols for communicational purposes.

Even though her drawings of the square, cross, and triangle were within normal limits, her drawing of the key demonstrated certain deficits that justified scoring of constructional dyspraxia on the NDS. The deficits on the key were shown particularly in her difficulty completing the circular structure of the handle and in a failure to achieve symmetry in the notches in the stem. She also had a problem achieving symmetry in the teeth of the key, but this difficulty by itself would not have been enough to score the performance as deficient. (The key obviously was facing the wrong direction, but this has been found to occur in normal controls as often as it occurs among persons with cerebral damage.) Thus, Ann received a total of 2 points for the Dysphasia and Related Variables section, scoring above the mean of 1.37 for normal children but not exceeding the cut-off of 3/4.

In summary, it is clear that Ann had difficulties mainly in speed of certain performances and on motor measures.

These problems were principally responsible for her total NDS score of 40, which was above the mean of 30.43 earned by control children but did not exceed the cut-off of 43/44.

Clinical Evaluation of the Test Results. Clinical interpretation of the test results requires additional analyses of the general and specific indicators. Ann performed fairly well on the general indicators, such as the Category Test (50 errors), the Total Time (7.2 min), Memory (5), and Localization (3) components of the TPT, and the Speech-Sounds Perception Test (7 errors). She performed a little poorly on the Seashore Rhythm Test (23 correct), but it must be remembered that factors other than brain damage may influence the performance on nearly any individual neuropsychological measure.

Ann was also slow on both Part A (26 sec) and Part B (40 sec) of the Trail Making Test. Her scores were within normal limits on the Tactile Form Recognition Test and finger-tip number writing, but on tactile finger localization she made a few more errors than expected for normal children. These results indicate that Ann performed relatively well on a considerable number of measures, taking into account the fact that normal children usually earn scores that fall in the brain-damaged range on at least a few measures.

In terms of lateralizing findings, Ann had no indications of left cerebral dysfunction. This finding stands in contrast to the only neurological indicator of lateralized impairment, namely the EEG, which showed maximal dysrhythmia in the left parietal area. We again emphasize that it is not at all uncommon to find disagreement between neuropsychological indicators and results of the EEG, particularly when the EEG findings stand alone and are not accompanied by other neurological signs or findings.

Certain of the test results did suggest the possibility of mild right cerebral dysfunction. The most definite sign was the evidence of constructional dyspraxia in Ann's drawing of the key (as described above). In addition, in both finger tapping speed and grip strength her performances with her left upper extremity were mildly reduced as compared with the right upper extremity. These findings, especially when considered within the context of relatively normal performances on higher-level neuropsychological measures, certainly would not constitute a basis for postulating significant involvement of the right cerebral hemisphere.

Summary

Ann's test results were essentially within the range of normal variability. The mild deviations from normal performances were probably due to a general illness factor, coupled with limited mobility during the month before the neuropsychological examination was performed. As noted earlier, even though Ann's tumor was highly malignant, her neuropsychological test results are quite consistent with a lesion below the level of the midbrain.

■

Supratentorial Brain Tumors in Children

Thalamic Tumors

The next case to be presented is of a youngster named Tom who had an astrocytoma that was located in the region of the thalamus.

Definition

An astrocytoma is a type of malignant brain tumor. Astrocytomas are the most common type of glioma, a tumor arising from the glial (supporting) cells within the nervous system. Among adult subjects, gliomas represent about half of all intracranial tumors.

Astrocytomas (which represent about 75% of all gliomas) are divided into four grades, principally represented by the particular cells from which they arise, their location, their rate of growth, and especially the degree of anaplasia or malignancy. A grade I astrocytoma is a slow-growing tumor that may spread widely throughout the brain and may be present for many years before causing symptoms. A grade IV astrocytoma is a very fast-growing tumor that causes rapid development of disabling symptoms. We have previously discussed other aspects of tumor classification (Reitan & Wolfson, 1992a), and the interested reader is referred to that publication for further information.

Incidence

Brain tumors, including both primary and metastatic lesions, are found at autopsy in between 1% and 2% of the population (Green, Waggener, & Kriegsfeld, 1976). About half of newly discovered tumors are primary in nature; the other half are metastatic.

The incidence of primary intracranial tumors is estimated to be about 8.2 cases per 100,000 persons per year (Annegers, Schoenberg, Okazaki, & Kurland, 1981). Primary brain tumors have a variable frequency in accordance with the age distribution. The incidence generally is lower among children, gradually rises to about the age of 40 years, and continues to show a sharper rise to a peak at about the age of 70 years before showing a decline (Walker, Robins, & Weinfeld, 1985).

Glial tumors occur about one hundred times as frequently as neuronal tumors (Green, Waggener, & Kriegsfeld, 1976), with the most common of these lesions representing the most malignant form (glioblastoma multiforme, about 50%).

Anaplastic astrocytomas, of the type shown by Tom, represent in total about 30%. Glioblastomas multiforme are rare in children, and astrocytomas in the region of the third ventricle constitute fewer than 1% of all intracranial gliomas. Thus, an anaplastic astrocytoma of the thalamus in a child is quite a rare condition. As noted by Harsh and Wilson (1990), neuroepithelial tumors (which include tumors arising from neuronal, glial, or neuroglial cells) have a "grim prognosis" and result in a yearly death rate that is essentially equivalent to their annual incidence (Gudmundsson, 1970).

Symptoms

Clinical signs and symptoms of intracranial tumors are often differentiated into those that are general and non-localizing and those that are focal and have localizing significance.

General neurological symptoms frequently include headache, vomiting, loss of equilibrium, generalized cerebral dysfunction, and seizures. Of course, many conditions other than neoplastic involvement of the brain may give rise to these nonspecific neurological symptoms, and additional diagnostic evidence is required to document the presence of a tumor.

Focal neurological symptoms and signs generally result from impairment of brain function in the tissue involved by (or adjacent to) the tumor. These symptoms vary greatly depending upon their location. In instances of tumors located in the diencephalon (as in Tom's case), clinical symptoms usually include the general manifestations noted above and frequently are accompanied by increased intracranial pressure.

Tumors involving the thalamus, as contrasted with other areas of the diencephalon, may produce more specific symptoms depending upon the part or parts of the thalamus involved. These symptoms include apathy, emotional lability, autonomic nervous system dysfunction, weakness, tremor, ataxia, choreoathetosis, facial paresis, dysphasia, and hemiparesis (particularly when the tumor extends into the internal capsule). Tactile symptoms are also sometimes present. Tumors involving the posterior thalamic area have been noted to cause visual field deficits (although this is much more common in tumors of the cerebral hemispheres) as well as loss of oculomotor and pupillary control and hearing loss. It is apparent that the range of clinical deficits that occurs with thalamic tumors is so extensive and overlapping with tumors in other areas that they usually do not provide an adequate basis for specific localization.

Diagnosis

The same procedures are used for diagnosis in children and adults. If the history and physical examination suggest the possibility of an intracranial mass, the definitive diagnostic information is usually obtained using CT scanning or MRI of the brain. Magnetic resonance imaging has a higher hit rate than does computed tomography in terms of specific diagnosis, especially because MRI avoids bone artifact, provides high contrast between gray and white matter, clearly identifies the tumor borders, and even provides information about histological differentiation between parts of the tumor which are different in this respect. Magnetic resonance imaging may also demonstrate larger areas of abnormality than a CT scan, due to the sensitivity of the MRI to both the tumor and edema. Specific areas of calcification, which are present in some tumors, are demonstrated less well by MRI than CT.

The use of other specialized neurological techniques such as cerebral angiography, radionuclide imaging, EEG, analysis of cerebrospinal fluid, and x-ray films rarely add anything to diagnosis of the lesion that is not available with a thorough history and physical examination, complemented by CT and/or MRI of the brain.

Treatment

Even though the prognosis is poor for long-term survival, children generally do considerably better than adults with similar lesions (Stage & Stein, 1975). Surgical resection of the tumor is required, and some researchers recommend that as much of the tumor as possible should be removed in order to increase the length of survival (Bruce, Schut, & Sutton, 1990). Biopsy is advantageous to identify the histological characteristics and type of tumor, but should be followed by surgery. Early diagnosis is a distinct advantage which allows surgical intervention before the lesion has involved additional brain tissue.

Although surgical intervention in the case of thalamic tumors may be far less complete in removal of neoplastic tissue than in tumors of the cerebral hemispheres or in other locations, some degree of removal of tumor tissue is usually possible, and an operative laser may be helpful in this respect.

The goals of the operation are to remove neoplastic tissue and, in many cases, to restore ventricular flow of cerebrospinal fluid. Surgical intervention is routinely supplemented by radiation therapy and chemotherapy, and these procedures have improved outcome and length of survival.

Prognosis

While surgery and radiation therapy have long been used to treat anaplastic astrocytomas, chemotherapy has been used routinely only more recently. The prognosis in individual cases is usually poor, and varies with the size, extent, and location of the lesion, the extent of resection, and the histological features (degree of anaplasia) of the tumor. In addition, it must be noted that while both radiation therapy and chemotherapy help to prolong life, each has frequent side effects that have not yet been overcome.

Case 6 — TOM

Age:	11-2	Gender:	Male
Education:	5	Handedness:	Right

Background Information

When Tom was 11 years, 2 months old he began having bifrontal headaches, stiffness of his neck, blurred vision, and episodes of horizontal diplopia. His parents became alarmed and took him to see a pediatric neurologist, who found that Tom had elevation of the optic discs and bilateral papilledema. Tom was admitted immediately to the hospital for further evaluation.

Neurological examination at the time of admission to the hospital revealed a latent internal strabismus which suggested a mild paresis of the 6th cranial nerve. Although no other abnormalities were detected on the medical examination, x-rays of the skull showed mild changes in the region of the sella turcica suggestive of increased intracranial pressure. An EEG demonstrated a generalized dysrhythmia, Grade II, compatible with a midline tumor either in the area of the third ventricle or in the posterior fossa.

Because of the evidence of intracranial hypertension, a ventriculogram was performed and a large tumor was visualized arising from the thalamic area and obstructing the foramen of Monro. A neurosurgeon was consulted and immediate surgery was recommended. A right frontal craniotomy revealed a moderately vascular tumor in the region of the thalamus. Because of its life-threatening location, no attempt was made to excise the tumor. A small amount of the tumor was removed for histological examination and the findings indicated that it was an astrocytoma. Tom had a difficult course following this surgery, and for the next four days went through a period of restlessness and acute illness, eventually developing hydrocephalus.

Tom was again taken to surgery and a blockage of both lateral ventricles was discovered. A bilateral Torkildsen procedure was done to re-establish CSF circulation. After this surgery Tom still remained partially obtunded, irritable, and had several episodes of vomiting. The next day a surgical re-exploration was done and the neurosurgeon found that the Torkildsen tubes had become occluded by herniation of edematous cerebellar tonsils. A modification of the tubes was done to restore the flow of CSF.

Following this procedure Tom continued to be obtunded and irritable. Cerebral tissue could be seen bulging through his burr holes, indicating continued increased intracranial pressure. A dye study performed to evaluate the circulation of the CSF indicated that the ventricular block was still present. Finally, a shunt procedure using a Holter valve was performed bilaterally and the flow of CSF was directed to the right atrium of the heart, circumventing both ventricles.

Following this surgery Tom gradually began to show improvement, and one month of x-ray therapy was instituted. At this time the intracranial hypertension had subsided entirely and the diplopia was no longer present. Although Tom was still somewhat weak, very unsteady, and unable to walk without considerable assistance, his doctor felt that he was medically stable and discharged him from the hospital to continue his recuperation at home.

Neuropsychological Examination

We tested Tom with the HRB for Older Children two days after he was admitted to the hospital (five days before the partial surgical excision of the tumor).

Considering the fact that Tom had a large tumor arising from the thalamus, one would expect to see some degree of neuropsychological impairment. However, with this condition the deficits should be considerably less than if a similar

The Halstead-Reitan Neuropsychological Test Battery for Older Children

Name Tom   Age 11 – 2

Gender M   Education 5   Handedness: RH 7 LH 0

Neuropsychological Deficit Scale (NDS) Summary

Level of Performance	Subject's score	Mean for controls	Mean for brain-damaged	Cut-off score
Motor Functions	13	6.29	14.05	
Sensory-perceptual Functions	6	5.15	10.77	
Attention and Concentration	2	1.91	3.78	
Immediate Memory and Recapitulation	4	2.23	3.31	
Visual-spatial Skills	3	4.06	7.69	
Abstraction, Reasoning, Logical Analysis	3	2.63	6.03	
Level of Performance–Total	31	22.27	45.63	33/34
Dysphasia and Related Variables	3	1.37	7.97	3/4
Right/Left Differences	11	6.79	13.74	9/10
Total NDS Score	45	30.43	67.34	43/44

WISC-R

VIQ	81
PIQ	111
FS IQ	94

Verbal Subtests		Performance Subtests	
Information	7	Picture Completion	16
Similarities	9	Picture Arrangement	12
Arithmetic	3	Block Design	8
Vocabulary	8	Object Assembly	13
Comprehension	8	Coding	9
(Digit Span)	(6)		

WRAT

	Grade Equivalent
Reading	3.8
Arithmetic	2.1
Spelling	2.9

Strength of Grip

Dominant hand	(R)	14.5 kg
Non-dominant hand	(L)	12.5 kg

Name Writing

Dominant hand	(R)	14 sec
Non-dominant hand	(L)	56 sec

Category Test

Number of errors   59

Tactual Performance Test

Dominant hand	(R)	2.8
Non-dominant hand	(L)	3.9
Both hands		2.4

Total Time	9.1
Memory	4
Localization	2

Seashore Rhythm Test

Number correct   25   6

Speech-sounds Perception Test

Number of errors   7

Finger Tapping Test

Dominant hand	(R)	40	40
Non-dominant hand	(L)	31	

Trail Making Test

Part A	17 sec	0	error(s)
Part B	36 sec	0	error(s)

Bilateral Simultaneous Sensory Stimulation

RH ___ LH ___	Both: RH ___ LH ___	
RH ___ LF ___	Both: RH ___ LF ___	
LH ___ RF ___	Both: LH ___ RF ___	
RE ___ LE ___	Both: RE ___ LE ___	
RV ___ LV ___	Both: RV ___ LV ___	
___ ___	___ ___	
___ ___	___ ___	

Tactile Finger Recognition

RH 1 ___ 2 ___ 3 ___ 4 ___ 5 ___   RH 0 / 20
LH 1 ___ 2 ___ 3 2 4 1 5 ___   LH 3 / 20

Finger-Tip Number Writing

RH 1 ___ 2 2 3 1 4 2 5 ___   RH 5 / 20
LH 1 1 2 1 3 3 4 1 5 ___   LH 6 / 20

Tactile Form Recognition Test

Dominant hand	(R)	8 sec	0 error(s)
Non-dominant hand	(L)	14 sec	0 error(s)

eitan-Indiana Aphasia
creening Test

m for Adults and Older Children

Name <u>Tom</u>　　　　　　　　Age <u>11 − 2</u>

Copy SQUARE	Repeat TRIANGLE
Name SQUARE	Repeat MASSACHUSETTS 　　　　　　Massachusess
Spell SQUARE	Repeat METHODIST EPISCOPAL 　　　　　　Methodis Episcopal
Copy CROSS	Write SQUARE
Name CROSS	Read SEVEN
Spell CROSS 　　　C - R - U - S - S	Repeat SEVEN
Copy TRIANGLE	Repeat/Explain HE SHOUTED THE WARNING
Name TRIANGLE	Write HE SHOUTED THE WARNING
Spell TRIANGLE 　　　T - R - I - N - G - L - E	Compute 85 − 27 =
Name BABY	Compute 17 x 3 =
Write CLOCK	Name KEY
Name FORK	Demonstrate use of KEY
Read 7 SIX 2	Draw KEY
Read MGW	Read PLACE LEFT HAND TO RIGHT EAR
Reading I	Place LEFT HAND TO RIGHT EAR
Reading II	Place LEFT HAND TO LEFT ELBOW

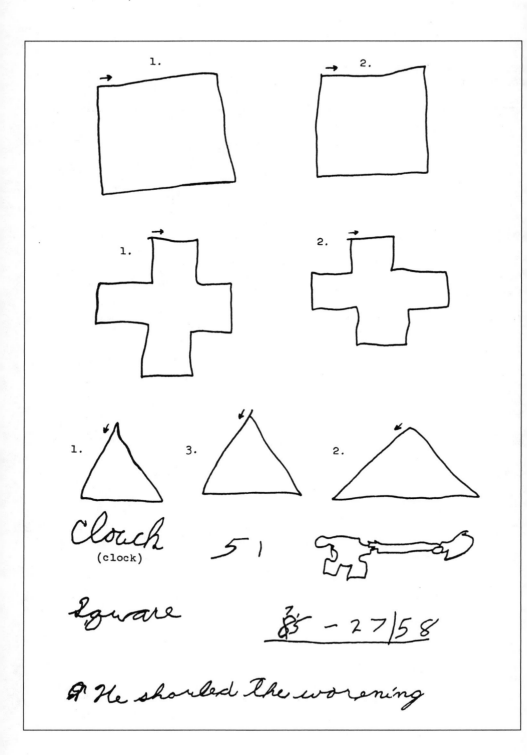

Clouch
(clock)

5 1

Square

$\frac{3}{8}5 - 27/58$

A He shoulded the worening

lesion were located within one of the cerebral hemispheres and exerted a more immediate effect upon cortical functioning. Because the tumor was represented bilaterally, the evidence of neuropsychological impairment should implicate both hemispheres, but it would be entirely possible that one cerebral hemisphere might be more involved than the other.

Wechsler Intelligence Scale for Children — Revised

On the WISC-R Tom earned a Verbal IQ of 81, a value that falls in the lower part of the Low Average range and exceeds only about 10% of his age peers. Tom's Performance IQ was 111, a score which is in the lower part of the High Average range and exceeds about 77%. These values yielded a Full Scale IQ of 94, a score that falls in the Average range and exceeds about 34%.

The more significant point of information to be gained from these results may well be represented by the 30-point difference between the Verbal and Performance IQ values. Silverstein's tables (1987) suggest that among normal subjects with a Performance IQ of 110 the 5% confidence band for Verbal IQ extends down to 83. Thus, in this case the difference in IQ values exceeds the usual confidence limits.

It may be, then, that Tom had experienced significant impairment of verbal intelligence as a result of his brain lesion. However, other factors are also known to be associated with low verbal intelligence. Some persons without documented cerebral damage, especially children with learning disability, show definite limitations of verbal intelligence. It might be that even without any effects of a brain lesion Tom may have had significant learning disabilities, a much lower Verbal IQ than Performance IQ, and distinct limitations of academic aptitude. Information relevant to these questions may sometimes be derived from a comprehensive history, but a complete neuropsychological examination may possibly indicate an organic basis for the impairment of verbal intelligence as discerned from measures other than the Wechsler Scale.

Except for an extremely poor performance on Arithmetic (3), the scaled scores for the individual Verbal subtests showed little variability. This one score considered by itself does little to resolve the question of cerebral damage vs. limited academic progress.

In general, the Performance subtests were at a higher level than the Verbal subtests. Coding might be performed poorly as a result of either cerebral damage or learning disability, and the relatively low score on Block Design (8) may suggest some right posterior cerebral dysfunction. However, as is usually the case, the overall conclusion from the Wechsler Scale is equivocal in its significance concerning the etiology of intellectual impairment.

As we have noted previously, the Wechsler Scales were not deliberately designed to evaluate brain-behavior relationships, and do not represent an adequate neuropsychological evaluation either in terms of content or methodology. Consequently, scores on the Wechsler Scales usually provide a very limited and insecure foundation for inferring brain damage as a basis for impairment of general intelligence or its various components.

Wide Range Achievement Test

When we questioned Tom's parents about his performance in school, they indicated that he had never done very well academically. He attended a small, semi-rural school and had been promoted through the grades despite his limited academic progress. He had completed five grades in school, but he had not made satisfactory progress in all of his subjects.

On the WRAT Tom obtained the following grade equivalents: Reading (word recognition) 3.8; Spelling, 2.9; and Arithmetic, 2.1. Tom had been in good health until about one month before this neuropsychological examination, but from the findings on the WRAT it appears that he had never made very adequate progress in school. Since he had just completed the fifth grade, the average grade equivalent would be 6.0.

Halstead-Reitan Battery for Older Children

Neuropsychological Deficit Scale. The NDS for Older Children yielded a total score of 45, which just exceeded the cut-off of 43/44. The total score of 31 for Level of Performance measures was intermediate to the means of 22.27 of control children and 45.63 of brain-damaged subjects and approaches the cut-off of 33/34. Tom's overall performances were therefore generally at a marginal level.

Tom performed rather poorly on the Motor Functions section, earning a score of 13. The scores on five of the seven measures in this section fell in the brain-damaged range, and the total score of 13 points was closer to the mean of brain-damaged children (14.05) than controls (6.29). Although his Total Time on the TPT (9.1 min) was within the normal range, his relatively poor scores on tapping, grip strength, and name writing may raise a question about impairment of basic motor functions. Research has shown that hospitalized patients often demonstrate impaired performances on motor tasks because of their restricted mobility and bedrest. However, since Tom was tested within two days after being admitted to the hospital, it is unlikely that his poor performances could be attributed to these influences.

On the Sensory-perceptual Functions section Tom did quite well on four of the seven measures, and his total score of 6 points was closer to the mean of controls (5.15) than brain-damaged subjects (10.77). Nevertheless, as we will show in the clinical evaluation of the neuropsychological test results, differences between performances on the two sides of the body added significant information to the interpretation.

Except for the relatively low score of 8 on Block Design (which was mentioned previously as a possible indicator of involvement or dysfunction of the posterior part of the right cerebral hemisphere), Tom's performances on the Visual-Spatial Skills section was within normal limits. He also did well on measures concerned with alertness and concentration, but scored in the brain-damaged range on both tasks that relate to immediate memory and recapitulation.

Finally, Tom had some difficulty in the area of abstraction, reasoning, and logical analysis. His performance on the Category Test (59 errors) earned a score of 2 on the NDS. On this section he accumulated a total of 3 points, compared with a mean of 2.63 for control children. As we noted, Tom's Level of Performance section score of 31 points approached the cut-off of 33/34, and raised a question of mild impairment of neuropsychological functions.

Similar results were obtained on the Right-Left Differences section of the NDS. On this section Tom earned a score of 11, which was just beyond the cut-off of 9/10 and closer to the mean of 13.74 for brain-damaged subjects than the average of 6.79 earned by controls. Again, this part of the NDS indicates that Tom's performances were marginal and indicative of possible impairment.

The final section of the NDS, concerned with dysphasia and related variables, had scores in the borderline range. On the Aphasia Screening Test Tom showed evidence of constructional dyspraxia and spelling dyspraxia. His score of 3 points for this section was just below the cut-off of 3/4. Although his score was somewhat closer to the mean of 1.37 for controls than the mean of 7.97 for brain-damaged subjects, the particular errors he made in his drawing of the key are strongly suggestive of right cerebral impairment.

A summary of the NDS results indicates that Tom's performances on each section were marginal and had scores falling just below or just above the cut-off point for brain damage. It is clear from these findings that Tom has a mild degree of neuropsychological impairment, although a more definitive indication of neuropsychological impairment depends upon clinical evaluation of the test results.

Clinical Evaluation of the Test Results. On the Trail Making Test Tom performed fairly well on Part A (17 sec) and Part B (36 sec). He also did well on the Seashore Rhythm Test (25 correct) and the Speech-sounds Perception Test (7 errors). These performances indicate that he is relatively alert and can focus his attention over time to specific stimuli. He also did well on the Total Time required for the Tactual Performance Test (9.1 min), demonstrating that he has fairly good ability to integrate and organize his activities to solve a difficult psychomotor task. His Performance IQ of 111 complements these findings. Tom had some difficulty on the Category Test (59 errors) and on the Memory (4) and Localization (2) components of the TPT. As expected, the clinical evaluation of the level of performance essentially confirms the findings already revealed by the NDS.

We will next direct our attention to the lateralizing findings to determine whether there are any further indications of impaired brain functions. On the Aphasia Screening Test Tom had some definite difficulties in simple spelling, manifested by his spelling of CROSS as C-R-U-S-S and the omission of the A in TRIANGLE. In his writing he also demonstrated spelling problems, first by writing CLOCK as C-L-O-A-C-K, and then misspelling WARNING as W-A-R-E-N-I-N-G.

As we noted when we discussed Tom's low Verbal IQ compared to his Performance IQ, there is a question about whether these difficulties represent inadequate academic progress or left cerebral damage. A total absence of other indicators of left cerebral damage strongly suggests that both the low Verbal IQ and the problems in spelling are attributable to limited academic aptitude and training rather than to specific involvement of the left cerebral hemisphere.

Lateralizing findings implicating the right cerebral hemisphere were much more definite. In placing the blocks for the TPT Tom was significantly slower with his left hand (3.9 min) than with his right hand (2.8 min). He made three errors in tactile finger localization on his left hand but no errors on his right hand, and was very slow in name writing speed with his left hand (56 sec) as compared with his right hand (14 sec).

Although he made no errors with either hand on the Tactile Form Recognition Test, the time he required for identifying the objects with the left hand (14 sec) was considerably longer than for the right hand (8 sec). Tom was also slow in finger tapping speed with his left hand (31) compared to his right hand (40). On grip strength his left hand (12.5 kg) was a little weak compared with the right hand (14.5 kg), but this difference was still within normal limits.

Although the square, cross, and triangle were drawn adequately, the second cross must be considered a marginal performance. Note, though, that Tom's drawing of the key was clearly deficient and indicative of constructional dyspraxia. He not only had great difficulty representing the various parts of the key, but made two mistakes that are almost pathognomonic. The first sign occurred near the handle of the key, where he drew the lower notch in the wrong direction and then had to make a correction. (This error was obvious to the examiner even though it is not perfectly clear on the drawing itself.)

The second error was just below the nose of the key where Tom initially extended the line too far and had to go back in order to achieve a more proper representation of the teeth. The handle of the key was also definitely deviant, with the total effort resulting in a figure that not only produced a poor overall representation, but also included specific errors of the type shown by persons with cerebral damage.

In summary, the right hemisphere indicators included poor performances on (1) the TPT with the left hand as compared with the right hand, (2) the Tactile Form Recognition Test, (3) tactile finger localization, (4) name writing, (5) finger tapping, and (6) the drawing of the key. All of these deficits complemented the low score on Block Design that we discussed previously.

Summary

These results contrast strikingly with those of Ann, and emphasize the importance of clinical interpretation of the test findings to complement the more formalistic analysis provided by the NDS. While Tom's NDS scores were sometimes borderline and suggestive of impaired brain functions, the pattern of deficits revealed in the clinical evaluation indicate clearly that (1) Tom's right cerebral hemisphere was not functioning as well as his left cerebral hemisphere (in spite of a Verbal IQ that was 30 points lower than his Performance IQ), and (2) the indications of right cerebral dysfunction fell in the context of mild generalized impairment.

We would postulate that the thalamic tumor had affected the right cerebral cortex to a greater extent than the left, but independent neurological information was not available to confirm this aspect of the neuropsychological findings. However, as is customarily seen with lesions principally involving the diencephalon, there is unequivocal evidence of cerebral impairment. (For a greater appreciation of the effects of lesion location on neuropsychological findings, compare Tom's test results with Ann's, which are typical for a child with a medulloblastoma of the fourth ventricle and with Rachel's, demonstrating the consequences of an intracerebral tumor.)

Although we did not have the opportunity to examine Tom postoperatively, we learned from his neurologist that he was apparently doing well five months after the surgery.

He occasionally had eye pain, but was active, alert, and generally happy, and his family felt that he had no significant symptoms.

As we have discussed in the cases of Ann and Rachel, pre- and postoperative neuropsychological findings are essentially similar in most evaluations of individuals with brain tumors. Considering the postoperative difficulties experienced by Tom, one might have expected a considerable and obvious degree of impairment in comparison with his preoperative status, but the brain is remarkably resilient in recovery from insult (as compared with disease). In most cases of tumors above the brainstem, the neoplasm has already compromised neuropsychological functions before surgical intervention, and removal of the tumor and surrounding damaged tissue does not result in a significant change in the patient's neuropsychological abilities.

■

Cerebral Tumors

Definition

A tumor, also known as a neoplasm, is an abnormal mass of tissue that forms when cells in a specific area reproduce at an increased rate. A number of different types of tumors may occur in the cerebral hemispheres of children. The most common are gliomas, tumors which arise from the supporting glial cells within the brain. The gliomas may be differentiated into anaplastic (or highly malignant tumors) and astrocytomas (in which the process of mitotic division of cells is much slower). Differentiation of the tumor, which is accomplished by histological evaluation of tumor tissue, is extremely important because of the very poor prognosis for long-term survival with anaplastic lesions.

Incidence

Glioblastomas multiforme in the cerebral hemispheres in children are rare, occurring in only 2% - 3% in one series of 163 tumors in children (Bruce, Schut, & Sutton, 1990). Low-grade gliomas (or astrocytomas) of the cerebral hemispheres represent approximately 50% of brain tumors in children (Heideman, Packer, Albright, & Freeman, 1990).

Symptoms

The most common symptom of a brain tumor in children is headache (Honig & Charney, 1982), although headaches obviously may be due to many other causes as well. Elevated intracranial pressure is not uncommon, and other symptoms may include vomiting, focal neurological deficits, seizures, and visual problems.

Bruce, Schut, and Sutton (1990) point out that tumors in children are often unrecognized for a considerable period of time. In their series, 25% of the children had received psychiatric or psychological counseling because the symptoms, attributable to the developing tumor, had been improperly diagnosed.

Diagnosis

A detailed medical history, clinical neurological examination, and imaging procedures are the most common bases for diagnosing cerebral tumors. Pre- and postinjection contrast-enhanced CT is valuable in identifying cerebral tumors. An MRI may identify low-grade as well as high-grade tumors, including lesions that are diffuse and infiltrating, even when CT is normal.

Treatment

Surgical resection of the tumor is the basic approach to treatment. Radiation therapy is not generally used with low-grade astrocytomas, but is used routinely with glioblastomas multiforme.

Prognosis

Even with surgical resection and postoperative treatment, the five-year survival rate for children with highly malignant tumors of the cerebral hemispheres is estimated to be only about 15% (Nelson, Nelson, Davis, et al., 1985). For children who have tumors which are not highly malignant, relatively long-term survival has increased strikingly during the last ten years. Among subjects with low-grade gliomas (such as that shown by Rachel), Bruce, Schut, and Sutton (1990) found that 48 of 60 (80%) of the children in their study were alive five years after diagnosis. Many of these children, however, demonstrated both neurological and neuropsychological deficits.

Case 7 — RACHEL

Age:	9-7 (Testing I) 9-8 (Testing II)	**Gender:**	Female
Education:	2	**Handedness:**	Right

Background Information

Testing I

Our first neuropsychological examination of Rachel was done when she was 9 years, 7 months old and in the latter part of the third grade. At that time she had been under the close medical supervision of her neurologist for just more than three years.

When she was six years old Rachel developed focal seizures, without loss of consciousness, that involved only her left arm. Over just more than a two-year period these seizures were brought under control with antiepileptic medication, but then over a period of several months Rachel developed a progressive hemiparesis involving the extremities on the left side. During this period her parents felt that she had become increasingly irritable, and her teachers reported that she was starting to have academic difficulties. Rachel was admitted to the hospital at this time, at the age of 9 years, for a more detailed neurological evaluation as well as a comprehensive neuropsychological examination.

On the neurological examination Rachel showed a number of abnormal signs, including a left central facial palsy, a left hemiparesis involving the arm to a greater extent than the leg, hyperactivity of deep tendon reflexes on the left side, a slight hypesthesia over the entire left side of the body, and pronounced papilledema bilaterally with evidence of retinal hemorrhages. Skull x-rays indicated some degree of suture separation, representing further evidence that the intracranial pressure was elevated. An EEG showed Delta waves, Grade I over the right frontal-temporal area.

A right carotid angiogram revealed a distinct tumor stain in the middle part of the right cerebral hemisphere. The day after the neuropsychological examination was completed, Rachel was taken to surgery for a subtotal resection of a tumor mass in the right posterior frontal area. Histological examination of the tumor tissue revealed it to be a slowly growing astrocytoma. Soon after the surgery was completed Rachel showed clinical evidence of marked improvement, and on the eighth postoperative day we repeated the neuropsychological examination. We will first present and describe the neuropsychological test results obtained preoperatively and then compare them with the postoperative findings.

Neuropsychological Examination

Intrinsic tumors of the cerebrum generally have very serious effects on neuropsychological functions. In addition, Rachel had a history of more than three years of neurological difficulties involving her brain. During this time the maturation of her brain-behavior relationships was probably adversely affected, because an impaired brain (as compared with a normal brain) was responsible for subserving her ability development. As we noted earlier in this volume (Chapter II), a presumption of the plasticity of the immature brain and its potential for recovery from the effects of damage is generally more than counterbalanced in clinical outcome by the limitations of neuropsychological development subserved by a damaged brain.

Secondly, the effects of even a lateralized or focal lesion are much more generalized in neuropsychological terms when a lesion is imposed upon the developing brain (as contrasted with the mature adult brain, in which cerebral

The Halstead-Reitan Neuropsychological Test Battery for Older Children

Name __Rachel I__ Age __9 – 7__

Gender __F__ Education __2__ Handedness: RH __7__ LH __0__

Neuropsychological Deficit Scale (NDS) Summary

Level of Performance	Subject's score	Mean for controls	Mean for brain-damaged	Cut-off score
Motor Functions	21	6.29	14.05	
Sensory-perceptual Functions	21	5.15	10.77	
Attention and Concentration	6	1.91	3.78	
Immediate Memory and Recapitulation	5	2.23	3.31	
Visual-spatial Skills	12	4.06	7.69	
Abstraction, Reasoning, Logical Analysis	9	2.63	6.03	
Level of Performance–Total	74	22.27	45.63	33/34
Dysphasia and Related Variables	13	1.37	7.97	3/4
Right / Left Differences	17	6.79	13.74	9/10
Total NDS Score	104	30.43	67.34	43/44

WISC-R

VIQ	72
PIQ	54
FS IQ	60

Verbal Subtests		Performance Subtests	
Information	7	Picture Completion	4
Similarities	5	Picture Arrangement	2
Arithmetic	6	Block Design	3
Vocabulary	5	Object Assembly	3
Comprehension	4	Coding	3
(Digit Span)	(10)	(Mazes)	(2)

WRAT

	Grade Equivalent
Reading	3.4
Arithmetic	2.7
Spelling	3.3

Strength of Grip

Dominant hand (R) __10.0__ kg
Non-dominant hand (L) __5.0__ kg

Name Writing

Dominant hand (R) __22__ sec
Non-dominant hand (L) __64__ sec

Tactile Form Recognition Test

Dominant hand (R) __14__ sec __3__ errors
Non-dominant hand (L) __26__ sec __2__ errors

Category Test

Number of errors __100__

Tactual Performance Test

Dominant hand (R) __10.0__ (0 blocks in)
Non-dominant hand (L) __10.0__ (0 blocks in)
Both hands __10.0__ (4 blocks in)

Total Time __30.0__ (4 blocks in)
Memory __3__
Localization __2__

Seashore Rhythm Test

Number correct __9__ __10__

Speech-sounds Perception Test

Number of errors __36__

Finger Tapping Test

Dominant hand (R) __20__ __20__
Non-dominant hand (L) __5__

Trail Making Test

Part A __73__ sec __0__ error(s)
Part B __375__ sec __4__ error(s)

Bilateral Simultaneous Sensory Stimulation

RH ___	LH ___		Both: RH ___	LH ___	
RH ___	LF ___		Both: RH _4_	LF ___	
LH ___	RF ___		Both: LH _3_	RF ___	
RE ___	LE ___		Both: RE ___	LE ___	
RV ___	LV ___		Both: RV ___	LV ___	

Tactile Finger Recognition

RH 1 ___ 2 _1_ 3 _3_ 4 _3_ 5 _2_ RH _9_ / _20_
LH 1 ___ 2 _3_ 3 _2_ 4 _1_ 5 _3_ LH _9_ / _20_

Finger-Tip Number Writing

RH 1 _3_ 2 _2_ 3 _2_ 4 _2_ 5 _2_ RH _11_ / _20_
LH 1 _4_ 2 _4_ 3 _3_ 4 _4_ 5 _4_ LH _19_ / _20_

Finger-Tip Symbol Writing

RH 1 ___ 2 ___ 3 ___ 4 ___ 5 ___ RH _0_ / _20_
LH 1 ___ 2 _1_ 3 _2_ 4 _2_ 5 ___ LH _5_ / _20_

Reitan-Indiana Aphasia Screening Test

Form for Adults and Older Children

Name: Rachel I   Age: 9 – 7

Copy SQUARE	Repeat TRIANGLE
Name SQUARE Window *Ex.?* Window pane	Repeat MASSACHUSETTS
Spell SQUARE S - Q - U - R - E	Repeat METHODIST EPISCOPAL
Copy CROSS	Write SQUARE
Name CROSS	Read SEVEN
Spell CROSS C - O - S - S *then* C - R - O - S	Repeat SEVEN
Copy TRIANGLE	Repeat/Explain HE SHOUTED THE WARNING
Name TRIANGLE Sign	Write HE SHOUTED THE WARNING
Spell TRIANGLE T - R - Y - A - N - G - L - Y	Compute $85 - 27 =$ 02 Second trial: 62 $96 - 43 = 53$
Name BABY	Compute $17 \times 3 =$ *Could not do* $3 \times 8 = 24$
Write CLOCK	Name KEY
Name FORK	Demonstrate use of KEY
Read 7 SIX 2	Draw KEY
Read MGW	Read PLACE LEFT HAND TO RIGHT EAR Place left hand to right E - A - R
Reading I	Place LEFT HAND TO RIGHT EAR *Placed left hand on left ear*
Reading II *Could not read "famous" or "winner"; otherwise OK.*	Place LEFT HAND TO LEFT ELBOW *Tried very hard, used right hand to help. Ex.? S said she should be able to do it.*

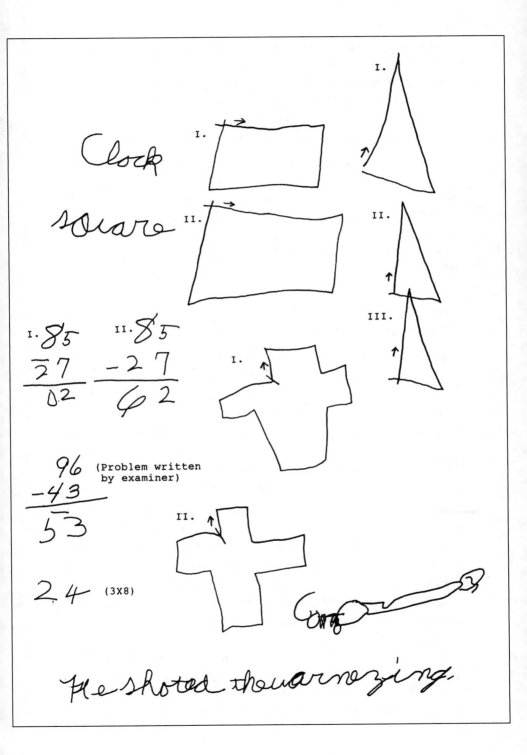

tissue appears to be more specifically dedicated to particu- lar functions). Thus, higher-level neuropsychological func- tions tend to be generally impaired in cases of this kind. Sensory-perceptual and motor functions are more closely tied in with particular areas of the cortex because the affer- ent and efferent pathways are anatomically determined.

Therefore, we would expect Rachel to have (1) relatively severe impairment of higher-level neuropsychological func- tions, (2) relatively little selective or specific loss of special- ized functions that ordinarily are presumed to be dependent upon the right cerebral hemisphere, and (3) definite motor and sensory-perceptual deficits involving the left side of the body.

Wechsler Intelligence Scale for Children — Revised

On the WISC-R Rachel earned a Verbal IQ of 72, a value that exceeds only 3% of her age peers and falls in the lower part of the classification of Borderline intelligence. Her Perform- ance IQ (54) was 18 points lower than her Verbal IQ, ex- ceeding less than 1% of her age peers, and falling in the range of mild Mental Retardation. These values yielded a Full Scale IQ of 60, which exceeds less than 1% and falls in the range of mild Mental Retardation.

Rachel's Verbal IQ was considerably higher than her Performance IQ and the brain tumor was located in her right cerebral hemisphere. In this case the relationship between verbal and performance intelligence, with respect to lateralization of the lesion, was in the direction usually seen in adults (i.e., a right cerebral lesion and a low Performance IQ). However, low Performance IQs are also frequently seen in children with left cerebral lesions. A consistent lateraliza- tion effect on VIQ/PIQ differences is not seen in children, but the Verbal IQ is sometimes the higher value. This observation may result from the frequency with which many parents who have children with a brain lesion work diligently to improve verbal intelligence (as contrasted with performance intelligence).

A review of Rachel's scores on the individual Verbal subtests indicates that only two of them (Information, 7; Digit Span, 10) were distinctly above the general level of the Performance subtests. Four of the six Verbal subtests approached or were at two standard deviations below the mean, and all of the Performance subtests were about two to three standard deviations below the mean. It is apparent from these scores that Rachel was far below the average child in terms of general intelligence measurements.

Wide Range Achievement Test

Considering these circumstances, one might wonder how Rachel was able to attend regular school. She was in fact having difficulty, but her problems were attributed (at least in part) to irregular attendance caused by her illness. From her performances on the HRB, it seems clear that Rachel's limited intellectual and adaptive capabilities would soon preclude any prospect of being able to make normal academic progress. However, she had developed some academic skills, as shown by the grade-equivalents she earned on the WRAT: Reading (word recognition) 3.4; Spelling, 3.3; and Arithmetic, 2.7. Although Rachel received a great deal of individual tutoring from her mother, it is still encouraging to see that she was able to make this much progress, considering the apparently serious effect of the brain lesion on her intelligence measurements and other adaptive abilities.

Halstead-Reitan Battery for Older Children

Neuropsychological Deficit Scale. Rachel's scores on the NDS for Older Children were consistently poor. In the Level of Performance section, 24 of the 25 variables had scores in the significantly impaired category. Rachel was not able to score in the normal range on a single test. On this section she earned a total of 74 points, well exceeding the cut-off of 33/34 and the mean of 45.63 of brain-damaged children. It is clear from these findings that a summarization of Rachel's test results is that she performed poorly in all areas of neuropsychological functioning, on low-level functions as well as higher-level abilities.

Results on the Right-Left Differences section of the NDS also contributed substantially to the total NDS score. On this section only two variables (Tactile Finger Localization and Tactile Form Recognition) had scores in the normal range, and this occurred because Rachel had defective performances which were about equivalent on the two sides of the body (and therefore did not have lateralizing significance). She earned a total of 17 points on this section.

In addition to constructional dyspraxia, the section concerned with Dysphasia and Related Variables revealed that Rachel had specific deficits in the use of language symbols for communicational purposes (despite the fact that the lesion was in her right cerebral hemisphere). This finding is not at all uncommon in children who have had impaired brain functions for an extended period of time during their developmental years.

Besides difficulty in naming common objects (dysnomia), Rachel also demonstrated spelling dyspraxia, dysgraphia, dyslexia, dyscalculia, and right-left confusion. Although she was able to perform satisfactorily on some of the items in the Aphasia Screening Test (she was able to identify numbers and letters, enunciate adequately, identify body parts, and understand verbal communications), her poor performances on this section earned a total of 13 points, well exceeding the mean of 7.97 points for brain-damaged children. These findings make it clear that Rachel performed poorly in terms of each of the approaches to data evaluation used to assess the adequacy of cerebral functions.

Other aspects of Rachel's performances can be further understood by comparing the lateralizing signs that implicate the left and right cerebral hemispheres. The evidence of specific deficits in dealing with language symbols would ordinarily reflect impairment of the left cerebral hemisphere, but in this case the developmental consequences of the right cerebral lesion appear to have been responsible for producing these deficits. Although Rachel had just a little more difficulty in tactile form recognition with her right hand (3 errors) than with her left hand (2 errors), this was the only lateralizing finding (using comparisons of identical performances on the two sides of the body) that suggested left cerebral dysfunction.

A number of right/left comparisons implicated the right cerebral hemisphere. Rachel's finger tapping speed was much faster with the right hand (20) than with the left hand (5). Although she was quite poor in finger-tip number writing perception on each hand, she made 19 errors on her left hand compared to 11 errors on her right hand.

We were concerned about the possibility that attentional deficits may have contributed to the errors on the right hand, since the anatomical pathways should have related specifically to the lesion of the right cerebral hemisphere. We explored this question by administering the Finger-tip Symbol Writing Test, which is customarily used with younger children. This task requires only that the child differentiate between X's and O's rather than discern individual numbers; therefore, careful attention to the specific stimulus configuration is less of a requirement on this test. On the Finger-tip Symbol Writing Test Rachel made no mistakes in 20 trials on her right hand but made 5 mistakes with her left hand. The lateralizing effect was still pronounced, but it would appear that the errors in finger-tip number writing perception on the right hand may well have reflected general rather than specific impairment.

Rachel also had definite difficulty perceiving a tactile stimulus to the left hand when it was given simultaneously with a stimulus to the right face. It must be noted, however, that she had just as much trouble appreciating a stimulus to the right hand when it was given in combination with a stimulus to the left face. In other words, Rachel had great difficulty perceiving a stimulus to the hand when it was given simultaneously with a stimulus to the contralateral side of the face, regardless of which hand/face combination was used. The explanation for this finding, which is sometimes seen in children with unilateral lesions that have been present long enough to have affected the course of their neurological development, is that the face is more sensitive than the hand in terms of brain functions, and under circumstances of bilateral simultaneous stimulation the more sensitive area (as represented in the cerebral cortex) predominates.

Summary

Our neuropsychological evaluation of this child demonstrated serious and widespread deficits, a finding that is not surprising in light of the nature of her lesion (intrinsic tumor). Even though the lesion involved the right cerebral hemisphere, lateralizing signs were seen only on tests that compared the same types of performances on the two sides of the body, findings which are determined by the anatomical organization of afferent and efferent pathways within the nervous system. Higher-level neuropsychological functions were generally impaired regardless of their conventional association with left or right hemisphere functions, a finding that reflects the influence of the brain lesion on developing abilities over the course of time.

Rachel responded very well to surgery and began to show definite improvement almost immediately. She appeared to be feeling much better generally than she had before the operation, and the clinical (neurological) examination demonstrated some increased function in her left arm and leg. Within five days postoperatively the papilledema had clearly decreased, but Rachel still had some minimal focal motor seizures involving muscles in her left hand. From a clinical viewpoint, it appeared that Rachel was improving physically, at least in terms of the effects of acute illness. However, results of the second (postoperative) neuropsychological examination, done about two weeks after the first testing, continued to reflect evidence of very serious impairment.

Testing II

On the second examination Rachel earned a score of 72 points on the Level of Performance section of the NDS. Although her score on the Right-Left Differences section actually was just a little worse (increasing from 17 to 20 points), on the Aphasia and Related Variables section her score improved from 13 points to 7 points. In summary, Rachel received a total NDS score of 104 points on the first examination and a total NDS score of 99 points on the second examination.

Comparing Rachel's performances on the two examinations test-by-test suggests that she made a little improvement. Her Performance IQ rose from 54 to 63; on Part B of the Trail Making Test she reduced the time required from 375 seconds to 302 seconds; on the Tactual Performance Test she was able to place a total of 8 blocks in 30 minutes (as compared with a total of 4 blocks during the same period of time on the initial examination); and her finger tapping speed with the left hand had risen from 5 taps to 9 taps in a 10-second period.

On the Aphasia Screening Test Rachel appeared to have less difficulty on some of the items. For example, she no longer had as much trouble with simple reading as she did initially, she was able to name common objects correctly,

The Halstead-Reitan Neuropsychological Test Battery for Older Children

Name __Rachel II__ Age __9 – 8__

Gender __F__ Education __2__ Handedness: RH __7__ LH __0__

Neuropsychological Deficit Scale (NDS) Summary

Level of Performance	Subject's score	Mean for controls	Mean for brain-damaged	Cut-off score
Motor Functions	20	6.29	14.05	
Sensory-perceptual Functions	20	5.15	10.77	
Attention and Concentration	6	1.91	3.78	
Immediate Memory and Recapitulation	6	2.23	3.31	
Visual-spatial Skills	11	4.06	7.69	
Abstraction, Reasoning, Logical Analysis	9	2.63	6.03	
Level of Performance–Total	72	22.27	45.63	33/34
Dysphasia and Related Variables	7	1.37	7.97	3/4
Right / Left Differences	20	6.79	13.74	9/10
Total NDS Score	99	30.43	67.34	43/44

WISC-R

VIQ __72__
PIQ __63__
FS IQ __65__

Verbal Subtests		*Performance Subtests*	
Information	7	Picture Completion	4
Similarities	4	Picture Arrangement	3
Arithmetic	6	Block Design	7
Vocabulary	6	Object Assembly	3
Comprehension	4	Coding	4
(Digit Span)	(5)	(Mazes)	(2)

WRAT

	Grade Equivalent
Reading	3.1
Arithmetic	2.7
Spelling	3.3

Strength of Grip

Dominant hand   (R) __10.5__ kg
Non-dominant hand (L) __4.0__ kg

Name Writing

Dominant hand   (R) __14__ sec
Non-dominant hand (L) __*__ sec

Tactile Form Recognition Test

Dominant hand   (R) __15__ sec   __2__ error(s)
Non-dominant hand (L) __22__ sec   __3__ error(s)

Category Test

Number of errors   106

Tactual Performance Test

Dominant hand   (R) __10.0__ (3 blocks in)
Non-dominant hand (L) __10.0__ (1 block in)
Both hands   __10.0__ (4 blocks in)

Total Time __30.0__ (8 blocks in)
Memory   __3__
Localization __1__

Seashore Rhythm Test

Number correct   __11__   __10__

Speech-sounds Perception Test

Number of errors   __27__

Finger Tapping Test

Dominant hand   (R) __21__   __21__
Non-dominant hand (L) __9__

Trail Making Test

Part A __48__ sec   __0__ error(s)
Part B __302__ sec   __2__ error(s)

Bilateral Simultaneous Sensory Stimulation

RH ___ LH ___		Both: RH ___ LH ___	
RH ___ LF ___		Both: RH ___ LF ___	
LH ___ RF ___		Both: LH ___ RF ___	
RE ___ LE ___		Both: RE ___ LE __1__	
RV ___ LV ___		Both: RV ___ LV __1__	
___ ___		___ ___	

Tactile Finger Recognition

RH 1 ___ 2 _2_ 3 _2_ 4 _3_ 5 _1_   RH _8_ / _20_
LH 1 _1_ 2 _1_ 3 _2_ 4 _2_ 5 _1_   LH _7_ / _20_

Finger-Tip Number Writing

RH 1 _4_ 2 _3_ 3 _4_ 4 _2_ 5 _2_   RH _15_ / _20_
LH 1 ___ 2 ___ 3 ___ 4 ___ 5 ___   LH _*_ / ___

Finger-Tip Symbol Writing

RH 1 _1_ 2 _1_ 3 _1_ 4 _1_ 5 _1_   RH _5_ / _20_
LH 1 _3_ 2 _1_ 3 _1_ 4 _2_ 5 _2_   LH _9_ / _20_

★ Unable to do

eitan-Indiana Aphasia
creening Test

m for Adults and Older Children

Name __Rachel II_____ Age _9 – 8_

Copy SQUARE	Repeat TRIANGLE
Name SQUARE	Repeat MASSACHUSETTS Massachuses
Spell SQUARE S - Q - U - A - R	Repeat METHODIST EPISCOPAL Methodiss Epise-cal
Copy CROSS	Write SQUARE
Name CROSS	Read SEVEN
Spell CROSS	Repeat SEVEN
Copy TRIANGLE	Repeat/Explain HE SHOUTED THE WARNING
Name TRIANGLE	Write HE SHOUTED THE WARNING
Spell TRIANGLE T - R - Y - A - N - G - L - Y	Compute $85 - 27 = 012$ (see) $18 - 6 = 22$ $6 - 3 = 3$
Name BABY	Compute $17 \times 3 =$ *Could not do* $3 \times 6 = 18$
Write CLOCK	Name KEY
Name FORK	Demonstrate use of KEY
Read 7 SIX 2	Draw KEY
Read MGW	Read PLACE LEFT HAND TO RIGHT EAR
Reading I	Place LEFT HAND TO RIGHT EAR
Reading II *Could not read "famous" or "winner"; otherwise OK.*	Place LEFT HAND TO LEFT ELBOW *S tried very hard before finally giving up.*

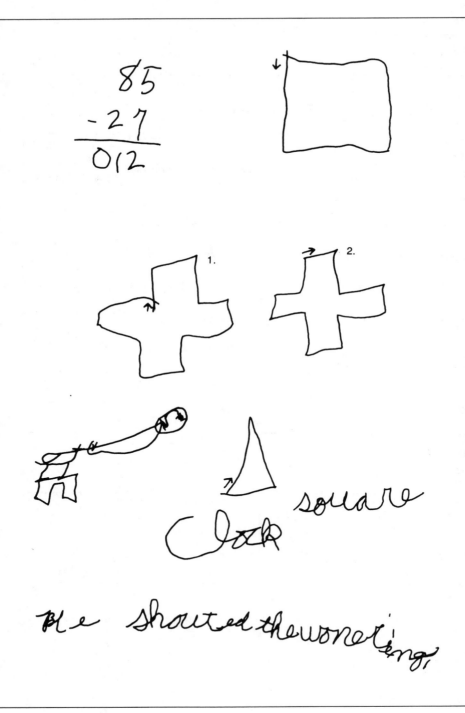

and she showed no evidence of right-left confusion. Nevertheless, she continued to demonstrate constructional dyspraxia, spelling dyspraxia, dysgraphia, and dyscalculia.

Rachel demonstrated some performances that were poorer than on the first testing. She had a tendency to fail to perceive an auditory stimulus and a visual stimulus on the left side with bilateral simultaneous stimulation. On the first examination on finger-tip symbol writing with the left hand she made 5 errors and on the second testing she made 9 errors. On this test she also had more difficulty with her right hand (5 errors) than she had experienced on the first testing (0 errors). Although on the first examination she had not done at all well in finger-tip number writing perception on the left hand (19 errors), on the second examination she was no longer able to do this task at all. In other respects, including all of the remaining tests, Rachel performed at essentially the same level as she had initially.

It is interesting to note that Rachel had no evidence of restriction of the visual fields at the time of either examination. The tumor primarily affected motor and tactile-perceptual functions, and considering its location in the posterior frontal region of the right cerebral hemisphere, these would be the expected findings. (Tactile losses are not uncommon in lesions of the posterior frontal area, considering that the parietal area is closely adjacent.)

The lesion (Testing I) and the lesion plus the effects of surgical intervention (Testing II) apparently did not extend posteriorly in their functional consequences to the extent that the radiations of the geniculostriate tract were involved. Considering the other evidence of lateralized involvement of the right cerebral hemisphere and the absence of a visual field defect, one would postulate that the structural aspects of the lesion were frontal in location. The absence of left homonymous visual field losses, particularly after surgical removal of the tumor, would tend to clear the posterior part of the right hemisphere and thus lead to an inference of anterior involvement.

Some readers might be under the impression that surgical intervention and extirpation of an intrinsic tumor would improve the individual's neuropsychological functioning. We have studied hundreds of patients pre- and postoperatively, and the results usually are quite similar. As we noted earlier, the tumor initially causes tissue damage which in turn produces the neuropsychological deficits. This tissue damage continues to be present postoperatively, and there is usually relatively little change in the patient's neuropsychological status. In other words, although the surgical intervention may be necessary and crucial to saving the individual's life, surgery does not repair the cortical tissue which has already been damaged by the tumor.

It is not entirely uncommon for neurosurgeons to claim "complete recovery" after such surgery, except possibly for obvious sensory and motor deficits. Such claims do not take into account the individual's neuropsychological status, and most patients (and, if they are children, their parents) do not understand why they cannot function as capably as they once had, when their doctor has told them the operation was a complete success. Neuropsychologists can play a critical role in the care and management of these persons, both in providing counseling that will help them to understand the nature and cause of their pre- and postoperative deficits and in adapting to their deficits.

■

Pseudotumor Cerebri

Definition

Persons who have the signs and symptoms of a cerebral tumor (particularly increased intracranial pressure) in the absence of any space-occupying lesion are said to have *pseudotumor cerebri*. The clinical symptoms of someone with pseudotumor cerebri are usually much less severe than the symptoms observed in a person with a neoplastic lesion.

Causes and Incidence

A number of conditions have been associated with pseudotumor cerebri. These include conditions which cause obstruction of intracranial venous drainage such as otitis media, mastoiditis, congenital atresia or stenosis of the primary venous sinus channels, and trauma. Improper drainage of cerebrospinal fluid through the venous sinuses has also been reported to result from a number of generalized diseases such as marasmus or certain hemoglobinopathies. A variety of conditions which cause obstruction of the drainage of the craniovenous system in the region of the neck and the thorax also have been reported.

Although no specific chemical or hormonal factors have been identified which relate to pseudotumor cerebri, certain hematological conditions, disorders of vitamin metabolism, and allergic or toxic reactions to drugs have been reported to have some connection with the condition. A number of other conditions have been implicated in producing intracranial hypertension, including Syndenham's chorea, infantile roseola, hypophosphatasia, sarcoidosis, and Paget's disease. Galactosemia has also been thought to be a causative factor, based on the hypothesis that impaired galactose metabolism results in accumulation of nondiffusible alcohol in the cerebrum which in turn attracts water by osmosis.

Pseudotumor cerebri is reported to be much more common in females than males, with the ratio as high as eight to one (Greer, 1990).

Signs and Symptoms

Intracranial hypertension is the principal indicator of pseudotumor cerebri, and the condition has even been described as *benign intracranial hypertension*. In general, overt indications of neurological impairment are absent, except for the relatively nonspecific signs associated with intracranial pressure — headache, nausea, vomiting, tinnitus, vague paresthesias, blurred vision, and diplopia. The incidence of impaired visual function, including significant losses of visual acuity, hemianopia, and sometimes even complete blindness, has been estimated to be as high as 22%. Unlike instances of tumors, it is unusual to see indications of either seizures or alteration of mental function in persons with pseudotumor cerebri.

Diagnosis and Treatment

Ophthalmological examination of the eyegrounds is frequently used to screen for intracranial hypertension, and papilledema is the most common finding. However, some patients have pseudopapilledema, a congenital anomaly that may be misleading in the diagnosis of pseudotumor cerebri. The diagnosis of pseudotumor cerebri is made after other causes of increased intracranial pressure, particularly mass lesions, are ruled out.

Treatment is directed toward maintaining the intracranial pressure within normal limits and, when possible, correcting the underlying cause of the hypertension. Osmotic diuretics and steroids have been used successfully in many cases (Menkes, 1980).

Prognosis

The prognosis is favorable when the increased intracranial pressure is maintained at a constant level. Recurrences of pseudotumor cerebri are reported to be less than 10% (Johnson & Paterson, 1974).

The Case of George

In the case of George, the next child to be presented, the history information was complemented by elevation of the optic discs (suggesting the presence of papilledema and intracranial hypertension) and left parietal slow-wave activity on the EEG. We would postulate retrospectively that in this case elevation of the optic discs may have been a congenital condition, and that the EEG abnormality may have been associated with prior traumatic injuries noted in the history (focal EEG abnormalities are unusual, although slow-wave activity has been reported with a frequency as high as 60% among children [Stewart, 1941]). Thus, it would appear that George represents a case of multiple and unrelated circumstances which combined in the history and his neurological examination to lead to the incorrect initial impression of a developing glioma in the left parietal area.

Case 8 — GEORGE

Age:	14-6	**Gender:**	Male
Education:	8	**Handedness:**	Right

Background Information

George was a ninth grader who had developed normally, without any significant medical, academic, or adjustmental problems. When we interviewed his parents, they recalled that two and one-half years earlier George had run into a tree while riding his bicycle, struck his head, and was unconscious for a short period of time. Six months after that incident he had been hit on the left side of his head by a baseball. He had been stunned by the blow, but had not lost consciousness. George had apparently recovered uneventfully from these accidents, and had no history of any other brain injury or disease.

Over the last one and one-half years, however, George had reported having four episodes of experiencing a tingling sensation in his right upper and lower extremities and on the right side of his face. During this time period he also had begun to have frequent headaches. Several days before the current hospital admission George again had complained of a severe headache and had experienced a tingling sensation on the right side. He also reported a severe episode of vomiting. The night before he was admitted to the hospital George's parents observed him having a major motor seizure while he was asleep. They immediately brought him to the hospital for a complete neurological evaluation.

The circumstances described above would raise the possibility of a developing brain lesion (such as a tumor). Although the results of the physical neurological examination were entirely negative, the presence of a brain tumor cannot be entirely ruled out. Considering the history, computed tomography or magnetic resonance imaging (MRI) of the head would have been advisable, but this child was examined before these procedures were widely available. An EEG demonstrated the presence of a generalized dysrhythmia, Grade I and Delta waves, Grade I in the left temporal-parietal area. This indication of focal slow wave activity was interpreted as suggesting the possibility of a destructive lesion.

Ophthalmological consultation was obtained, and an examination of the eye grounds revealed signs of early papilledema. This suggestion of increased intracranial pressure caused additional concern about the presence of an intracranial tumor in the left temporal-parietal area. At this time the attending physician requested that George have a comprehensive neuropsychological examination.

Neuropsychological Examination

Wechsler Intelligence Scale for Children — Revised

On the WISC-R George earned a Verbal IQ of 135, a value that exceeds more than 99% of his age peers and falls within the Very Superior range. His Performance IQ of 112 was considerably lower, but still exceeded 79% and fell in the lower part of the High Average range. His Full Scale IQ was 126.

The individual subtest scores indicated that George did well on each of the Verbal subtests and did not show a pattern that had any particular neurological significance. Except for a relatively poor score on Picture Arrangement (9), he also did well on the Performance subtests. The next lowest score was on Coding (11), a finding which was not sufficiently low to suggest that there was any definite impairment. Since Picture Arrangement has been related to the status of the right anterior-temporal area, we noted that the score of 9 on this variable may possibly have significance for

The Halstead-Reitan Neuropsychological Test Battery for Older Children

Name __George__   Age __14 – 6__

Gender __M__ Education __8__   Handedness: RH __7__ LH __0__

Neuropsychological Deficit Scale (NDS) Summary

Level of Performance	Subject's score	Mean for controls	Mean for brain-damaged	Cut-off score
Motor Functions	2	6.29	14.05	
Sensory-perceptual Functions	11	5.15	10.77	
Attention and Concentration	1	1.91	3.78	
Immediate Memory and Recapitulation	2	2.23	3.31	
Visual-spatial Skills	3	4.06	7.69	
Abstraction, Reasoning, Logical Analysis	0	2.63	6.03	
Level of Performance–Total	19	22.27	45.63	33/34
Dysphasia and Related Variables	0	1.37	7.97	3/4
Right / Left Differences	7	6.79	13.74	9/10
Total NDS Score	26	30.43	67.34	43/44

WISC-R

VIQ __135__
PIQ __112__
FS IQ __126__

Verbal Subtests
Information __13__
Similarities __17__
Arithmetic __18__
Vocabulary __15__
Comprehension __14__
(Digit Span) (__11__)

Performance Subtests
Picture Completion __14__
Picture Arrangement __9__
Block Design __13__
Object Assembly __12__
Coding __11__

Strength of Grip
Dominant hand (R) __26.0__ kg
Non-dominant hand (L) __23.5__ kg

Name Writing
Dominant hand (R) __8__ sec
Non-dominant hand (L) __20__ sec

Category Test
Number of errors __11__

Tactual Performance Test
Dominant hand (R) __6.1__
Non-dominant hand (L) __5.3__
Both hands __2.7__   Total Time __14.1__   Memory __5__   Localization __3__

Seashore Rhythm Test
Number correct __28__   __1__

Speech-sounds Perception Test
Number of errors __9__

Finger Tapping Test
Dominant hand (R) __40__   __40__
Non-dominant hand (L) __37__

Trail Making Test
Part A __23__ sec __0__ error(s)
Part B __23__ sec __0__ error(s)

Bilateral Simultaneous Sensory Stimulation

RH ___ LH ___   Both: RH ___ LH ___
RH ___ LF ___   Both: RH ___ LF __1__
LH ___ RF ___   Both: LH ___ RF ___

RE ___ LE ___   Both: RE ___ LE ___

RV ___ LV ___   Both: RV ___ LV ___

Tactile Finger Recognition
RH 1 __ 2 __ 3 __ 4 __1__ 5 __   RH __1__ / 20
LH 1 __ 2 __ 3 __ 4 __ 5 __   LH __0__ / 20

Finger-Tip Number Writing
RH 1 __2__ 2 __2__ 3 __2__ 4 __0__ 5 __2__   RH __8__ / 20
LH 1 __ 2 __1__ 3 __1__ 4 __ 5 __   LH __2__ / 20

Tactile Form Recognition Test
Dominant hand (R) __8__ sec __2__ error(s)
Non-dominant hand (L) __8__ sec __2__ error(s)

© 1991, Ralph M. Reitan, Ph.D.   Reitan Neuropsychology Laboratory   Tucson, Arizona

**eitan-Indiana Aphasia
creening Test**

m for Adults and Older Children

Name ___George___   Age ¹⁴ ⁻ ⁶

Copy SQUARE	Repeat TRIANGLE
Name SQUARE *Rectangle then self-corrected*	Repeat MASSACHUSETTS Massatusits
Spell SQUARE	Repeat METHODIST EPISCOPAL Methodist Epistopal
Copy CROSS	Write SQUARE
Name CROSS	Read SEVEN
Spell CROSS	Repeat SEVEN
Copy TRIANGLE	Repeat/Explain HE SHOUTED THE WARNING
Name TRIANGLE	Write HE SHOUTED THE WARNING
Spell TRIANGLE	Compute 85 − 27 =
Name BABY	Compute 17 x 3 =
Write CLOCK	Name KEY
Name FORK	Demonstrate use of KEY
Read 7 SIX 2	Draw KEY
Read MGW	Read PLACE LEFT HAND TO RIGHT EAR
Reading I	Place LEFT HAND TO RIGHT EAR
Reading II	Place LEFT HAND TO LEFT ELBOW

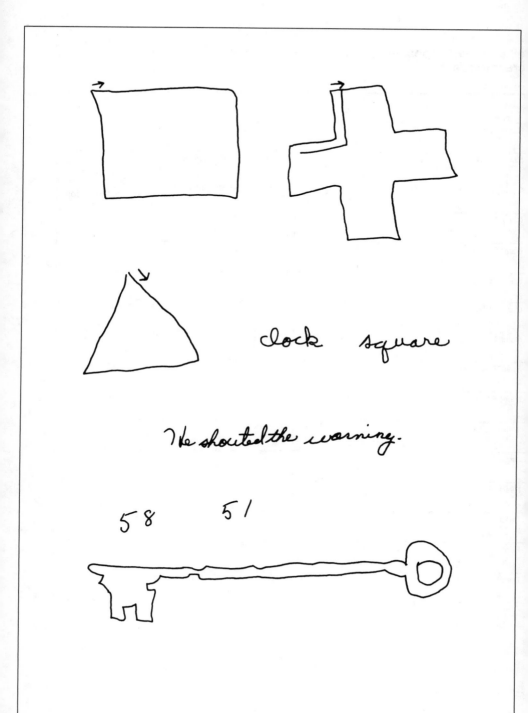

brain dysfunction, but an inference of this nature based on the WISC-R would be questionable. In addition, if a destructive lesion of the left cerebral hemisphere in this right-handed youngster was suspected, the relationship between the Verbal and Performance IQ values was in the wrong direction.

Halstead-Reitan Battery for Older Children

Neuropsychological Deficit Scale. The next step in George's evaluation is to consider his results on the NDS for Older Children. Except on the Sensory-perceptual Functions section, he performed well in each of the areas included under Level of Performance. On the Sensory-perceptual Functions section he earned a total score of 11 points, as compared with a mean of 5.15 points for control subjects and 10.77 points for brain-damaged subjects.

In total, George earned 19 points on the Level of Performance section of the NDS. The average control subject earns 22.27 points on this section, and the cut-off score is 33/34. On the Right-Left Differences section George's performances yielded a total of 7 points, which is just slightly greater than the mean of 6.79 for control subjects. The cut-off score for this section is 9/10. George had no difficulties on the section concerned with Aphasia and Related Variables, earning a score of 0. His total NDS score was 26 points, compared with a mean score of 30.43 for control subjects and a cut-off score of 43/44.

It is apparent from these results that George's overall performances on the Halstead-Reitan Battery were well within normal limits. This finding complemented the direction of the difference between the Verbal and Performance IQ values to suggest than an intrinsic tumor of the brain was not a likely possibility. However, since the presence of this type of lesion is frequently a life or death consideration, it is important to evaluate the findings in greater detail and analyze their full significance.

Clinical Evaluation of the Test Results. Most children with intrinsic brain tumors (regardless of the location of the lesion) show significant and serious deficits on the general indicators of the HRB; it was therefore particularly encouraging to find that George did very well on a number of tests. His excellent score on the Category Test (11 errors) argues strongly against a recent or rapidly developing focal lesion such as an intrinsic cerebral tumor. His score on Part B of the Trail Making Test (23 sec) has the same level of significance. Except for sensory-perceptual tasks, the only individual measures that had scores in the impaired range were Part A of the Trail Making Test (23 sec) and the Total Time on the Tactual Performance Test (14.1 min). It must be remembered that even persons with generally excellent abilities are occasionally likely to do poorly on some tests. As George's total NDS score of 26 indicates, his performances were generally very good.

At this point we will turn to a clinical evaluation of the lateralizing indicators. One test result stood out very prominently as an indicator of left cerebral involvement: on finger-tip number writing perception George made 8 mistakes on his right hand but only 2 mistakes on his left hand. This performance clearly deviates beyond normal expectancy, and generated a converted score of 3 on the Right-Left Differences section of the NDS. Although George also was just a little slow in finger tapping speed with his right hand (40) as compared with his left hand (37), this finding was clearly minimal.

In the context of the results shown by the finger-tip number writing procedure, it is very important to note that George showed no evidence of aphasia, and also scored within the normal range on the Speech-sounds Perception Test (9 errors). These findings, considered with the 8 errors on finger-tip number writing perception on the right hand, suggest that George had some discrete dysfunction in the left parietal area, but that the lesion was not sufficiently destructive of cerebral tissue to produce aphasia, impairment on the Speech-sounds Perception Test, any appreciable reduction of verbal intelligence, or a significant difference between the two hands on finger tapping speed. Thus, although the lateralizing indicators provided evidence that could be considered consistent with the EEG findings, they argued against a destructive lesion such as an intrinsic tumor. Obviously, as noted above, this conclusion was also supported by the excellent scores on some of the tests in the HRB which are most sensitive to the general biological condition of the brain, such as the Category Test and Part B of the Trail Making Test.

Lateralizing findings were also present to implicate the right cerebral hemisphere. These included (1) a somewhat poor performance on the Tactual Performance Test with the left hand (5.3 min) as compared with the right hand (6.1 min), (2) the possible significance of a score of only 9 on the Picture Arrangement subtest of the Wechsler Scale, and (3) a slight tendency toward failing to perceive a tactile stimulus to the left side of the face when it was given simultaneously with a stimulus to the right hand. (Since it is unusual for a stimulus to the face to not be perceived, this error may have increased significance. However, a single error sometimes occurs merely because the subject is not paying close attention.)

George's drawing of the key should also be evaluated carefully. The drawing is barely adequate, and although on the NDS we did not score his performance as representing constructional dyspraxia, the elongation of the stem and the lack of symmetry at both the handle and the teeth should be noted clinically.

These results would suggest that George's right cerebral hemisphere may be somewhat more generally involved than his left hemisphere, even though the strongest single indicator he demonstrated (8 errors on finger-tip number writing perception on the right hand) implicated the left cerebral hemisphere. Finally, we should note that George performed quite poorly in tactile form recognition. With each hand he made two errors in four trials. This is definitely not a normal performance, but it has no lateralizing significance because the deficits were equivalent on each hand.

It is clear from the above findings that despite the results of the NDS, the neuropsychological test results do not fall perfectly within the normal range. We included this case particularly to emphasize the importance of a detailed clinical neuropsychological evaluation rather than depending only upon summarical procedures (such as the NDS). It is critical for the neuropsychologist to realize that in this case the test results are definitely not compatible with a diagnosis of an intrinsic tumor of the left temporal-parietal area. Instead, the findings implicate each cerebral hemisphere to a mild degree, with the good test scores suggesting that the brain impairment is chronic and static in nature and consistent with some type of prior insult to the brain (such as the head injuries that were noted in the history).

After the neuropsychological examination George underwent cerebral angiography, and the results were entirely normal. On the basis of the medical findings and the neuropsychological results, a decision was made to treat George's epilepsy with antiepileptic medications and to follow him closely for any signs of progression of neurological deficits or manifestations. George remained seizure-free for the next several months. Ophthalmological examination was repeated several times during this period, and the finding of mild papilledema remained constant and showed no evidence of progression. The overall situation seemed to represent a stable, chronic condition which was not consistent with a brain tumor. The results of the EEG were never fully explained, especially the appearance of slow wave activity, but presumably the abnormalities were associated with the prior head traumas.

We must once again repeat our caution that inexperienced neuropsychologists should never accept the clinical responsibility for differentiating between intrinsic neoplasms and residual effects of head trauma solely on the basis of neuropsychological test results. There are highly valid techniques, such as computed tomography and magnetic resonance imaging, which are currently available to provide such diagnostic information (Reitan & Wolfson, 1985b).

The principal purpose of neuropsychological evaluation is to assess the behavioral correlates of brain functions and their implications for adjustments in living. Nevertheless, unless we know which variables relate to the biological condition of the brain and the ways in which they affect behavior, it is not possible to be certain that our psychological assessments are related to the condition of the brain (and therefore within the field of neuropsychology as contrasted with psychology more generally). Our principal strategic approach in this regard has been to study neuropsychological test results in persons with brain lesions of various types to identify variables (and combinations of variables) that are valid in drawing inferences about brain-behavior relationships.

■

Cerebral Abscess

Definition

An abscess is a collection of pus in a solid tissue, formed as a result of infection by micro-organisms (usually bacteria). The pus is composed of destroyed tissue cells, leukocytes, and bacteria. A protective lining or wall (pyogenic membrane) gradually develops around the abscess. A cerebral abscess is a type of mass (space-occupying) lesion, surrounded by inflamed tissues, in the brain or on its surface. The cerebral tissue surrounding the abscess frequently becomes edematous.

Cathy, the child whose test results we will discuss next, had an abscess of the superior portion of the left posterior frontal area that developed from a viral infection represented initially as an upper respiratory flu. Before reviewing the pathology of cerebral abscess, we will give brief consideration to some of the other types of bacterial infections that may involve the central nervous system.

The skull is relatively resistent to infection, and osteomyelitis (infection of the bone) of the skull secondary to sinusitis and mastoiditis has become less common with the use of antibiotics. Osteomyelitis of the skull may cause the formation of epidural abscesses and, in some cases, even abscesses of the cerebrum. Bacterial meningitis (inflammation of the meninges) involves infection of the cerebrospinal fluid, the pia arachnoid, and the subarachnoid space, and may also lead to the development of a cerebral abscess.

Causes and Incidence

The organisms that cause meningitis usually enter the bloodstream from an infection elsewhere in the body, such as otitis media (inflammation of the middle ear), sinusitis (particularly of the paranasal sinuses), or mastoiditis.

About 40% of brain abscesses result from middle ear or sinus infections. Infection of the cerebrum may also occur from a penetrating brain injury, or from air-borne organisms entering the cranial cavity after a compound fracture of the skull. In a considerable number of cases, however, the source of the infection cannot be identified. Abscesses due to blood-borne infections are often found in multiple sites.

Symptoms

Clinical symptoms and neurological deficits vary greatly depending upon the location and size of the abscess, but it is common for most patients to experience headaches, drowsiness, seizures, and focal neurological deficits. In patients who have a cerebral abscess, headaches that increase in severity and do not respond to symptomatic treatment have been reported in up to 70%, altered consciousness in 66%, and hemiparesis in 38%. Seizures occur in 30% - 50% of the patients. Other focal neurological signs include dysphasia and visual field deficits. Nausea and vomiting, which may be associated with increased intracranial pressure, occur in 25% - 50% of cases.

Diagnosis and Treatment

Routine laboratory tests are usually not helpful in diagnosing a brain abscess, but CT scanning and MRI of the brain are usually quite accurate in identifying the lesion. The definitive treatment is a craniotomy either to drain (aspirate) the abscess or excise it. Preoperative antibiotic therapy has not been shown to be of much benefit, although parenteral antibiotic therapy is often used for four to eight weeks following surgery. For patients who show progressive neurological deficits, significant impairment of alertness, or a risk of tentorial herniation, corticosteroid therapy may be instituted. However, corticosteroids significantly inhibit the host defenses that lead to walling off and eventual resolution of the brain abscess, and therefore are not routinely used.

Prognosis

Mortality associated with a brain abscess is relatively high, with studies of large series of patients showing rates ranging up to 33% (Haines, Mampalam, Rosenblum, & Nagib, 1990). Surviving patients often demonstrate some residual impairment of brain function, and may experience a recurrence of the abscess (especially when foreign bodies remain in the brain). Since epilepsy is a common sequela in this population, anticonvulsant drugs are often prescribed postoperatively.

Case 9 — CATHY

Age:	9-6	Gender:	Female
Education:	3	Handedness:	Right

Background Information

Cathy had been in good health and was developing quite normally until the age of 8 years, 5 months, when she contracted an upper respiratory flu and symptoms of a viral infection. Cathy's illness appeared to be following a routine and uneventful course until one day when she started to complain of numbness in her right face and arm. Within 24 hours she also started experiencing weakness of her right arm and drooping of her right cheek. Her parents took her to the hospital emergency room, and she was admitted for a complete neurological workup.

The neurological examination at that time revealed a paresis of the right upper extremity, some drooping of the right face, and deviation of the tongue to the right. The day after admission to the hospital Cathy experienced a focal clonic convulsive seizure that was limited to the right upper extremity, the right back, and the right side of the face, especially involving the mouth and eyelid. Following this seizure Cathy demonstrated additional neurological findings, including a Babinski sign and hyperactive deep tendon reflexes on the right side. Despite being on antiepileptic medication, she also had brief episodes of twitching of the right side of her body. At this time her neurologist noted blurring of the optic discs, a sign of increased intracranial pressure. Cathy continued to demonstrate a Babinski sign on the right side and had no gag reflex.

An EEG done the day after admission showed Delta waves, Grade II in the left frontal-temporal area as well as dysrhythmia, Grade II involving the left cerebral hemisphere. The EEG was repeated three days later and showed very similar results. Carotid angiography done on the fourth hospital day revealed a space-occupying lesion in the superior portion of the posterior frontal area on the left side, and was judged to be compatible with a tumor or abscess.

A neurosurgeon was immediately consulted to evaluate Cathy. After reviewing the medical evidence, he recommended exploratory surgery to determine the exact nature and extent of the lesion demonstrated on angiography.

Surgery was performed the next day. The neurosurgeon reported that the frontal cortex appeared to be relatively normal, but needling of the superior precentral gyrus produced a small amount of serous drainage and necrotic brain tissue. A cortical incision was made and a total of about 15cc of this material was evacuated. The pathology report indicated that the lesion was an abscess.

Following the surgery Cathy recovered very well and showed improvement of strength in her right upper extremity and right lower face. After discharge from the hospital about ten days later she continued her excellent recovery course, and was reported to have been in nearly perfect health except for occasional episodes of numbness of her right upper extremity.

Thirteen months after the initial illness Cathy was rehospitalized for surgical repair of an unusual fragmentation of the bone flap. At this time her neurological examination was entirely normal except for a slight weakness of the right upper extremity. Our neuropsychological examination was performed before this second surgery (about 13 months after the surgery performed to remove the abscess).

Neuropsychological Examination

All of Cathy's test findings suggest that she had a focal lesion in the superior-posterior portion of the left frontal lobe which was successfully treated. It appeared that she had made an excellent recovery. In a case of this kind we

The Halstead-Reitan Neuropsychological Test Battery for Older Children

Name: Cathy   Age: 9 – 6
Gender: F   Education: 3   Handedness: RH 7 LH 0

Neuropsychological Deficit Scale (NDS) Summary

Level of Performance	Subject's score	Mean for controls	Mean for brain-damaged	Cut-off score
Motor Functions	15	6.29	14.05	
Sensory-perceptual Functions	1	5.15	10.77	
Attention and Concentration	1	1.91	3.78	
Immediate Memory and Recapitulation	1	2.23	3.31	
Visual-spatial Skills	2	4.06	7.69	
Abstraction, Reasoning, Logical Analysis	4	2.63	6.03	
Level of Performance–Total	24	22.27	45.63	33/34
Dysphasia and Related Variables	5	1.37	7.97	3/4
Right / Left Differences	9	6.79	13.74	9/10
Total NDS Score	38	30.43	67.34	43/44

WISC-R

VIQ	105
PIQ	142
FS IQ	125

Verbal Subtests

Information	11
Similarities	13
Arithmetic	10
Vocabulary	10
Comprehension	10
(Digit Span)	(10)

Performance Subtests

Picture Completion	16
Picture Arrangement	18
Block Design	15
Object Assembly	16
Coding	15

WRAT

	Grade Equivalent
Reading	3.4
Arithmetic	2.1
Spelling	2.5

Strength of Grip

Dominant hand	(R)	8.0 kg
Non-dominant hand	(L)	11.0 kg

Name Writing

Dominant hand	(R)	17 sec
Non-dominant hand	(L)	37 sec

Category Test

Number of errors — 63

Tactual Performance Test

Dominant hand	(R)	3.9
Non-dominant hand	(L)	1.2
Both hands		0.7

Total Time	5.8
Memory	5
Localization	4

Seashore Rhythm Test

Number correct — 29   1

Speech-sounds Perception Test

Number of errors — 9

Finger Tapping Test

Dominant hand	(R)	26	26
Non-dominant hand	(L)	30	

Trail Making Test

Part A	24 sec	0	error(s)
Part B	39 sec	0	error(s)

Bilateral Simultaneous Sensory Stimulation

RH ___ LH ___	Both: RH ___ LH ___	
RH ___ LF ___	Both: RH ___ LF ___	
LH ___ RF ___	Both: LH ___ RF ___	
RE ___ LE ___	Both: RE ___ LE ___	
RV ___ LV ___	Both: RV ___ LV ___	

Tactile Finger Recognition

RH 1 ___ 2 ___ 3 ___ 4 _1_ 5 ___	RH 1 / 20
LH 1 ___ 2 ___ 3 ___ 4 _1_ 5 ___	LH 1 / 20

Finger-Tip Number Writing

RH 1 _1_ 2 ___ 3 ___ 4 ___ 5 ___	RH 1 / 20
LH 1 ___ 2 ___ 3 ___ 4 ___ 5 ___	LH 0 / 20

Tactile Form Recognition Test

Dominant hand	(R)	8 sec	0 error(s)
Non-dominant hand	(L)	8 sec	0 error(s)

Reitan-Indiana Aphasia Screening Test

Form for Adults and Older Children

Name Cathy   Age 9 – 6

Copy SQUARE	Repeat TRIANGLE
Name SQUARE	Repeat MASSACHUSETTS Massatucite
Spell SQUARE S - Q - U - R - A - E	Repeat METHODIST EPISCOPAL
Copy CROSS	Write SQUARE
Name CROSS	Read SEVEN
Spell CROSS C - O - R - S - S	Repeat SEVEN
Copy TRIANGLE	Repeat/Explain HE SHOUTED THE WARNING
Name TRIANGLE	Write HE SHOUTED THE WARNING
Spell TRIANGLE T - R - I - A - N - C - L - E	Compute 85 − 27 =
Name BABY	Compute 17 x 3 = 14 4 × 6 = 2
Write CLOCK	Name KEY
Name FORK	Demonstrate use of KEY
Read 7 SIX 2	Draw KEY
Read MGW	Read PLACE LEFT HAND TO RIGHT EAR
Reading I	Place LEFT HAND TO RIGHT EAR
Reading II *Could not read "famous," but read everything else correctly.*	Place LEFT HAND TO LEFT ELBOW

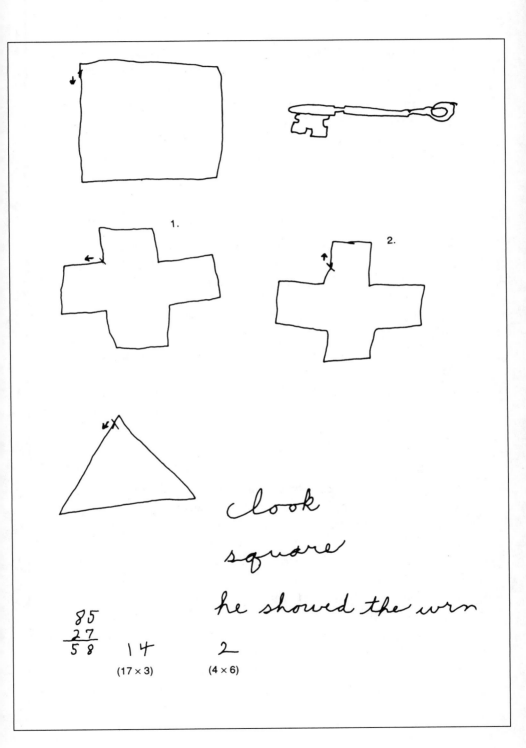

would expect to find evidence of motor impairment (especially involving the right side), possibly some impairment of verbal intelligence and dysphasic manifestations, and probably some evidence of impairment on general indicators. However, it is likely that Cathy would not show any significant deficits on additional tasks that were specific in nature (such as sensory-perceptual losses), considering the frontal location of the lesion.

Wechsler Intelligence Scale for Children — Revised

At the time of the neuropsychological examination Cathy was 9 years, 6 months of age and had completed 4.5 years of school. On the WISC-R she earned a Verbal IQ of 105, a value that falls at the 63rd percentile and is in the upper part of the Average range. Cathy did extremely well on the Performance subtests, earning a Performance IQ of 142, a value that falls at the 99th percentile and is well into the Superior range. The Verbal subtests were all at the average level except for a score of 13 on Similarities; the Performance subtest scores ranged from 15 to 18. Cathy earned a Full Scale IQ of 125, a value in the Superior range exceeding 95% of her age peers.

On the basis of these findings, it would appear that Cathy had a verbal intelligence that was lower than her performance intelligence, but there would be no way to know definitely that her verbal intelligence had been impaired. Evaluation of the frequency with which differences between Verbal and Performance IQs occur in the normal population have been made by Silverstein (1987). With a Verbal IQ of 105, a Performance IQ of 142 would occur less than 1% of the time. Considering the history information (including the fact that Cathy had developed normally and then suddenly had sustained a lesion of the left cerebral hemisphere), and the significant disparity between the Verbal and Performance IQ values, it seems likely that some impairment of verbal intelligence has occurred.

The Halstead-Reitan Battery
for Older Children

Neuropsychological Deficit Scale. The NDS for Older Children succinctly recapitulates the results of the neuropsychological examination. On the Level of Performance section Cathy performed very well, except in the areas evaluating motor functions (in which she was strikingly impaired) and abstraction, reasoning, and logical analysis abilities (the general indicators of cerebral functioning). Her score of 15 on the Motor Functions section exceeded the mean of 14.05 for brain-damaged children, and reflected the mild but definite impairment she demonstrated on each of the measures in this section (except for Total Time on the Tactual Performance Test).

Cathy performed very well on the Sensory-perceptual Functions section, earning scores that were in the perfectly normal range on six of the seven measures. Her total score of 1 on this section was well below the mean of 5.15 for control children. This finding certainly would suggest that the lesion causing her difficulties was quite discrete and limited to the frontal lobe rather than having any significant influence on the functional status of the parietal cortex.

It is interesting to note, however, that Cathy showed evidence of mild impairment on the Category Test (63 errors) and Part B of the Trail Making Test (39 sec), two of the three measures included in the Abstraction, Reasoning and Logical Analysis section. Research has demonstrated that these tests are generally sensitive to cerebral damage regardless of its location. On this section Cathy earned a total of 4 points, a score intermediate to the mean of control children (2.63) and brain-damaged children (6.03).

As noted above, Cathy had a Verbal IQ that was 37 points below her Performance IQ, despite the fact that her Verbal IQ was still in the upper part of the Average range. We raised a question about whether this disparity may reflect damage involving the left cerebral hemisphere, and the

results on the Aphasia Screening Test provided the definitive answer. Cathy demonstrated specific deficits involving
the use of language symbols for communicational purposes,
and earned an NDS score of 5 on the Aphasia and Related
Variables section. This score does not reach the mean of 7.97
earned by children with brain damage, but it definitely
exceeds the cut-off point of 3/4 for this section.

On the Right-Left Differences section of the NDS Cathy
earned a score of 9, which did not quite exceed the cut-off
point of 9/10. On this section the mean is 6.79 for control
children and 13.74 for brain-damaged children.

Clinical Evaluation of the Test Results. Analysis of the
details of the test results yields additional important information. On the Aphasia Screening Test Cathy showed clear
evidence of spelling dyspraxia. She confused the sequence
of letters in SQUARE and CROSS and substituted a C for a
G in the word TRIANGLE. Her difficulty in reading was
sufficiently severe to qualify for a classification of dyslexia.
(Even though she was in the latter part of the fourth grade,
she was not able to read the word "famous.")

Cathy also showed definite evidence of confusion in
dealing with simple arithmetical problems. She was able to
solve the problem $85 - 27 =$ correctly, but apparently did so
on a rote basis. When she was asked to mentally multiply
17×3, she responded by saying "14." She was even more
confused when asked to multiply 4×6, and answered "2."
These responses may have resulted from an attempt to subtract instead of multiply, but children with Cathy's ability
level rarely make these kinds of errors unless cerebral damage or dysfunction is present.

Cathy demonstrated additional manifestations of left
cerebral dysfunction. Her grip strength was clearly less in
her right upper extremity (8 kg) than in her left upper extremity (11 kg), and her finger tapping speed was definitely
slower with her right hand (26) than with her left hand (30).
On the Tactual Performance Test she performed relatively

well in terms of overall time (5.8 min), indicating that the problem-solving elements of the task were not difficult for her. However, she required more than three times as much time to complete the task with her right hand (3.9 min) than with her left hand (1.2 min). Despite the good scores with each hand, the difference between the two hands must be noted in clinical interpretation of the results.

In individual cases a variety of circumstances can affect the comparative performances on each hand of the Tactual Performance Test, and in the Right-Left Differences section of the NDS we have decided to follow a fairly conservative approach toward scoring differences between the two hands. Even though the variability in circumstances from one child to another has made us reluctant to adopt stringent criteria, it was apparent in this case that Cathy was well motivated to perform to the best of her ability and that no unusual testing problems affected her performance. Thus, the comparatively slow performance with the right hand may well be of significance in comparing the status of the two cerebral hemispheres. This instance serves as an example of the advantages often implicit in clinical interpretation as contrasted with a stereotyped scoring procedure (such as represented by the Neuropsychological Deficit Scale).

It is interesting to note that except for the indications of dysphasia (and in all probability, a depressed Verbal IQ), the only general higher-level deficits encountered in the entire test protocol were shown on the Category Test (63 errors) and Part B of the Trail Making Test (39 sec). The Verbal IQ and the evidence of dysphasia are probably related to impairment of specialized functions and the fact that the brain lesion involved the left cerebral hemisphere. In this sense the only indicators of generalized impairment were the Category Test and the Trail Making Test.

Cases of this kind have led psychologists to assume that the Category Test and Part B of the Trail Making Test are specifically and selectively sensitive to frontal lesions.

However, such conclusions are drawn without careful consideration and comparison of results obtained in persons with nonfrontal lesions. Our research and experience suggest that in this case the Category Test and the Trail Making Test would, in all probability, have been performed just as poorly if the lesion had been located in an area other than the frontal lobe (although if this had been the case it is likely that certain other tests would have been performed more poorly as well), and the test configuration, based on the relationships of measures of lower-level and higher-level brain functions, would have been substantially different.

Wide Range Achievement Test

Finally, we should note that Cathy appeared to be below grade level in her academic progress, a prediction that could have been made fairly confidently on the basis of her Verbal IQ and the additional indications of left cerebral impairment. Although she had presently completed about 4.5 grades of school, the WRAT yielded the following grade-equivalents: Reading (word recognition), 3.4; Spelling, 2.5; and Arithmetic, 2.1. There is no doubt that these scores reflect, at least in part, the specific deficits in spelling, reading, and calculating that were shown on the Aphasia Screening Test. Such effects probably are only to be expected with lesions of the left cerebral hemisphere.

We frequently observe difficulties in making adequate academic progress even in children whose evidence of left cerebral hemisphere dysfunction is derived from comparisons of performances on the two sides of the body. Cathy demonstrated impairment not only on the right side of the body, but had specific deficits in dealing with language symbols as well. Moreover, it seems likely that her verbal intelligence has been strikingly reduced.

Although Cathy's parents reported that she was making excellent progress since her brain surgery, it definitely appears that the neuropsychological test results serve as a warning and even as an indicator of problems in the area of academic performance which are likely to become more obvious and pronounced in time. Cathy's performances indicate that she needs cognitive brain retraining, starting with Track C of REHABIT and progressing through Tracks B and A. She is not likely to receive the focused and individual attention that she needs in the regular classroom, and it is probable that she will fall farther and farther behind her peers unless specific remediation efforts are employed.

It is also likely that this set of circumstances will be confusing and emotionally upsetting for Cathy. In many areas she is still quite capable, and will not understand why she cannot perform as well as her peers on many tasks (particularly when the physician has told Cathy and her parents that she has made "an excellent and full recovery.") Unless Cathy receives individualized help directed toward remediating her specific neuropsychological deficits, she is likely to experience a great deal of anxiety and apprehension. In all probability, she will be evaluated on the basis of her good abilities, and may be blamed for "not trying hard enough" when her neuropsychological impairment limits her performances in other areas.

It is interesting to observe the pattern of specific and general indicators of cognitive impairment shown by a child who has had most of her life to develop neuropsychological functions with a normal brain and then sustains a focal brain lesion. There is almost no doubt that Cathy generally was much more competent in many of her abilities than she would have been if she had sustained a similar lesion early in life. In this case the test findings principally reflect a loss of previously acquired cognitive abilities, due to a brain lesion. Although the brain lesion was sustained about one year before the neuropsychological testing was done, not enough time has passed to limit the development of neuropsychological functions to the extent that will, in all probability, become apparent in later years. For more than eight years Cathy had the advantage of a normal brain to subserve the development of her neuropsychological functions, and she still retains many good abilities.

This case illustrates the importance of using both general and specific neuropsychological tests in the evaluation of brain-behavior relationships. At the time of our neuropsychological examination Cathy had a focal lesion involving a very specific area of the brain. The neurosurgeon reported that while removing the abscess he had been careful to do as little damage to the cerebral cortex as possible, merely making an incision in the cortex and removing the abscess through the incision. Thus, as expected, the principal manifestations of deficit related to rather specific (lateralized or even localized) abilities. In this case, considering the posterior frontal location of the lesion, these abilities related to motor functions on the right side of the body and lateralized abilities concerned with verbal intelligence and the use of language and related symbols. However, any brain lesion (even when it is focal in location) can also be expected to have certain general implications.

During the last three decades the emphasis in neuropsychology on the specialized (lateralized) functions of the cerebral hemispheres has tended to preclude and overshadow recognition of the types of neuropsychological deficits which occur with any lesion, regardless of lateralization or location. There are certain abilities that are generally distributed throughout the cerebral cortex, even pervading areas that subserve more specific abilities. For example, the abilities of attention and concentration will be affected when the lesion is sufficiently severe or widespread. In the case of this child, the first level of central processing was essentially intact, but the highest level, concerned with abstraction, reasoning, and logical analysis skills, showed definite evidence of impairment.

For Cathy, the general indicators as well as the more specific indicators contributed to an understanding of the significance of the cerebral lesion. In many cases, impairment of general neuropsychological functions is the critical factor that limits adequacy and efficiency of performance in everyday living. Specific difficulties (such as lateralized motor dysfunction) are readily recognized, remediated, or allowed for; however, impairment in the area of reasoning, basic understanding, being able to discern the essential nature of problems, and identify the aspect of the problem that needs adjustment is not subject to specific identification, and therefore is rarely understood or properly handled in a rehabilitation program. Instead, the child is labeled as "unmotivated," "slow," "lazy," or even "stupid." As we have noted elsewhere (Reitan & Wolfson, 1988b), one of the major weaknesses in approaches to neuropsychological rehabilitation is represented by the tendency to identify specific deficits as targets of remediation and to fail to recognize the general neuropsychological deficits, which are even more important in affecting an individual's efficiency of everyday behavior, emotional status, and quality of life.

■

Cerebral Hemispherectomy for Intractable Epileptic Seizures

The next patient to be discussed, Donald, had a right cerebral hemispherectomy performed when he was twelve years old as treatment for intractable epilepsy. Before discussing his case, we will present a brief description of this procedure and its history.

In 1950 Krynauw, a South African neurosurgeon, reported results of cerebral hemispherectomy on twelve children who suffered from infantile hemiplegia and severe, medically refractory seizures. These children were screened to include those who had documented evidence of lateralized cerebral damage and an epileptic focus arising from the damaged cerebral hemisphere.

The rationale was that when electrical storms arose within the brain and caused epileptic seizures, it might be better to remove a damaged and perhaps atrophic cerebral hemisphere (which was probably doing little more than causing severe electrical abnormalities involving the entire brain) rather than to let the hemisphere continue to produce these episodes of seizures. Frequently, in fact, children who are considered candidates for cerebral hemispherectomy have suffered episodes of major status epilepticus.

Krynauw (1950) reported that when he removed the "offending" cerebral hemisphere, there was a substantial reduction in seizure frequency and the child seemed to be somewhat more alert. Although the group of children who are appropriate for this operation is small compared to the total number of children with cerebral disorders, Krynauw's results were quite impressive and led to further study in neurological centers in various parts of the world. Rasmussen and Villemure (1989) reported that by 1961 nearly 300 cases had been published (White, 1961). A complete or nearly complete reduction of seizures occurred in 80% - 85% of these children; motor dysfunction on the side contralateral to the removed cerebral hemisphere, which already had been significantly impaired, seemed to show no further deterioration. The alertness and abilities of the children, as well as their general behavior, seemed to improve.

However, complications began to be noted in children who had undergone cerebral hemispherectomy, beginning four or more years after the surgery. This was first reported by Laine, Pruvet, and Osson (1964). The children developed gradually progressive neurological deterioration, loss of alertness and mental slowing, somnolence, tremor, ataxia, and evidence of chronic increased intracranial pressure. CT scans showed enlargement of the remaining ventricle associated with narrowing of the central aqueduct or of the foramen of Monro. This late complication, which was sometimes fatal, developed in one-fourth to one-third of the patients who had previously undergone cerebral hemispherectomy. Surgical re-exploration showed that the hemispherectomy cavity was filled with a dark, viscid fluid containing high levels of protein and iron.

Tinuper, Andermann, Villemure, Rasmussen, and Quesney (1988) indicate that they believe that this syndrome occurs after hemispherectomy because of lack of adequate support of the remaining hemisphere within the skull and its "vulnerability to minimal jolts to the head or brief physiological increases in intracranial pressure (e.g., coughing, sneezing) leading to repeated leakage of red blood cells into the intracranial cavity." This condition is referred to as *superficial cerebral hemosiderosis.*

Hemispherectomy in children with hemiplegia and intractable seizures was largely discontinued after discovery of this condition. However, Rasmussen and Villemure (1989) have reported excellent results in a series of 57 patients who have undergone a modification of the operation (referred to as "subtotal hemispherectomy") in which two-thirds to four-fifths of the hemisphere is removed. The procedure actually consists of removing the central part of the hemisphere and the temporal lobe, leaving the anterior half of the frontal lobe and the posterior third of the hemisphere intact and vascularized. Following this extirpation the remaining frontal and posterior areas of the hemisphere are disconnected from the remaining cerebral hemisphere by sectioning white matter connections from the brainstem as well as the remaining hemisphere.

With blood supply remaining intact to these isolated areas, it appears that the patient is protected against gradual seepage of red blood cells into the cavity created by extirpation of the brain tissue. Donald had a hemispherectomy before this modified procedure was widely available. In addition, he had striking atrophic changes of the right cerebral hemisphere and a complete occlusion of the internal carotid artery.

A suggestion has been made that sectioning the corpus callosum, and thereby separating the cerebral hemispheres, might be an adequate alternative to hemispherectomy (Spencer, Spencer, Williamson, & Mattson, 1985). However, Tinuper, et al. (1988) note that callosotomy eliminates seizures in only 5% of the patients, even though drop attacks are substantially improved.

The small number of instances in which seizures are eliminated following section of the corpus callosum is a revealing statistic, considering the fact that seizure control has served as the clinical justification for sectioning the corpus callosum (as contrasted with the research interest in an experimental model in which the human being had been subjected to separation and isolation of the two cerebral hemispheres).

Case 10 — DONALD

Age:	12-8 (Testing I)	**Gender:**	Male
	13-0 (Testing II)		
Education:	1	**Handedness:**	Right
	(Both testings)		

Neuropsychological Examination

Donald was a child who had been ill essentially all of his life. When he was born at seven and one-half months gestation he weighed only 4 pounds, 10 ounces. His development was obviously slow. At 20 months of age, when he had just learned to take a few steps, he had an acute onset of spastic left hemiparesis. Specialized neurological studies indicated that he had right cerebral cortical atrophy. Although he was hemiparetic, he did learn to walk within the next year. When he was five years of age he began to have major motor seizures which occurred relatively frequently from that time on.

Donald was admitted to the hospital when he was 11 years old because of an increase in the frequency of his falling episodes. A right carotid angiogram done at that time revealed that his internal carotid artery was completely occluded at about a centimeter distal to the bifurcation at the common carotid artery. Angiographic visualizations of the left carotid and the vertebral arteries were normal.

At about the time of his 12th birthday Donald suffered a head blow and was unconscious for about ten minutes. Two months later he again fell and struck his head, and even though he did not lose consciousness, the effects were sufficient to require hospitalization. An EEG done at this time showed a generalized dysrhythmia, Grade II, with abnormal tracings more prominent over the right cerebral hemisphere than the left.

During this entire period, since the age of 5 years, Donald continued to have major motor seizures that did not respond to medication. Finally, at the age of 12 years, 8 months, he was admitted to the hospital to be evaluated for a right hemispherectomy.

At that time the neurological examination documented a spastic quadraparesis with muscle atrophy and spastic hemiparesis on the left side, a strikingly ataxic gait, bilateral extensor toe signs, and hyperactive reflexes generally. Renewed efforts to control Donald's epilepsy with medication were unsuccessful, and a right hemispherectomy was performed two weeks after he had been admitted to the hospital.

For the first ten days postoperatively, Donald was somewhat lethargic and febrile. He then began to show improvement, became more alert, and it was possible to decrease his antiepileptic medication. He improved steadily and was discharged from the hospital one month after the operation. At the time of his discharge the diagnoses included spastic left hemiparesis, major motor epilepsy, complete occlusion of the right internal carotid artery, and surgical removal of a severely atrophic right cerebral hemisphere.

Neuropsychological Examination

Testing I

Two weeks before the hemispherectomy was done we administered a comprehensive neuropsychological examination. Donald demonstrated serious and general limitations in his abilities. We will first summarize his performances and then discuss his scores in more detail.

The Halstead-Reitan Neuropsychological Test Battery for Older Children

Name: Donald I   Age: 12 – 8
Gender: M   Education: 1   Handedness: RH 7 LH 0

Neuropsychological Deficit Scale (NDS) Summary

Level of Performance	Subject's score	Mean for controls	Mean for brain-damaged	Cut-off score
Motor Functions	21	6.29	14.05	
Sensory-perceptual Functions	21	5.15	10.77	
Attention and Concentration	6	1.91	3.78	
Immediate Memory and Recapitulation	(6)	2.23	3.31	
Visual-spatial Skills	12	4.06	7.69	
Abstraction, Reasoning, Logical Analysis	9	2.63	6.03	
Level of Performance–Total	75	22.27	45.63	33/34
Dysphasia and Related Variables	18	1.37	7.97	3/4
Right / Left Differences	22	6.79	13.74	9/10
Total NDS Score	115	30.43	67.34	43/44

WISC-R

VIQ 50
PIQ 45
FS IQ 43

Verbal Subtests		Performance Subtests	
Information	2	Picture Completion	5
Similarities	3	Picture Arrangement	1
Arithmetic	3	Block Design	1
Vocabulary	1	Object Assembly	1
Comprehension	1	Coding	1
(Digit Span)	(3)	(Mazes)	(3)

Tactile Form Recognition Test

Dominant hand (R) 10 sec   4 errors
Non-dominant hand (L) 14 sec   6 errors

Strength of Grip

Dominant hand (R) 13.0 kg
Non-dominant hand (L) * kg

Name Writing

Dominant hand (R) _____ sec   Could not print
Non-dominant hand (L) * sec   or write letters but used pencil in RH.

Category Test

Number of errors   119

Tactual Performance Test

Dominant hand (R) 6.5   One block was placed; then test was discontinued.
Non-dominant hand (L) ___
Both hands ___   Total Time ___
Memory ___
Localization ___

Seashore Rhythm Test

Number correct   18   10

Speech-sounds Perception Test

Number of errors   42

Finger Tapping Test

Dominant hand (R) 24   24
Non-dominant hand (L) *

Trail Making Test

Part A   61 sec   0 error(s)
Part B   300 sec   6 error(s)
Discontinued at 4-D

Bilateral Simultaneous Sensory Stimulation

RH___ LH___   Both: RH 1 LH 3
RH___ LF___   Both: RH 2 LF 1
LH___ RF___   Both: LH 3 RF 0

RE___ LE___   Both: RE___ LE 2

RV___ LV___   Both: RV___ LV___
___ ___   ___ ___ } *
___ ___   ___ ___

Tactile Finger Recognition

RH 1 1 2 2 3 2 4 1 5___   RH 6 / 20
LH 1___ 2 2 3 2 4 3 5 1   LH 8 / 20

Finger-Tip Number Writing *

RH 1___ 2___ 3___ 4___ 5___   RH ___ / ___
LH 1___ 2___ 3___ 4___ 5___   LH ___ / ___

Finger-Tip Symbol Writing

RH 1 1 2___ 3___ 4 1 5___   RH 2 / 20
LH 1 1 2___ 3 2 4___ 5 1   LH 4 / 20

©1991, Ralph M. Reitan, Ph.D. Reitan Neuropsychology Laboratory Tucson, Arizona   * Unable to do

Reitan-Indiana Aphasia Screening Test

Form for Adults and Older Children

Name __Donald I__ Age __12 – 8__

Copy SQUARE	Repeat TRIANGLE *Slurred enunciation, but OK.*
Name SQUARE	Repeat MASSACHUSETTS *Massatusess*
Spell SQUARE *Cannot do.*	Repeat METHODIST EPISCOPAL *Subject would not attempt.*
Copy CROSS	Write SQUARE
Name CROSS *Cannot do.*	Read SEVEN *Cannot read. Read letters S - E - V - E - N.*
Spell CROSS *Cannot do.*	Repeat SEVEN
Copy TRIANGLE	Repeat/Explain HE SHOUTED THE WARNING *He shout da war. Could not explain.*
Name TRIANGLE *Cannot do.*	Write HE SHOUTED THE WARNING
Spell TRIANGLE	Compute 85 – 27 =
Name BABY *Boy. Ex.? No further response.*	Compute 17 x 3 = *Cannot multiply.*
Write CLOCK *Attempted to draw.*	Name KEY
Name FORK *Spoon.*	Demonstrate use of KEY *Could not do.*
Read 7 SIX 2 *S - I - X - 2. Ex.? 2 - X - I - S.*	Draw KEY
Read MGW *A - G - W. Ex.? G - W - Y*	Read PLACE LEFT HAND TO RIGHT EAR *Cannot read.*
Reading I *Cannot read.*	Place LEFT HAND TO RIGHT EAR
Reading II *Cannot read.*	Place LEFT HAND TO LEFT ELBOW

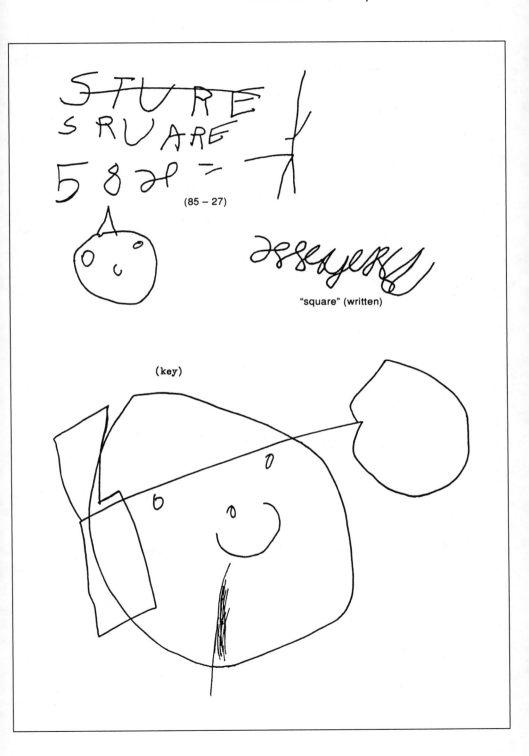

(85 – 27)

"square" (written)

(key)

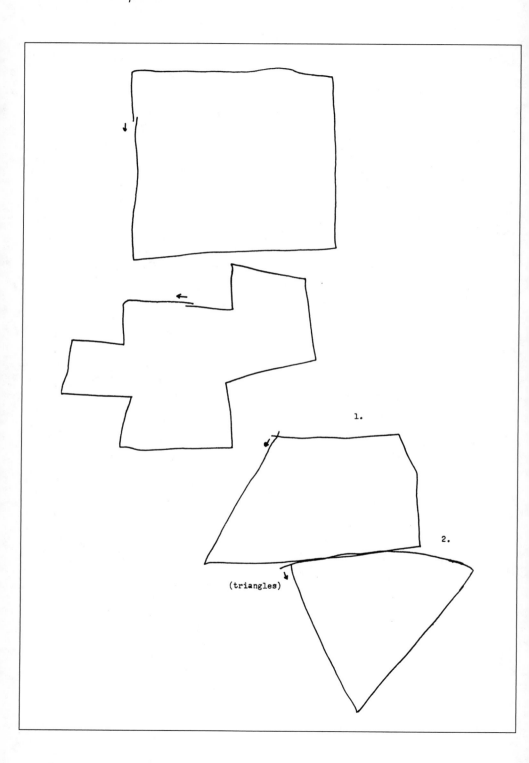

1.

2.

(triangles)

Wechsler Intelligence Scale for Children — Revised

On the WISC-R Donald earned a Verbal IQ of 50, a Performance IQ of 45, and Full Scale IQ of 43. Although he was not able to read even the simplest material, he was able to name several of the objects on the Aphasia Screening Test and recognized both numbers and letters. It was somewhat difficult to obtain reliable results on the sensory-perceptual tests, but it was clear that Donald had more difficulty perceiving stimuli to the left side than to the right side. The motor dysfunction of Donald's left upper extremity was so pronounced that he was not able to perform any tasks with it.

Halstead-Reitan Battery for Older Children

Neuropsychological Deficit Scale. The NDS for Older Children showed very severe impairment. Every variable in the Level of Performance section earned a score of 3, yielding a total score of 75 points on that section. Donald also had a total of 22 points for the Right-Left Differences section. Every variable had a score in the range of impairment and although deficits were demonstrated principally on the left side, some tasks were clearly defective on the right side as well.

Despite conservative scoring of the Dysphasia and Related Variables section, Donald's performances still produced a score of 18 points. He was able to identify body parts correctly and showed no evidence of right-left confusion on the test items. Although he could repeat TRIANGLE and MASSACHUSETTS understandably and without evidence of central dysarthria, his enunciation was far from distinct. The test results clearly indicated that his right cerebral hemisphere was much more deficient than the left, an inference drawn mainly from comparisons of performances on the two sides of the body. Donald was generally impaired on higher level tasks, as exemplified by the Verbal IQ of 50 and the Performance IQ of 45.

Testing II

We re-examined Donald four months after the hemispherectomy. Although he showed some degree of improvement in his ability to attempt the various tasks involved (and even in some of his performances), he continued to demonstrate severe generalized neuropsychological impairment. The results indicated that the operation was beneficial not only in controlling Donald's epilepsy, but also in improving certain aspects of his neuropsychological functioning.

On the second examination Donald earned both Verbal and Performance IQ values that were similar to those of the first testing, with scores in the range of Mental Retardation. Comparisons of his actual performances suggested that he had in fact done a little better on the second examination, but he had also entered an older age category, resulting in approximately equivalent IQ values.

Neuropsychological Deficit Scale. The NDS score based on the first testing totaled 115 points, but had been reduced to 108 on the second testing. Donald had improved 6 points on Level of Performance and 3 points on Dysphasia and Related Variables. However, he was 2 points worse on the Right-Left Differences section. The improvement on the Level of Performance section resulted from reducing scores from 3 to 2 on four measures relating to the right upper extremity and his ability to remember four shapes on the Memory component of the TPT.

On the second examination Donald showed only mild impairment in finger tapping and grip strength with the right hand as well as finger-tip number writing perception and tactile form recognition. Although he showed some degree of improvement in other respects (as will be detailed below), his scores on the NDS still fell in the range of serious impairment.

The Halstead-Reitan Neuropsychological Test Battery for Older Children

Name __Donald II__   Age __13 – 0__

Gender __M__ Education __1__   Handedness: RH __7__ LH __0__

Neuropsychological Deficit Scale (NDS) Summary

Level of Performance	Subject's score	Mean for controls	Mean for brain-damaged	Cut-off score
Motor Functions	18	6.29	14.05	
Sensory-perceptual Functions	19	5.15	10.77	
Attention and Concentration	6	1.91	3.78	
Immediate Memory and Recapitulation	5	2.23	3.31	
Visual-spatial Skills	12	4.06	7.69	
Abstraction, Reasoning, Logical Analysis	9	2.63	6.03	
Level of Performance–Total	69	22.27	45.63	33/34
Dysphasia and Related Variables	15	1.37	7.97	3/4
Right / Left Differences	24	6.79	13.74	9/10
Total NDS Score	108	30.43	67.34	43/44

WISC-R

VIQ	47
PIQ	46
FS IQ	42

Verbal Subtests

Information	3
Similarities	1
Arithmetic	1
Vocabulary	1
Comprehension	2
(Digit Span)	(2)

Performance Subtests

Picture Completion	4
Picture Arrangement	1
Block Design	3
Object Assembly	1
Coding	1
(Mazes)	(4)

WRAT

	Grade Equivalent
Reading	1.2
Arithmetic	1.8
Spelling	1.2

Strength of Grip

Dominant hand	(R)	16.5 kg
Non-dominant hand	(L)	* kg

Name Writing

Dominant hand	(R)	24 sec
Non-dominant hand	(L)	* sec

*Unable to do

©1991, Ralph M. Reitan, Ph.D. Reitan Neuropsychology Laboratory Tucson, Arizona

Category Test

Number of errors	119

Tactual Performance Test

Dominant hand	(R)	4.8	
Non-dominant hand	(R)	3.7	
Both hands	R	6.2	

Total Time	14.7
Memory	4
Localization	1

Seashore Rhythm Test

Number correct	18	10

Speech-sounds Perception Test

Number of errors	37

Finger Tapping Test

Dominant hand	(R)	31	31
Non-dominant hand	(L)	*	

Trail Making Test

Part A	76 sec	1	error(s)
Part B	163 sec	4	error(s)

Discontinued at 3-C

Bilateral Simultaneous Sensory Stimulation

RH ___ LH ___	Both: RH ___ LH ___	
RH ___ LF ___	Both: RH 1 LF 1	
LH ___ RF ___	Both: LH 2 RF ___	
RE ___ LE ___	Both: RE ___ LE ___	
RV ___ LV 2	Both: RV ___ LV 4	
___ 1	___ 3	
___ 2	___ 4	

Tactile Finger Recognition

RH	1 ___	2 ___	3 2	4 2	5 1	RH	5 / 20
LH	1 ___	2 2	3 2	4 4	5 2	LH	10 / 20

Finger-Tip Number Writing

RH	1 1	2 ___	3 2	4 2	5 1	RH	6 / 20
LH	1 ___	2 ___	3 ___	4 ___	5 ___	LH	* / ___

Tactile Form Recognition Test

Dominant hand	(R)	12 sec	1	error(s)
Non-dominant hand	(L)	* sec		error(s)

**Reitan-Indiana Aphasia
Screening Test**

Form for Adults and Older Children

Name <u>Donald II</u>   Age <u>13 – 0</u>

Copy SQUARE	Repeat TRIANGLE *OK, but slurred.*
Name SQUARE	Repeat MASSACHUSETTS Maschusess
Spell SQUARE C - A - E - H	Repeat METHODIST EPISCOPAL Me – dist Sp
Copy CROSS	Write SQUARE
Name CROSS *Cannot name.*	Read SEVEN *Read individual letters.*
Spell CROSS B - H - G	Repeat SEVEN
Copy TRIANGLE	Repeat/Explain HE SHOUTED THE WARNING He shotted at warning. *Could not explain.*
Name TRIANGLE Square. *Could not offer another name.*	Write HE SHOUTED THE WARNING
Spell TRIANGLE C - A - E	Compute 85 − 27 = *Cannot do. See attempt.*
Name BABY	Compute 17 x 3 = *Cannot do. See attempt.*
Write CLOCK Write the whole thing? *Instructions repeated and subject encouraged.*	Name KEY
Name FORK Spoon	Demonstrate use of KEY *Pointed index and middle fingers toward examiner.*
Read 7 SIX 2 S - I - X - 2 *Ex.? Repeated S - I - X - 2.*	Draw KEY
Read MGW	Read PLACE LEFT HAND TO RIGHT EAR *Cannot read.*
Reading I *Could not read. Named individual letters.*	Place LEFT HAND TO RIGHT EAR
Reading II *Could not read.*	Place LEFT HAND TO LEFT ELBOW *Right hand to left elbow.*

1.

2.

1.

1. SQUDRE 2. SQURE

"square" (written)

1.

2. SENE (He shouted the warning.)

PRQTietoWMY

8⁵/₁₂₃ − 2 7⁼/₁₃₉₁₀

BAMCKTY (clock)

Although Donald showed some improvement on the Aphasia Screening Test, he demonstrated many of the same basic difficulties on both examinations. He could now write his name legibly, even though the letters were not always correctly formed. He had initially reversed numbers when copying the problem 85 – 27 = , but now was able to copy the problem correctly (even though he could not make any progress in solving it). He initially demonstrated no ability in reading, but was now able to read the individual letters correctly. On the initial examination he would not attempt to spell any words, but when now requested to spell he was willing to name letters (though his responses were entirely inappropriate).

On the first examination Donald was entirely unwilling to try to enunciate METHODIST EPISCOPAL; after the operation, when given the words individually, he was able to say "Medist" and to make the sound "sp" in attempting to repeat EPISCOPAL. He made only one mistake on the Aphasia Screening Test that was not present on the first examination; when asked to place his left hand to his left elbow, he put his right hand on his left elbow. On the first examination he had recognized that compliance with the request was impossible. We are not certain that these performances on the Aphasia Screening Test represent anything more than a willingness to attempt tasks he could not perform.

Clinical Evaluation of the Test Results. Analysis of the neuropsychological test results indicates that Donald continued to have striking difficulties on the left side of his body, involving both motor and sensory-perceptual functions. In addition, his level of performance was generally very deficient. The test findings on the second examination therefore continued to demonstrate severe deficits in brain-related abilities generally, with findings of specific dysfunction of the right cerebral hemisphere (which, of course, had been removed).

A test-by-test comparison of Donald's performances indicates that during the four months since the first examination Donald had improved in certain respects. He did much better on the TPT than he had initially. On the first examination he worked for 6.5 minutes on the first trial but had managed to place only one block successfully. He was unable to make any further progress and the test was discontinued. On the postoperative examination he completed the task on three successive trials, requiring a total of 14.7 minutes to place the 18 blocks (6 blocks on each trial). Note that he used his right hand for all three trials because he was totally unable to use his left upper extremity.

Donald's finger tapping speed with the right hand had increased from 24 to 31 taps and his grip strength increased from 13 kg to 16.5 kg. Results of the sensory-perceptual examination can be summarized by noting that there were somewhat fewer errors on the post-hemispherectomy examination, but more distinct lateralization effects were demonstrated essentially by somewhat fewer errors on the right side. When his right hand was tested it appeared that Donald was able to pay better attention and thus perform at a somewhat improved level.

As noted above, Donald may also have shown some improvement on individual items on the Aphasia Screening Test, although his apparent improvement may have been only a greater willingness to attempt to perform the tasks. On the Speech-sounds Perception Test his errors decreased from 42 to 37, but it would not be possible to conclude that this represented any genuine improvement.

Donald's scores remained essentially the same on Verbal IQ, Performance IQ, the Category Test, the Seashore Rhythm Test, and the quality of his drawings on the Aphasia Screening Test. None of his scores deteriorated except on Part A of the Trail Making Test; on the second examination he required 76 seconds to complete the test whereas he had required only 61 seconds on the first examination. However, considering Donald's general level of impairment, this change may have been within the range of chance variation. As noted above, he also demonstrated right-left confusion that was not present on the first examination. In total, it appears that Donald was somewhat more alert, cooperative, had improved functions particularly on motor tasks (finger tapping speed, complex manipulatory skills, and perhaps grip strength), and showed some possible improvement on certain sensory-perceptual tasks.

Finally, it is of definite interest to note that Donald still had some remaining sensory-perceptual abilities on the left side despite the fact that his right cerebral hemisphere had been removed. In testing for perception of bilateral simultaneous auditory stimulation, Donald made no errors on either side, although on the first examination he had made two errors. In tactile finger localization he made ten errors on the left hand, just two errors more than he had made before his right hemisphere was removed.

On the first examination we were not able to test for perception of bilateral simultaneous visual stimuli because Donald was not able to pay close enough attention to respond reliably. However, on the second examination he made no errors at all when the stimulus was given toward his right side, failed in 5 of 12 trials to identify a unilateral stimulus when it was given to his left side (indicating quite clearly that he did perceive the stimulus in 7 of 12 trials), and was able to identify the stimulus on both sides with bilateral simultaneous stimulation in 1 of 12 trials. In the other 11 trials he consistently failed to report the stimulus toward the left side.

These results make it clear that even certain sensory-perceptual functions can be perceived by a single hemisphere when there has, in effect, been only a single hemisphere functionally available for neuropsychological development during the maturational process. Thus, a minor degree of sharing even of sensory-perceptual abilities between the cerebral hemispheres is noted in this case, although it is quite clear that the absence of the right cerebral hemisphere had profound effects on sensory-perceptual and motor functions of the contralateral side of the body.

In this case the neuropsychological examination illustrates the generalized impairment associated with even lateralized lesions that occur early in life. Children with such lesions routinely show devastating impairment on higher-level functions, regardless of whether they are the kind of abilities that would later be normally subserved by the left or right cerebral hemisphere. Obviously, there is a degree of plasticity in the immature brain in the sense that a single cerebral hemisphere learns to subserve the entire range of higher-level brain functions, but the adequacy of those cerebral functions is seriously compromised across the board.

This finding clearly argues against a concept of redundancy of cerebral tissue, indicating that when a significant amount of cerebral tissue is compromised biologically the result usually is a lowering of abilities in a general sense. One cerebral hemisphere by itself cannot totally subserve normal neuropsychological development. It is interesting that in this case the total of Verbal and Performance IQ values approximates what each of them might have been had early brain damage not occurred. This case serves as an example of the issues discussed in Chapters I and II.

■

Arteriovenous Malformations

Definition

An arteriovenous malformation (AVM) is a tangle of abnormal blood vessels of various sizes. In an AVM there is usually one or more large feeding arteries and a number of abnormal draining veins. The brain tissue in the area of the arteriovenous malformation may show evidence of old hemorrhages, and the overlying leptomeninges are frequently thickened and stained. Microscopic examination may reveal hemorrhage, gliosis, and astroglial proliferation.

Incidence

Following berry aneurysms, arteriovenous malformations are the second leading cause of primary subarachnoid hemorrhage. These lesions represent 2% - 4% of intracranial masses and are particularly common in young adults. Although they may be found in any part of the brain or spinal cord and may occasionally be multiple, the most common site is in the parietal lobe. They may be quite small or large enough to cover the greater part of a cerebral hemisphere.

Symptoms

Even before any bleeding from an AVM occurs, the subject may experience a number of abnormal signs and symptoms, including epilepsy. It is not uncommon for these seizures to begin with auditory or visual phenomena, a factor that may relate to the location of the AVM. Even before any bleeding has occurred, it is not uncommon for the patient to have migraine-like headaches. These headaches are often unilateral, although not necessarily on the same side of the brain as the AVM.

Neurological deficits associated with AVMs are more prominent when the lesion has bled, causing additional damage to the brain tissue. They may range from minimal to severe, depending upon the degree of damage to the cerebral tissue caused by the hemorrhage. The neurological deficits are associated with the location of the lesion and include hemiparesis, hemisensory deficits, homonymous hemianopia, and dysphasia.

Diagnosis

Arteriovenous malformations are readily identified by CT scans, MRI, and cerebral angiography. Serial angiograms are sometimes helpful in identifying abnormal feeding arteries and veins which drain the area, and thus facilitate evaluating the feasibility of surgery and the approach to treatment. When an arteriovenous malformation has ruptured there may be evidence of blood in the cerebrospinal fluid. Electroencephalography often shows focal spike and slow-wave activity in the area of the AVM, although sometimes there is only evidence of focal slowing.

Treatment

Generally, the consensus has been that surgical excision and repair of the lesion should be performed when possible. However, if the location of the lesion causes concern about production of dysphasia or contralateral motor dysfunction, many neurosurgeons are hesitant to operate. Thus, there has been a considerable amount of controversy about whether AVMs should be managed conservatively or treated by surgical intervention.

Brown, Wiebers, Whisnant, O'Fallon, Piepgras, Marsh, and Maciunas (1987) have performed a long-term follow-up study of 168 patients who had clinically unruptured intracranial arteriovenous malformations. Follow-up information was obtained over an 11-year period on 166 patients until death, surgery, or other intervention occurred, or in some cases at least four years after the diagnosis was made. On the average each patient was followed for 8.2 years.

These investigators reported that 19% of these subjects suffered intracranial hemorrhage, representing a rupture rate of 2.2% per year. However, the frequency of hemorrhage increased as time went by. The risk of death associated with intracranial hemorrhage was 29%. Among those who survived hemorrhage, however, significant long-term morbidity was present in 23%. The size of the AVM and the presence or absence of hypertension were of no significance in predicting rupture. Because of the relatively high risk of death from rupture in arteriovenous malformations, together with the potential for significant long-term morbidity among survivors, the results of this study support a recommendation for surgical therapy even in cases in which there has been no evidence of prior hemorrhage.

Case 11 — TED

Age:	12-1	Gender:	Male
Education:	6	Handedness:	Left

Background Information

Ted was a youngster who had experienced no significant illnesses during his childhood and appeared to be developing quite normally. However, one day when he was 10 years 7 months of age, he had a sudden onset of symptoms that began with several episodes of vomiting and difficulty in swallowing (dysphagia). Over the next few hours his condition deteriorated rapidly to convulsions and a state of unconsciousness. His parents rushed him to the local hospital and he was immediately admitted for a complete work-up.

It was difficult to complete an initial medical examination on Ted because of his impaired state of consciousness. It was obvious that he had limited spontaneous movement in his right arm and leg, and there seemed to be a flaccid paralysis of both lower extremities with decreased deep tendon reflexes on both sides. A Babinski sign was questionably present on the right. Repeated neurological examinations done the day after admission revealed diminished strength in both the right arm and leg, hypoactive deep tendon reflexes on the right side, and a Babinski sign on the right side. While the left leg seemed to be dysfunctional to a certain extent, it clearly could be used better than the right leg.

A neurological examination done three days after admission to the hospital indicated that Ted had a definite right hemiplegia as well as a central facial paralysis on the right side. Two EEGs done during the first week showed

Delta waves Grade II in the left frontal-temporal area. Bilateral carotid angiography done on the sixth hospital day revealed an extensive vascular mass over the left frontal-parietal area. This lesion appeared to be a large arterio-venous malformation (AVM) which involved almost the entire left cerebral hemisphere. The diagnostic procedures also revealed a subarachnoid hemorrhage which occurred as a result of the lesion. In addition to the right hemiplegia, Ted had also developed dysphasia.

During the next few days Ted began to show striking improvement and was soon discharged from the hospital. Over the next month he received intensive physical therapy and speech therapy and showed definite progress in his gait and articulation. However, he continued to have serious motor dysfunction of his right upper extremity, and it was necessary for him to start using his left hand to perform the tasks he had previously done with his right hand.

About 19 months following this initial episode Ted was readmitted to the hospital for further angiographic evaluation and neuropsychological testing. Since his discharge from the hospital one and one-half years earlier he had essentially recovered from the pronounced dysphasia and had shown improvement from the spastic hemiplegia on his right side. He had experienced no convulsions since his discharge and had only occasional mild headaches. He was able to walk without assistance or bracing, and had shown minor improvement in the ability to use his right hand. He had returned to school and was able to maintain B and C grades.

At this time the medical (neurological) examination documented a minimal right facial paralysis, moderate right hemihypesthesia, a definite spastic right hemiparesis, a spastic gait, hyperactive deep tendon reflexes on the right side, Babinski and Hoffmann signs on the right side, absent right abdominal reflexes, and impairment of palm-writing perception on the right side. Bilateral carotid angiograms and a left vertebral angiogram performed two days after the neuropsychological testing was done revealed the presence of a huge arteriovenous malformation occupying nearly the entire left hemisphere and appearing to be fed mainly by the left middle cerebral and the left posterior cerebral arteries. Comparisons made with the angiogram done 19 months earlier showed that a number of vessels had now returned to a more normal position, indicating that the vessel displacement noted at the time of the initial examination probably was related to intracranial bleeding.

Because of the size of the arteriovenous malformation, the physicians felt that the lesion would be impossible to treat surgically without causing severe neurological (and probably neuropsychological) deficits. Surgeons are often hesitant to operate on an AVM which involves a large area of the left hemisphere, and in this instance it was decided that no surgical treatment would be attempted. In cases of this kind it is often difficult to determine which course of treatment should be pursued. In this particular instance, no medical treatment was given, and Ted was discharged from the hospital.

Just after midnight one day 16 months later Ted awoke complaining of a severe headache on the anterior left side of his head. Over the next half-hour he became more and more lethargic and experienced several right-sided seizures. By the time he was examined in the emergency room at 4:30 AM he was comatose with decerebrate rigidity. His left pupil was fixed and dilated and he showed no purposeful response to painful stimuli. A lumbar puncture revealed grossly bloody spinal fluid, and Ted was diagnosed as having suffered a massive hemorrhage from the AVM. His condition continued to deteriorate, and he expired within 24 hours after admission.

As reported previously by Reitan and Wolfson (1985, 1992a), arteriovenous malformations are variable in the associated neuropsychological deficits they produce. The type of neuropsychological deficit produced by an AVM depends heavily upon the location of the lesion; the degree of deficit depends on the amount of damage sustained by the cerebral cortex. Damage to the cerebral cortex, in turn, is caused principally by episodes of bleeding from the lesion.

Arteriovenous malformations which have not bled are usually associated with relatively mild neuropsychological impairment. When the bleeding has been substantial, the patient will show significant cognitive deficits shortly after the bleeding has occurred and generally will demonstrate gradual recovery of function in time, much as from any other insult to the cerebrum. In Ted's case, the initial episode of bleeding had occurred 19 months before the neuropsychological examination; therefore, we would expect that improvement had occurred following the initial bleeding episode and that higher-level neuropsychological functions would not necessarily be grossly impaired.

Neuropsychological Examination

Wechsler Intelligence Scale for Children — Revised

On the WISC-R Ted earned a Verbal IQ of 118, a value that falls in the upper part of the High Average range and exceeds about 89% of comparably-aged children. He earned a Performance IQ of 115, a value that also falls in the High Average range and exceeds about 84%. These values yielded a Full Scale IQ of 119, which falls in the upper part of the High Average range and exceeds approximately 88%.

Compared to his other scores, Ted did somewhat poorly on the Digit Span (7) and Coding (9) subtests. Because experience and prior research (Reitan, 1959a) have indicated that low scores on Digit Span frequently occur among hospitalized subjects (including those who do not have brain damage), it appears that a number of factors

The Halstead-Reitan
Neuropsychological Test Battery
for Older Children

Name Ted   Age 12 – 1

Gender M   Education 6   Handedness: RH 0   LH 7

Neuropsychological Deficit Scale (NDS) Summary

Level of Performance	Subject's score	Mean for controls	Mean for brain-damaged	Cut-off score
Motor Functions	14	6.29	14.05	
Sensory-perceptual Functions	11	5.15	10.77	
Attention and Concentration	4	1.91	3.78	
Immediate Memory and Recapitulation	0	2.23	3.31	
Visual-spatial Skills	2	4.06	7.69	
Abstraction, Reasoning, Logical Analysis	1	2.63	6.03	
Level of Performance–Total	32	22.27	45.63	33/34
Dysphasia and Related Variables	2	1.37	7.97	3/4
Right / Left Differences	24	6.79	13.74	9/10
Total NDS Score	58	30.43	67.34	43/44

WISC-R

VIQ 118
PIQ 115
FS IQ 119

Verbal Subtests

Information	13
Similarities	13
Arithmetic	12
Vocabulary	13
Comprehension	14
(Digit Span)	(7)

Performance Subtests

Picture Completion	14
Picture Arrangement	11
Block Design	13
Object Assembly	14
Coding	9

WRAT

Grade Equivalent

Reading	6.9
Arithmetic	5.6
Spelling	5.4

Strength of Grip

Dominant hand (L) 28.0 kg
Non-dominant hand (R) 3.5 kg

Name Writing

Dominant hand (L) 23 sec
Non-dominant hand (R) 93 sec

Category Test

Number of errors   30

Tactual Performance Test

Dominant hand	(L)	2.4
Non-dominant hand	(L)	3.0
Both hands	(L)	1.8

Total Time 7.2
Memory 6
Localization 5

Seashore Rhythm Test

Number correct   20   10

Speech-sounds Perception Test

Number of errors   10

Finger Tapping Test

Dominant hand (L) 38   38
Non-dominant hand (R) 0

Trail Making Test

Part A	22	sec	1	error(s)
Part B	26	sec	0	error(s)

Bilateral Simultaneous Sensory Stimulation

RH ___ LH ___	Both: RH ___ LH ___	
RH ___ LF ___	Both: RH 2 LF ___	
LH ___ RF ___	Both: LH ___ RF ___	
RE ___ LE ___	Both: RE ___ LE ___	
RV ___ LV ___	Both: RV ___ LV ___	
___ ___	___ ___	
___ ___	___ ___	

Tactile Finger Recognition

RH 1 1   2 3   3 1   4 3   5 3   RH 11 / 20
LH 1 ___ 2 1   3 ___ 4 ___ 5 ___   LH 1 / 20

Finger-Tip Number Writing

RH 1 3   2 4   3 3   4 2   5 3   RH 15 / 20
LH 1 ___ 2 ___ 3 ___ 4 ___ 5 ___   LH 0 / 20

Tactile Form Recognition Test

Dominant hand	(L)	9 sec	0	error(s)
Non-dominant hand	(R)	14 sec	5	error(s)

Reitan-Indiana Aphasia Screening Test

Form for Adults and Older Children

Name ___Ted___ Age ___12 – 1___

Copy SQUARE	Repeat TRIANGLE
Name SQUARE	Repeat MASSACHUSETTS
Spell SQUARE S - Q - U - A - R - A *self-corrected to* S - Q - U - A - R - E	Repeat METHODIST EPISCOPAL Methodist Epistopal
Copy CROSS	Write SQUARE
Name CROSS Plus *Ex.?* Red Cross	Read SEVEN
Spell CROSS	Repeat SEVEN
Copy TRIANGLE	Repeat/Explain HE SHOUTED THE WARNING
Name TRIANGLE	Write HE SHOUTED THE WARNING
Spell TRIANGLE	Compute 85 − 27 =
Name BABY	Compute 17 x 3 =
Write CLOCK	Name KEY
Name FORK	Demonstrate use of KEY
Read 7 SIX 2	Draw KEY
Read MGW	Read PLACE LEFT HAND TO RIGHT EAR
Reading I	Place LEFT HAND TO RIGHT EAR
Reading II	Place LEFT HAND TO LEFT ELBOW

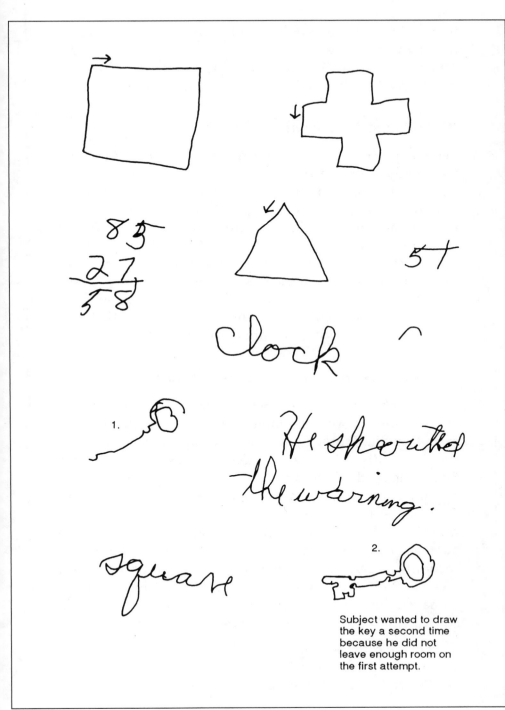

Subject wanted to draw
the key a second time
because he did not
leave enough room on
the first attempt.

besides brain damage may produce low scores on this sub-test. However, Ted's score on Coding is very probably a reflection of some impairment of brain-related abilities, or possibly was influenced by using his left hand for the task.

Wide Range Achievement Test

Ted had just completed the sixth grade in school; therefore, an average score on the WRAT would have been 7.0. His test scores suggested that he was lagging behind somewhat in both spelling and arithmetic abilities. On the WRAT he earned the following grade-equivalents: Reading (word recognition) 6.9; Spelling, 5.4; and Arithmetic, 5.6. Even though it had been reported that Ted had recovered completely from his dysphasia, these mild deficits in academic performances may well have been due to involvement of the left cerebral hemisphere and the dysphasia that had been present following the initial hospitalization.

Halstead-Reitan Battery for Older Children

Neuropsychological Deficit Scale. Results on the NDS for Older Children were essentially within the normal range except for the Motor Functions, Sensory-perceptual Functions, and Right-Left Differences sections. On the Motor Functions section Ted scored a total of 14 points. On this section control subjects average 6.29 points and brain-damaged subjects average 14.05 points. Ted's score was therefore almost exactly at the mean level for brain-damaged subjects. On the Sensory-perceptual Functions section Ted earned a score of 11 points (compared with a mean of 5.15 points for controls and 10.77 points for brain-damaged subjects). On this section his scores were again equivalent to the average for brain-damaged subjects.

On the Attention and Concentration section, Ted earned a score of 4 points, which is slightly greater than the mean of 3.78 produced by brain-damaged children. His high score on this section was particularly due to a poor score on the Seashore Rhythm Test (20 correct). However, on the Immediate Memory and Recapitulation, Visual-spatial Skills, and Abstraction, Reasoning and Logical analysis sections, his scores were somewhat better than the average of control subjects. Ted therefore scored within the normal range on many of the areas of higher-level brain functions, but as we will see on close clinical analysis of the data, he demonstrated some difficulties which suggested the presence of mild residual dysphasia.

On the Right-Left Differences section of the NDS, Ted earned 24 points, a score that exceeds the mean of 13.74 points for brain-damaged subjects and falls far beyond the cut-off of 9/10 points. He performed relatively well on the Aphasia and Related Variables section of the NDS, earning only 2 points (for dysgraphia). On this section the mean for brain-damaged subjects is 7.97 and the cut-off is 3/4 points. As we will describe below, his writing attempts were quite characteristic of children with impaired left cerebral functions. Ted had a total NDS score of 58 points, which well exceeds the mean of 30.43 points for control subjects and approaches the mean of 67.34 points for brain-damaged subjects. Considering the cut-off of 43/44 points, there appears to be no question that Ted's results on the Halstead-Reitan Battery fall definitely into the brain-damaged range.

Clinical Evaluation of the Test Results. The clinical significance of the test results contributes further understanding of Ted's deficits. The left cerebral hemisphere was implicated by a number of findings, including a grip strength of only 3.5 kg with his right upper extremity compared to 28.0 kg with the left upper extremity. Ted was not able to register any finger tapping speed at all with his right hand, but had a score in the normal range (38) with his left hand.

Ted also had tactile-perceptual deficits on the right side, showing a definite tendency to fail to perceive a stimulus to the right hand when it was given simultaneously with a stimulus to the left face. Further evidence of tactile-perceptual losses was clearly manifested in testing for tactile finger localization; Ted had 11 errors on the right hand but only one error on the left hand. On finger-tip number writing perception he made 15 errors on the right hand and none on the left hand. On the Tactile Form Recognition Test Ted made 5 errors on the right hand and none on the left hand.

The probability of the responsible lesion being at the cerebral level is greatly increased when lateralized manifestations involve motor as well as sensory-perceptual deficits. In this case, however, evidence of involvement of the left cerebral hemisphere was further supported by mild, though definite, indications of dysphasia. On the NDS we did not give Ted any points for spelling dyspraxia, but he made a very unusual mistake when he spelled SQUARE with an A at the end of the word instead of an E (even though he spontaneously corrected this error).

The errors Ted made in writing HE SHOUTED THE WARNING are quite characteristic of the problems in letter formation shown by persons with dysgraphia. When writing SHOUTED Ted obviously had difficulty forming the O as well as the ED. Even in writing WARNING he was apparently confused about the direction of the line used to represent the A. He also demonstrated a minor degree of confusion with numerical symbols when he initially wrote a 3 instead of a 5 when proceeding with his computation of 85 − 27 = . Although Ted was originally right-handed, he now used his left hand for writing. This fact may have caused some impairment of motor control in his writing and drawings, but would not be responsible for the brain-related errors he made.

Although there was no striking evidence of right cere-bral dysfunction, Ted did have some mild difficulty in drawing the shape of the cross. When drawing the key he started in a position on the paper which had insufficient space for the drawing, and when drawing the key in another location he distorted the spatial configuration somewhat. We did not feel that the drawing difficulties were suffi-ciently pronounced to qualify for a deficient score on the NDS, but such problems certainly must be noted clinically.

In cases of arteriovenous malformations it is not uncom-mon to see evidence of dysfunction that sometimes occurs in the homologous area of the noninvolved cerebral hemi-sphere, a manifestation that may be a reflection of the vas-cular "steal" phenomenon that has been reported in the literature. Thus, considering the type of lesion that was present, we would not consider the difficulties in drawing the cross and key to be an indication of specific involvement of the right cerebral hemisphere.

Ted had been able to maintain adequate academic progress despite the findings that reflected mild dysphasia. Persons who manifest significant motor and sensory-perceptual involvement of the left cerebral hemisphere not uncommonly have academic difficulties, even when the Verbal IQ is adequate. At this point we cannot offer a defi-nite explanation for the fact that Ted was getting B's and C's in school; however, we have found that children who have experienced a serious illness are often graded less strin-gently than their peers. In any case, it is likely that his relatively high level of verbal intelligence had been a signif-icant advantage in maintaining his grades. Nevertheless, despite his school grades, the results of the Wide Range Achievement Test suggested that Ted was having some dif-ficulty maintaining academic progress.

Encephalitis

Definition

Encephalitis is an inflammation of the brain, usually due to viral infection. In many cases the meninges are also affected. The infection may be congenital or it may occur as a complication of an infectious systemic disease contracted later in life.

The virus most commonly responsible for encephalitis is the herpes simplex virus type 1, but the inflammatory condition may be caused by any of a large number of viruses, including a range of arthropod-borne viruses, rabies, varicella (chicken pox), herpes zoster (shingles), measles, mumps, cytomegalovirus infection, infectious mononucleosis, enterovirus infections (including three types of poliomyelitis viruses), a great number of coxsackie and echo viruses, Epstein-Barr virus, cat-scratch fever, syphilis, and HIV infections (AIDS).

Although the vast majority of encephalitides represent an acute illness, the infection is sometimes chronic. In these instances reference is made to a "slow virus infection," and the progressive course of the disease often leads to death.

Causes

Marshall (1983) states that, ". . . there is a paucity of accurate data on both the incidence of CNS involvement in individual virus infections and the overall incidence of virus infections in the causation of CNS disease. Most figures probably underestimate the problem for several reasons." He goes on to state that the underestimate of CNS involvement may be due to inadequate evaluation of the patient, inadequate diagnostic procedures or their lack of use, or failure to identify the signs and symptoms which indicate brain infection.

Some data concerning incidence has been published. Aseptic meningitis in mumps has been estimated to involve 0.5% - 2% of the cases. Measles encephalitis has been estimated at 1-2 cases per 1000. Chicken pox encephalitis is thought to be somewhat less frequent than measles encephalitis, and has been estimated to occur in 1 in 1000 cases. It is clear that the actual incidence of encephalitis in these infectious illnesses cannot be accurately estimated. In all probability, as indicated by Marshall, more instances of brain involvement actually occur than are identified, diagnosed, and entered into the record.

Signs and Symptoms

Aseptic meningitis resulting from the mumps virus often causes headache, fever, vomiting, and neck stiffness. In addition, there may be inflammation of the parotid gland. In cases of viral encephalitis, the symptoms may range from mild to relatively severe. However, the onset of brain inflammation is usually represented by symptoms which occur quite abruptly, including high fever, headaches, drowsiness, irritability, and possible obtundity, stupor, nuchal rigidity and muscle pain, and nausea followed by episodes of vomiting. Epileptic seizures are not uncommon, and motor deficits and cranial nerve palsies may also be present.

Diagnosis and Treatment

In general, there is no effective treatment for viral infection of the central nervous system. Usually the treatment is supportive and symptomatic in nature, and aimed toward prevention of secondary infections. A number of drugs have been used, but the results of treatment must considered to be equivocal in terms of effectiveness.

Prognosis

Aseptic meningitis resulting from mumps usually leads to a fairly rapid recovery, but nerve deafness (often unilateral) may result. The prognosis regarding various types of viral encephalitis is variable, depending upon the type of virus involved. For example, rabies encephalitis is an acute, fatal encephalitis. With other viral infections, outcomes range from death to instances of definite residual neurological deficits to apparently complete recovery.

It must be remembered that medical evaluation tends to equate complete recovery with findings on the physical neurological examination that are within normal limits. In neuropsychological examination it is not uncommon to find clear evidence of definite impairment of cerebral functions, even when the results of the neurological examination are within normal limits (Reitan & Wolfson, 1985, 1986, 1988b).

Case 12 — CINDY

Age:	9-11	**Gender:**	Female
Education:	3	**Handedness:**	Left

Background Information

Cindy was a little girl who had been in good health and apparently developing normally until shortly after her ninth birthday. At that time she contracted a febrile condition that was diagnosed as encephalitis. Eleven days after this illness began she experienced a major motor seizure which lasted approximately ten minutes and was accompanied by urinary incontinence. After the seizure Cindy lapsed into an extremely lethargic state.

Several hours later that same day Cindy experienced another seizure which progressed into status epilepticus and required admission to a local hospital and treatment with antiepileptic drugs. The medication finally brought the seizures under control, and Cindy was discharged from the hospital. When she returned to school a few days later, Cindy's teachers felt that she was "dull" and appeared unable to grasp the subject matter of her studies as quickly as she had previously.

Approximately two months after this initial episode, Cindy had an aura that consisted of dizziness and scotomata in her visual fields and she experienced another major motor seizure. She was again hospitalized briefly, and her antiepileptic medication was increased. Two months later she started having major motor seizures which did not respond well to medication, and hospitalization was usually necessary to control each seizure.

Both socially and emotionally Cindy was having a very difficult time adjusting to her condition. She was withdrawing from her friends at school and becoming contentious and difficult at home. More and more frequently she verbalized intentions of harming or killing her parents and younger sister. About nine months after her illness began she ran away from home and was not found for several hours. Because of these circumstances, her parents hospitalized her for comprehensive neurological, neuropsychological, and psychiatric evaluations.

Neurological Findings

On the physical neurological examination Cindy showed no abnormalities except for a mild Romberg sign; when she stood with her eyes closed she consistently demonstrated a tendency to lean to the left. An EEG revealed a generalized dysrhythmia, Grade III, consistent with a chronic, diffuse cortical disorder that was entirely compatible with a prior viral infection of the brain.

The child psychiatrist who evaluated Cindy explored the background of her adjustmental status. He felt that there was a serious personality conflict between Cindy and her parents prior to this illness, and that the encephalitis and the seizures had precipitated these problems. The physician recommended outpatient psychiatric treatment.

This example emphasizes the fact that it is not uncommon for brain disease or damage to exacerbate previous tendencies toward behavioral abnormalities (Aita & Reitan, 1948). In addition, it is well recognized that the occurrence of major motor seizures frequently places an extreme degree of stress on a child (as well as an adult).

Neuropsychological Examination

Wechsler Intelligence Scale for Children — Revised

On the WISC-R Cindy earned a Verbal IQ of 95, a value that falls in the lower part of the Average range and exceeds

The Halstead-Reitan Neuropsychological Test Battery for Older Children

Name __Cindy_____ Age _9 – 11_

Gender __F__ Education __3_____ Handedness: RH _6_ LH _1_

Neuropsychological Deficit Scale (NDS) Summary

Level of Performance	Subject's score	Mean for controls	Mean for brain-damaged	Cut-off score
Motor Functions	17	6.29	14.05	
Sensory-perceptual Functions	7	5.15	10.77	
Attention and Concentration	4	1.91	3.78	
Immediate Memory and Recapitulation	6	2.23	3.31	
Visual-spatial Skills	7	4.06	7.69	
Abstraction, Reasoning, Logical Analysis	7	2.63	6.03	
Level of Performance–Total	48	22.27	45.63	33/34
Dysphasia and Related Variables	3	1.37	7.97	3/4
Right/Left Differences	11	6.79	13.74	9/10
Total NDS Score	62	30.43	67.34	43/44

WISC-R

VIQ __95__

PIQ __90__

FS IQ __91__

Verbal Subtests		Performance Subtests	
Information	9	Picture Completion	10
Similarities	10	Picture Arrangement	7
Arithmetic	8	Block Design	11
Vocabulary	11	Object Assembly	8
Comprehension	8	Coding	7
(Digit Span)	(8)	(Mazes)	(9)

WRAT

	Grade Equivalent
Reading	4.3
Arithmetic	3.2
Spelling	3.3

Strength of Grip

Dominant hand   (L) __14.0__ kg

Non-dominant hand (R) __16.5__ kg

Name Writing

Dominant hand   (L) __30__ sec

Non-dominant hand (R) __54__ sec

Category Test

Number of errors   __82__

Tactual Performance Test

Dominant hand   (L) __7.4__

Non-dominant hand (R) __6.1__

Both hands   __2.3__   Total Time __15.8__

                                       Memory   __2__

                                       Localization __1__

Seashore Rhythm Test

Number correct   __22__   __10__

Speech-sounds Perception Test

Number of errors   __12__

Finger Tapping Test

Dominant hand   (L) __29__   __29__

Non-dominant hand (R) __28__

Trail Making Test

Part A   __28__ sec   __0__ error(s)

Part B   __158__ sec   __1__ error(s)

Bilateral Simultaneous Sensory Stimulation

RH ___ LH ___	Both: RH ___ LH ___
RH ___ LF ___	Both: RH ___ LF ___
LH ___ RF ___	Both: LH ___ RF ___
RE ___ LE _1_	Both: RE ___ LE ___
RV ___ LV _1_	Both: RV ___ LV ___
___ ___	___ ___
___ ___	___ ___

Tactile Finger Recognition

RH 1 ___ 2 ___ 3 ___ 4 ___ 5 ___   RH _0_ / 20

LH 1 _1_ 2 ___ 3 _2_ 4 ___ 5 ___   LH _3_ / 20

Finger-Tip Number Writing

RH 1 _1_ 2 ___ 3 _2_ 4 ___ 5 _2_   RH _5_ / 20

LH 1 ___ 2 _1_ 3 ___ 4 _2_ 5 _1_   LH _4_ / 20

Tactile Form Recognition Test

Dominant hand   (L) __9__ sec   __0__ error(s)

Non-dominant hand (R) __9__ sec   __1__ error(s)

Reitan-Indiana Aphasia Screening Test

Form for Adults and Older Children

Name: Cindy   Age: 9 – 11

Copy SQUARE	Repeat TRIANGLE — triango
Name SQUARE	Repeat MASSACHUSETTS — Massachusess
Spell SQUARE — S - U - A - R	Repeat METHODIST EPISCOPAL — Methadis Episcopal
Copy CROSS	Write SQUARE
Name CROSS	Read SEVEN
Spell CROSS — C - A - R - S	Repeat SEVEN
Copy TRIANGLE	Repeat/Explain HE SHOUTED THE WARNING
Name TRIANGLE	Write HE SHOUTED THE WARNING
Spell TRIANGLE — T - R - A - G - L	Compute 85 − 27 = 59
Name BABY	Compute 17 x 3 = 23 2 × 5 = 10 4 × 4 = 6 *(verbally)*
Write CLOCK	Name KEY
Name FORK	Demonstrate use of KEY
Read 7 SIX 2	Draw KEY
Read MGW	Read PLACE LEFT HAND TO RIGHT EAR — Please let hand to right ear.
Reading I	Place LEFT HAND TO RIGHT EAR
Reading II — *S could not read "famous"; otherwise correct.*	Place LEFT HAND TO LEFT ELBOW

I.   II.

Clock Square

He showed the

woreind.

$$\begin{array}{r} 7 \\ 8.15 \\ -2\,7 \\ \hline 5\ 9 \end{array}$$

23   (17x3)

about 37% of her age peers. Her Performance IQ of 90 was in the lower limit of the Average range and exceeded 25%. These values yielded a Full Scale IQ of 91, a score which also falls in the lower part of the Average range and exceeds 27%.

The scaled scores for the individual Verbal subtests indicate relatively little variability. The Performance subtest scores were somewhat more scattered, with scores ranging from 7 (Picture Arrangement and Coding) to 11 (Block Design). However, the subtest variation is not particularly remarkable, and would not serve as a basis for postulating the presence of cerebral disease or damage. One could suggest retrospectively that Coding and Picture Arrangement were mildly impaired, but the pattern of scores would not necessarily deviate from results obtained by many children who have absolutely no evidence of brain damage.

Wide Range Achievement Test

Since Cindy had completed three grades in school and was just about to begin the fourth grade when this neuropsychological examination was done, we would expect her results on the WRAT to be at a level of 4.0. She earned the following grade equivalents: Reading (word recognition), 4.3; Spelling, 3.3; and Arithmetic, 3.2. These findings indicate that she is a little behind her grade-level in spelling and arithmetic, but this is perhaps not entirely unexpected in a child who has a Full Scale IQ of 91. These test results suggest that Cindy may need some additional help to facilitate her academic progress, but the first step should be a comprehensive evaluation of her neuropsychological abilities.

Halstead-Reitan Neuropsychological Test Battery

Neuropsychological Deficit Scale. The NDS for Older Children demonstrated quite clearly that Cindy's basic adaptive abilities have been compromised. She earned a total NDS score of 62, which exceeds the cut-off of 43/44 and approaches the mean of 67.34 earned by brain-damaged children. In fact, Cindy consistently scored in the brain-damaged range in the various areas of function represented by the NDS. Her scores were worse than the average for brain-damaged children in the sections representing motor functions, attention and concentration, abstraction, reasoning, and logical analysis skills, and especially, immediate memory and recapitulation. She was a little better than the average brain-damaged subject in the area of visual-spatial skills and sensory-perceptual functions. Her total Level of Performance score of 48 is clearly beyond the cut-off of 33/34 points, and exceeds the mean of 45.63 for brain-damaged children.

Cindy's score of 11 on the Right-Left Differences section of the NDS approaches the average score of 13.74 earned by brain-damaged children and exceeds the cut-off of 9/10. It is interesting to note that Cindy's performances were more similar to controls than to brain-damaged children only on the Dysphasia and Related Variables section. In this area she earned 3 points, and the cut-off score is between 3 and 4. Since brain involvement is generally diffuse rather than focal in most cases of encephalitis, this finding is consistent with expectation. These overall test findings indicate that Cindy has generalized neuropsychological impairment, and her pattern of results is representative of a near-typical child with cerebral damage.

Clinical Evaluation of the Test Results. A more detailed evaluation of Cindy's test scores revealed evidence implicating both the left and right cerebral hemispheres and identified significant generalized impairment of neuropsychological functions. Probably the most serious indications of generalized deficit occurred on the Category Test (82 errors) and on Part B of the Trail Making Test (158 sec). These scores indicate that Cindy has a great deal of difficulty drawing meaningful conclusions from her observations and is relatively slow in organizing diverse stimulus material.

With impairment of this kind Cindy is probably rather inflexible in her thought processes. It is likely that in complex situations she is unable spontaneously to generate a range of alternatives to consider, and as a result appears concrete and arbitrary in her attitudes. Almost certainly she is a difficult child to deal with, *particularly* since her IQ values are within the normal range. The neuropsychological test results indicate quite clearly that Cindy's ability structure represents a series of conflicts. Considering her IQ values, on casual contact she probably appears to have fairly normal intelligence. On the other hand, the deficits she demonstrates on the general neuropsychological indicators make it obvious that her abilities are significantly impaired.

Evaluation of the lateralizing findings yielded evidence to implicate both the left and right cerebral hemispheres. The Aphasia Screening Test demonstrated that Cindy's spelling ability deviated strikingly from normal, and the several mistakes she made in her attempts to read were sufficient to score 2 points for dyslexia. Although Cindy preferred her left hand for writing, she used her right hand for all other tasks included in the Lateral Dominance Examination. We would presume that the indications of deficit on the Aphasia Screening Test relate to impairment of the left cerebral hemisphere. Other left hemisphere indicators were seen on the second trial of the TPT, when Cindy performed poorly with her right hand (6.1 min) as compared with her left hand (7.4 min) and on the Tactile Form Recognition Test, when she made one relatively serious error with her right hand (mistaking a cross for a triangle).

Cindy also demonstrated significant deviations from expected performances that implicate the right cerebral hemisphere. Her finger tapping speed was scarcely faster with the left hand (29) than with the right hand (28), and her grip strength was clearly less with her left hand (14 kg) than with her right hand (16.5 kg). She demonstrated a mild tendency toward failure to perceive auditory or visual stimuli toward her left side when the stimulus was given unilaterally (even though she did not make any errors with bilateral simultaneous stimulation). On tactile finger localization she had a clearly deficient performance with the left hand; she made no mistakes with her right hand in 20 trials, but made three mistakes with her left hand. We considered Cindy's drawing of the cross and the key to be marginally adequate. Even though when scoring the NDS we did not consider these performances to represent constructional dyspraxia, they should still be viewed as somewhat deviant from normal, and should be considered important clinically.

Cindy was confused in her attempt to mentally multiply 17×3, and she wrote "23" as her answer. She was able to multiply 2×5 satisfactorily, but responded "6" when given the problem 4×3. Although these responses might be considered sufficiently poor to assign a score of 2 for dyscalculia on the NDS, we were conservative in our scoring and did not classify the incorrect answers in this manner.

Summary and Recommendations

In summary, Cindy demonstrated some definite lateralizing signs, implicating each cerebral hemisphere, in the context of generalized brain dysfunction. The most significant areas of her impairment appear to involve complex higher-level problem-solving abilities. Unless these deficits are remediated, they will certainly have a limiting effect on the eventual development of her academic skills.

The appropriateness of brain retraining should be considered routinely in conjunction with neuropsychological evaluation. As we have noted, it may be more important to identify the general neuropsychological impairment than the specific deficits, particularly because the specific deficits are more obvious. Secondly, the general deficits, regardless of their nature, tend to pervade efficiency of performances in everyday living, while the more specific deficits can often be circumvented.

We routinely begin our cognitive rehabilitation program of a brain-impaired individual by focusing on remediation of the generalized deficits. Retraining of the more
specialized (lateralized) functions is better addressed after
the general neuropsychological functions have been improved. This approach obviously contrasts strikingly with
the usual procedure employed by both psychologists and
speech pathologists in retraining dysphasic subjects. The
rather specific deficits shown by dysphasics are the focus for
retraining and the general deficits, which are almost invariably present to some degree, are frequently not even identified through comprehensive neuropsychological testing, let
alone dealt with in cognitive retraining.

Considering the fact that Cindy is a rather typical example of a brain-damaged child, her case is not an exception to
this general approach. Her principal needs concerning cognitive rehabilitation relate to the higher-level aspects of
brain functions and the more difficult types of problem-
solving activities. We recognize that Cindy does have some
limitation of academic skills resulting from brain damage,
and the remediation of these deficits should be considered
part of the total rehabilitation program. However, the principal area that must first be remediated concerns abstraction, reasoning, and concept formation skills. Even her poor
scores on the Memory (2) and Localization (1) components
of the TPT probably represent generalized difficulties in basic
problem-solving skills rather than primary manifestations of
memory impairment.

We would initially start Cindy's cognitive rehabilitation
program by using materials in Track C of REHABIT and
then move to Tracks D and E. The most important components to be emphasized are the problem-solving and logical-
organization aspects of the stimulus material. When
working with Cindy, every effort should be made to focus
on reinforcing memory and recapitulation of events to
which she has been exposed.

Even an item such as *Attribute Beads* could be used very
effectively with this child. The therapist could string the

beads, alternating shape, color, size, and position, and have Cindy identify the principle and reproduce the pattern from memory. This would not only give Cindy additional practice in developing manipulatory skills (note her poor performance on the TPT Total Time), but also help her learn to organize and reproduce stimulus material.

The serious impairment Cindy demonstrated on the Category Test (82 errors) and Part B of the Trail Making Test (158 sec) indicates that she needs to practice (1) observing stimulus material, (2) determining which of the stimuli are relevant to the solution of a problem, (3) recognizing causal relationships, and (4) drawing reasonable and accurate conclusions from her observations.

The severity of Cindy's deficit in this area indicates that training should start at a very simple level. We would recommend that a considerable amount of therapy time be spent with items such as the *Sorting and Order Kit,* because the diversity of the material would give her an opportunity to sort, classify, and organize a great deal of stimulus material in accordance with various principles. It might be necessary at first to suggest principles to Cindy that should be used for sorting purposes. Eventually, however, she should be encouraged to think of principles on her own and to follow through in accordance with that idea. It would also be valuable to use the workbooks included in Track C which teach various thinking skills, such as the identification of cause-and-effect relationships.

Much of the material in Track D should be used in the same way as the material in Track C. These items would permit practice in (1) sorting and classifying according to a number of variables, such as color, shape, size, etc., (2) establishing patterns and relationships among various stimuli, and (3) organizing material in a temporal sequence.

As we described above in the analysis of her test results, it is also probable that Cindy is impaired in her ability to deal with language and verbal symbolic material. Training Cindy in abstraction, reasoning, and logical analysis skills and teaching her how to organize stimulus material and recapitulate events to which she has been exposed will provide the basic foundation for mastering the specific content of academic subject material.

Following such training, it will be extremely important to work with material from Track A, which contains many items which emphasize listening skills, staying on task, and following directions as well as conventional academic subjects such as spelling, reading, arithmetic, and writing. Considering the fact that Cindy's neuropsychological test results provided some specific indications of left cerebral dysfunction, it is likely that she will need training in all of these academic areas.

In summary, we can say that Cindy's deficits are generalized and extensive in nature and involve the cerebral cortex as a whole. The task of comprehensive brain retraining for this child also promises to be relatively extensive, and the test results suggest that it would be necessary to use training materials included in all five tracks of REHABIT. Unless Cindy receives intensive, appropriate rehabilitation specifically directed to the remediation of her neuropsychological deficits, there is minimal chance that she will be able to keep up academically with her age-peers. Without such help, Cindy will fall further behind, and become more confused and discouraged than she is presently.

As is common rather than uncommon, neither Cindy nor her parents understood the ramifications of her condition, and in their anxiety and concern, knew only how to strike out at (or withdraw from) the obvious problems they were facing. This situation is also true (given the obvious motivation to seem informed) of the neuropsychologist who has not done an examination that covers neuropsychological functions both generally and in a balanced manner.

Epilepsy

Definition

Epilepsy is a condition characterized by the experience of seizures which are usually recurrent. Seizures are transient neurological abnormalities caused by aberrant electrical activity of the brain.

Epileptic seizures can be classified into two broad groups: generalized seizures and partial seizures. The form a seizure assumes depends on (1) the part of the brain in which the aberrant electrical activity arises, and (2) how widely and rapidly the electrical activity spreads from its point of origin.

Generalized Seizures. There are two main types of generalized seizures — grand mal and petit mal (absence) seizures.

Generalized seizures affect the whole body bilaterally and involve both hemispheres. During a grand mal seizure the person usually falls and loses consciousness. The entire body initially stiffens, and then jerks uncontrollably. During the seizure, breathing may become very irregular or stop entirely. Following the seizure the person may be incontinent. The person rarely remembers having the seizure.

Absence seizures occur mainly in children. During this type of seizure there is a momentary loss of consciousness with only a minimal amount of abnormal movement. The seizure may last from a few seconds up to 30 seconds or longer. Frequently the child appears to be daydreaming or not paying attention. Absence seizures may occur hundreds of times in a single day.

Partial Seizures. Partial seizures are divided into simple seizures (in which consciousness is maintained) and complex seizures (in which there is an alteration of consciousness). Partial seizures are usually caused by an abnormality in a more limited area of one cerebral hemisphere. Although partial seizures begin in a relatively circumscribed area, the electrical disturbance may spread and affect the entire brain, causing a generalized seizure.

In simple partial seizures the person experiences an abnormal twitching, tingling sensation, or even a gustatory, visual, auditory, or olfactory hallucination. The seizure may last several minutes, and the person retains consciousness and may recall the events of the seizure.

During complex partial seizures the individual experiences an altered state of consciousness. Involuntary motions (called automatisms), such as lip smacking, may occur. The person usually does not remember the seizure.

Incidence

As pointed out by Dodrill (1981), most psychologists seem to be unaware of the fact that epilepsy appears to be more prevalent than all psychotic disorders combined. It has been reported that at least 2% of the population of the United States suffers from some form of epilepsy, and over 75% of all epilepsy begins before the age of 15 years.

Epilepsy may be associated with a wide range of diseases or events, such as head trauma, stroke, metabolic disorders, tumors, encephalitis, and drug intoxication. However, in the majority of cases epilepsy is described as *idiopathic*, meaning that the cause is unknown. In children the incidence of idiopathic epilepsy is greater than 50%, and among adults the percentage is only somewhat smaller.

It should be noted, however, that epilepsy is only a symptom of a brain disorder, and the range of disorders underlying epilepsy extend from significant and seriously destructive lesions of the brain to disorders of brain function that are relatively mild and have little if any neuropsychological consequences (Reitan, 1976).

Neurological and Neuropsychological Deficits

There is an extensive body of literature documenting the neuropsychological impairment associated with epilepsy. In general, the degree of impairment varies, depending upon the particular type of epilepsy involved. Although many patients with epilepsy demonstrate no positive findings on neurological examination, there usually is some neuropsychological element of brain dysfunction that is associated with epilepsy that can be identified (Kløve & Matthews, 1966; Matthews & Kløve, 1967).

Diagnosis

The diagnosis of epilepsy is made essentially on the basis of observation of the epileptic seizures or reports of such an attack obtained from a witness. An EEG is often of value in confirming the diagnosis. A CT or MRI scan is frequently done to check for conditions associated with epilepsy.

Treatment and Prognosis

A great number of antiepileptic drugs have been developed, some of which are more effective for patients with certain symptoms than others. For example, partial complex seizures are by far the most difficult to treat effectively. In general, either complete control or substantial improvement of seizure frequency and intensity can be achieved in over 85% of epileptic patients when appropriate evaluation and antiepileptic drug treatment is instituted. In a small proportion of cases, seizures are intractable and anticonvulsant medications are not effective. In such instances, if there is documented evidence of a consistent and stable epileptogenic focus, surgical removal of the area of the epileptogenic focus has proved to be an effective treatment.

In summary, it must be noted that one of the major problems of epileptic patients concerns the fact that they never know the duration of their current state of consciousness, which may cease when the next epileptic attack occurs. In addition, there seems to be a continuing but entirely unreasonable and prejudiced attitude toward epileptic patients with relation to the nature of the attacks, the clonic-tonic movements that are sometimes involved, and the impairment of consciousness.

For the reader who would like more information, detailed reviews of neuropsychology and epilepsy have been published by Reitan (1976) and Dodrill (1981).

Case 13 — OSCAR

Age:	15-4	**Gender:**	Male
Education:	8	**Handedness:**	Left

Background Information

Oscar was an adolescent who had always had difficulty learning academic subject matter, and his problems were severe enough to cause the school authorities to require him to repeat the fourth grade. When Oscar was eight years old he experienced his first petit mal seizure. Over the next six years these episodes occurred once or twice a year, and apparently were not considered to be a major problem by either Oscar or his parents.

When Oscar was 14 years, 9 months of age, just before the beginning of his ninth grade school year, he experienced a major motor seizure which resulted in a fairly extended period of unconsciousness, violent tonic-clonic movements, and urinary incontinence. Oscar experienced three more such episodes during the first two months of school. His classmates became apprehensive and began to distance themselves from Oscar, causing him to become very upset and embarrassed. He was performing even more poorly academically than he had previously, and began acting out in the classroom. Oscar's anxiety and distress in school (and the apparent conflict it generated) became so intense that by November he refused to attend school any longer.

Oscar's mother told us that at home her son was also having significant problems, which intensified just after the first major motor seizure. The mother seemed to have relatively little insight about the stresses that Oscar was experiencing, and felt that he was a behavior problem. She told us that Oscar very much resented his older brother (who apparently was more able and successful than Oscar) and that

Oscar had run away from home four times since his first grand mal seizure seven months ago. However, the mother did not see any relationship between these problems and the seizures, and reluctantly admitted that epilepsy might be a factor influencing her son's behavior only after it had been suggested to her.

On the neurological examination Oscar showed no evidence of abnormalities, but did report that he had experienced severe headaches for about one year. He also stated that about three months before the neuropsychological examination he experienced an episode in which he had a sensation of "pins and needles" affecting his right shoulder and arm. About one month before the neuropsychological examination Oscar's medical care was undertaken by a neurologist who had extensive experience managing epilepsy. The neurologist felt that changes in Oscar's antiepileptic medication might significantly improve the level of seizure control.

Oscar was apprehensive and withdrawn during the initial phases of the neuropsychological examination. However, the examiner was soon able to establish a trusting relationship with him and he even began to discuss his problems and difficulties. It was apparent that Oscar definitely did not want to return to school, not only because of his academic difficulties, but especially because of apprehension concerning the reaction of his classmates to his epileptic attacks. He admitted to feeling a great deal of distress about his family situation, and at one time mentioned to the examiner that he was going to "go to court to get new parents."

The difficulties experienced by this adolescent, relating both to the school and family situation, make it quite clear that problems in the area of clinical neuropsychology frequently involve clinical psychology much more generally. Although Oscar's basic difficulty may have related to impaired brain functions and the neurological manifestations of epilepsy, a failure to understand the overall situation by any of the significant parties involved (the parents, classmates, teachers, and Oscar himself) greatly compounded his difficulties. The first step in rehabilitation obviously is to perform a comprehensive neuropsychological evaluation and determine the nature of behavioral correlates or deviations as related to brain functions. However, in this case as in many others, this type of information would only serve as a basis for further counseling Oscar and the significant persons in his life.

Neuropsychological Examination

Wechsler Intelligence Scale for Children — Revised

The WISC-R indicated that Oscar had a Verbal IQ of 92, a value that falls in the lower part of the Average range and exceeds about 30% of his age peers. He earned a Performance IQ of 90, a score that falls at the lower limit of the Average range and exceeds 25%. These values yielded a Full Scale IQ of 90, corresponding with the 25th percentile.

The scaled scores indicate that Oscar was at the average level on Vocabulary (10) and Comprehension (11), well above average on Similarities (14), and a little below average on Information (8) and Digit Span (7). He was essentially able to make no progress on the Arithmetic subtest (1), being able to answer only the question, "How much is $4 and $5?"

It is interesting to note that Oscar achieved a grade equivalent of 6.3 on the Arithmetic subtest of the WRAT. Some children, particularly when impaired in basic aspects of abstraction and reasoning (as Oscar was) have great difficulty on the Arithmetic subtest of the Wechsler Scale. This apparently is related to difficulties in arithmetical reasoning, as contrasted with rote performance of arithmetical procedures.

The Halstead-Reitan Neuropsychological Test Battery for Adults

Name Oscar   Age 15 – 4

Gender M   Education 8   Handedness: RH 0 LH 7

Neuropsychological Deficit Scale (NDS) Summary

General NDS

Level of Performance	21
Pathognomonic Signs	0
Patterns	1
Right / Left Differences	12

Total G-NDS Score   34

WISC-R

VIQ	92
PIQ	90
FS IQ	90

Verbal Subtests

Information	8
Similarities	14
Arithmetic	1
Vocabulary	10
Comprehension	11
(Digit Span)	(7)

Performance Subtests

Picture Completion	12
Picture Arrangement	8
Block Design	9
Object Assembly	7
Coding	7

WRAT

Grade Equivalent

Reading	7.7
Arithmetic	6.3
Spelling	8.1

Strength of Grip

Dominant hand	(L)	36.0 kg
Non-dominant hand	(R)	40.0 kg

Name Writing

Dominant hand	(L)	10 sec
Non-dominant hand	(R)	27 sec

Category Test

Number of errors   76

Tactual Performance Test

Dominant hand	(L)	6.9	Total Time	17.6
Non-dominant hand	(R)	8.1	Memory	7
Both hands		2.6	Localization	4

Seashore Rhythm Test

Number correct   20   10

Speech-sounds Perception Test

Number of errors   7

Finger Tapping Test

Dominant hand	(L)	43	43
Non-dominant hand	(R)	34	

Impairment Index   0.7

Trail Making Test

Part A	21 sec	0 error(s)	
Part B	67 sec	0 error(s)	

Bilateral Simultaneous Sensory Stimulation

RH ___ LH ___   Both: RH ___ LH ___
RH ___ LF ___   Both: RH ___ LF ___
LH ___ RF ___   Both: LH ___ RF ___

RE ___ LE ___   Both: RE ___ LE ___

RV ___ LV ___   Both: RV ___ LV ___
___ ___   ___ ___
___ ___   ___ ___

Tactile Finger Recognition

RH	1 __	2 1	3 2	4 1	5 __	RH 4 / 20
LH	1 __	2 __	3 __	4 __	5 __	LH 0 / 20

Finger-Tip Number Writing

RH	1 __	2 1	3 1	4 __	5 __	RH 2 / 20
LH	1 __	2 __	3 2	4 1	5 __	LH 3 / 20

Tactile Form Recognition Test

Dominant hand	(L)	8 sec	1 error(s)	
Non-dominant hand	(R)	8 sec	0 error(s)	

Reitan-Indiana Aphasia Screening Test

orm for Adults and Older Children

Name ___Oscar___ Age 15 – 4

Copy SQUARE	Make it the same size or make it look the same size on my paper?	Repeat TRIANGLE
Name SQUARE		Repeat MASSACHUSETTS *Massatusetts*
Spell SQUARE		Repeat METHODIST EPISCOPAL *Spoken slowly but correctly.*
Copy CROSS		Write SQUARE
Name CROSS		Read SEVEN
Spell CROSS		Repeat SEVEN
Copy TRIANGLE		Repeat/Explain HE SHOUTED THE WARNING
Name TRIANGLE		Write HE SHOUTED THE WARNING
Spell TRIANGLE		Compute 85 − 27 =
Name BABY		Compute 17 x 3 =
Write CLOCK		Name KEY
Name FORK		Demonstrate use of KEY
Read 7 SIX 2	7 plus - - - 7 - 6 - 2	Draw KEY
Read MGW		Read PLACE LEFT HAND TO RIGHT EAR
Reading I		Place LEFT HAND TO RIGHT EAR
Reading II		Place LEFT HAND TO LEFT ELBOW *No. Immediately and with a smile.*

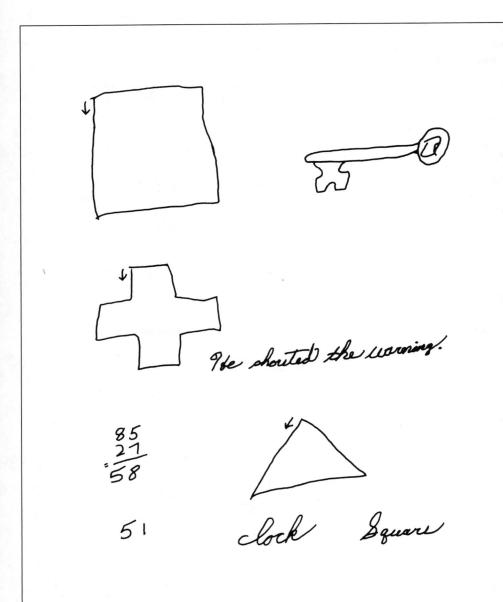

He shouted the warning.

85
27
=58

51

clock   Square

Regardless of the explanation for the poor performance on the Arithmetic subtest, it is apparent that Oscar showed a considerable degree of variability in his performances. Even on the Performance subtests his scores ranged from 7 (Object Assembly and Coding) to 12 (Picture Completion). Although results on the Wechsler Scale would not necessarily permit one to conclude that Oscar had significant brain damage, the variability among the subtest scores could certainly raise a question about the consistency of development of various aspects of general intelligence, and the prospect that on certain subtests the development of his abilities was restricted or impaired.

Wide Range Achievement Test

Results on the WRAT showed that Oscar was somewhat behind his expected current grade placement. He earned the following scores: Reading (word recognition), 7.7; Spelling, 8.1; and Arithmetic, 6.3. It must be noted that Oscar was approximately at a grade placement of 9.3 when he quit attending classes about five months before the neuropsychological testing. Findings on the WRAT were, however, approximately consistent with expectation in terms of school reports of his academic progress. On the basis of the IQ values, we might also expect to see some degree of academic retardation. It is apparent that in school Oscar was not doing as well as the average child, and probably felt some degree of stress because of the difficulties he experienced in making academic progress.

Halstead-Reitan Neuropsychological Test Battery

The adult version of the Halstead-Reitan Battery was administered because Oscar had passed his 15th birthday. Even though his chronological age placed him in the age range to be tested with the Adult Battery, we deliberately included Oscar in our series of children's case studies. It is important to recognize the fact that problems of childhood do not correspond necessarily with the age categories used for administration of particular psychological test batteries.

Neuropsychological Deficit Scale. Results on the NDS for Adults summarize Oscar's performances. He earned a total NDS score of 34, which well exceeds the cut-off point of 25/26 and is nearly twice the mean score of 17.20 earned by control subjects. The total NDS score suggests strongly that Oscar has mild impairment of brain functions.

Evaluation of the individual sections of the NDS indicated that Oscar earned 21 points on the Level of Performance section (as compared with a mean of 11.95 points for controls). He performed well on the Pathognomonic Signs and Patterns and Relationships sections, earning scores which fell just below the average level. However, on the Right-Left Differences section Oscar earned 12 points (compared with a mean of 3.37 points for controls). These results suggest that at least in certain respects, Oscar does not have the abilities of control subjects. He demonstrates disparities between functions of the two cerebral hemispheres that well exceed the range of control subjects.

The score of 12 on the Right-Left Differences section was based on some fairly definite deviations from normal expectancy. Oscar earned 2 points for differences between the left and right hand in finger tapping speed, and earned 3 points on the variables comparing the two sides of the body on the Tactual Performance Test, Grip Strength, and Tactile Finger Localization.

Clinical Evaluation of the Test Results. The above results provide an overview of Oscar's general level of intelligence and his brain-behavior relationships. For a complete assessment it is always necessary to proceed with a more detailed clinical evaluation of the test results as well. Oscar's HRB scores must be considered with relation to his IQ values, which were somewhat below average. One might therefore expect Oscar to perform a little more poorly than a child with higher IQ values (unless the IQ values had been impaired as a result of brain damage, just as might be the case for other test scores).

Oscar's score of 7 on the Speech-sounds Perception Test demonstrated that he has relatively good ability to attend to specific stimulus material. Even though his score on the Seashore Rhythm Test (20 correct) was considerably poorer, it may have been the result of some specific impairment rather than a primary loss of ability to register incoming stimuli.

In terms of level of performance, the most significant deficit clearly occurred on the Category Test (76). Oscar demonstrated impairment in the ability to observe simple stimulus material, draw reasonable hypotheses, and test these hypotheses (with the bell and buzzer) to see if they were correct. Results of this kind are seen in persons who are impaired in the ability to recognize the significance of information and appreciate the cause-and-effect relationships among events in their environment. In other words, it would be difficult for Oscar to draw reasonable conclusions or make appropriate judgments on the basis of his observations. Therefore, in addition to having relatively low IQ values, it appears that Oscar can easily become confused and somewhat bewildered in his assessment of the complex circumstances that characterize everyday living.

Probably the most convincing indications of cerebral impairment were derived from the lateralizing findings. Measures of lateral dominance indicated that Oscar was definitely and strongly left-handed. Taking this into account, he performed poorly with his right hand as compared with his left hand on both the Tactual Performance Test and in finger tapping speed.

It is also important to note that Oscar's deficits on the right side were not limited to motor performances. He made

4 mistakes in 20 trials in tactile finger localization with his right hand, but performed perfectly with his left hand. He also made one error with his left hand on the Tactile Form Recognition Test. Finally, he demonstrated mild difficulties on both hands in finger-tip number writing perception. When there are both motor and sensory-perceptual findings implicating one of the hemispheres, the probability is increased that the cause is at the cerebral level (rather than peripheral).

In addition, it should also be noted that Oscar had some difficulty in reading simple material. When presented with the item 7 SIX 2 Oscar first read 7 PLUS, paused, and then was able to give the correct answer. He apparently experienced a mild degree of confusion in performing this task, a situation that is not uncommon in children with cerebral impairment.

Comparable findings implicating the right cerebral hemisphere were considerably less marked. In fact, the only right hemisphere sign Oscar demonstrated was a significant detriment in grip strength with his left (preferred) upper extremity as compared with his right upper extremity.

In summary, the overall comparisons of performances on the two sides of the body strongly indicate that Oscar has more impairment of his left cerebral hemisphere than the right. In this respect we should comment that many persons who show evidence of impairment of the left cerebral hemisphere develop a preference for the left upper extremity. Our clinical observation is that this situation occurs particularly among children with long-standing brain impairment. It would appear that early impairment of the left cerebral hemisphere may cause some degree of dysfunction of the contralateral (right) upper extremity and, in the course of developing hand preference, the more able side (left) is naturally selected.

It seems possible (and perhaps likely) that Oscar developed left-handedness because of left cerebral damage and resulting impairment (even though to a mild degree) of the right upper extremity. This finding, in turn, may provide some basis for expectation that the left cerebral hemisphere may continue to serve language functions, since a transposition of language functions between the two cerebral hemispheres may be more difficult to accomplish than a gravitation toward hand preference.

It should also be noted that Oscar's overall test results are suggestive of a long-standing developmental condition rather than of a recent or progressive type of brain disease or damage. The facts that his IQ values were somewhat below average, his academic achievement was probably somewhat restricted, and the neuropsychological test findings were not indicative of highly focal or specific deficits all support a hypothesis that he has a condition of brain dysfunction that has imposed its effects on his cognitive development.

Summary and Recommendations

In addition to the needs for counseling and education (in its broadest sense) that have already been mentioned, Oscar has certain specific neuropsychological deficits that clearly need remediation. We would strongly recommend that Track C of REHABIT be used initially in order to provide Oscar with better basic ability in learning how to learn. In fact, it is somewhat surprising that he was able to make as much progress on the WRAT as he did. We would postulate that this has come about only through very special application and effort on Oscar's part. He has a somewhat dysfunctional left cerebral hemisphere, significant impairment in basic abilities in abstraction and reasoning, and IQ values that certainly do not predispose him to excellence in academic achievement. It is likely that he has made progress in developing academic skills in spite of these factors, and probably because of consistent and constant effort on his own part.

Oscar appears finally to have reached the point at which he cannot continue. It is apparent that he needs not only emotional support, but specific cognitive training of brain functions. If the material in Track C can be used effectively in the initial phases of training to provide him with a better approach to analysis, understanding, and problem-solving capabilities, he may be able to make better progress in other areas as well. Secondly, he obviously needs specific training in dealing with language and verbal material. It would be beneficial to use Track B, because of its emphasis on abstraction and reasoning using verbal and symbolic material. Oscar definitely needs assistance in upgrading specific skills of the left cerebral hemisphere, and materials from Track A should be integrated into his rehabilitation program.

Finally, although Oscar demonstrated his principal difficulties in abstraction, reasoning, logical analysis, and use of language, verbal, and numerical symbols for communicational and analytical purposes, his performances representing right cerebral functions were hardly outstanding. Materials in Tracks D and E should be used to upgrade his abilities in visual-spatial skills. As is true with most children who have some degree of impairment of brain functions, Oscar needs the entire range of materials included in REHABIT in order to achieve adequate cognitive retraining.

This case demonstrates the range of complications and difficulties that not uncommonly occurs among persons with cerebral disease or damage. The consequences affect not only the afflicted individual, but significant others in his life as well as the full range of environmental activities.

Obviously, the starting point in rehabilitation must necessarily be directed toward assessment of the brain-impaired person. However, since it must also be recognized that every person lives in an extensive environment and depends upon interactions and meeting expectations imposed by the environment and the significant persons in it, the entire situation inevitably becomes complicated. This volume is not directed toward the involvement of family members, teachers, and others who should be involved in the brain-injured child's rehabilitation program, but the importance of the contributions made by these individuals must always be considered when planning a comprehensive rehabilitation program.

■

Traumatic Brain Injury

Definition

Head injuries may be described in various ways. An acceleration injury refers to a blow to the head when it is struck by a more rapidly moving object. A deceleration injury occurs when the head itself is propelled into a fixed or solid object.

Head injuries may also be described as open or closed. In an open head injury a penetrating object establishes a direct path from outside the head to the brain. Depressed skull fractures are sometimes classified as open head injuries because in many instances there is nothing but soft tissue intervening between the outside of the head and the brain. In a closed head injury the skull remains intact following the head blow (even though there may be a linear fracture).

The major forces by which head trauma causes brain injury include: (1) direct compression of brain tissue, in which the tissues are penetrated by a propelled object or pushed together in some other manner; (2) tension or tearing tissues apart; and (3) shearing or sliding of tissues over other tissues either as a result of differential pressure gradients (acting on tissues of approximately the same density) or a movement of brain tissues across tissues of greater density (such as bony ridges).

Head injuries may cause damage to neurons, supporting tissues within the brain, and blood vessels. Primary brain damage refers to damage of these tissues resulting directly from the immediate forces of the head blow. Secondary structural damage is damage that occurs in response to primary damage, and is represented either by bleeding or edema. Extensive damage to the brain, in accordance with the nature and severity of the injury, may be associated either with primary or secondary structural damage.

It should be noted that even when surgical observation identifies only relatively focal damage within a cerebral hemisphere, pathology studies of head-injured patients have indicated that damage is frequently much more extensive. Mitchell and Adams (1973) studied the brains of a group of persons who manifested clinical signs of brainstem involvement and in whom increased intracranial pressure and brain shift did not appear to have been significant factors. These researchers found evidence of more widespread damage in essentially every case and concluded that localized brainstem damage, independent of extensive involvement of the brain, does not exist as a pathological entity.

Oppenheimer (1968) examined the brains of patients who had sustained relatively mild closed head injuries after they had died from other causes, and found evidence of microscopic lesions diffusely distributed in the white matter of the cerebral hemispheres.

Adams, Mitchell, Graham, and Doyle (1977) studied a series of 152 fatal head injuries and found widespread damage in the brain whenever the brainstem had been injured. Thus, shearing and compression, together with tearing of brain tissue and blood vessels over rough and irregular surfaces of the internal table of the skull, may give rise to extensive and diffuse cerebral damage in cases of either open or closed head injury.

Similar results have been found in survivors of head injury. Gentry, Godersky, and Thompson (1989) reported that in patients with head injury of both a hemorrhagic and nonhemorrhagic type, MRI results frequently showed evidence of brainstem injury. These patients with brainstem injury also demonstrated indications of extensive axonal shear lesions.

Incidence

Matson (1969) states that head injury is the major cause of accidental death in childhood and adolescence. Runyan and Gerken (1989) reported that head injuries are the leading cause of death for persons between the ages of 1 and 44 years, and account for 40% of all years of potential life loss before 65 years of age. Because head injuries usually occur so much earlier in a person's life, this loss of life-years far exceeds the figures for cancer and heart disease.

Head injuries are responsible for 57% of all deaths among children aged 10 through 14 years. Study of the trend over recent decades indicates that deaths attributed to head injury are rising rather than falling in frequency. Of course, nonfatal injuries far outnumber instances of death from head injury. For each death among teen-agers, there were an estimated 41 cases that required hospitalization and 1,100 cases that were treated in emergency rooms. Approximately 5% - 10% of persons below the age of 25 years who suffer a head injury do not survive, and most survivors experience long term medical, neuropsychological, and social sequelae. There is no doubt that in our society head injury represents a very major factor in accidental death and disability.

Neurological Deficits

Research findings (see Reitan & Wolfson, 1986, 1988b) have indicated that neuropsychological impairment is much more common than neurological deficits, and in many cases represents the sole but major residual of traumatic brain injury. Bond (1976) and Oddy, Humphrey, and Uttley (1978) have documented the special significance of psychological and social problems (as compared with physical problems) following head injury. Neurological deficits may include a great number of disabilities, covering essentially the entire range of neurological impairment. The type and severity of the neurological deficits depends upon location, size, and severity of tissue destruction in the brain.

Diagnosis

The diagnosis of brain injury following head trauma is established from the history, findings revealed on the physical neurological examination, and results of CT scanning, MRI, and in some cases, cerebral angiography. An EEG may show abnormalities, particularly in cases of epilepsy.

Treatment

The initial phases of treatment following head injury are determined by the findings of neurological evaluation. Surgery may be required to repair areas of damaged tissue and bleeding and to control intracranial hypertension resulting from edema. Neuropsychological treatment generally involves cognitive retraining.

Prognosis

There have been a considerable number of outcome studies in cases of traumatic brain injury and, as noted above, neuropsychological and social consequences seem to be of more significance in eventual outcome than physical manifestations of brain injury. The prognosis is extremely variable in individual cases. However, it should be recognized that even mild head injuries, involving short (if any) periods of unconsciousness, may result in significant neuropsychological impairment. In general, however, the more serious the initial indications of brain damage are, the greater the residual impairment.

The late complications of head injury have been reviewed by Eisenberg (1982), a neurosurgeon, who indicated that neuropsychological deficits represent a serious and pervasive complication of head injury. He recommended that a neuropsychological assessment should be part of the follow-up of any child who has sustained a head injury, particularly one associated with loss of consciousness. Only if the neuropsychological deficits are recognized can steps be taken either for direct remediation and retraining of such impairment or planning an adaptation in a manner that is meaningful and pertinent.

Extensive and detailed information about the epidemiology, mechanisms, and types of head injury, together with a detailed discussion of primary structural damage and secondary structural damage, has been presented in an earlier publication by Reitan and Wolfson (1986). Additional extensive information about recovery and rehabilitation, in terms of structural, physiological and neurochemical factors as well as spontaneous and facilitated neuropsychological recovery has also been reviewed (Reitan & Wolfson, 1988b). In each of these volumes the neuropsychological consequences of traumatic brain injury in adult subjects has been considered in great detail and integrated with the medical, neurological, and neurosurgical aspects of head injury.

Case 14 — MARGARET

Age:	9-0 (Testing I)	**Gender:**	Female
	10-1 (Testing II)		
Education:	2 (Testing I)	**Handedness:**	Right
	3 (Testing II)		

Background Information

Just after her eighth birthday Margaret was struck by a car as she was riding her bicycle. The impact was so great that she was thrown onto the hood of the car and broke the windshield with her head. Emergency services arrived within minutes, and she was immediately transported to the local trauma center and admitted to the hospital.

During the first six hours after the injury she progressed from a state of unconsciousness to a dazed and somewhat confused condition. A comprehensive evaluation performed by a neurosurgeon revealed no evidence of abnormalities except a questionable nystagmus on right lateral gaze. The physician noted a swollen, discolored area behind the left ear, and remarked that it may indicate a basilar skull fracture. Skull x-rays demonstrated a linear fracture in the left parietal area.

On the day following the accident Margaret was still quite dizzy, and became nauseated whenever she changed the position of her head. Over the next two days the dizziness gradually resolved and she was alert and oriented. She was discharged from the hospital on the third day post-injury. At that time the neurosurgeon reported that he felt that Margaret had not sustained any permanent brain injury.

Once at home Margaret resumed her normal activities, but her parents felt that she was not as bright and competent as she had been before the accident. They noted that she seemed unable to concentrate and that her mind wandered. They brought these problems to the attention of the neurosurgeon, but he reassured them that there was no evidence of any permanent injury.

Nine months later, Margaret's parents were still greatly concerned about her, and contacted the neurosurgeon again. He re-examined Margaret and once more reported that she had a perfectly normal neurological examination. However, because the parents insisted that Margaret was not as alert as she previously had been, an appointment was made for an electroencephalogram.

The EEG was interpreted as definitely abnormal, reflecting a chronic type of paroxysmal dysfunction. The abnormalities were slightly more apparent over the left cerebral hemisphere than the right, but were not judged to be specifically diagnostic of a seizure disorder. The EEG was repeated in another laboratory about a month later and again showed definite abnormalities consisting of generalized paroxysmal activity. These findings, in conjunction with the parents' assessment, led to this neuropsychological examination.

Neuropsychological Examination

Testing I

Our first evaluation was done about eleven months after Margaret sustained her head injury. At that time she was nearing the end of the third grade and was making adequate progress in school.

Wechsler Intelligence Scale for Children — Revised

Margaret's performances on the WISC-R yielded a Verbal IQ of 111, a value that exceeds 77% of her age peers and falls

The Halstead-Reitan Neuropsychological Test Battery for Older Children

Name: Margaret I   Age: 9 – 0
Gender: F   Education: 2   Handedness: RH 7 LH 0

Neuropsychological Deficit Scale (NDS) Summary

Level of Performance	Subject's score	Mean for controls	Mean for brain-damaged	Cut-off score
Motor Functions	16	6.29	14.05	
Sensory-perceptual Functions	5	5.15	10.77	
Attention and Concentration	4	1.91	3.78	
Immediate Memory and Recapitulation	0	2.23	3.31	
Visual-spatial Skills	3	4.06	7.69	
Abstraction, Reasoning, Logical Analysis	7	2.63	6.03	
Level of Performance–Total	35	22.27	45.63	33/34
Dysphasia and Related Variables	1	1.37	7.97	3/4
Right / Left Differences	11	6.79	13.74	9/10
Total NDS Score	47	30.43	67.34	43/44

WISC-R

VIQ 111
PIQ 93
FS IQ 102

Verbal Subtests

Information 13
Similarities 15
Arithmetic 12
Vocabulary 12
Comprehension 7
(Digit Span) (10)

Performance Subtests

Picture Completion 13
Picture Arrangement 8
Block Design 9
Object Assembly 11
Coding 5
(Mazes) (7)

WRAT

	Grade Equivalent
Reading	4.3
Arithmetic	4.1
Spelling	3.3

Strength of Grip

Dominant hand (R) 14.5 kg
Non-dominant hand (L) 13.0 kg

Name Writing

Dominant hand (R) 22 sec
Non-dominant hand (L) 59 sec

Category Test

Number of errors   58

Tactual Performance Test

Dominant hand	(R)	2.9	
Non-dominant hand	(L)	7.3	
Both hands		1.5	

Total Time 11.7
Memory 6
Localization 6

Seashore Rhythm Test

Number correct   15   10

Speech-sounds Perception Test

Number of errors   6

Finger Tapping Test

Dominant hand (R) 35   35
Non-dominant hand (L) 32

Trail Making Test

Part A   16 sec   0 error(s)
Part B   51 sec   0 error(s)

Bilateral Simultaneous Sensory Stimulation

RH ___ LH ___   Both: RH ___ LH ___
RH ___ LF ___   Both: RH ___ LF 1
LH ___ RF ___   Both: LH ___ RF ___

RE ___ LE ___   Both: RE ___ LE ___

RV ___ LV ___   Both: RV ___ LV 1

Tactile Finger Recognition

RH 1 ___ 2 1 3 1 4 ___ 5 ___   RH 2 / 20
LH 1 ___ 2 1 3 ___ 4 1 5 ___   LH 2 / 20

Finger-Tip Number Writing

RH 1 ___ 2 ___ 3 ___ 4 ___ 5 ___   RH 0 / 20
LH 1 ___ 2 1 3 1 4 ___ 5 ___   LH 2 / 20

Tactile Form Recognition Test

Dominant hand (R) 8 sec   0 error(s)
Non-dominant hand (L) 8 sec   0 error(s)

Reitan-Indiana Aphasia Screening Test

Form for Adults and Older Children

Name <u>Margaret I</u>   Age <u>9 — 0</u>

Copy SQUARE	Repeat TRIANGLE
Name SQUARE	Repeat MASSACHUSETTS Massachusess

Spell SQUARE
        S - Q - U - E - R
	Repeat METHODIST EPISCOPAL
	                Methodist Epistipal

Copy CROSS	Write SQUARE
Name CROSS	Read SEVEN
Spell CROSS Q - R - S - S Ex.? C - R - S - S	Repeat SEVEN
Copy TRIANGLE	Repeat/Explain HE SHOUTED THE WARNING
Name TRIANGLE	Write HE SHOUTED THE WARNING
Spell TRIANGLE T - R - I - G - L - E - N -D	Compute 85 − 27 =
Name BABY	Compute 17 x 3 = *Cannot do.* 3 × 4 = 12
Write CLOCK	Name KEY
Name FORK	Demonstrate use of KEY
Read 7 SIX 2	Draw KEY
Read MGW	Read PLACE LEFT HAND TO RIGHT EAR
Reading I	Place LEFT HAND TO RIGHT EAR
Reading II He is a friendly animal, a famous winner of a dog show. *Second attempt correct.*	Place LEFT HAND TO LEFT ELBOW

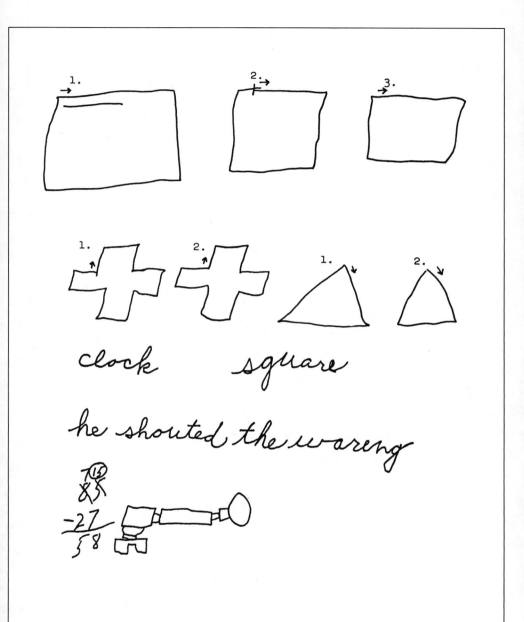

in the lower part of the High Average range. Her Performance IQ of 93 was in the lower part of the Average range and exceeded 32%. Her Full Scale IQ was 102.

Given a Verbal IQ of 111, Silverstein's (1987) tables indicate that a Performance IQ as low as 84 would occur 5% of the time. Therefore, the difference between Margaret's Verbal and Performance IQ values cannot necessarily be considered pathological.

The scaled scores for the individual subtests, however, showed a considerable degree of variability. The scores for both the Verbal and Performance subtests ranged from a low of 5 (Coding) to a high of 15 (Similarities). The scores of 5 (Coding) and 7 (Mazes) suggest that there may have been some impairment of brain functions. As is customarily the case, though, it is difficult to draw any definitive conclusions about brain damage from the Wechsler Scale alone.

Wide Range Achievement Test

Margaret's scores on the WRAT indicated that she was making adequate progress in developing academic skills. She earned the following grade-equivalents: Reading (word recognition), 4.3; Spelling, 3.3; and Arithmetic, 4.1. Considering her grade placement, average scores would be about 3.7 or 3.8. Although the measures of academic progress might be considered consistent with her Verbal IQ of 111, one wonders how much of the academic achievement she demonstrated on the WRAT had been accomplished before the head injury.

Halstead-Reitan Neuropsychological Test Battery

Neuropsychological Deficit Scale. The results of Margaret's neuropsychological examination are summarized by her scores on the NDS for Older Children. Her total NDS score of 47 exceeds the cut-off of 43/44, and falls at a position intermediate to the means of 30.43 for control subjects and 67.34 for brain-damaged children.

The NDS includes four of the WISC-R Performance subtests, but none of the Verbal subtests. It is therefore sometimes helpful to compare the total NDS score with the Verbal IQ. Margaret earned a Verbal IQ of 111, suggesting that her verbal intelligence did not place her at any particular disadvantage in terms of producing a normal NDS score. Therefore, her NDS score of 47 would be particularly disconcerting, because it may well represent some mild impairment of brain functions.

The Level of Performance section of the NDS yielded a total score of 35 points, a value that exceeds the mean of 22.27 for control children as well as the cut-off point of 33/34. The scores for the sections included under Level of Performance showed a considerable degree of variability. Margaret earned 16 points on the Motor Functions section, a score slightly greater than the mean of 14.05 points for brain-damaged subjects. She also performed somewhat poorly on the tests concerned with attention and concentration. Her score of 4 points on this section is slightly greater than the mean of 3.78 for brain-damaged children. On the abstraction, reasoning, and logical analysis measures her score of 7 exceeded the average of 6.03 for children with brain damage. However, Margaret's scores in the areas concerned with sensory-perceptual functions (5), immediate memory and recapitulation (0), and visual-spatial skills (3) were essentially comparable to or better than scores earned by control children.

Margaret also scored in the brain-damaged range on the Right-Left Differences section, earning a total of 11 points and exceeding the cut-off of 9/10. The Dysphasia and Related Variables section revealed that she had significant difficulty in spelling and mild problems in copying spatial configurations (although her drawings were considered to be just within the borderline normal range).

Clinical Evaluation of the Test Results. Margaret appeared particularly to have trouble on tasks that were complex and required her to keep several elements of a task in mind at the same time. Her scores indicated mild impairment on the Category Test (58 errors), Part B of the Trail Making Test (51 sec), and the Total Time for the TPT (11.7 min).

It should be noted that on the TPT the scores for the first trial (2.9 min) and third trial (1.5 min) were perfectly normal, and the score on Total Time was largely due to a very poor performance on the second trial (7.3 min) with the left upper extremity. Although the Total Time for the TPT is included in the Motor Functions section of the NDS, because of its complexity it can be considered to complement the relatively poor scores in the Abstraction, Reasoning, and Logical Analysis section in identifying significant neuropsychological problems.

As mentioned above, Margaret also performed poorly on the Attention and Concentration section. Three of the 4 points she earned were contributed by her performance on the Seashore Rhythm Test (15 correct). Note, though, that Margaret did relatively well on the Speech-sounds Perception Test (6 errors) and Part A of the Trail Making Test (16 sec), suggesting that the Rhythm Test score may have been due to factors other than an inability to attend to and concentrate on the stimulus material. It is possible, however, that Margaret does have some degree of impairment in her ability to focus her attention and keep her mind from wandering (as her parents reported).

The specific indicators implicating the left cerebral hemisphere were not prominent. Margaret's spelling difficulty was most apparent in her attempt to spell CROSS. She first responded Q-R-S-S and, when asked by the examiner to try again, responded C-R-S-S. Omitting the vowel when spelling a word is fairly characteristic of children with brain-related deficiencies. Margaret also had difficulty spelling TRIANGLE, but this word may have been somewhat too difficult for a child in the latter part of the third grade. We noted that when writing the word SQUARE she substituted a G for a Q, but this error may also be due to limited education rather than reflecting dysgraphia. The spelling difficulties, in conjunction with indications of mild impairment of brain functions, are sufficiently severe to alert the neuropsychologist to the possibility that Margaret may be developing academic problems.

A number of findings implicated the right cerebral hemisphere. The most prominent finding was the very poor performance on the TPT with the left hand (7.3 min) compared with the right hand (2.9 min). Note that Margaret performed excellently on the third trial (using both hands), when she again had the facility of her right hand available; this makes it clear that the difficulty was specific to the left hand.

On finger-tip number writing perception, Margaret made two errors with her left hand but no errors with her right hand. She also had a mild tendency toward failure to perceive a tactile stimulus to the left face when it was given simultaneously with a stimulus to the right hand. Margaret made one mistake in 12 trials toward her left side with bilateral simultaneous visual stimulation, but this error conceivably could have been due to inattention.

Margaret used her left hand quite ineffectively for writing her name compared with her right hand performance. Finally, as noted before, even though her drawings of the cross and key did not quite qualify as constructional dyspraxia on the NDS, they were not very adequate compared with many of her other abilities.

Summary and Recommendations

In summary, these results are perfectly consistent with residual effects of a closed head injury. The general indicators were complemented by possible mild deficits in the area of dysphasia to implicate the left cerebral hemisphere and by a number of deviant findings to implicate the right cerebral hemisphere. The test results quite definitely confirm the observation by the parents that Margaret was not as bright and capable as she had been before the injury.

Unfortunately, eleven months had passed before the nature of Margaret's neuropsychological deficits were identified. It would have been advantageous if she had been assessed shortly after the injury so that her neuropsychological deficits could have been identified and a program for brain retraining could have been instituted.

The critical area in which Margaret needs remediation is in the area of abstraction, reasoning, and logical analysis abilities. She should first begin training using Track C of REHABIT. Once she has made progress in this area, the focus of training should expand to include remediation of left cerebral functions (Tracks B and A) as well as right hemisphere functions (Tracks D and E).

In cases of head trauma it is common to find generalized impairment as well as specific lateralized deficits. Thus, the neuropsychological deficits are usually relatively widespread even though they may reflect particular impairment in one part of a cerebral hemisphere.

In Margaret's case it appears that the right cerebral hemisphere was more involved than the left, but the overall results suggest that her brain functions are mildly compromised on a general basis. Findings of this kind, even with the indication of a specific deficit with the left upper extremity on the TPT, would not suggest that a specific or focal lesion could be identified through neurological diagnostic procedures.

Testing II

We had the opportunity to retest Margaret at a routine follow-up visit just more than one year after the first examination (approximately two years after her head injury). At that time her mother indicated that she thought that Margaret still had a little trouble concentrating and was very apprehensive, anxious, and "nervous."

Upon further questioning, Margaret's mother explained that she felt that her daughter seemed to tolerate stress and pressure less well than she had before the accident. Obviously, it would be difficult to know the degree to which complaints of this kind were valid and the extent to which they may be reflecting the mother's anxiety and apprehension. Apparently it had been quite a shock to her to have been told initially that there was no permanent brain injury and that Margaret would have no ensuing problems, and then later learn that her daughter did in fact have residual neuropsychological deficits.

Neuropsychological Examination

Wechsler Intelligence Scale for Children — Revised

Margaret demonstrated substantial improvement on the WISC-R, currently earning a Verbal IQ of 123 (compared with the previous score of 111), a Performance IQ of 111 (compared with the previous score of 93) and a Full Scale IQ of 120 (compared with 102). Her previous low score of 5 on Coding had increased to 10. However, her Object Assembly score had decreased from 11 to 7, but this was due principally to a very poor performance on one of the items.

It would appear that the increment in IQ values was well beyond expectation in terms of positive practice-effect, and confirms the hypothesis that the results of the first examination genuinely reflected a diminution in general

The Halstead-Reitan Neuropsychological Test Battery for Older Children

Name: Margaret II   Age: 10 – 1
Gender: F   Education: 3   Handedness: RH 7 LH 0

Neuropsychological Deficit Scale (NDS) Summary

Level of Performance	Subject's score	Mean for controls	Mean for brain-damaged	Cut-off score
Motor Functions	9	6.29	14.05	
Sensory-perceptual Functions	6	5.15	10.77	
Attention and Concentration	1	1.91	3.78	
Immediate Memory and Recapitulation	0	2.23	3.31	
Visual-spatial Skills	2	4.06	7.69	
Abstraction, Reasoning, Logical Analysis	3	2.63	6.03	
Level of Performance–Total	21	22.27	45.63	33/34
Dysphasia and Related Variables	1	1.37	7.97	3/4
Right / Left Differences	8	6.79	13.74	9/10
Total NDS Score	30	30.43	67.34	43/44

WISC-R

VIQ 123
PIQ 111
FS IQ 120

Verbal Subtests

Information 15
Similarities 16
Arithmetic 12
Vocabulary 12
Comprehension 14
(Digit Span) (12)

Performance Subtests

Picture Completion 15
Picture Arrangement 11
Block Design 15
Object Assembly 7
Coding 10
(Mazes) (7)

WRAT

Grade Equivalent
Reading 5.4
Arithmetic 4.5
Spelling 4.0

Strength of Grip

Dominant hand (R) 15.5 kg
Non-dominant hand (L) 15.5 kg

Name Writing

Dominant hand (R) 16 sec
Non-dominant hand (L) 37 sec

Category Test

Number of errors 46

Tactual Performance Test

Dominant hand (R) 2.1
Non-dominant hand (L) .9
Both hands .8   Total Time 3.8
  Memory 6
  Localization 5

Seashore Rhythm Test

Number correct 24   8

Speech-sounds Perception Test

Number of errors 2

Finger Tapping Test

Dominant hand (R) 41   41
Non-dominant hand (L) 35

Trail Making Test

Part A 13 sec   0 error(s)
Part B 60 sec   1 error(s)

Bilateral Simultaneous Sensory Stimulation

RH ___ LH ___   Both: RH ___ LH ___
RH ___ LF ___   Both: RH 1 LF ___
LH ___ RF ___   Both: LH ___ RF ___

RE ___ LE ___   Both: RE ___ LE ___

RV ___ LV ___   Both: RV ___ LV ___

    1

Tactile Finger Recognition

RH 1 ___ 2 1 3 ___ 4 ___ 5 ___   RH 1 / 20
LH 1 ___ 2 1 3 ___ 4 ___ 5 1   LH 2 / 20

Finger-Tip Number Writing

RH 1 1 2 1 3 ___ 4 ___ 5 2   RH 4 / 20
LH 1 1 2 ___ 3 ___ 4 ___ 5 ___   LH 1 / 20

Tactile Form Recognition Test

Dominant hand (R) 10 sec   0 error(s)
Non-dominant hand (L) 9 sec   0 error(s)

Reitan-Indiana Aphasia Screening Test

Form for Adults and Older Children

Name <u>Margaret II</u>   Age <u>10 – 1</u>

Copy SQUARE	Repeat TRIANGLE Triango
Name SQUARE	Repeat MASSACHUSETTS Massachuses
Spell SQUARE S - Q - U - A - R	Repeat METHODIST EPISCOPAL Methodist Ebiscobal
Copy CROSS	Write SQUARE
Name CROSS	Read SEVEN
Spell CROSS	Repeat SEVEN
Copy TRIANGLE	Repeat/Explain HE SHOUTED THE WARNING
Name TRIANGLE	Write HE SHOUTED THE WARNING
Spell TRIANGLE T - I - R - A - N - G - L - E	Compute 85 − 27 =
Name BABY	Compute 17 x 3 =
Write CLOCK	Name KEY
Name FORK	Demonstrate use of KEY
Read 7 SIX 2	Draw KEY
Read MGW	Read PLACE LEFT HAND TO RIGHT EAR
Reading I	Place LEFT HAND TO RIGHT EAR
Reading II	Place LEFT HAND TO LEFT ELBOW

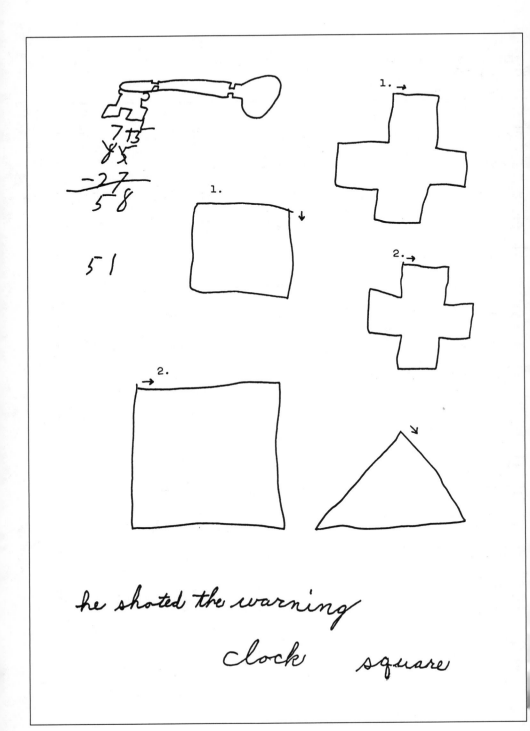

7 +3
8 ✗
−2 7
5 8

5 1

1.

1.

2.

2.

he shoted the warning

clock   *square*

intelligence (as the parents had claimed). Although her total NDS score (30) was now exactly at the average level, this finding should be considered with relation to the fact that her current IQ values were well above average. In other words, it seems possible that there is still some degree of residual impairment, as reflected by an average NDS score in a child who is well above average in general intelligence.

Wide Range Achievement Test

Unfortunately, Margaret did not show as much improvement on measures of academic achievement as might have been expected. On the WRAT she did improve considerably on Reading (word recognition), progressing from a grade equivalent of 4.3 to 5.4. However, on Spelling she improved only from 3.3 to 4.0 and on Arithmetic from 4.1 to 4.5. The test results suggest that brain damage may well have been the significant limiting factor that kept Margaret from progressing at the expected rate in the areas of spelling and arithmetic.

Halstead-Reitan Neuropsychological Test Battery

Neuropsychological Deficit Scale. The NDS indicated that a substantial degree of improvement had occurred over the past twelve months, with the total NDS score dropping from 47 to 30. Margaret now earned 21 points on the Level of Performance section, compared with 22.27 points for control children. As her decrease from 11 to 8 points on the Right-Left Differences section illustrates, she also showed some degree of improvement on this section. She continued to have some difficulty with spelling, and this earned 1 point on the Dysphasia and Related Variables section.

Margaret's scores in the various areas of function represented by the Level of Performance section were consistently at about the average level or better (except for the area on Motor Functions). Margaret was somewhat weak on both sides in grip strength and slow with both hands in name writing.

Analysis of the additional neuropsychological test results reflects further improvement in a number of areas. Margaret had the same (or better) NDS score on each of the 25 variables in the Level of Performance section except for Object Assembly (as we discussed above) and an increase in the number of errors on the right hand in finger-tip number writing perception.

On the second testing Margaret had no difficulty on the Aphasia Screening Test except for spelling. She omitted the E in spelling SQUARE and confused the sequence of the I and R in her spelling of TRIANGLE. This error suggests that she still has a brain-related problem in this respect. She also demonstrated her difficulty in spelling when she wrote SHOUTED as SHOTED. However, with respect to left cerebral dysfunction, this error does not have the same significance as confusing the sequence of letters in TRIANGLE.

Margaret's substantial improvement on tests of right hemisphere functioning was most apparent in her performance of the left hand on the TPT. She previously had required 2.9, 7.3, and 1.5 minutes to complete the three trials; on the second testing she required 2.1, 0.9, and 0.8 minutes. There seems to be little doubt that she had regained a substantial degree of proficiency with her left upper extremity in performing complex manipulatory tasks.

An analysis of the entire set of test results suggested that there were very mild remaining deficiencies. Although not scored as constructional dyspraxia, Margaret had a little difficulty with symmetry of the extremities of the cross and a similar problem when drawing the key, especially with the nose. Scattered instances of imperception of bilateral simultaneous sensory stimuli represented a deviation from normal expectancy in a child of this intelligence. Occasional mistakes in tactile finger localization and the difficulties on the right hand in finger-tip number writing perception also suggest that there is still a degree of neuropsychological impairment.

Results of this kind have been noted clinically to relate to impaired ability to tolerate stressful circumstances. At this point it appeared that psychological counseling oriented toward minimizing stress that Margaret might experience and diminishing anxiety and tension within the family constellation was indicated.

■

Case 15 — MILLIE

Age:	12-7 (Testing I)	Gender:	Female
	13-10 (Testing II)		
Education:	5 (Testing I)	Handedness:	Right
	6 (Testing II)		

Background Information

Testing I

When Millie was 12 years, 6 months old she fell and struck the left side of her head on a rock. She did not lose consciousness, but was in a dazed and somewhat confused condition as she walked home. Her parents noted immediately that it was difficult for her to speak intelligibly, and she complained of numbness of her right arm. She was immediately taken to the local hospital.

In the emergency room Millie's general physical examination was essentially within normal limits. However, the neurological examination revealed a slight weakness of the sixth cranial nerve, nystagmus on lateral gaze to both the right and left sides, a slight facial asymmetry with a questionable weakness on the right side, a minimal degree of weakness of the right upper extremity, and minimal impairment in stereognosis and skin-writing perception on the right side. X-rays indicated that there was a depressed skull fracture in the left parietal area, and Millie was transferred to a major medical center for further treatment.

The next day Millie was taken to surgery for elevation of the left parietal depressed skull fracture. She showed excellent improvement almost immediately following the surgery, and was able to be up and around her room within two days. The neurosurgeon had noted a small area of contusion in the lower part of the left parietal-temporal area, but he felt that no surgical intervention was necessary. We examined Millie with the Halstead-Reitan Battery three days postoperatively. At that time both her speech and the sense of feeling in her right arm were reported to be normal.

Neuropsychological Examination

Wechsler Intelligence Scale for Children — Revised

Millie earned Wechsler scores that consistently fell well below the average level and yielded IQ values in the range of Borderline intelligence. Her Verbal IQ of 75 exceeded only about 5% of her age peers. Her Performance IQ of 77 exceeded 6%, and her Full Scale IQ of 74 exceeded only 4%.

There was relatively little variability among the subtest scores, with eight of the eleven subtests having scaled scores of 5 or 6. Three additional subtests had scores of 7 or 8, and Digit Span had a score of 10. Considering the scores on the WISC-R alone, there would be no way to infer that the recent head injury had caused any neuropsychological impairment.

Wide Range Achievement Test

On the WRAT Millie earned the following grade-equivalents: Reading (word recognition), 5.6; Spelling, 3.8; and Arithmetic, 4.8. She was presently about half way through the sixth grade, and average scores for her would be 6.5.

Considering her scores on the WRAT, it seems likely that Millie was never a particularly good student. Although pre-injury intelligence data were not available, we would postulate that she had probably never been very high in verbal intelligence. These inferences, coupled with specific language deficits and the other indications of left-hemisphere impairment to be described below, all suggest that Millie will have an especially difficult time making adequate academic progress when she returns to school.

The Halstead-Reitan Neuropsychological Test Battery for Older Children

Name Millie I   Age 12 – 7

Gender F   Education 5   Handedness: RH 7 LH 0

Neuropsychological Deficit Scale (NDS) Summary

Level of Performance	Subject's score	Mean for controls	Mean for brain-damaged	Cut-off score
Motor Functions	19	6.29	14.05	
Sensory-perceptual Functions	2	5.15	10.77	
Attention and Concentration	2	1.91	3.78	
Immediate Memory and Recapitulation	5	2.23	3.31	
Visual-spatial Skills	8	4.06	7.69	
Abstraction, Reasoning, Logical Analysis	5	2.63	6.03	
Level of Performance–Total	41	22.27	45.63	33/34
Dysphasia and Related Variables	9	1.37	7.97	3/4
Right/Left Differences	9	6.79	13.74	9/10
Total NDS Score	59	30.43	67.34	43/44

WISC-R

VIQ 75
PIQ 77
FS IQ 74

Verbal Subtests		*Performance Subtests*	
Information	6	Picture Completion	6
Similarities	6	Picture Arrangement	8
Arithmetic	6	Block Design	5
Vocabulary	6	Object Assembly	7
Comprehension	6	Coding	7
(Digit Span)	(10)	(Mazes)	(5)

WRAT

	Grade Equivalent
Reading	5.6
Arithmetic	4.8
Spelling	3.8

Strength of Grip

Dominant hand   (R)   11.5 kg
Non-dominant hand (L)   11.0 kg

Name Writing

Dominant hand   (R)   14 sec
Non-dominant hand (L)   46 sec

Category Test

Number of errors   65

Tactual Performance Test

Dominant hand   (R)   10.0 (4 blocks in)
Non-dominant hand (L)   10.0 (1 block in)
Both hands   5.6 (10 blocks in)

Total Time 25.6
Memory 2
Localization 2

Seashore Rhythm Test

Number correct   24   8

Speech-sounds Perception Test

Number of errors   7

Finger Tapping Test

Dominant hand   (R)   32   32
Non-dominant hand (L)   30

Trail Making Test

Part A   24 sec   _____ error(s)
Part B   35 sec   _____ error(s)

Bilateral Simultaneous Sensory Stimulation

RH ___ LH ___   Both: RH ___ LH ___
RH ___ LF ___   Both: RH ___ LF ___
LH ___ RF ___   Both: LH ___ RF ___

RE ___ LE ___   Both: RE ___ LE ___

RV ___ LV ___   Both: RV ___ LV ___

Tactile Finger Recognition

RH 1 ___ 2 ___ 3 ___ 4 ___ 5 ___   RH 0 / 20
LH 1 ___ 2 ___ 3 ___ 4 ___ 5 ___   LH 0 / 20

Finger-Tip Number Writing

RH 1 2 2 ___ 3 1 4 ___ 5 1   RH 4 / 20
LH 1 ___ 2 ___ 3 ___ 4 ___ 5 1   LH 1 / 20

Tactile Form Recognition Test

Dominant hand   (R)   10 sec   0 error(s)
Non-dominant hand (L)   10 sec   0 error(s)

Reitan-Indiana Aphasia Screening Test

orm for Adults and Older Children

Name __Millie I__   Age __12 – 7__

Copy SQUARE	Repeat TRIANGLE
Name SQUARE	Repeat MASSACHUSETTS
Spell SQUARE	Repeat METHODIST EPISCOPAL
Copy CROSS	Write SQUARE
Name CROSS	Read SEVEN
Spell CROSS	Repeat SEVEN
Copy TRIANGLE	Repeat/Explain HE SHOUTED THE WARNING
Name TRIANGLE	Write HE SHOUTED THE WARNING

Spell TRIANGLE
    T - L - R - A - - - T - R - I - A - N - G - E
	Compute 85 − 27 =
	     What is it — divide? It's not right

Name BABY	Compute 17 x 3 = 53 6 × 4 = 24
Write CLOCK	Name KEY
Name FORK	Demonstrate use of KEY
Read 7 SIX 2	Draw KEY
Read MGW M - G - Y *Ex.?* M - G - W	Read PLACE LEFT HAND TO RIGHT EAR
Reading I	Place LEFT HAND TO RIGHT EAR
Reading II	Place LEFT HAND TO LEFT ELBOW *S placed LH on* *right elbow. Ex.? S responded correctly.*

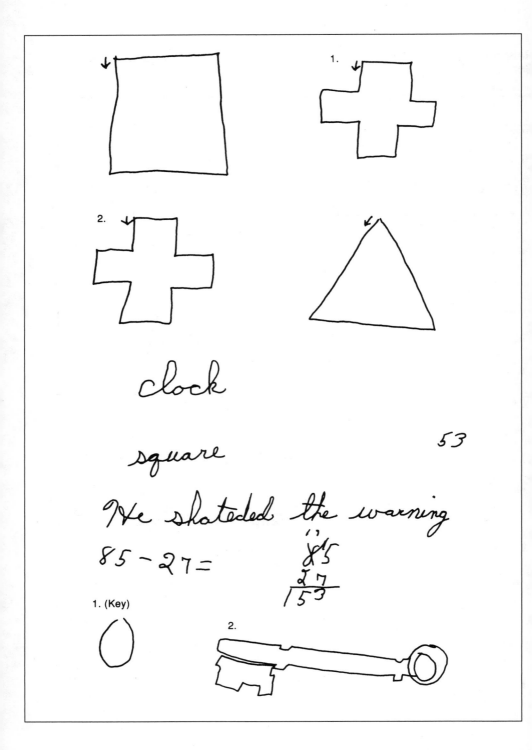

clock

square

53

He shateded the warning

85 − 27 =

$$\begin{array}{r}\overset{\prime\prime}{8}5\\ 2\,7\\ \hline 1\,5\,3\end{array}$$

1. (Key)

2.

Halstead-Reitan Battery for Older Children

Neuropsychological Deficit Scale. Millie showed definite evidence of cerebral damage on the NDS for Older Children. She earned 41 points on the Level of Performance section, which surpasses the cut-off score of 33/34 and approaches the mean of 45.63 of brain-damaged children. She obtained a score of 9 points on the Right-Left Differences section (cut-off, 9/10), and earned 9 points on the Dysphasia and Related Variables section (cut-off, 3/4). These values yielded a total NDS score of 59 points, which is a little better than the mean of 67.34 points of brain-damaged subjects, but clearly exceeds the cut-off score of 43/44. Thus, Millie's scores on two of the three sections of the NDS fell in the brain-damaged range.

Even though the damage was described by the neurosurgeon as being relatively focal, Millie demonstrated impairment on the general neuropsychological measures as well as on the measures that reflect the competency of the left and right cerebral hemispheres. In terms of the Reitan-Wolfson neuropsychological model, she performed relatively well at the first level of central processing (attention and concentration), earning adequate scores on both the Seashore Rhythm Test (24 correct) and the Speech-sounds Perception Test (7 errors).

On the Aphasia Screening Test Millie showed definite left-hemisphere deficits, including spelling dyspraxia, visual letter dysgnosia, dyscalculia, and right-left confusion. She also demonstrated difficulties that relate to the specialized functions of the right cerebral hemisphere, primarily by her drawing of the key. Although the general configuration of her key was fairly adequate, Millie consistently drew the notches on the stem in the same direction, a finding that is quite typical of persons with right cerebral damage. In addition, she failed to achieve symmetry in drawing the teeth of the key, again drawing the notch in different directions (drawing it correctly on the right side but in the wrong direction on the left side). Finally, the line connecting the lower part of the stem with the handle extends past the first line of the handle and on to the second line. This kind of mistake is rarely (if ever) made by normal subjects.

Millie also showed evidence of impairment on the third level of central processing, which involves abstraction, reasoning, and logical analysis abilities. She performed poorly on the Category Test (65 errors), indicating that she has a particular problem in organizing and analyzing simple material based upon her observations and in appreciating cause-and-effect relationships.

Except for the NDS sections concerned with sensory-perceptual functions and alertness and concentration, Millie consistently performed more poorly than normal children on the Level of Performance section, and approached or reached the means shown by brain-damaged children. Her scores on the Motor Functions section (19), Immediate Memory and Recapitulation (5), and Visual- spatial skills (8) were actually worse than the means earned by brain-damaged children. Thus, it would appear that in Millie's case the neuropsychological consequences of brain damage are rather diffuse and generalized in nature.

Considering Millie's relatively low IQ values, a question could be raised about whether a poor total NDS score should have been anticipated. It is difficult on the basis of a single testing to discern the exact degree to which IQ values may have been depressed by brain damage. However, it is rarely possible to depend upon the IQ values alone to determine whether cerebral damage is present.

Clinical Evaluation of the Test Results. Millie's responses on the Aphasia Screening Test indicate quite definitely that her left cerebral hemisphere was compromised. She was obviously confused when trying to spell TRIANGLE.

She began with T-L-R-A, paused, and made another attempt with T-R-I-A-N-G-E. Her spelling deficiencies were even more clearly demonstrated in her attempt to write SHOUTED.

Millie also had difficulties trying to do the arithmetic problem 85 – 27 = . She first wrote the numbers down as they appeared on the stimulus card, then correctly placed the 85 over the 27 and proceeded with the computation. However, at this point she seemed very confused. She apparently recognized the need to carry, crossed out the 8 and made it a 17, and subtracted 2 from 17 after first having recorded a 3. It is obvious that she was not able to deal with numerical relationships, even in solving this simple problem. Even though she corrected her error, Millie also demonstrated evidence of right-left confusion when asked to PLACE LEFT HAND TO LEFT ELBOW.

These deficits on the Aphasia Screening Test were complemented by a slightly slow finger tapping speed with the right hand (32) as compared with the left hand (30), grip strength that was scarcely greater with the right hand (11.5 kg) than the left hand (11.0 kg), and four errors with the right hand in finger-tip number writing perception but only one error with the left hand. While these findings implicated the left cerebral hemisphere, the deficits noted in drawing the key and a severe deficiency on the TPT with the left hand (10.0 min, one block placed) point toward significant damage of the right cerebral hemisphere. These findings fell in the context of generalized impairment shown on a number of variables, and are summarized in the Level of Performance section of the NDS.

We will now return to the question of Millie's low IQ values and their possible pre-injury significance. The other test findings strongly suggest that Millie had experienced neuropsychological impairment due to the head injury. The rather specific deficits shown by the Aphasia Screening Test and the clear and striking deficits shown on tests that compare the two sides of the body are of the type which result from a specific insult to the brain rather than from a life-long developmental deficit.

This case illustrates very well the importance of assessment with a test battery that is designed to use complementary approaches in evaluation of the subject. If only a series of tests had been employed (regardless of how many tests were given) and they were interpreted according to a level-of-performance approach, there would have been no way to know that Millie had been seriously impaired by the head injury (as contrasted with the possibility of having only life-long developmental limitations).

The results of the neuropsychological evaluation were communicated to Millie's neurosurgeon so that he could discuss the findings and implications with Millie and her family and the school personnel. We learned later that the he had not accepted these responsibilities very seriously.

Neurosurgeons are usually not well versed in neuropsychology, and often do not appreciate the significance of neuropsychological findings and their implications for practical aspects of everyday living. Although some neurosurgeons are competent in this area, many are not. Over the years we have learned that the responsibility of communicating the results of the neuropsychological examination to the patient and his/her family should not routinely be left to someone other than the neuropsychologist.

In this case, because they had not been prepared, it came as a total shock to Millie and her family and teachers that Millie had a considerable degree of difficulty in school following her brain injury. Many of these problems could have been avoided if the results of the neuropsychological examination had been discussed with Millie and her family.

About fifteen months after the surgical repair of the depressed skull fracture Millie was readmitted to the hospital for a complete neurological and neuropsychological re-evaluation.

Neuropsychological Examination

Testing II

The results of the neurological examination were essentially within normal limits, but an EEG showed a generalized dysrhythmia, Grade I. The neuropsychological examination indicated that a substantial degree of spontaneous recovery had occurred, as would be expected (Reitan & Wolfson, 1988b).

Wechsler Intelligence Scale for Children — Revised

Millie's results on the WISC-R showed relatively little change on the Verbal subtests, but a very substantial improvement on the Performance subtests. The scaled scores for the two testings indicated that she did somewhat better on Arithmetic (from 6 to 7) and Similarities (from 6 to 10). However, only the improvement on Similarities represented a very substantial change among the Verbal subtests, and even this change was almost counterbalanced by a deterioration on Digit Span from 10 to 7.

Millie's Verbal IQ of 75 on the first examination increased only to 80 on the second examination. Notice, though, that her Performance IQ increased to 93, a gain of 16 points. Prior studies of the recovery process have indicated that the major improvement due to spontaneous recovery (which occurs especially during the first twelve months after injury) will be demonstrated in the areas originally showing the greatest deficit (Reitan & Wolfson, 1986, 1988b).

On this basis, one would presume that Millie had perhaps always had a somewhat depressed Verbal IQ, but that her Performance IQ was impaired as a result of the brain injury. Nevertheless, it was clear from the neuropsychological testing that she had specific deficits in dealing with

The Halstead-Reitan Neuropsychological Test Battery for Older Children

Name __Millie II__   Age __13 – 10__

Gender __F__ Education __6__   Handedness: RH __7__ LH __0__

Neuropsychological Deficit Scale (NDS) Summary

Level of Performance	Subject's score	Mean for controls	Mean for brain-damaged	Cut-off score
Motor Functions	11	6.29	14.05	
Sensory-perceptual Functions	2	5.15	10.77	
Attention and Concentration	0	1.91	3.78	
Immediate Memory and Recapitulation	4	2.23	3.31	
Visual-spatial Skills	6	4.06	7.69	
Abstraction, Reasoning, Logical Analysis	2	2.63	6.03	
Level of Performance–Total	25	22.27	45.63	33/34
Dysphasia and Related Variables	3	1.37	7.97	3/4
Right/Left Differences	9	6.79	13.74	9/10
Total NDS Score	37	30.43	67.34	43/44

WISC-R

VIQ __80__
PIQ __93__
FS IQ __85__

Verbal Subtests		*Performance Subtests*	
Information	6	Picture Completion	8
Similarities	10	Picture Arrangement	12
Arithmetic	7	Block Design	7
Vocabulary	6	Object Assembly	8
Comprehension	5	Coding	11
(Digit Span)	(7)	(Mazes)	(10)

WRAT

	Grade Equivalent
Reading	6.8
Arithmetic	5.9
Spelling	5.2

Strength of Grip

Dominant hand   (R) __21.0__ kg
Non-dominant hand (L) __17.0__ kg

Name Writing

Dominant hand   (R) __23__ sec
Non-dominant hand (L) __50__ sec

Category Test

Number of errors   __49__

Tactual Performance Test

Dominant hand	(R)	4.8		
Non-dominant hand	(L)	10.4		
Both hands		1.2	Total Time	16.4
			Memory	3
			Localization	3

Seashore Rhythm Test

Number correct   __28__   2

Speech-sounds Perception Test

Number of errors   3

Finger Tapping Test

Dominant hand   (R) 35   35
Non-dominant hand (L) 35

Trail Making Test

Part A   __19__ sec   0 error(s)
Part B   __33__ sec   0 error(s)

Bilateral Simultaneous Sensory Stimulation

RH___ LH___	Both: RH___ LH___
RH___ LF___	Both: RH___ LF___
LH___ RF___	Both: LH___ RF___
RE___ LE___	Both: RE___ LE___
RV___ LV___	Both: RV___ LV___
___ ___	___ ___
___ ___	___ ___

Tactile Finger Recognition

RH 1__ 2__ 3_1_ 4__ 5__   RH _1_ / 20
LH 1__ 2__ 3_1_ 4__ 5__   LH _1_ / 20

Finger-Tip Number Writing

RH 1__ 2__ 3__ 4__ 5__   RH _0_ / 20
LH 1__ 2_1_ 3__ 4__ 5__   LH _1_ / 20

Tactile Form Recognition Test

Dominant hand   (R) 8 sec   0 error(s)
Non-dominant hand (L) 9 sec   0 error(s)

Reitan-Indiana Aphasia Screening Test

Form for Adults and Older Children

Name Millie II   Age 13 – 10

Copy SQUARE	Repeat TRIANGLE
Name SQUARE	Repeat MASSACHUSETTS
Spell SQUARE	Repeat METHODIST EPISCOPAL
Copy CROSS	Write SQUARE
Name CROSS	Read SEVEN
Spell CROSS	Repeat SEVEN
Copy TRIANGLE	Repeat/Explain HE SHOUTED THE WARNING
Name TRIANGLE	Write HE SHOUTED THE WARNING
Spell TRIANGLE T - R - A - N - G - L - E	Compute 85 − 27 =
Name BABY	Compute 17 x 3 =
Write CLOCK	Name KEY
Name FORK	Demonstrate use of KEY
Read 7 SIX 2	Draw KEY

Read MGW	Read PLACE LEFT HAND TO RIGHT EAR
	   Please _____ (self-corrected).
	   Place left hand on right ear.

Reading I	Place LEFT HAND TO RIGHT EAR *Hesitated, but done correctly.*
Reading II	Place LEFT HAND TO LEFT ELBOW

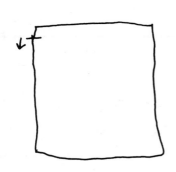

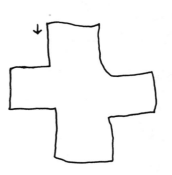

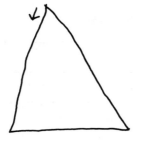

clock

square

he souwoued

the warning

$$
\begin{array}{r}
85 \\
27 \\
\hline
58
\end{array}
\qquad 51
$$

language symbols for communicational purposes. Impairment in this area, together with the indications of generalized impairment, almost certainly would have caused her to do more poorly in school than if she had not sustained a head injury.

Wide Range Achievement Test

The WRAT also showed improvement. Millie increased her scores in Reading (word recognition) from 5.6 to 6.8, in Spelling from 3.8 to 5.2, and in Arithmetic from 4.8 to 5.9. Although each of the present scores was still below the expected grade level of 7.6, the results suggest quite definitely that Millie was making some progress in developing her academic skills.

Halstead-Reitan Neuropsychological Test Battery

Neuropsychological Deficit Scale. On the second testing Millie earned a total NDS score of 37, a value somewhat worse than the mean of 30.43 earned by control subjects, but not exceeding the cut-off of 43/44 points. Her total NDS score for the first examination had been 59 points, a value that fell well into the brain-damaged range.

Millie's scores on the Level of Performance section were somewhat better than the means for controls for attention and concentration, abstraction, reasoning, and logical analysis abilities, and sensory-perceptual functions. Her score of 4 in the area of immediate memory and recapitulation was slightly worse than the average of 3.31 earned by brain-damaged subjects, but Millie's score was influenced considerably by a poor performance on the Memory component (3) of the TPT.

Millie's score of 6 on the Visual-Spatial Skills section was intermediate to the means of normals (4.06) and brain-damaged children (7.69). She continued to perform poorly on the Motor Functions section, earning 11 points (compared with means of 6.29 for control subjects and 14.05 for brain-damaged subjects). She earned a total of 25 points for the Level of Performance section, a score just a little above the mean of 22.27 points for control subjects and well below the cut-off of 33/34.

It is apparent that Millie's general level of performance on the second testing was substantially improved over the results obtained shortly after she had the sustained traumatic brain injury. However, she showed no improvement on the Right-Left Differences section, earning scores of 9 on both examinations. The cut-off score for this section is 9/10 points. Although Millie had reduced her score from 9 to 3 on the Dysphasia and Related Variables section, she still demonstrated some deficits in this area.

There was no doubt that Millie had shown a substantial degree of spontaneous improvement, a finding that was expected in consideration of the first set of test results. However, it is important to note that the second set of test results documents the fact that significant impairment was initially present.

Clinical Interpretation of the Test Results. A more detailed evaluation of the test results indicates that although Millie performed relatively well in terms of level of performance, she continued to show certain findings that implicated both the left and right cerebral hemispheres. The results on the Aphasia Screening Test clearly demonstrate her difficulty in spelling. For example, she omitted the I in spelling TRIANGLE. Although this error is not particularly serious, she wrote SHOUTED as SOUWOUOD.

Millie also demonstrated just a little difficulty in reading, which should be noted clinically even though it was not sufficiently poor to be scored as dyslexia on the NDS. When she was asked to read PLACE LEFT HAND TO RIGHT EAR, she read the first word as PLEASE. She then corrected herself and read the rest of the sentence correctly.

Millie's finger tapping speed with the right (preferred) hand (35) was no faster than with the left hand (35), although there had been some increase in speed on each hand since the time of the first examination.

Millie continued to show some signs of right cerebral dysfunction as well. In her drawing of the key she had difficulties that were very similar to the problems she manifested at the time of the first examination, and they were sufficiently severe to classify as constructional dyspraxia. She had shown a very substantial improvement on all three trials of the TPT, but she still required twice as much time with her left hand (10.4 min) as her right hand (4.8 min). From these findings there is no doubt that Millie continues to experience significant impairment in performing complex manipulatory functions with her left hand.

On the first examination Millie's grip strength had been somewhat reduced with the right hand as compared with the left hand. On the second testing the relationship was reversed, and she was a little weaker with her left hand (17 kg) compared to her right hand (21 kg). On the first examination Millie's performance on finger-tip number writing perception had shown definite impairment with the right hand, but at the present time her results were essentially within the normal range.

It is not uncommon for persons who sustain traumatic brain injury to return to their normal activities only to find that they are not able to function as efficiently as they had previously. This is true for grade-school children returning to the daily classroom, college students resuming their academic work, or adults in demanding occupational situations. It seems that many persons who sustain head injuries are (at least initially) relatively oblivious to the fact that the brain is the organ of behavior.

As it turned out in this case, it is not uncommon for specialists in the neurological sciences to fail to communicate information about the neuropsychological deficits experienced by persons with head injuries, and the kinds of problems that they are likely to encounter because they have such deficits. It appears that Millie actually made a fairly good recovery, but it was also clear that she and her parents were unprepared to deal with the deficits that were revealed by the first neuropsychological examination.

The present concern about difficulty in academic progress was, in all probability, certainly justified during the preceding interval, but the test results suggest that many of these major difficulties have resolved. Spontaneous recovery, which occurs principally during the first year following traumatic brain injury, had taken place. Unless the trauma of the past fifteen months had created new problems over and beyond the neuropsychological consequences of the head injury, Millie currently had an opportunity to do somewhat better in terms of her brain-behavior relationships.

This case serves to illustrate the importance of adequate communication to head-injured persons and their families shortly after the injury has occurred. Millie clearly demonstrates how critical it is to enroll persons with neuropsychological deficits in brain retraining programs and establish a counseling relationship to help them through this difficult and stressful period. With brain-injured children it is particularly important to include the parents and teachers in rehabilitation conferences, not only to help them understand the child's neuropsychological deficits, but to enlist them whenever possible in the cognitive retraining efforts and to allay the natural anxieties and even fears that spring from ignorance about the effects of brain damage and the outlook of the future.

■

Case 16 — EUNICE

Age:	10-8	Gender:	Female
Education:	3	Handedness:	Right

Background Information

Eunice was a little girl who was just starting the 4th grade in school when she was referred for a neuropsychological examination. We were asked to evaluate this child because she was having difficulty making adequate academic progress, particularly with reading and spelling.

Eunice's parents reported that their daughter had previously sustained a head injury on two separate occasions. The first occurred when Eunice was three years old and she fell and injured the right side of her head. She was unconscious briefly and in a dazed condition for about one hour. The skull x-ray taken at the hospital emergency room documented that Eunice had sustained a linear fracture of the right parietal area. When she was four years old she sustained another head injury. Although this accident was considered less serious, it also rendered her unconscious for a brief period of time.

Because the medical evaluations had demonstrated no neurological signs, the parents originally felt that Eunice had not sustained any significant permanent impairment from these injuries. However, it was difficult for her to keep up with her classmates in school subjects, and the parents had begun to suspect that their daughter may have sustained some degree of mild brain damage as a result of these two head injuries.

A complete neurological evaluation was done at the time the neuropsychological testing was performed. Except for an EEG showing a generalized cerebral dysrhythmia, Grade I, the neurological examination was entirely within normal limits.

This case represents a typical example of the serious, generalized consequences of cerebral damage in the early developmental years.

Neuropsychological Examination

Wechsler Intelligence Scale for Children — Revised

We have noted previously that it is very uncommon to encounter normal IQ values in children who have had the disadvantage of having a damaged brain to subserve their developmental years. As would be expected in this case, Eunice had IQ values that were below the average level.

On the WISC-R Eunice earned a Verbal IQ of 78, a value that falls in the range of Borderline intelligence and exceeds 7% of her age peers. Her Performance IQ of 73 was a few points lower, also falling in the Borderline range of intelligence and exceeding 4%. These values yielded a Full Scale IQ of 74, a score which falls in the lower part of the Borderline range and exceeds only 4%.

The variability of the subtest scores was not particularly useful in helping us draw conclusions about differential involvement of the various areas of the cerebral cortex. The Verbal subtest scores ranged from 4 (Comprehension) to 9 (Similarities and Vocabulary), and the Performance scores ranged from 5 (Picture Completion and Object Assembly) to 7 (Picture Arrangement and Coding). These results make it quite clear that Eunice's general intelligence is consistently and considerably below the average level. On this basis alone one would not expect this child to make normal academic progress.

The Halstead-Reitan Neuropsychological Test Battery for Older Children

Name: Eunice   Age 10 – 8
Gender: F   Education: 3   Handedness: RH 7 LH 0

Neuropsychological Deficit Scale (NDS) Summary

Level of Performance	Subject's score	Mean for controls	Mean for brain-damaged	Cut-off score
Motor Functions	18	6.29	14.05	
Sensory-perceptual Functions	12	5.15	10.77	
Attention and Concentration	5	1.91	3.78	
Immediate Memory and Recapitulation	5	2.23	3.31	
Visual-spatial Skills	11	4.06	7.69	
Abstraction, Reasoning, Logical Analysis	6	2.63	6.03	
Level of Performance–Total	57	22.27	45.63	33/34
Dysphasia and Related Variables	15	1.37	7.97	3/4
Right / Left Differences	8	6.79	13.74	9/10
Total NDS Score	80	30.43	67.34	43/44

WISC-R

VIQ 78
PIQ 73
FS IQ 74

Verbal Subtests
Information 6
Similarities 9
Arithmetic 4
Vocabulary 9
Comprehension 4
(Digit Span) (6)

Performance Subtests
Picture Completion 5
Picture Arrangement 7
Block Design 6
Object Assembly 5
Coding 7

WRAT

	Grade Equivalent
Reading	2.7
Arithmetic	2.6
Spelling	2.2

Strength of Grip
Dominant hand (R) 5.0 kg
Non-dominant hand (L) 4.0 kg

Name Writing
Dominant hand (R) 19 sec
Non-dominant hand (L) 40 sec

Category Test
Number of errors 58

Tactual Performance Test
Dominant hand (R) 6.4
Non-dominant hand (L) 3.8
Both hands 4.4
Total Time 14.6
Memory 4
Localization 0

Seashore Rhythm Test
Number correct 22   10

Speech-sounds Perception Test
Number of errors 21

Finger Tapping Test
Dominant hand (R) 26   26
Non-dominant hand (L) 20

Trail Making Test
Part A 39 sec 0 error(s)
Part B 86 sec 1 error(s)

Bilateral Simultaneous Sensory Stimulation

RH ___ LH ___   Both: RH ___ LH ___
RH ___ LF ___   Both: RH ___ LF ___
LH ___ RF ___   Both: LH ___ RF ___

RE ___ LE ___   Both: RE ___ LE ___

RV ___ LV ___   Both: RV ___ LV ___

Tactile Finger Recognition
RH 1 0 2 4 3 2 4 3 5 0   RH 9 / 20
LH 1 0 2 1 3 2 4 1 5 2   LH 6 / 20

Finger-Tip Number Writing
RH 1 3 2 2 3 4 4 4 5 2   RH 15 / 20
LH 1 3 2 3 3 4 4 3 5 4   LH 17 / 20

Tactile Form Recognition Test
Dominant hand (R) 10 sec 0 error(s)
Non-dominant hand (L) 8 sec 0 error(s)

Reitan-Indiana Aphasia Screening Test

Form for Adults and Older Children

Name <u>Eunice</u>　　　　　　　　　Age <u>10 – 8</u>

Copy SQUARE	Repeat TRIANGLE
Name SQUARE	Repeat MASSACHUSETTS
Spell SQUARE　S – *Could not go further.*	Repeat METHODIST EPISCOPAL　*Methodis Epistopal*
Copy CROSS	Write SQUARE
Name CROSS　Oval. *Could not give another name.*	Read SEVEN
Spell CROSS　T – *Could not go further.*	Repeat SEVEN
Copy TRIANGLE	Repeat/Explain HE SHOUTED THE WARNING　*OK*　Indians were coming.
Name TRIANGLE　Oval. *Could not give another name.*	Write HE SHOUTED THE WARNING
Spell TRIANGLE　"Starts with T- O." *Could not do better.*	Compute 85 – 27 =　*See confusion and errors.*
Name BABY	Compute 17 x 3 = *Could not do.*　$12 \times 2 = 14$　$3 \times 3 = 6$　$2 \times 3 = 6$
Write CLOCK	Name KEY
Name FORK	Demonstrate use of KEY
Read 7 SIX 2	Draw KEY
Read MGW	Read PLACE LEFT HAND TO RIGHT EAR　Please leave here to right here.
Reading I	Place LEFT HAND TO RIGHT EAR
Reading II　He is a fraid animal, a farmer with a _____ of big show.	Place LEFT HAND TO LEFT ELBOW　*Tried hard to place left hand to left shoulder. Finally OK.*

1.

2.

3.

4.

ocoL e

souake.

he show the were -

$$\begin{array}{r} 8\ 5 \\ -7\ 2 \\ \hline 1\ \ 3 \end{array}$$

$$\begin{array}{r} 8\ 5 \\ -2\ 7 \\ \hline 6\ 2 \end{array}$$

(Written by examiner)

$$\begin{array}{r} 4\ 6 \\ -2\ 3 \\ \hline 2\ 3 \end{array}$$

1 4 (12 × 2)

4 (3 × 3)

6 (2 × 3)

Wide Range Achievement Test

At the time of this neuropsychological examination Eunice was just starting the fourth grade in school, and the average score for her grade level would therefore be about 4.0. On the WRAT she earned the following grade-equivalents: Reading (word recognition) 2.7; Spelling, 2.2; and Arithmetic, 2.6. These results confirm the expectation based on the IQ values that Eunice would exhibit a relatively serious lag in the development of her academic skills.

Halstead-Reitan Neuropsychological Test Battery

Neuropsychological Deficit Scale. In contrast to the medical examination, the neuropsychological evaluation indicated that Eunice had serious and significant generalized neuropsychological impairment. On the NDS for Older Children, her total score of 80 exceeded the cut-off point of 43/44 as well as the mean of 67.34 earned by brain-damaged children.

On the Level of Performance section of the NDS Eunice scored above the mean for brain-damaged children in each of the six component areas: Motor Functions, Sensory-perceptual Functions, Attention and Concentration, Immediate Memory and Recapitulation, Visual-spatial Skills, and Abstraction, Reasoning, and Logical Analysis. The scores on these various sections yielded a total of 57 points for the Level of Performance section, which exceeds the cut-off score of 33/34 and is greater than the mean of 45.63 for brain-damaged children.

By inspecting Eunice's performances on each of the 25 measures in this section we can see that she had NDS scores of 2 or 3 (impaired range) on all measures except bilateral imperception, tactile form recognition with each hand, and the Coding subtest. Eunice showed some degree of impairment on the Right-Left Differences section of the NDS, but her score of 8 was just below the cut-off point of 9/10 and intermediate to the means of control children (6.79) and brain-damaged children (13.74). It should be emphasized that this finding is directly in line with expectation for a child with chronic cerebral damage.

Strong lateralized effects are seen most commonly in children with focal, lateralized lesions that are either recent in origin or rapidly progressive in nature. Many children with generalized cerebral damage demonstrate some deficits that implicate one cerebral hemisphere more than the other, but the fact that Eunice scored in the normal range on the Right-Left Differences section of the NDS would serve, in the context of the other test findings, to suggest that her brain damage was chronic and static in nature.

Eunice's scores on the tests in the Dysphasia and Related Variables section yielded significant evidence of brain impairment. She accumulated 15 points on this section, a score which is nearly twice the mean score of 7.97 for brain-damaged children and well beyond the cut-off parameter of 3/4. As we will discuss in more detail below, Eunice demonstrated evidence of dysnomia, constructional dyspraxia, spelling dyspraxia, dysgraphia, dyslexia, dyscalculia, and body dysgnosia.

Clinical Evaluation of the Test Results. A more detailed analysis of the results of the Halstead-Reitan Battery provides further information about the impairment of this child's brain functions. The fact that Eunice has generalized impairment of neuropsychological abilities was already well established by the approaches described above. The test results also suggest that her left cerebral hemisphere is more seriously dysfunctional than her right cerebral hemisphere. This outcome is not particularly surprising, even though the blow to her head which resulted in a right parietal linear fracture was on the right side (see pp. 672-673).

Eunice's NDS score of 8 on the Right-Left Differences section was not quite into the brain-damaged range. Her difficulties tended to involve the right side of her body to a greater extent than her left side. For example, although she had difficulty on both sides in tactile finger recognition, she made more mistakes on the right hand (9) than on the left hand (6).

On the Tactual Performance Test the disparity between performances of the two hands was not strikingly deviant from expectation, but it should be noted that Eunice had increased difficulty on the third trial (4.4 min) as compared with the second trial (3.8 min). Thus, instead of demonstrating continued improvement on the third trial (when using both hands), her performance regressed when her right hand participated in the task. The total pattern of the time required for the three trials on the TPT suggests the presence of left cerebral dysfunction.

As noted above, on the Aphasia Screening Test Eunice also demonstrated a number of specific deficits. Difficulties of this kind tend to be associated with early brain damage in children (Reitan, 1985), but it is likely that they also indicate impairment of left cerebral functioning. We can see that Eunice showed clear difficulties in spelling. She was unable to name more than the first letter in attempting to spell SQUARE, responded only with T in attempting to spell CROSS, and answered T-O when asked to spell TRIANGLE. Her serious deficiency in the ability to use letters to form words was also demonstrated by her attempts at writing. A naming deficit was manifested by her identification of both the cross and the triangle as an "oval."

Eunice's attempts at writing showed clear evidence of dysgraphia. In most instances she was able to form the letters legibly, but she failed to write a proper Q and R in writing SQUARE. It may be that formation of a Q is beyond her training and ability level, but improper formation of the R suggests that she has definite difficulty in writing.

Eunice also demonstrated confusion in her reading of simple material. When trying to read HE IS A FRIENDLY

ANIMAL, A FAMOUS WINNER OF DOG SHOWS, she responded, "He is a fraid animal, a farmer with a —— of big show." She also made reading errors when asked to read PLACE LEFT HAND TO RIGHT EAR; she responded, "Please leave here to right here."

Eunice also showed evidence of dyscalculia, apparently confusing arithmetical processes on some occasions. Although she performed certain arithmetic problems correctly, she gave "62" as the answer to $85 - 27 = $. Derivation of this answer either represents a combination of addition and subtraction, or subtraction of 5 from 7 and 2 from 8. In either case, the confusion represents a fairly typical manifestation of a deficit in understanding arithmetical procedures and numerical relationships. Eunice further demonstrated this kind of difficulty by answering "14" when given the problem 12×2 and responding "6" when asked for the answer to 3×3.

Finally, Eunice displayed body dysgnosia, a rather unusual deficit that is associated with left cerebral damage. When she was asked to place her left hand to her left elbow, she tried diligently to place her left hand to her left shoulder.

Eunice also demonstrated the kind of impairment that indicates right cerebral involvement. Her finger tapping speed was somewhat slow with the left hand (20) as compared with the right hand (26). Although her drawing of the cross was marginally acceptable, her third attempt to draw the triangle clearly distorted the spatial configuration. Her drawing of the key was sufficiently poor to merit a scoring of constructional dyspraxia on the NDS.

Summary and Recommendations

In summary, Eunice showed serious and generalized impairment of adaptive abilities dependent upon the biological condition of the brain. We would estimate that her left cerebral hemisphere was somewhat more dysfunctional than the right, but as we commonly find in cases of traumatic brain injury, the neuropsychological findings implicated both cerebral hemispheres (Reitan & Wolfson, 1986).

The immediate consequences of a child's neuropsychological deficits will be reflected principally in the area of academic progress. Because of her brain damage, Eunice is on a learning curve different from that of her age-peers, and it is almost certain that as she gets older she will fall further and further behind children of her age in terms of academic achievement.

The primary question is, of course, What can be done for a child like Eunice, who has significant generalized neuropsychological impairment? Can cognitive retraining be effective with a child who has spent the past six years trying to develop her neuropsychological abilities with an impaired brain? Is it appropriate to recommend training for a child who has a neuropsychological ability structure that is depressed and limited in such a wide range of functional areas?

We have attempted brain retraining in a number of children with significant neuropsychological impairment. As might be expected, our most striking successes have occurred with children who have specific and delimited neuropsychological deficits. In these cases one can proceed through training to remediate the "weak link" in the chain and thereby restore a significant degree of functional competence.

This is not, however, to imply that a child like Eunice would not benefit from an intensive cognitive retraining program, even six years after the last head injury occurred. It is critical to realize, though, that these children will not progress as rapidly as children who have specific deficits in the context of some good neuropsychological abilities. Although the training program generally takes longer and skills need to be reviewed and rehearsed frequently, we have found that we are able to make significant progress with these children as well.

Finally, this case again causes us to bemoan the fact that traumatic head injuries (and the concomitant brain damage) are often treated in such a casual manner. It seems likely that the head injuries Eunice sustained when she was three and four years old were responsible for her present neuropsychological impairment and academic difficulties. If the parents, teachers, physicians, and others who undoubtedly felt a concern for this child had sought early evaluation, it might have been possible to remediate her identified deficits, rather than to permit the original impairment of brain functions to diffuse through her entire ability structure in the course of her development.

■

Case 17 — BOYD

Age:	14-3	**Gender:**	Male
Education:	7	**Handedness:**	Right

Background Information

Nineteen months prior to this neuropsychological examination, when Boyd was 12 years, 8 months old, he was
riding in the back of a pickup truck that collided with an
automobile. The impact was so severe that he was thrown
from the truck, and as he landed, struck the right side of his
head against a streetlight pole. When the paramedics arrived at the scene of the accident minutes later, Boyd was
unconscious and unresponsive to verbal or physical stimuli. He was immediately transported to the local hospital.

In the hospital Boyd remained comatose for the next
twenty days. He gradually began to regain consciousness on
the twenty-first day, and was able to recognize his family
about twenty-six days following the injury. He remained in
the hospital for almost three months.

Although Boyd gradually improved during his hospitalization, he still had many difficulties after he was
discharged. At the time of Boyd's neuropsychological examination, his parents enumerated a number of problems that
they felt their son was having: (1) difficulty with his balance
when attempting to perform complex or coordinated activities, (2) impairment in his overall awareness of situations,
frequently including a failure to consider the consequences
of his actions, (3) a tendency to become angry more quickly
than he did before the injury, (4) frequent failure to perform
normally expected behavior (such as writing messages
when answering the phone), and (5) an inability to carry out
tasks that involve several steps or elements.

Concerning this latter problem, Boyd's parents indicated that in order to have him complete a task satisfactorily, it was necessary to give him a single instruction at a time and require him to come back and be told about the next step to be done. The parents also indicated that after the accident Boyd had experienced a degree of paralysis on the right side of his body, but they felt that he had essentially recovered from this.

At the present time, the parents' major concern centered around Boyd's limitations of academic ability and achievement. It must be recognized that the ability to make normal academic progress is greatly valued in our society, and probably represents the principal and best-defined challenge faced by children. Therefore, when a child is impaired in the academic area, it frequently is the major cause of concern for parents.

This case was involved in litigation, and neuropsychological testing was done to obtain information about Boyd's condition in seeking compensation for damages. In addition, the parents were very much concerned about the neuropsychological consequences of brain injury, and were anxious to take any steps possible to assist in their son's eventual recovery and development.

Since the accident Boyd's progress had been monitored by his neurologist. Boyd had initially demonstrated evidence of mild right hemiparesis, but this has gradually improved. He had been placed prophylactically on antiepileptic medication, but it was discontinued after approximately one year because his EEG was normal and he had shown no indications of developing epilepsy. At the time of the neuropsychological testing, the medical (neurological) examination was considered to be within normal limits.

Neuropsychological Examination

The technician who administered the Halstead-Reitan Neuropsychological Test Battery for Older Children noted that Boyd was a well-groomed and pleasant young man who seemed to be very interested in the tests and was completely cooperative. He put forth a good effort and seemed to do his best on all of the tests. The examiner noted, however, that in many situations Boyd was quite slow to respond and frequently seemed to have difficulty comprehending instructions. With careful attention to make sure that Boyd understood the instructions before a test was begun, it was possible to administer all of the tests in the Battery and obtain valid results. A review of the intrinsic characteristics of the test results also suggested that they were a consistent set of findings which appeared to reflect Boyd's abilities validly.

Wechsler Intelligence Scale for Children — Revised

The WISC-R yielded a Verbal IQ of 85, a score which exceeds 16% of Boyd's age peers and falls in the Low Average range. Boyd's Performance IQ was 90, a score that exceeds 25% and falls at the lower limits of the Average range. His Full Scale IQ was 86, exceeding 18% and falling in the Low Average range. These summary values were consistently well below the 50th percentile.

The scaled scores indicate a considerable degree of variability among the subtests. On the Verbal subtests the scores ranged from 3 (Digit Span) to 9 (Comprehension and Similarities), and on the Performance subtests from 4 (Coding) to 11 (Picture Completion and Block Design). However, it must be remembered that the specificity of results on individual WISC-R subtests and their relation to brain damage is much less than with the Wechsler Adult Intelligence Scale (WAIS). Therefore, even though the degree of variability in Boyd's set of test results suggests that aspects of his general

The Halstead-Reitan Neuropsychological Test Battery for Older Children

Name __Boyd__   Age __14 – 3__
Gender __M__ Education __7__   Handedness: RH __7__ LH __0__

Neuropsychological Deficit Scale (NDS) Summary

Level of Performance	Subject's score	Mean for controls	Mean for brain-damaged	Cut-off score
Motor Functions	7	6.29	14.05	
Sensory-perceptual Functions	7	5.15	10.77	
Attention and Concentration	4	1.91	3.78	
Immediate Memory and Recapitulation	4	2.23	3.31	
Visual-spatial Skills	5	4.06	7.69	
Abstraction, Reasoning, Logical Analysis	7	2.63	6.03	
Level of Performance–Total	34	22.27	45.63	33/34
Dysphasia and Related Variables	5	1.37	7.97	3/4
Right / Left Differences	17	6.79	13.74	9/10
Total NDS Score	56	30.43	67.34	43/44

WISC-R

VIQ __85__
PIQ __90__
FS IQ __86__

Verbal Subtests		Performance Subtests	
Information	6	Picture Completion	11
Similarities	9	Picture Arrangement	8
Arithmetic	6	Block Design	11
Vocabulary	8	Object Assembly	9
Comprehension	9	Coding	4
(Digit Span)	(3)		

WRAT

	Grade Equivalent
Reading	6.9
Arithmetic	3.9
Spelling	5.4

Strength of Grip

Dominant hand (R) __32.5__ kg
Non-dominant hand (L) __26.5__ kg

Name Writing

Dominant hand (R) __11__ sec
Non-dominant hand (L) __14__ sec

©1991, Ralph M. Reitan, Ph.D. Reitan Neuropsychology Laboratory Tucson, Arizona

Category Test

Number of errors __43__

Tactual Performance Test

Dominant hand (R) __3.1__
Non-dominant hand (L) __5.1__
Both hands __2.3__   Total Time __10.5__
  Memory __4__
  Localization __2__

Seashore Rhythm Test

Number correct __22__   10

Speech-sounds Perception Test

Number of errors __14__

Finger Tapping Test

Dominant hand (R) __28__   28
Non-dominant hand (L) __35__

Trail Making Test

Part A __45__ sec __0__ error(s)
Part B __72__ sec __1__ error(s)

Bilateral Simultaneous Sensory Stimulation

RH ___ LH ___	Both: RH ___ LH _1_
RH ___ LF ___	Both: RH ___ LF ___
LH ___ RF ___	Both: LH ___ RF ___
RE ___ LE ___	Both: RE ___ LE ___
RV ___ LV ___	Both: RV ___ LV ___

Tactile Finger Recognition

RH 1 __ 2 __ 3 __ 4 _1_ 5 __   RH _1_ / 20
LH 1 __ 2 __ 3 _3_ 4 _3_ 5 __   LH _6_ / 20

Finger-Tip Number Writing

RH 1 __ 2 __ 3 __ 4 __ 5 __   RH _0_ / 20
LH 1 _1_ 2 __ 3 __ 4 __ 5 __   LH _1_ / 20

Tactile Form Recognition Test

Dominant hand (R) __9__ sec __0__ error(s)
Non-dominant hand (L) __9__ sec __0__ error(s)

**Reitan-Indiana Aphasia
Screening Test**

Name ___Boyd_____ Age ___14 – 3___

Form for Adults and Older Children

Examiner's Note: S was extremely slow and required frequent repetition of instructions.

Copy SQUARE	Repeat TRIANGLE
Name SQUARE	Repeat MASSACHUSETTS
Spell SQUARE S - Q - U - A - R	Repeat METHODIST EPISCOPAL Methodik Ebisoble
Copy CROSS	Write SQUARE *After writing the word, S said,* Oh, that's square. I thought those were just letters.
Name CROSS It's an - - - an addition sign - - - a plus sign. *Ex.?* Cross	Read SEVEN
Spell CROSS	Repeat SEVEN
Copy TRIANGLE	Repeat/Explain HE SHOUTED THE WARNING
Name TRIANGLE	Write HE SHOUTED THE WARNING *S had difficulty forming the letter g and added the loop later.*
Spell TRIANGLE T - R - Y - A - N - G - L - E	Compute 85 − 27 =
Name BABY	Compute 17 x 3 = 20 2 × 4 = 8
Write CLOCK	Name KEY
Name FORK	Demonstrate use of KEY
Read 7 SIX 2	Draw KEY
Read MGW	Read PLACE LEFT HAND TO RIGHT EAR
Reading I	Place LEFT HAND TO RIGHT EAR *S placed right hand to right ear, then placed left hand to left ear, then placed left hand to right ear.*
Reading II	Place LEFT HAND TO LEFT ELBOW

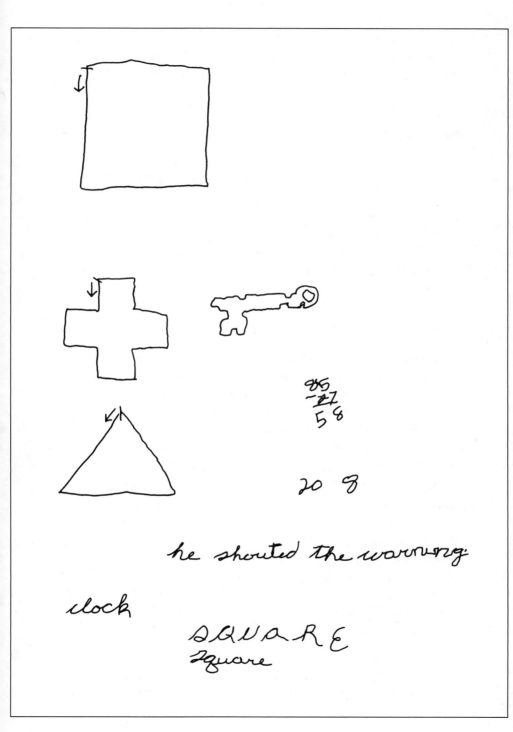

intelligence (as measured by the WISC-R) may be impaired, we are reluctant to use results on the WISC-R to draw conclusions about lateralization or regional localization of cerebral damage in children.

Wide Range Achievement Test

On the WRAT Boyd earned the following grade-equivalents: Reading (word recognition), 6.9; Spelling, 5.4; and Arithmetic, 3.9. His level of performance is below the expected level (eighth grade), and it may well be that he is not receiving the specific kind of training necessary to improve his academic skills. As we will describe, Boyd will need intensive individual tutorial help in order to make any significant progress.

Halstead-Reitan Battery for Older Children

Neuropsychological Deficit Scale for Older Children. Boyd earned a total NDS score of 56, a value that exceeds the cutoff of 43/44 and falls in the range characteristic of brain damage. Control children have a mean total NDS score of 30.43 and brain-damaged children average 67.34 points. Boyd's score of 56 is at an intermediate position, but it is also necessary to keep in mind that Boyd was 14 years, 3 months of age at the time the neuropsychological examination was done; therefore, he fell at the extreme end of the age distribution for the 9- through 14-year age range. Although an age-related breakdown of scores for normal and brain-damaged children has not yet been compiled for the NDS, it certainly can be assumed that older children should perform better than younger children. Therefore, it is reasonable to say that Boyd's total NDS score of 56 is definitely deviant.

It is helpful to evaluate scores for each of the NDS sections in order to identify the areas in which the principal deficits occurred. Integrating the Reitan-Wolfson neuropsychological model with the sections of the NDS provides a useful framework for understanding an individual's strengths and weaknesses, and allows the clinician to construct an appropriate remediation program.

As shown by his impaired scores on both the Seashore Rhythm Test (22 correct) and the Speech-sounds Perception Test (14 errors), Boyd had particular difficulty in the area of alertness and concentration. His performances earned him a score of 4 points for this section, which exceeds the mean score of 3.78 earned by brain-damaged subjects. These results indicate that Boyd definitely needs remediation of abilities concerned with registration and initial analysis of incoming information. Unless Boyd is helped to improve his ability to maintain his attention over time and organize incoming stimuli in a meaningful manner, it is unlikely that he will be able to make any progress in remediating his other deficits.

Boyd also demonstrated difficulty with the tasks in the Immediate Memory and Recapitulation section, scoring in the impaired range on both the Memory (4) and Localization (2) components of the Tactual Performance Test. His score of 4 points on this section was above the mean of 3.31 for brain-damaged children.

These results suggest that it was difficult for Boyd to register any incoming information, regardless of whether his attention was directed specifically to the task at hand or whether the incoming information was only incidentally available. This type of finding has significant implications for understanding Boyd's behavior as well as for developing a rehabilitation program. As we will emphasize in a later section, unless Boyd receives specific and intensive training with materials that focus on attention, concentration, and reasoning skills, it is unlikely that efforts in other areas will have any degree of success.

Except in the area of dysphasia, the NDS is not organized to evaluate language and verbal skills, and the Verbal

IQ should also be considered in this area. As we pointed out, Boyd not only showed quite variable scores on the individual subtests of the WISC-R, he earned a Verbal IQ of only 85 (16th percentile). We did not score any specific deficits on the Dysphasia and Related Variables section except for dyscalculia, right-left confusion, and constructional dyspraxia. However, it was clear from Boyd's responses that he performed relatively poorly on a number of other items. He omitted the E in spelling SQUARE, was somewhat confused in naming the CROSS, repeated METHODIST EPISCOPAL as "Methodik Episoble," seemed to be somewhat deficient in writing ability, and demonstrated repeated difficulties in understanding the examiner's instructions. Boyd's conservative total score of 5 points on the Dysphasia and Related Variables section was intermediate to the mean score of 1.37 for controls and 7.97 for brain-damaged subjects.

The reader will note that the results on the Aphasia Screening Test identified problems which went well beyond the specific difficulties identified in the Dysphasia and Related Variables section of the Neuropsychological Deficit Scale. In several individual instances Boyd's responses did not meet the explicit criteria for earning points on the NDS; nevertheless, from a clinical point of view, these problems in performance must be taken into account. From his results on the Aphasia Screening Test we can conclude that Boyd shows evidence of some deficiencies in using language and verbal symbols for communicational purposes, which in turn might well reflect some degree of left cerebral dysfunction.

As he demonstrates in his drawings, Boyd also had difficulty in copying simple spatial configurations. Although we would not have scored his drawing of the cross as evidence of constructional dyspraxia, his drawing of the key demonstrated a significant problem with spatial relationships. Even though Boyd did not have specific difficulty on the Picture Arrangement (8), Block Design (11), or Object Assembly (9) subtests, his poor performance on Trails A (45 sec) contributed 3 points to the Visual-spatial Skills section of the NDS.

Boyd's deficient scores on Part B of the Trail Making Test (72 sec) and the Coding subtest (4) of the WISC-R demonstrated his impairment in the area of abstraction, reasoning, and logical analysis. He earned 7 points on this section of the NDS, a score which exceeds the mean of 6.03 for brain-damaged children.

These findings indicate quite clearly that Boyd had difficulties which pervaded each of the areas and levels of central processing. On the Motor Functions and Sensory-perceptual Functions sections of the NDS Boyd earned scores that were closer to the means for controls than the average for brain-damaged subjects. However, as we will indicate below in the more detailed analysis of the test results, Boyd's difficulties on certain of these tests contributed to the impression of lateralized cerebral dysfunction. Boyd's score of 17 on the Right-Left Differences section of the NDS reflected these problems in summarical form. On this section control children average 6.79 points and brain-damaged children average 13.74 points.

In summary, Boyd's total score of 56 points on the NDS well exceeds the cut-off of 43/44 points, indicating that his overall performances clearly fell in the brain-damaged range (despite the fact that he was 14 years of age when he was given the Battery and the normative data was based upon performances across the entire 9-year through 14-year age range).

Clinical Evaluation of the Test Results. As we have cautioned frequently, the formalized aspect of analysis of the test results using the NDS should never be a substitute for clinical organization and interpretation of the test results.

In clinical interpretation we would note initially that Boyd's IQ values were clearly below the 50th percentile, and that the scaled scores for the individual subtests showed a striking degree of variability which might suggest some impairment. We also note, however, that the IQ scores are not out of the normal range, and by themselves do not necessarily indicate the presence of brain damage.

The results on the general neuropsychological measures indicated impairment of cognitive functioning. Except for the adequate score on the Category Test (43), Boyd showed clear evidence of impairment on Part A (45 sec) and Part B (72 sec) of the Trail Making Test, on all components of the Tactual Performance Test (including Total Time [10.5 min], Memory [4], and Localization [2]). The general indicators therefore definitely suggest that Boyd was experiencing a mild to moderate impairment of cerebral functioning.

This inference of impairment was firmly supported by indications of lateralized cerebral dysfunction. In finger tapping speed Boyd was definitely slow with his right hand (28) as compared with his left hand (35). He was also somewhat slow in the time required for name writing with his right hand (11 sec) as compared with his left hand (14 sec). On the Aphasia Screening Test Boyd demonstrated evidence of dyscalculia and right-left confusion, and produced marginal performances on a number of other items. In the context of the rest of the test scores, these findings would be considered to be valid indicators of left cerebral dysfunction.

The results were equally if not more striking concerning right cerebral involvement. On the Tactual Performance Test Boyd showed distinct difficulty with the left hand (5.1 min) as compared with the right hand (3.1 min), and on tactile finger localization he had more problems with his left hand (6) than his right hand (1). In addition, there were minor tendencies in the direction of impairment on the left side of the body in grip strength, bilateral simultaneous stimulation of the hands, and finger-tip number writing perception. The evidence of constructional dyspraxia would also be considered to be a right hemisphere indicator.

Summary and Recommendations

The overall findings of impaired brain functions are quite compatible with (and even suggestive of) a traumatic etiology. Some of the test results implicated the left cerebral hemisphere, whereas others indicated right cerebral hemisphere dysfunction. All of the deficits fell in a context of some degree of impairment on the general indicators. The adequacy of certain performances (such as the time required on the first and third trials of the TPT and the score on the Category Test) suggests that Boyd's cerebral damage is relatively stabilized and is probably chronic in nature. Adequate scores on a number of the subtests of the WISC-R indicate that Boyd had made reasonably satisfactory progress in developing certain aspects of general intelligence, a finding that also supports the hypothesis that the obvious neuropsychological deficits were acquired relatively recently rather than being representative of impairment sustained in early childhood.

The fact that impairment seems to be present (at least to a degree) in essentially all of the areas of neuropsychological functioning indicates that Boyd would require rather extensive cognitive rehabilitation in order to remediate his deficits. At the present time the principal challenge for Boyd probably relates to the academic area. He is definitely at risk for failing to understand instructions in the normal course of events and he needs individualized attention, such as that given in a special educational setting. However, it would be very important to avoid letting this special attention remove Boyd from the normal academic arena.

As many experienced neuropsychologists have learned, there are no simple or easy solutions to remediating the generalized kinds of deficits shown by this adolescent. As time goes by he will almost certainly need continuing assistance in the development of his academic abilities in order to successfully complete the equivalent of a high school education, and his results on the WRAT suggest that this possibility may already essentially have been lost.

Finally, we should note that the neuropsychological test results obtained in this case would be relatively characteristic and routine for a child classified as having a learning disability. Boyd had been making good progress academically until he sustained a head injury. It seems reasonable to conclude that the brain damage caused by the head injury is the factor responsible for the current set of problems.

In cases of learning disability the responsible factor(s) are usually not specifically identified; nevertheless, some type of biological interference with brain functions has probably occurred. The fact that the etiology may be established in one case but not in another does not change the essential nature of the neuropsychological impairment, the need for remediation, or the approaches that should be utilized to rehabilitate the individual with neuropsychological deficits.

With respect to litigation, Boyd's parents had retained a local lawyer and his partner, neither of whom had any experience in representing a child with possible brain injury. The defense had retained a large, experienced law firm, and it was apparent that Boyd's lawyer was intimidated by the prospect of facing such an opponent. Liability was not an issue, and the defendant's insurance was sufficient to cover a large judgement. However, Boyd's attorney was very apprehensive, because Boyd had improved since the accident. At the time of the neuropsychological testing Boyd had no medical signs or symptoms, and a competent and highly respected neurologist was prepared to testify that Boyd had made a full recovery.

The defense attorneys took a "discovery" deposition which explored the full range of possible weaknesses of neuropsychological findings. Questions were particularly focused on the published evidence for validity of the neuro-psychological tests as indicators of brain injury; the reasons we (as neuropsychologists) could know that Boyd had suffered any loss or impairment when we had no test findings obtained before the accident to use for comparisons; how we could possibly expect our test results to be accepted over the conclusion of the neurologist that Boyd had fully recovered; and the possibility that Boyd had deliberately performed poorly on the tests in order to affect the outcome of the litigation.

Following this day-long deposition that focused on the neuropsychological findings, the case was settled for an amount that was entirely satisfactory to Boyd, his parents, and his lawyer.

■

The Neuropsychology of Learning Disabilities

The field of learning disabilities has a long history, but recently there has been a large number of publications that have placed reading deficits and other learning disabilities squarely in the context of human neuropsychology. This development owes a great deal to the work of Doehring (1968), Rourke (1975), Knights and Bakker (1976), and Gaddes (1980). In this volume we will not try to review the extensive contributions to this area, and the interested reader is referred to the many publications available (e.g., Doehring, Trites, Patel, & Fiedorowicz, 1981; Duffy & Geschwind, 1985; Hynd, 1986; Kirk, 1983; Knights & Bakker, 1980; Pirozzolo, 1979; Pirozzolo & Wittrock, 1981; Rourke, 1981, 1985, 1989; Rourke, Bakker, Fisk, & Strang, 1983; Rourke, Fisk, & Strang, 1986; Rourke & Strang, 1983; Rutter, 1983; Spreen, Tupper, Risser, Tuokko, & Edgell, 1984).

The review below is obviously selective and related to the particular purposes of the present volume.

Theories and Subtypes of Learning Disability

A number of investigators have proposed theories to explain learning disabilities as well as subtypes of learning-disabled children. The majority of these theories are based upon two factors which relate to the differential specialized functions of the two cerebral hemispheres. Subtypes of learning disability have been defined according to various criteria, including relationships between measures of academic achievement (high arithmetic and low reading skills, low arithmetic and high reading skills, etc.), patterns of observed behavioral deficits, or patterns of neuropsychological test scores.

The problem with these approaches to learning disability is that they propose oversimplified theories or oversimplified criteria for identifying the subtypes. Most children with learning disabilities have neuropsychological deficits that represent complex and individualistic configurations rather than a particular pattern of test scores or behavioral manifestations that have been independently described.

Several points argue against the proposed theories or subtypes:

1. It is well recognized that the behavioral manifestations of impaired brain functions are extremely diversified, encompassing the full range of intellectual and cognitive abilities. In other words, it is clear that the biological condition of the brain is relevant to a very broad range of neuropsychological functions. This has been well established in a great number of studies.

2. Recent research (Reitan & Wolfson, 1988c and this volume; Rourke, 1975, 1985) has indicated that many learning-disabled children have a subtle form of impairment of neuropsychological abilities and, presumably, of brain functions. Most of these children do not show gross evidence of abnormality on the physical neurological examination. In the past there was a tendency to attribute poor academic performance to factors such as phobic reactions to the classroom and other types of emotional disturbances. The current trend is to recognize that a subtle form of impaired brain functions is probably more often a significant factor.

3. If learning disabilities are due principally to neuropsychological and brain-related deficits, and impairment of this type is broadly diversified, one would necessarily presume that the children who are found to have a learning disability have the types of deficits that are manifested in the classroom and limit academic progress. However, such deficits may be broad rather than specific, and affect learning abilities in diverse and subtle ways. They may not be strictly limited to verbal and language skills. In fact, Rourke (1989) has recently published a book on nonverbal learning disabilities.

It is not surprising that many brain-related abilities which do not explicitly involve verbal and language functions may affect learning aptitudes. We have found that difficulties with abstraction, reasoning, and logical analysis are fundamental and practically universal deficits among children classified as having learning disabilities (see Chapter VII). REHABIT, our cognitive retraining program, usually begins by training the individual child not with verbal and academic tasks, but in the area of abstraction and reasoning.

Many children with other types of impairment due to obvious or subtle impairment of brain functions presumably manage satisfactorily in academic situations because the nature of their impairment is not limiting in this particular respect. However, it must be recognized that basic academic skills are, in their own right, very complex both in their acquisition as well as their competent performance. Many investigators have identified reading as an extremely complex function, and one that, when impaired, could hardly be explained by postulating either discrete or selective neuropsychological deficits or a highly focal area of cerebral damage. Writing, spelling, and arithmetic skills appear to be equally complex types of abilities. Thus, each of these psychological functions may very well include a broad diversity of brain-related abilities.

4. The theories of learning disability are customarily two-factor propositions which relate to the differential or specialized functions of either the left or right cerebral hemisphere. Obviously, a two-factor theory would hardly be adequate to represent the complex neuropsychological functions that are involved in the broad range of abilities represented by academic skills. The subtypes of learning disabilities are customarily based upon observations of clinical deficits or upon relationships among either academic achievement or neuropsychological test scores.

Once again, the criteria defining subtypes of learning disability seem grossly oversimplified compared to either the complexity of most academic skills or the broad range of neuropsychological functions dependent upon the biological condition of the brain. This critique has been answered in part by Rourke (1989) in his recognition and exposition of nonverbal deficits as one basis for learning disabilities.

5. A review of the variables involved in learning disability, as they relate to the neuropsychological aspects of brain functions or the complexity of academic skills, suggests that a simplified set of relationships or criteria for categorization probably would be inadequate to characterize the individual learning-disabled child. It would seem likely that a host of neuropsychological deficits, in varying relationships and patterns, might be needed to characterize actual children with learning disorders.

6. Finally, it is important to consider the need for agreement in neuropsychological classification of learning disabilities and demonstration of learning disabilities in the classroom, in conjunction with the sequential aspect of biological and learning factors. The learning-disabled child presumably has had some kind of subtle biological disorder of brain functions which has precluded normal development of academic progress. In other words, the child becomes recognized as having a learning disability because of a pre-existing neuropsychological deficit represented by certain clinical characteristics or patterns of test results. If this premise is accepted, it becomes clear that for the classification to have practical meaning, these children must also demonstrate learning disabilities in the classroom. The requirements of the classroom situation, or the learning environment, must in effect be able to sort out or select children with specifically identified clinical symptoms or patterns among test scores.

If the child with specific neuropsychological clinical symptoms that supposedly served to diagnose learning

disability (or configurations of test scores that serve to identify subtypes of learning disability) is not identified as
learning-disabled in the classroom, these criteria would be
inadequate and of limited practical significance. In other
words, the end result in the practical classroom situation
must be the final test for validating the diagnosis.

Considering the complexity of academic subjects and
the diversity of neuropsychological deficits associated with
impaired brain functions, it seems unlikely that only children with specific sets of symptoms or specific patterns
among test scores would fail to make academic progress and
be classified as learning-disabled. In all probability the
learning requirements of the classroom, from one classroom
to the next, would not be sufficiently consistent to select and
classify the children who meet particular criteria for subtypes of learning disabilities. In other words, the children
who fall in various subtypes, according to neuropsychological criteria, would probably show overlapping rather than
distinctive differences in the classroom itself.

In practice, it is much more likely that learning-disabled
children will show a great diversity of neuropsychological
deficits, all of which, in various combinations, relate to limited academic aptitude and skill. If this is the case, one must
question how many actual children with learning disabilities will qualify for categorization according to one of the
theories or subtypes of learning disabilities that have been
proposed. If the theories do not apply to a significant number of the actual children with learning disabilities — or if a
significant proportion cannot be classified into existing subtypes — the theories and subtypes lose practical significance.

There would be little point, for example, in having a
diagnostic category of measles if the criteria for diagnosis
were not sufficiently specific to include all of the children
with measles and to exclude those without measles. If most
of the children with measles did not qualify for the diagnosis, one would wonder about the value of the diagnosis

except, possibly, as an intellectual exercise of some type. One must raise the same type of question about both theories and subtypes of learning disability that have been proposed.

Rourke (1985) offers an answer to this critique by suggesting that subtypes of learning disability represent a first step toward identifying the neuropsychological diversity and uniqueness of individual children with learning disabilities. If individual children fell validly in one subtype or another this would be true; however, extensive neuropsychological evaluation of the individual child frequently identifies him/her as sharing the features of several subtypes.

Assessment of Neuropsychological Impairment in Children with Learning Disabilities

Selz and Reitan (1979a) and Reitan and Wolfson (1988c) have shown that test results on the Halstead-Reitan Neuropsychological Test Battery for Older Children differentiate at significant levels between normal, learning-disabled, and brain-damaged children. The children with learning disabilities show impairment compared with most normal children, but considering all areas of neuropsychological functioning, they are not as consistently impaired as children with documented brain damage. Nevertheless, on the Halstead-Reitan Battery, children with learning disabilities show a great deal of neuropsychological diversity, defying the current attempts to define any but the most preliminary approaches to clinically meaningful subtypes.

Our comparisons of normal, learning-disabled and brain-damaged children have yielded a general insight into differences among these groups concerning a distinction between the so-called higher and lower behavioral correlates of brain function. Higher-level brain functions include the various aspects of central processing described in the

Reitan-Wolfson model. Lower-level behavioral correlates are represented principally by motor and sensory-perceptual abilities.

Non-brain-damaged (normal) children generally perform well on both higher and lower level tasks; children with documented brain damage perform more poorly in both areas. However, many children with learning disabilities demonstrate different levels of performance in these two areas. In general, they are able to perform relatively well on the lower level tasks, but show definite impairment on the higher level functions.

Thus, on sensory-perceptual and motor tasks (often including overall speed of performance of the complex motor skills required by the Tactual Performance Test), the learning-disabled children frequently approach the unimpaired performances of normal children, but perform almost as poorly as brain-damaged children on the higher level aspects of brain functions. We must emphasize, however, that even these broad categorizations represent only trends shown in group analyses, and often break down when applied to the individual child.

This generalization can be understood more completely when placed in the framework of the Reitan-Wolfson model of neuropsychological functioning. Learning-disabled children perform input (sensory-perceptual) and output (motor) tasks relatively well, but have difficulty with the higher level aspects of central processing (especially attention and concentration, verbal and language skills, and abstraction, logical analysis and reasoning, and in a few cases, even visual-spatial abilities). Individual learning-disabled children often show differential ability levels among these areas of central processing, and this fact further emphasizes the necessity of individual neuropsychological testing to obtain the information necessary for developing and prescribing appropriate procedures and emphases in cognitive retraining.

In terms of a highly practical assessment procedure, the reader should keep in mind that normal children rarely show any significant deficits on the Reitan-Indiana Aphasia Screening Test (see Chapter VII of this volume and Reitan, 1985). However, children with either brain damage or a learning disability regularly demonstrate deficient performances on the simple tasks included in this test. With information from the Aphasia Screening Test as a starting point and using the guidelines presented above, the results from the remainder of the Halstead-Reitan Battery for Older Children often provide a clear basis for differentiating between the child with definite brain damage and the learning-disabled child.

Case 18 — ROGER

Age:	10-6	**Gender:**	Male
Education:	4	**Handedness:**	Right

Background Information

Roger was being treated by a child psychiatrist as a result of a court order stemming from his behavioral problems. After ten months of therapy, the physician reported that Roger had shown no improvement at all in his destructive, aggressive behavior. In addition to demonstrating evidence of learning disability, the psychiatrist noted that Roger was malicious, had severe temper tantrums, and was considered to be potentially dangerous.

Roger's past behavioral problems had included breaking the windows in various homes in the neighborhood, spraying paint on a neighbor's house, and putting boards on the railroad tracks in an attempt to derail a train. In a recent incident in a local park, Roger apparently had attempted to molest a younger girl.

Roger's mother admitted that she received little support from her husband in raising the child, and that she was almost totally responsible for any discipline the child received. At this point she felt entirely unable to control her son's behavior. Thus, in addition to his difficulty making academic progress, Roger had a host of other behavioral problems, a situation not at all uncommon among children with learning disabilities. The neuropsychological results reported below are relevant not only in appreciating the bases of Roger's learning disability, but in understanding his behavioral problems as well.

Roger was reported to have experienced only the usual childhood illnesses. His EEG was within normal limits, and on the physical neurological examination he showed no evidence of significant abnormalities.

Neuropsychological Examination

The results of the examination with the HRB for Older Children were far from falling within the range of normal variation. From a neuropsychological point of view, the test results indicated that Roger had (1) impairment in a number of areas of function, (2) differences in performances on the two sides of the body that were somewhat greater than normally expected, and (3) indications of specific deficits that were even more pronounced than expected in the average brain-damaged child.

Roger's scores on academic achievement tests were well below the expected grade level, and on the Aphasia Screening Test he demonstrated specific deficits in his ability to deal with language symbols for communicational purposes. However, the information contributing the greatest insight to Roger's overall behavioral picture was the evidence of impairment in the area of abstraction, reasoning, logical analysis, and planning abilities, and we will discuss the importance of this finding below.

Wechsler Intelligence Scale for Children — Revised

Roger's scores on the WISC-R showed evidence of somewhat limited general intelligence. He earned a Verbal IQ of 86, a value that exceeded only 18% of his age peers. His Performance IQ of 92 exceeded 30%. These values yielded a Full Scale IQ of 88 that fell in the Low Average range and exceeded 21%.

The scaled scores for the Verbal subtests indicated that Roger had his lowest score (5) on the Arithmetic subtest. On the Performance subtests his lowest score (6) was on Picture Arrangement. However, it must be remembered that on the WISC-R the distribution of subtest scores cannot be used reliably to infer lateralization or localization of cerebral dysfunction in children. It should be noted that Roger was at or

The Halstead-Reitan Neuropsychological Test Battery for Older Children

Name: Roger Age: 10 – 6

Gender: M Education: 4 Handedness: RH 7 LH 0

Neuropsychological Deficit Scale (NDS) Summary

Level of Performance	Subject's score	Mean for controls	Mean for brain-damaged	Cut-off score
Motor Functions	10	6.29	14.05	
Sensory-perceptual Functions	10	5.15	10.77	
Attention and Concentration	5	1.91	3.78	
Immediate Memory and Recapitulation	3	2.23	3.31	
Visual-spatial Skills	6	4.06	7.69	
Abstraction, Reasoning, Logical Analysis	6	2.63	6.03	
Level of Performance–Total	40	22.27	45.63	33/34
Dysphasia and Related Variables	11	1.37	7.97	3/4
Right / Left Differences	8	6.79	13.74	9/10
Total NDS Score	59	30.43	67.34	43/44

WISC-R

VIQ 86
PIQ 92
FS IQ 88

Verbal Subtests

Information	9
Similarities	8
Arithmetic	5
Vocabulary	9
Comprehension	8
(Digit Span)	(6)

Performance Subtests

Picture Completion	10
Picture Arrangement	6
Block Design	11
Object Assembly	10
Coding	8
(Mazes)	(9)

WRAT

	Grade Equivalent
Reading	3.8
Arithmetic	3.6
Spelling	3.6

Strength of Grip

Dominant hand (R) 20.0 kg
Non-dominant hand (L) 17.5 kg

Name Writing

Dominant hand (R) 20 sec
Non-dominant hand (L) 49 sec

Category Test

Number of errors 85

Tactual Performance Test

Dominant hand (R) 4.2
Non-dominant hand (L) 3.2
Both hands 1.8

Total Time 9.2
Memory 4
Localization 3

Seashore Rhythm Test

Number correct 16 10

Speech-sounds Perception Test

Number of errors 16

Finger Tapping Test

Dominant hand (R) 36 36
Non-dominant hand (L) 35

Trail Making Test

Part A 25 sec 1 error(s)
Part B 41 sec 2 error(s)

Bilateral Simultaneous Sensory Stimulation

RH ___ LH ___	Both: RH ___ LH ___	
RH ___ LF ___	Both: RH 1 LF 1	
LH ___ RF ___	Both: LH 1 RF ___	
RE ___ LE ___	Both: RE ___ LE ___	
RV ___ LV ___	Both: RV ___ LV ___	
___ 1	2 2	

Tactile Finger Recognition

RH 1 ___ 2 1 3 2 4 1 5 ___   RH 4 / 20
LH 1 ___ 2 ___ 3 1 4 1 5 ___   LH 2 / 20

Finger-Tip Number Writing

RH 1 2 2 ___ 3 ___ 4 2 5 1   RH 5 / 20
LH 1 2 2 1 3 ___ 4 ___ 5 1   LH 4 / 20

Tactile Form Recognition Test

Dominant hand (R) 10 sec 0 error(s)
Non-dominant hand (L) 10 sec 0 error(s)

.eitan-Indiana Aphasia
creening Test

'm for Adults and Older Children

Name <u>Roger</u>   Age <u>10 – 6</u>

Copy SQUARE	Repeat TRIANGLE
Name SQUARE	Repeat MASSACHUSETTS
Spell SQUARE S - Q - U - R	Repeat METHODIST EPISCOPAL *Mesodis Episopal*
Copy CROSS	Write SQUARE
Name CROSS	Read SEVEN
Spell CROSS	Repeat SEVEN
Copy TRIANGLE	Repeat/Explain HE SHOUTED THE WARNING
Name TRIANGLE *Rectangle - - I mean, triangle*	Write HE SHOUTED THE WARNING
Spell TRIANGLE T - R - I - A - C - L	Compute $85 - 27 = 85$ $75 - 48 = 37$ $22 - 16 = 6$
Name BABY	Compute $17 \times 3 =$ $17 \times 3 = 61$ $12 \times 5 = 70$ $8 \times 4 = 42$ $2 \times 3 = 6$
Write CLOCK	Name KEY
Name FORK	Demonstrate use of KEY
Read 7 SIX 2	Draw KEY
Read MGW	Read PLACE LEFT HAND TO RIGHT EAR
Reading I *. . . back dog . . . self-corrected*	Place LEFT HAND TO RIGHT EAR *S was slow to respond, then placed right hand to left ear.*
Reading II *. . . of the - - of dog shows.*	Place LEFT HAND TO LEFT ELBOW *S placed right hand to left elbow, then tried right hand to right elbow.*

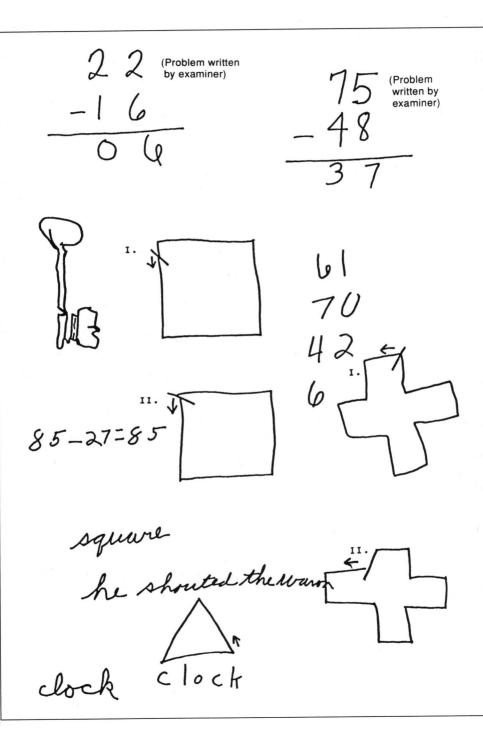

approached the average level on a number of the subtests; therefore, the results on the WISC-R would hardly be sufficient to account for the range and types of problems that he demonstrated.

Wide Range Achievement Test

We administered the WRAT to obtain an overview of Roger's academic progress. At the time of the examination he was in the latter part of the fifth grade, and his expected level of academic competence would be about 5.8 grades. On the WRAT he earned the following grade-equivalents: Reading, 3.8; Spelling, 3.6; Arithmetic, 3.6. It is clear from these results that Roger had not made progress even approaching the level expected of a normal child.

Neuropsychological Examination

Roger's IQ levels do not appear to be sufficiently low to account for such a definite indication of academic retardation, and these kinds of observations contributed to the decision to refer him for a neuropsychological evaluation. The child psychiatrist treating Roger recognized the presence of significant problems in the areas of academic achievement as well as social behavior. He found no evidence of environmental or neurological problems that appeared to be sufficiently severe to account for the child's difficulties, and thus referred Roger for neuropsychological examination. As we will discuss below, the comprehensive neuropsychological examination yielded findings that provided a basis for understanding Roger's learning disorder as well as his behavioral problems.

Halstead-Reitan Neuropsychological Test Battery

Neuropsychological Deficit Scale. An analysis of the test results using the NDS for Older Children identifies Roger's neuropsychological strengths and weaknesses. He earned a total NDS score of 59, a value that falls well above the cut-off score of 43/44. This finding would indicate that in an overall sense Roger's performances were significantly impaired.

Reference to the individual sections of the NDS indicates that in most instances Roger performed more like the brain-damaged subjects than the normal control children. On the Motor Functions section he earned a total of 10 points, a value somewhat below the mean of 14.05 points for brain-damaged subjects. His performances were within the normal range on finger-tapping speed, grip strength, and Total Time for the Tactual Performance Test, but he performed poorly with each hand on the Name Writing Test.

Roger's score of 10 on the Sensory-perceptual Functions section closely approximated the mean score of 10.77 earned by brain-damaged subjects. On tests of bilateral simultaneous sensory perception he showed evidence of significant impairment. He had particular difficulty on finger localization (6 errors) and finger-tip number writing perception (9 errors).

Roger's score of 6 on the NDS section concerned with visual-spatial skills was intermediate to the mean for controls (4.06) and brain-damaged subjects (7.69). It should also be noted that he performed poorly on the Picture Arrangement subtest of the WISC-R, earning a score of 6.

Roger's performances on measures in the Attention and Concentration section earned him a score of 5, which is somewhat worse than the mean of the average brain-damaged subject (3.78). Research has shown that impairment in this area is not unusual among children with learning disabilities (see Chapter VII). Roger also performed almost as poorly as the average brain-damaged subject on the two measures in the Immediate Memory and Recapitulation section. This suggests that he does not do particularly well when required to reconstruct the stimulus dimensions of tasks to which he previously has been exposed.

As we have already noted, Roger performed much more poorly than the average control child on the Abstraction, Reasoning, and Logical Analysis section of the NDS. He earned a score of 6 points on this section, almost exactly at the mean of 6.03 for brain-damaged children. Although his score of 8 on the Coding subtest of the WISC-R was adequate, he scored in the impaired range on both Part B of the Trail Making Test (41 sec) and the Category Test (85 errors). His scores yielded a total of 40 points for the Level of Performance section of the NDS, which compares with a mean of 22.27 points for control children and a mean of 45.63 points for children with documented brain damage.

On the Dysphasia and Related Variables section Roger performed very poorly, earning a score of 11 points (as compared with average scores of 1.37 for control children and 7.97 for brain-damaged children). As we have noted before, on this section of the NDS it is not unusual for children with learning disabilities to perform as poorly as children with documented cerebral disease or damage.

These results of the NDS make it quite clear that Roger's scores were much worse than those of normal children. A starting point in understanding this child's difficulties is to recognize that he has significant neuropsychological impairment that extends over a broad area of behavioral abilities dependent upon brain functions.

Clinical Evaluation of the Test Results. The next step in assessing Roger's neuropsychological status requires a review of his performances on specific tests. First, he performed poorly on both the Rhythm Test (16 correct) and the Speech-sounds Perception Test (16 errors), indicating that the first level of central processing (attention and concentration) is at least moderately compromised. In other words, Roger appears to have a basic problem in perceiving and registering simple incoming stimuli. Undoubtedly, this constitutes a significant deficit, at least in terms of certain areas of function.

On other measures Roger showed variable results. He performed poorly on some tasks that required simple cognitive skills, and showed quite variable performances on more complex cognitive tasks. For example, Roger showed a definite tendency to fail to perceive simple stimuli when administered to each side of the body simultaneously. These results were not of lateralizing significance, because they tended to occur nearly as frequently on the left side of the body as on the right side, but it is noteworthy that Roger had problems perceiving even the most simple stimuli.

Roger also had much more difficulty than would normally be expected in tactile finger localization, but in this case he made more mistakes on the right hand (4) than on the left hand (2). In finger-tip number writing perception he also had a significant degree of difficulty. Once again, the critical point of information is that Roger demonstrated a striking degree of confusion in registering and understanding even simple incoming stimuli.

Analyzing Roger's performances on more complex tasks, we see that on the Tactual Performance Test he performed quite well, both in terms of the Total Time (9.2 min) and the Localization component (3). Scores with each hand, which measured the functional status of the right and left upper extremities, also were in the normal relationship. Roger's score of 4 on the Memory component showed that although he did have some difficulty on this component of the TPT, it would appear that his performances on this test were among the best that he demonstrated.

Roger performed quite poorly on complex problem-solving tasks that required abstraction and reasoning, but in which the motor response component was not limiting (Category Test and Part B of the Trail Making Test). Roger's poor score (85) on the Category Test indicates that he is significantly impaired in his ability to analyze situations, recognize relationships, draw inferences from his observations, and utilize cause-and-effect reasoning. This type of deficit is almost certainly of major significance in understanding his deviant behavior and the apparently incorrigible nature of this problem.

In fact, the combination of adequate psychomotor skills (shown on the TPT as well as finger tapping speed) and the poor Category Test score suggests that Roger can use his hands quite effectively for completing even relatively complex tasks, but that these skills do not have the advantage of being tempered by balanced judgment or an appreciation of cause-and-effect consequences. Thus, the relationship between the test scores provides a considerable degree of insight about Roger's impaired cognitive structure, which in turn predisposes him to behave in socially unacceptable ways.

Roger's specific difficulties in dealing with symbolic material in the language area were quite evident. On the Aphasia Screening Test he showed distinct evidence of deficits in spelling ability, manifesting a striking tendency to neglect the sound of the letters selected for spelling the word. This was clearly shown in his omission of the A in his attempt to spell SQUARE and his spelling of TRIANGLE as T-R-I-A-C-L. He showed a tendency toward dysnomia when he initially identified the triangle as a rectangle. The reading deficiencies he demonstrated on both the first and second reading items were not gross errors, but they did demonstrate that Roger had limited ability in this area. Although he tended to slur his enunciation of METHODIST

EPISCOPAL (and the result is mildly suggestive of impairment), we did not give him any points for this particular item on the NDS.

Roger also demonstrated confusion in performing simple arithmetical calculations. We did not count the mistakes on 75 − 48, 17 × 3, 12 × 5, or 8 × 4 as definite indications of dyscalculia, but when he recorded "85" as his answer to 85 − 27 =, we concluded that he was definitely impaired in his ability to understand simple arithmetical relationships. One might attribute this latter error to a perseverative tendency, since he had just written "85" in the problem initially; however, regardless of the reason, the error must be viewed as a basic deficit in understanding arithmetical relationships. Finally, Roger showed evidence of right-left confusion. All of these deficits in performance are quite characteristic of children with learning disabilities.

Roger also demonstrated difficulty in dealing with simple spatial configurations. His first drawing of the cross was marginal, but his second attempt demonstrated a type of distortion of the configuration characteristic of persons with brain damage. (Note the disparity of the lateral extremities that goes beyond acceptable limits.)

The most convincing demonstration of Roger's deficit in visual-spatial relationships was in his drawing of the key. The notches in the stem close to the handle are not symmetrical and constitute one indication of impaired brain functions. The most important indication, however, related to the notches near the teeth of the key and a failure to connect the teeth to the stem. This particular manifestation of confusion is almost a certain indication of impaired brain functions.

An assessment of the lateralizing indicators suggests that Roger's left cerebral hemisphere is more dysfunctional than his right hemisphere. Left hemisphere indicators included the evidence of dysphasic deficits and a greater impairment of tactile finger localization on the right hand (4) than on the left hand (2). In addition, Roger was scarcely any faster in finger tapping with his right (preferred) hand (36) than with his left hand (35). Thus, a series of deficits was present to implicate the left cerebral hemisphere, and fell in the context of a range of general indicators of impaired brain functions.

The only findings to implicate the right cerebral hemisphere were (1) evidence of constructional dyspraxia (deficits in drawing the cross and key, as well as the planning error on the first square that resulted in a problem of closure), and (2) a failure to perceive a tactile stimulus to the left hand when it was given simultaneously with a stimulus to the right face. This latter error, however, must be viewed in the context of a number of scattered errors on both tactile and visual tests of bilateral simultaneous stimulation.

Summary and Recommendations

Even though the findings from the physical neurological examination were in the normal range, neuropsychological results of this kind are quite characteristic of brain dysfunction. There appears to be no doubt that Roger has significant impairment of brain-related abilities that is manifested not only by general indicators, but also by specific indicators that implicate both the right and left cerebral hemispheres. It is clear that he has impairment in both receptive (sensory-perceptual) and expressive (motor) functions as well as deficits at all levels of central processing.

As we noted, Roger is impaired in attention, concentration, and the ability to register even simple material at the cortical level. His poor performances on the Aphasia Screening Test document the significant deficits he has in dealing with verbal and language symbols for communicational purposes. Evidence of constructional dyspraxia, manifested by the types of errors made in his drawings (and probably supplemented by the low Picture Arrangement score) all point toward deficits in the area of visual-spatial skills.

Finally, Roger demonstrated a critical deficit by his poor score on the Category Test. His inability to do well on this test demonstrates a serious impairment of abstraction, reasoning, logical analysis, and planning abilities. This deficit almost certainly underlies Roger's erratic, impulsive, socially inappropriate behavior, and clearly implies that he is unlikely to change these behaviors until he gains an ability to understand his actions and their consequences. As with the great majority of children with learning disabilities, the basic problems Roger is demonstrating are neuropsychological in nature rather than medical (neurological).

The best approach toward remediating Roger's deficits would be to use REHABIT to provide training in the areas of his deficits and thus establish a normal neuropsychological ability structure. As his results on the Halstead-Reitan Battery have demonstrated, his cognitive deficits are rather widespread and relate to all levels of neuropsychological functioning. However, since he showed such significant difficulties in the area of abstraction and reasoning, initially it would be important to teach Roger how to approach problems in an organized manner, and to develop his basic problem-solving capabilities before beginning training with more specific subject matter.

We would begin Roger's cognitive rehabilitation program by using items from Track C, giving special emphasis to the attention, concentration, and memory types of procedures that can be built into these tasks. This type of approach would have two particular objectives: (1) to teach Roger to pay closer attention to the stimulus material that he observes, and (2) to educate Roger about the ways that cues can be used to determine the organization of material.

For example, one of the REHABIT items consists of simple material for stringing wooden beads that vary in size, shape and color. We know that Roger has the motor skills to string beads easily; however, based on his score on the Category Test, it is almost certain that he would have difficulty understanding meaningful sequences and the organization of stimulus material according to the different variables of shape, size, color, and position. Thus, one important way to use this material would be to teach Roger to arrange the beads according to principles relating to shape or color or size (or a combination of these variables), to verbalize the principles, and to reproduce the configuration at a later time using the principle that he previously had learned. This same type of training activity can be applied with many of the items in Track C and D because of their emphasis on sorting, classification, and organization.

After extensive training with items from Track C, we would recommend using tasks concerned with sequential arrangement of pictures. A number of items in Track D would provide this training and extend from simple to very complex arrangements. We would emphasize this type of training particularly for Roger because of his poor score on the Picture Arrangement subtest of the WISC-R. Items included in Track E may be used to develop skills in expressive aspects of simple drawing, and Roger should also receive practice with such items as well.

We would then move to Track B for the next set of training exercises. It is important to remember that it is necessary to go back and forth among the Tracks as the training experiences develop in order to effect integration of abilities. In terms of the general sequence of retraining Roger, we would use items from Track B to relate abstraction and reasoning abilities to verbal stimulus material.

Finally, it was clear that Roger had very limited abilities in reading, spelling and arithmetic. Many of the items in Track A emphasize the development of academic skills and would be appropriate for Roger. He needs to start by developing familiarity with phonics, and then progress to word-building exercises, sentence building, and eventually reading. Roger also appears to need training in understanding numerical relationships, and may need additional teaching in specific and rote arithmetical exercises. A number of items designed to develop such abilities are included in Tracks A and B, and include tasks that teach the concept of fractions in terms of relationships to a whole configuration.

While we have recited a sequence of training procedures, it is important to keep in mind that a child with neuropsychological deficits such as those shown by Roger frequently appears to have mastered a task at one time only to demonstrate striking regression at a later point. Therefore, it is always important to rehearse and review the skills that have recently been developed, recognizing that they are not established as well for a child with neuropsychological impairment as they would be for a child with normal brain functions.

It is also important to note that our approach to cognitive remediation involved academic subject matter toward the end of the training procedure rather than at the beginning. Basically, we postulate that children like Roger are impaired in certain fundamental respects that interfere with their ability to learn academic skills, and that the neuropsychological prerequisite abilities must be developed before the academic training can hope to be successful.

In the existing school situation much effort had been expended attempting to teach Roger academic skills, but because his basic neuropsychological deficits had not been identified, there was no attempt to remediate these problems. A comprehensive neuropsychological examination was able to identify these critical basic aspects of impaired brain function which must be addressed in order to deal with the overall problem. In addition, it is likely that training in the area of abstraction, reasoning, and logical analysis will constitute a much more appropriate approach to Roger's behavioral problems than the conventional therapeutic procedures in the area of child psychiatry.

The neuropsychological deficits described above defined the basic nature of Roger's problems even though other diagnostic approaches had been noncontributory. It therefore seems only reasonable that the remediation would relate to Roger's neuropsychological deficits rather than to approaches that were not of demonstrated relevance.

■

Case 19 — STEVE

Age:	10-5	Gender:	Male
Education:	3	Handedness:	Right

Background Information

Steve was referred for a neuropsychological examination by his pediatric neurologist, who had performed a comprehensive neurological examination but could not find any medical basis for the child's behavioral and academic achievement problems. Although we are presenting Steve as a child with a rather characteristic pattern of neuropsychological test results relating to learning disability, the difficulties which led to his evaluation were identified as behavioral disorders that occurred primarily in the classroom.

Although we were unable to learn many specific details, we did know that Steve had an unfortunate early childhood. Steve's father had a history of committing minor crimes and was in prison when Steve was born. Steve's mother led a somewhat erratic lifestyle and deserted Steve when he was three years old. After living in foster homes for a year, Steve was adopted shortly after his fourth birthday. Steve's adoptive parents soon noted that he seemed to be rather undisciplined, easily angered, and resistive to suggestion or direction. These behavior and personality characteristics had continued until the present time and appeared to be getting worse.

Steve's adoptive mother had worked very diligently with him to develop his reading skills, but both she and Steve's teachers had noted that the child was becoming increasingly resistive to academic instructions. In many instances his actions were overtly hostile and defiant. Steve's unmanageable behavior was reaching significant proportions, and he was referred for a neurological evaluation as well as assessment and treatment in a child guidance clinic. Steve would probably have been treated only for emotional problems of adjustment if his pediatric neurologist had not been aware of the relevance of neuropsychological examination for children with these types of problems.

Neuropsychological Examination

When we administered the Lateral Dominance Examination, we found that Steve was one of the few children who showed evidence of mixed dominance on the seven-item questionnaire. He performed four of the tasks with his left hand and three of the tasks (including name writing) with his right hand; he therefore met the criterion for testing as a right-handed child. The evidence of Steve's mixed dominance should be borne in mind when interpreting the test results, because he might not be expected to perform as much better with his right hand than with his left hand compared with most strongly right-handed children.

Wechsler Intelligence Scale for Children — Revised

Steve's results on the WISC-R were not remarkable. He earned a Verbal IQ of 95, a value that falls in the lower part of the Average range and exceeds about 37% of his age peers. His Performance IQ of 90 exceeded 25%. The overall results yielded a Full Scale IQ of 91, which falls in the lower part of the Average range and exceeds about 27%.

The scaled scores for the individual subtests showed no striking areas of deficit. The lowest score of 7 was earned on the Comprehension, Block Design, Object Assembly, and Mazes subtests. Interestingly, Steve had a score of 10 on Information and a score of 12 on Vocabulary. Thus, the pattern of scores on the WISC-R was not particularly suggestive of learning disability, although we must note that in

The Halstead-Reitan Neuropsychological Test Battery for Older Children

Name: Steve Age: 10 – 5
Gender: M Education: 3 Handedness: RH 3 LH 4

Neuropsychological Deficit Scale (NDS) Summary

Level of Performance	Subject's score	Mean for controls	Mean for brain-damaged	Cut-off score
Motor Functions	9	6.29	14.05	
Sensory-perceptual Functions	13	5.15	10.77	
Attention and Concentration	3	1.91	3.78	
Immediate Memory and Recapitulation	4	2.23	3.31	
Visual-spatial Skills	5	4.06	7.69	
Abstraction, Reasoning, Logical Analysis	5	2.63	6.03	
Level of Performance–Total	39	22.27	45.63	33/34
Dysphasia and Related Variables	8	1.37	7.97	3/4
Right/Left Differences	11	6.79	13.74	9/10
Total NDS Score	58	30.43	67.34	43/44

WISC-R

VIQ 95
PIQ 90
FS IQ 91

Verbal Subtests		Performance Subtests	
Information	10	Picture Completion	11
Similarities	8	Picture Arrangement	9
Arithmetic	9	Block Design	7
Vocabulary	12	Object Assembly	7
Comprehension	7	Coding	9
(Digit Span)	(9)	(Mazes)	(7)

WRAT

	Grade Equivalent
Reading	5.5
Arithmetic	3.2
Spelling	3.5

Strength of Grip

Dominant hand (R) 13.5 kg
Non-dominant hand (L) 14.0 kg

Name Writing

Dominant hand (R) 9 sec
Non-dominant hand (L) 22 sec

Category Test

Number of errors 77

Tactual Performance Test

Dominant hand (R) 3.4
Non-dominant hand (L) 4.6
Both hands 1.9
Total Time 9.9
Memory 5
Localization 0

Seashore Rhythm Test

Number correct 26 5

Speech-sounds Perception Test

Number of errors 11

Finger Tapping Test

Dominant hand (R) 32 32
Non-dominant hand (L) 32

Trail Making Test

Part A 13 sec 0 error(s)
Part B 49 sec 1 error(s)

Bilateral Simultaneous Sensory Stimulation

RH___ LH___ Both: RH___ LH___
RH___ LF___ Both: RH _1_ LF___
LH___ RF___ Both: LH___ RF___

RE___ LE___ Both: RE___ LE___

RV___ LV___ Both: RV___ LV___

Tactile Finger Recognition

RH 1___ 2_1_ 3_1_ 4_2_ 5_1_ RH 5/20
LH 1___ 2_2_ 3_2_ 4_1_ 5___ LH 5/20

Finger-Tip Number Writing

RH 1___ 2_2_ 3_1_ 4___ 5_1_ RH 4/20
LH 1_2_ 2_2_ 3_1_ 4_1_ 5_1_ LH 7/20

Tactile Form Recognition Test

Dominant hand (R) 11 sec 0 error(s)
Non-dominant hand (L) 8 sec 1 error(s)
Δ for □

Reitan-Indiana Aphasia Screening Test

Form for Adults and Older Children

Name <u>Steve</u>   Age <u>10 − 5</u>

Copy SQUARE	Repeat TRIANGLE
Name SQUARE	Repeat MASSACHUSETTS
Spell SQUARE S - Q - A - R - E	Repeat METHODIST EPISCOPAL *Mebidis Etisible*
Copy CROSS	Write SQUARE
Name CROSS	Read SEVEN
Spell CROSS C - R - O - O - S	Repeat SEVEN
Copy TRIANGLE	Repeat/Explain HE SHOUTED THE WARNING *Well, like he told somebody something.*
Name TRIANGLE	Write HE SHOUTED THE WARNING
Spell TRIANGLE T - R - I - N - A - G - L	Compute $85 - 27 =$
Name BABY	Compute $17 \times 3 = 20$ $6 \times 7 =$ *(S unable to do)* $5 \times 4 = 20$
Write CLOCK *See writing of "clook"*	Name KEY
Name FORK	Demonstrate use of KEY
Read 7 SIX 2	Draw KEY
Read MGW	Read PLACE LEFT HAND TO RIGHT EAR
Reading I	Place LEFT HAND TO RIGHT EAR *S placed left hand to left ear, then self-corrected.*
Reading II	Place LEFT HAND TO LEFT ELBOW

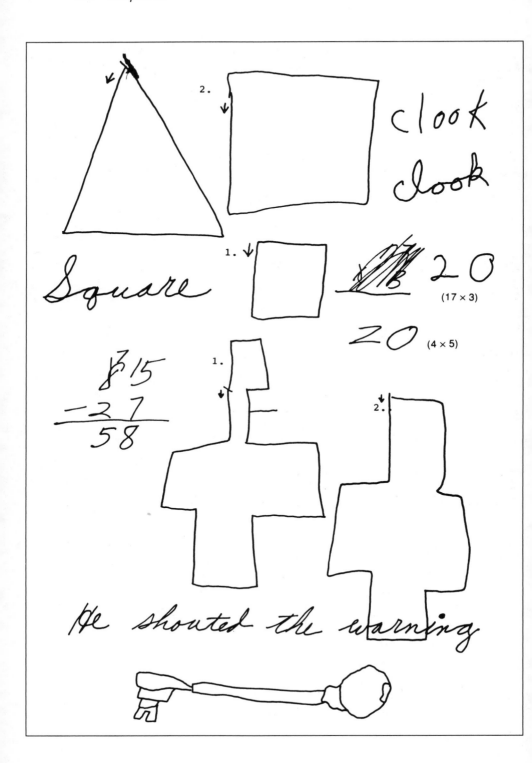

our experience with learning-disabled children the distribution of WISC-R subtests scores does not always fit any particular pattern.

Wide Range Achievement Test

At the time of this neuropsychological examination Steve was nearing the end of the fourth grade. He was older than the other children in his class because he had been required to repeat the third grade. Steve's teachers indicated that he was making variable progress; his reading and writing seemed to be progressing fairly well, but he was having definite difficulty in spelling and arithmetic. On the WRAT Steve earned the following grade-equivalents: Reading, 5.5; Spelling, 3.5; and Arithmetic, 3.2. Considering the history information, it seemed likely that Steve's progress in word recognition was largely due to the training efforts of his adoptive mother.

The Halstead-Reitan Neuropsychological Test Battery

Neuropsychological Deficit Scale. Evaluating Steve's performances on the HRB for Older Children by using the NDS revealed critical information. The Level of Performance section yielded a score of 39, a value that exceeds the cut-off score of 33/34 and falls in the range characteristic of brain-damaged performances. Steve's score of 11 points on the Right-Left Differences section exceeds the cut-off of 9/10, and is intermediate to the mean score of 6.79 earned by control children and the mean of 13.74 produced by brain-damaged subjects. Steve did very poorly on the Dysphasia and Related Variables section, earning a score of 8 and exceeding the cut-off of 3/4. Control children usually have very little difficulty with the performances required in this section, and earn a mean score of 1.37 (as compared with a mean of 7.97 for brain-damaged children). Steve's total

NDS score of 58 points fell in the brain-damaged range and was well above the cut-off score of 43/44.

These scores represent another instance in which the validity and usefulness of using only conventional medical criteria, based upon the history and various aspects of the neurological evaluation, must be brought into question. Despite the fact that medical information had classified Steve as normal, there is no doubt that this child had significant neuropsychological impairment. This set of circumstances occurs very commonly among children with learning problems, and it is imperative that these children are recognized as brain-impaired even though they have only inferential evidence of cerebral dysfunction. These procedural considerations often have definite significance concerning treatment approaches and eventual outcome. Steve had been referred to a child guidance clinic because of his apparent emotional problems; in reality his difficulties clearly related to his significant neuropsychological deficits.

A review of the areas of function within the Level of Performance section of the NDS indicates that Steve had rather generalized deficits. His score of 9 on the tests comprising the Motor Functions section was intermediate to the mean of 6.29 for control children and the mean of 14.05 for brain-damaged children. Steve's score of 13 on the Sensory-perceptual Functions section was well above the average score of 10.77 points for brain-damaged children. On the Visual-spatial Skills section Steve earned 5 points, just above the mean of 4.06 for control children. In the area of Attention and Concentration he earned 3 points, a score that is intermediate to the means of controls (1.91) and brain-damaged children (3.78). Steve's score of 4 on the Immediate Memory and Recapitulation section was just slightly greater than the mean of 3.31 for brain-damaged subjects. Steve's particularly poor raw score of 0 on the Localization component of the Tactual Performance Test contributed significantly to his high score on this section.

Finally, in the area of abstraction, reasoning, and logical analysis skills, Steve scored 5 points, performing nearly as poorly as brain-damaged children (6.03). A very deficient performance on the Category Test (77 errors) and a relatively poor performance on Part B of the Trail Making Test (49 sec) contributed to his high score in this area.

In terms of a general assessment of the test results, we would summarize by saying that Steve performed best on the Reading (word recognition) test of the WRAT and showed evidence of mild to serious impairment in all other areas of cognitive performances.

Clinical Evaluation of the Test Results. Clinical analysis of the complete set of test results indicates that Steve has generalized as well as lateralized cerebral dysfunction. He performed relatively well on the Seashore Rhythm Test (26 correct), and did well enough on the Speech-sounds Perception Test (11 errors) to indicate that his ability to concentrate over time and his basic alertness skills were sufficient to allow him to perform satisfactorily on other neuropsychological measures. Therefore, poor performances on other tests are not attributable to impairment at the first level of central processing (attention and concentration). Steve also did relatively well on the Total Time of the TPT (9.9 min), indicating that even under adverse conditions (blindfolded) he has the ability to use his hands effectively to perform a complex task.

Steve also did well on Part A of the Trail Making Test (13 sec), further demonstrating a satisfactory degree of alertness and quickness in his responses. However, he had significant difficulty when the tasks became more complicated and involved an element of abstract reasoning or flexibility in thought processes. As we noted above, he did somewhat poorly on Part B of the Trail Making Test (49 sec) and showed evidence of significant impairment on the Category Test (77 errors). This latter result indicates that Steve had considerable difficulty in drawing meaningful conclusions from his observations, a type of problem that almost certainly suggests that he needs intensive training in learning how to learn.

In addition to the indications of generalized impairment, Steve also demonstrated neuropsychological deficits related to the function of the left cerebral hemisphere. His performance on both motor and sensory-perceptual tasks as well as his use of language and related symbols revealed a certain amount of difficulty. Steve was no faster in finger tapping speed with his right hand (32) than with his left hand (32), and had somewhat less grip strength in his right upper extremity (13.5 kg) than in his left upper extremity (14.0 kg). It should be noted, though, that the failure to demonstrate greater ability with his right upper extremity may have been attenuated by his strong tendency toward ambidexterity.

However, Steve also showed some mild difficulties in tactile perception on the right side, a finding which would not relate to lateral dominance. He made one mistake on the right hand when a stimulus was delivered simultaneously with the left face. On the Tactile Form Recognition Test he also required a little more time with his right hand (11 sec) than his left hand (8 sec). Although he made one mistake with his left hand on this test, the error represented confusion between the triangle and the square, a mistake which sometimes occurs when the subject tries to perform the task very quickly.

The errors Steve made on the Aphasia Screening Test were quite characteristic of the types of problems demonstrated by children with learning disabilities as well as by brain-damaged children. As we have remarked previously, these two groups of children do not differ significantly in their performances on the Aphasia Screening Test (Reitan, 1985); however, both groups are very sharply differentiated from control children, who make very few (if any) errors on this test.

Note that Steve demonstrated a distinct limitation of his spelling ability. He omitted the U in SQUARE, used two O's instead of two S's in spelling CROSS, wrote CLOOK for CLOCK, and confused the sequence of letters by spelling TRIANGLE as T-R-I-N-A-G-L. When asked to repeat METHODIST EPISCOPAL Steve responded Mebidis Etisible. The confusion of the consonant sound B for TH in Methodist and T for P in Episcopal, together with the omission of the hard C sound, appears to constitute enough of an enunciation problem to merit scoring of central dysarthria on the NDS.

Steve appeared to have some rote ability in simple arithmetical calculations, and was able to perform $85 - 27 =$ correctly. Although he also was able to give the correct answer to the problem 5×4, he had no idea of how to solve somewhat more complex multiplication problems, such as 6×7. When asked to multiply 17×3 he responded "20." This answer frequently is given by children with basic difficulties in dealing with arithmetical processes, and appears to represent confusion between addition and multiplication. Finally, although he corrected himself, Steve demonstrated evidence of mild right-left confusion. Considered in total, these findings appear to be quite sufficient to imply a degree of dysfunction of the left cerebral hemisphere.

As is true with most children who have learning deficits, Steve demonstrated specific positive findings indicating impairment of each cerebral hemisphere as well as general neuropsychological deficits. There were several performances implicating dysfunction of the right cerebral hemisphere. On the Tactual Performance Test Steve performed more slowly with his left hand (4.6 min) than with his right hand (3.4 min), but the overall performance (9.9 min) was adequate. In finger-tip number writing perception he also had significantly more difficulty with his left hand (7 errors) than with his right hand (4 errors).

Finally, Steve demonstrated evidence of constructional dyspraxia in his first attempts to copy the shape of a cross. His deficit in the first drawing was quite apparent. Although his second attempt was somewhat better, he clearly failed to achieve symmetry of the vertical and horizontal extremities. Even his second attempt to copy the shape of a square demonstrated some difficulty in dealing with simple spatial configurations. It is obvious that when it was time to close the figure Steve discovered that he was well above his starting point, and he needed to make a downward adjustment to compensate for the prior misjudgment and achieve closure.

Summary and Recommendations

The test results demonstrate clearly that Steve has a broad range of neuropsychological problems that extend far beyond the specific tasks involved in academic performances. We often find that the learning-disabled child's neuropsychological deficits are not limited to the academic area. In fact, we would identify Steve's basic and most debilitating problem as impairment in the area of abstraction, reasoning, and logical analysis skills. He clearly needs to learn how to learn before he can proceed effectively to master the more specific kinds of abilities that are required for adequate academic performances. He obviously has made some progress in developing word recognition skills (apparently through his adoptive mother's tutelage), but he still has striking language-related deficits. Note that although these deficits are pronounced, they are probably no worse than his difficulty in visual-spatial skills (as demonstrated particularly by his first attempt to copy the cross).

The major reason that Steve was referred for professional evaluation was his misbehavior (especially in the classroom) and his increasing hostility and even defiance directed toward the academic situation. It is apparent that

Steve would have much more difficulty in developing academic skills than most children with his IQ values, and that the special problems he was experiencing, probably in the face of expectations from both his teachers and parents, would engender a degree of resentment. His behavioral difficulties would therefore appear to relate, at least in part, to the conflict implicit in the situation and the lack of understanding of Steve's neuropsychological deficits.

Considering his neuropsychological ability pattern, Steve also shows a definite tendency toward developing socially inadequate reactive patterns in his general behavior. A poor Category Test score and a tendency to be able to perform psychomotor activities (TPT) adequately represents a combination that predisposes a child toward behaviors that are viewed as ill-considered, inappropriate, and often destructive. Steve has the skill to do things effectively with his hands, but he does not have the advantage of calculated judgment or the ability to infer cause-and-effect relationships and appreciate the ways in which his behavior will affect other people in his environment.

It is apparent that the complete neuropsychological assessment revealed that Steve had significant impairment of brain functions which was not identified by the medical and neurological examination. In fact, at his age, the primary testing ground for displaying such behaviors is in the classroom and on academic performances. It is not surprising, therefore, that the emerging problems center in this area. These difficulties in turn are then described as behavioral problems relating to the school situation, learning disabilities, or both. Upon more complete examination, however, a host of brain-related neuropsychological problems is revealed.

The brain impairment of children like Steve, even though exposed and demonstrated in the academic area, does not fit into neat packages that emanate from descriptive information based on deficiencies noted in the classroom. It therefore becomes very important for the individual child to be evaluated comprehensively to assess the full range of brain-behavior relationships. The neuropsychological test results for individual children who have been thought to fit subtypes of learning disabilities reveal significant deficits that are much more extensive than originally believed, and the simplistic categories relating to learning disability subtypes are definitely blurred. In practice, instead of finding children who fit into simplified categories of learning disabilities, comprehensive neuropsychological testing identifies children who have a broad range of neuropsychological deficits that are present in varying degrees. Obviously, a full evaluation and understanding of the brain-behavior relationships for the individual child is a prerequisite to effective treatment.

In this case, it is apparent that Steve needs an approach to cognitive retraining similar to the one we recommended for Roger, the child in the previous case. Steve requires intensive training with Track C (abstraction, reasoning, organizational ability, and planning skills) to help him develop an appreciation of the effects of his behavior on the environment and understand the relationships between various components of a situation. We would also aim to improve his ability to deal with spatial relationships, especially as they relate to reasoning and abstraction types of tasks. Only after these fundamentals have been accomplished would we integrate materials focusing on verbal and language skills. We would use items from Track B to establish abilities in verbal reasoning and logical analysis, and then introduce specific instruction in academic subject matter.

The fundamental difficulty with many children who are described as having learning disabilities is that they have general neuropsychological deficits which represent an inadequate groundwork or a failure of prerequisites for making academic progress. In addition, disparities in neuropsychological ability structure may predispose the child toward unacceptable social behavior. Only through a comprehensive neuropsychological examination is it possible to reveal these difficulties and then develop a treatment program for the individual child which is specific to his/her particular deficits.

■

Case 20 — RUDY

Age:	12-5	**Gender:**	Male
Education:	5	**Handedness:**	Right
(repeated 2 grades)			

Background Information

Rudy was an adolescent who had always experienced a great deal of difficulty making academic progress. Now in the fifth grade, he is unable to keep up with his school work, has not learned to read, and is showing signs of increasing anxiety, self-doubt, and lowered self-esteem because of his limited academic ability and achievement.

Rudy's parents were concerned that a medical disorder may be the cause of their son's problems, and they took him to see a pediatric neurologist for a complete examination. The physician could find no medical basis to explain why Rudy was having such trouble making normal academic progress, and referred the child to our laboratory for a comprehensive neuropsychological examination.

When Rudy was about six years old he sustained a blow to the head as he was playing with his friends after school. He had apparently lost consciousness for about two minutes, but seemed alert and oriented immediately upon regaining consciousness. Nevertheless, his parents took him to the local emergency room as a precautionary measure. The EEG and the neurological examination done in the ER revealed no abnormalities, and Rudy was not admitted to the hospital. There were no complications from the accident, and Rudy's parents believed that their son had not sustained any permanent effects from the blow to his head. Rudy's medical history was otherwise negative for any brain disease or damage which might have caused neuropsychological impairment.

Neuropsychological Examination

Wechsler Intelligence Scale for Children — Revised (WISC-R)

We administered the WISC-R to evaluate Rudy's general level of intelligence. The most striking finding was the disparity between Verbal and Performance IQ values. Rudy's Verbal IQ of 75 fell in the Borderline range of intelligence and exceeded only 5% of his age peers. However, his Performance IQ of 115 was in the High Average range, exceeding 84%. Although these values yielded a Full Scale IQ of 92, falling in the Average range at the 30th percentile, the more meaningful observation of his scores relates to the disparity between verbal and performance intelligence. Silverstein's (1987) tables indicate that with a Performance IQ of 115 a Verbal IQ as low as 82 would occur as infrequently as 1% of the time, and Rudy had a Verbal IQ of 75.

The weighted scores for the Verbal subtests suggest that Rudy tended to do most poorly on those subtests that required accumulation of verbal information (Information, 5 and Vocabulary, 6) and the development of arithmetical competence (Arithmetic, 1). Verbal tests that depended more upon use of available information rather than recapitulation of accumulated facts were performed somewhat better (Comprehension, 9 and Similarities 9). It should also be noted that although Rudy performed poorly in repetition of digits, earning a score of 3 on Digit Span, this subtest has never been related very closely or explicitly to impaired brain functions (Black, 1986).

The Performance subtests were done adequately except for Coding (8), and this subtest often is performed poorly by children who have impairment of academic abilities. The Picture Arrangement score of 10 also appears to be somewhat low compared to the other Performance subtest scores, but it should be noted that even this score is at the average level and higher than any of the Verbal subtest scores.

The Halstead-Reitan Neuropsychological Test Battery for Older Children

Name: Rudy   Age 12 – 5

Gender M   Education 5   Handedness: RH 7 LH 0

Neuropsychological Deficit Scale (NDS) Summary

Level of Performance	Subject's score	Mean for controls	Mean for brain-damaged	Cut-off score
Motor Functions	5	6.29	14.05	
Sensory-perceptual Functions	2	5.15	10.77	
Attention and Concentration	3	1.91	3.78	
Immediate Memory and Recapitulation	0	2.23	3.31	
Visual-spatial Skills	3	4.06	7.69	
Abstraction, Reasoning, Logical Analysis	6	2.63	6.03	
Level of Performance–Total	19	22.27	45.63	33/34
Dysphasia and Related Variables	13	1.37	7.97	3/4
Right / Left Differences	6	6.79	13.74	9/10
Total NDS Score	38	30.43	67.34	43/44

WISC-R

VIQ   75
PIQ   115
FS IQ   92

Verbal Subtests

Information	5
Similarities	9
Arithmetic	1
Vocabulary	6
Comprehension	9
(Digit Span)	(3)

Performance Subtests

Picture Completion	14
Picture Arrangement	10
Block Design	13
Object Assembly	16
Coding	8

WRAT

	Grade Equivalent
Reading	2.7
Arithmetic	2.1
Spelling	1.9

Strength of Grip

Dominant hand   (R)   23.5 kg
Non-dominant hand (L)   22.0 kg

Name Writing

Dominant hand   (R)   5 sec
Non-dominant hand (L)   12 sec

Category Test

Number of errors   52

Tactual Performance Test

Dominant hand   (R)   5.3
Non-dominant hand (L)   3.3
Both hands   1.7

Total Time   10.3
Memory   6
Localization   6

Seashore Rhythm Test

Number correct   26   5

Speech-sounds Perception Test

Number of errors   14

Finger Tapping Test

Dominant hand   (R)   37   37
Non-dominant hand (L)   31

Trail Making Test

Part A	33	sec	0	error(s)
Part B	80	sec	1	error(s)

Bilateral Simultaneous Sensory Stimulation

RH ___ LH ___   Both: RH ___ LH ___
RH ___ LF ___   Both: RH ___ LF ___
LH ___ RF ___   Both: LH ___ RF ___

RE ___ LE ___   Both: RE ___ LE ___

RV ___ LV ___   Both: RV ___ LV ___
___ ___   ___ ___
___ ___   ___ ___

Tactile Finger Recognition

RH 1 ___ 2 ___ 3 1 4 1 5 ___   RH 2 / 20
LH 1 ___ 2 1 3 ___ 4 ___ 5 ___   LH 1 / 20

Finger-Tip Number Writing

RH 1 ___ 2 ___ 3 1 4 ___ 5 ___   RH 1 / 20
LH 1 ___ 2 ___ 3 ___ 4 ___ 5 ___ LH 0 / 20

Tactile Form Recognition Test

Dominant hand (R)	9	sec	0	error(s)
Non-dominant hand (L)	8	sec	0	error(s)

Reitan-Indiana Aphasia Screening Test

Form for Adults and Older Children

Name _Rudy_____ Age _12 – 5_

Copy SQUARE	Repeat TRIANGLE
Name SQUARE	Repeat MASSACHUSETTS Masstachusess
Spell SQUARE S - Q - U - W - A - R	Repeat METHODIST EPISCOPAL Methis Episipal
Copy CROSS	Write SQUARE
Name CROSS Triangle *Ex.?* Cross	Read SEVEN Seem *Ex.?* Seem
Spell CROSS S-H - - - I don't know. *Ex. urged S to try and S responded* G - R - A - S - E	Repeat SEVEN
Copy TRIANGLE	Repeat/Explain HE SHOUTED THE WARNING
Name TRIANGLE	Write HE SHOUTED THE WARNING
Spell TRIANGLE T - R - I - T - A - N - I - L	Compute 85 − 27 =
Name BABY	Compute 17 x 3 =
Write CLOCK	Name KEY
Name FORK	Demonstrate use of KEY
Read 7 SIX 2	Draw KEY
Read MGW	Read PLACE LEFT HAND TO RIGHT EAR Police leaf than to _____ ear.
Reading I	Place LEFT HAND TO RIGHT EAR *S placed left hand on left ear.*
Reading II He is a _____ only, a _____ of dog show.	Place LEFT HAND TO LEFT ELBOW

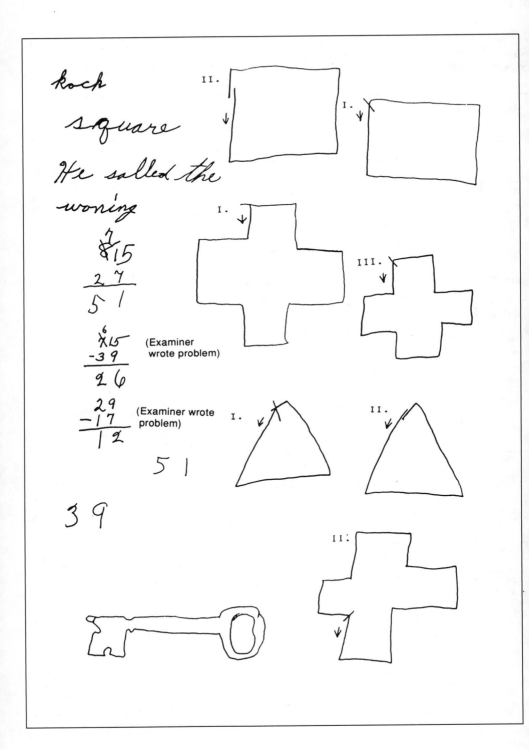

kock

square

He salled the

woning

8̸15
2 7
5 1

6
X̸15   (Examiner
-3 9   wrote problem)
2 6

2 9   (Examiner wrote
-1 7   problem)
1 2

5 1

3 9

Wide Range Achievement Test

It was apparent from both the history information and the VIQ that Rudy would have significant problems developing academic skills, and the Wide Range Achievement Test documented his limitations in this area. Rudy earned the following grade-equivalents: Reading, 2.7; Arithmetic, 2.1; and Spelling, 1.9. These findings make it quite apparent that Rudy was not at all prepared to deal with academic material at the sixth grade level, and it was not surprising that he was becoming increasingly anxious and concerned. Any child with a degree of insight that even approached normal comprehension would be uneasy (and perhaps frightened) about being in such a situation, particularly if the child had any feeling of responsibility with regard to making normal academic progress.

Halstead-Reitan Battery for Older Children

Neuropsychological Deficit Scale. Further insight into the nature and distribution of neuropsychological strengths and weaknesses was revealed by the results of the NDS for Older Children. Rudy earned a total NDS score of 38, a value that is somewhat closer to the mean of 30.43 shown by control children than to the mean of 67.34 earned by children with documented brain damage. The recommended cut-off for the total NDS score is 43/44, and Rudy's score of 38 approaches this level.

Rudy performed quite adequately on several sections of the NDS: Motor Functions, Sensory-perceptual Functions, and Immediate Memory and Recapitulation. However, on the sections reflecting skill in abstraction, reasoning and logical analysis, his scores were essentially at the level shown by brain-damaged children. Rudy's score of 3 on the Visual-spatial Skills section was the result of a particularly poor performance on Part A of the Trail Making Test (33 sec). Two of the three measures that contributed to the Abstraction, Reasoning, and Logical Analysis section — the

Category Test and Part B of the Trail Making Test — had scores in the impaired range. After the complete set of neuropsychological results has been reviewed, it will be important to bear in mind this area of deficiency in recapitulating the neuropsychological weaknesses of this child.

On the Right-Left Differences section of the NDS, all but one of Rudy's scores fell essentially in the normal range. However, he performed very poorly on the Dysphasia and Related Variables section. On this section he earned a score of 13 points, which is far worse than the mean score of 7.97 earned by brain-damaged children. When we recall that on this section the mean for control children is only 1.37 and the cut-off is 3/4, it is apparent that Rudy had great difficulties with the simple tasks included in the Aphasia Screening Test. Although many children with learning disabilities show evidence of more generalized impairment on the Level of Performance section of the NDS, Rudy's particular pattern of results (including the low Verbal IQ compared with the Performance IQ) is quite typical of children with learning disabilities.

Clinical Evaluation of the Test Results. Clinical analysis of the test results adds important details that should be noted. First, it is apparent that Rudy has certain cognitive strengths. Although he showed evidence of mild impairment on the Total Time score of the Tactual Performance Test (10.3 min), he remembered and correctly localized all six of the figures. The relationship between the performances on the right hand (5.3 min) and the left hand (3.3 min) also was well within the normal range.

Rudy demonstrated his ability to pay attention and maintain concentration over time by responding correctly to 26 of the 30 items on the Seashore Rhythm Test. The Speech-sounds Perception Test score (14 errors) fell in the impaired range, but this performance almost certainly reflected part of the general picture of difficulty in dealing with verbal symbols. In fact, for Rudy this score might be considered to be fairly good, considering the problems he had on the Aphasia Screening Test. He showed little evidence of sensory-perceptual deficits, demonstrating no problems with perception of unilateral or bilateral sensory stimulation, made only relatively minor errors in tactile finger localization, finger-tip number writing perception, and earned normal scores on tactile form recognition.

Although it might be noted that Rudy was a little slow in finger tapping speed with his left hand (31) as compared with his right hand (37), the difference was not striking. His grip strength might be considered to be a little weak with the right hand (23.5) as compared with the left hand (22.0), but again the difference was minor. The relative integrity of motor and sensory-perceptual functions would constitute a strong basis for predicting that the medical (neurological) examination would be within normal limits.

Results of the Aphasia Screening Test are of critical significance for identifying Rudy's neuropsychological deficits. As shown by his responses, Rudy had many difficulties that are quite similar to those shown by children with documented cerebral damage. We concluded that he demonstrated evidence of dysnomia when he named the CROSS as a triangle. After the examiner questioned Rudy and urged him to think of another possible name, he was able to name the figure correctly.

Rudy's spelling showed evidence of significant deficiencies, and he deviated particularly from phonics in his attempt to spell CROSS. Although he had no problems on the first reading item, he had great difficulty on the second item and was able to read only the more simple words. Evidence of central dysarthria was clearly manifested by his confusion of the sequence of sounds involved when he attempted to repeat MASSACHUSETTS and his omission of part of METHODIST. Rudy had great difficulty reading SEVEN, suggesting a particular difficulty when reading material out of context.

Rudy demonstrated evidence of prior training in dealing with simple arithmetical problems, but his ability to perform computations was seriously limited. Nevertheless, he was able to respond correctly to 17 × 3 and 13 × 3, suggesting that his difficulty stemmed more from failure to have properly learned the basics as compared with impairment of the arithmetical processes involved.

On the NDS scale we did not score dysgraphia as being present, although a judgment in this respect is sometimes difficult. Rudy's writing attempts appeared to demonstrate an impaired spelling ability rather than an inability to form the individual letters.

Rudy showed additional significant impairment in reading when he attempted to read PLACE LEFT HAND TO RIGHT EAR. He also demonstrated at least a mild degree of right-left confusion when asked to perform this task.

Finally, although Rudy was able to draw simple spatial configurations reasonably well, it is interesting to note that his second drawing of the Greek cross was actually poorer than his first drawing. On the basis of the significant imbalance of the lateral extremities on the second drawing, together with having had to add the "nose" of the key, we felt that Rudy just qualified for scoring of constructional dyspraxia on the NDS.

These results make it quite clear that Rudy performed relatively well on "lower level" neuropsychological test scores and comparatively less well on the "higher level" neuropsychological measurements. In addition, he demonstrated significant and serious deficits on the Aphasia Screening Test. This pattern of test scores is very typical of children with learning disabilities who are classified as normal on the basis of their negative neurological examination. As we have previously noted, the great majority of children with learning disabilities demonstrate impaired neuropsychological findings on the Halstead-Reitan Battery, despite

the fact that they are routinely judged to be normal according to the conventional neurological evaluation.

One might raise a question about whether this configuration of test results would suggest the presence of serious
behavioral problems, particularly in light of the striking
disparity between the Verbal and Performance IQ values. If
we consider the components of the "terrible triad" (see the
introduction to the cases concerned with behavioral problems and the results and discussion of Gary), we find that
Rudy does not meet the criteria for two specific reasons: his
Category Test score (52) was not sufficiently impaired, and
his Total Time on the TPT (10.3 min) was not sufficiently
good. Therefore, the low Verbal IQ as compared with Performance IQ is the only element of the "terrible triad" that
Rudy demonstrates. With this set of test results, it is likely
that Rudy would be a more subdued and withdrawn child
and, as suggested by the history, inclined to be intimidated
and anxious in the face of his problems rather than hostile
and belligerent.

Summary and Recommendations

In summary, Rudy's performances on the Aphasia Screening Test, the Category Test and Part B of the Trail Making
Test and the Wechsler Scales indicate that his principal
difficulties fall in the areas of (1) abstraction, reasoning,
and logical analysis skills, (2) the ability to deal with visual-
spatial relationships, and (3) impairment of verbal intelligence and competence in using language symbols for
communicational purposes.

In terms of remediation, we recommended that the initial training efforts be directed toward upgrading Rudy's
insight and understanding of causal relationships. The principal requirement, however, clearly centers on the development of specific academic skills, and Rudy needs a
considerable degree of assistance in this area. Without help

over and beyond the regular classroom situation, he would certainly continue to fall farther and farther behind his peers. The test results indicate that Rudy needs individual tutorial help in order to develop academic abilities in which he is so seriously deficient at present.

Rudy's extensive range of deficits indicated that he could benefit from material in all five tracks of REHABIT. We began our cognitive retraining with Rudy by using materials in Track C that focused on abstraction skills, recognizing cause-and-effect relationships, and discerning sequential patterns. We initially used materials that were fairly simple, in order to give Rudy a chance to experience success in the program and develop a stronger sense of self-confidence. We also realized that it would be important for Rudy to establish a trusting relationship with the cognitive rehabilitation technician, who would be asking Rudy to do tasks that would be difficult and frustrating for him.

We progressed to more difficult material in Track C and gradually introduced tasks from other tracks. It was also necessary to work closely with Rudy's teachers, so that we could use material that would complement his school subjects. Rudy made steady progress, but it was often necessary to repeat tasks at various intervals to ensure that the learning was reinforced and solidified.

■

Behavioral Problems of Children with Cerebral Damage or Dysfunction

More than 30 years ago our research in neuropsychology made us aware that cognitive impairment, particularly when represented by striking intra-individual disparities in various areas of function, can cause significant behavioral problems of adjustment (see Chapter VII). At that time, however, not many professionals felt that "brain damage" represented anything more than a generalized impairment of intellectual abilities, and psychologists were much more impressed with emotional trauma (particularly early in life) as a determinant of later emotionally-based behavioral problems.

During the past three decades there has been growing awareness that cognitive functions interact in a significant way with behavior. However, the emphasis still is usually directed toward the use of cognitive approaches in therapy and behavior modification. Although emotional and behavioral problems have received increasing attention, particularly in the area of traumatic brain injury (Prigatano, 1986), the emphasis has been on personality problems and areas of cognitive dysfunction rather than on intra-individual ability disparities of the brain-damaged person. There has not yet developed much of an understanding that abnormal cognitive patterns of the individual, determined by cerebral impairment interacting with environmental influences, can be a potent force in producing significant behavioral disorders.

In the 1960s, when we described the behavioral disturbances and persistently incorrigible activities that could be expected of a particular youngster because of his or her neuropsychological deficits, the attending child psychiatrist invariably said, "That is exactly how he behaves, but I sent him over to your lab just to have him tested for organicity." Many members of our professional society still seem to be committed in practice to a separation of the "emotional" and "organic" bases of behavior. One is almost forced to postulate that the basic presumption underlying this problem is the existence of a deep and unshakable belief that the brain has little if anything to do with aberrant and normal social behavior.

Even though little understanding has developed in the mental health community about the role of neuropsychological impairment in producing deviant behavior, there is at present a growing belief that learning deficits and disabilities may result from brain damage or dysfunction. Thirty years ago such disorders were in many instances related to an unexplained impairment of learning aptitude, if not selected or more generalized manifestations of mental retardation. Mental retardation, in turn, was rarely explained in terms of impaired brain functions unless the subject had suffered a medically diagnosed injury or disease of the brain.

Although learning disability has reached a point of acceptability within the framework of neuropsychological impairment, significant behavioral disturbances are still usually thought of as representing emotional problems which arise from environmental circumstances and factors. This attitude is quite remarkable, considering the fact (as demonstrated by the case-studies that follow), that we can actually predict the kinds of behavioral disturbances that many children will manifest based exclusively on evaluation of their brain-behavior relationships.

The pattern of neuropsychological test results that frequently is associated with socially unacceptable behavior (such as disruptive behavior in the classroom, impulsive and uncontrolled behavior, lack of respect for authority figures and unwillingness to accept guidance, disregard for the property and rights of others, and even direct violation not only of socially-accepted conventions but legal regulations) is usually represented by three characteristics that we have termed the "terrible triad":

1. Impairment of basic insight and understanding of fundamental cause-and-effect relationships; a deficient ability in the skills of abstraction, reasoning and logical analysis; and serious limitation in being able to postulate meaningful principles or explanations of how things interact and make sense in practical terms (functions that are best reflected in neuropsychological testing by the Category Test);

2. Limited ability in both receptive (input) and expressive (output) aspects of verbal intelligence and language skills which in effect have at least partially isolated the individual from this extremely important avenue of contact with society and influence by persons who would normally be very significant in molding the behavior of the child (best reflected by verbal intelligence measures and Verbal IQ);

3. Relatively unimpaired (or sometimes even excellent) abilities in motor and manipulatory skills by which the child is able to accomplish even complex performances (best shown by the Total Time score on the Tactual Performance Test).

Deficits in areas (1) and (2) above represent loss of control, impaired self-monitoring of behavior, lessened ability to be affected by environmental influences, and basic impairment of judgment and the ability to appreciate events in terms of their more general implications and consequences. Area (3) above represents intact abilities in accomplishing expressive psychomotor tasks, and when this ability is preserved and available to the child, the child often has a strong tendency to use it. The combination of (1), (2), and (3) in the individual child represents a set of predisposing neuropsychological factors in which an acting-out tendency is only minimally modified by the controls implicit in normal brain functions.

It should be noted that areas (1) and (2) above not only tend to characterize children with socially unacceptable behavior, but also are frequently seen in children with learning disabilities. There is, of course, a substantial overlap of learning disability and behavioral problems, and common neuropsychological patterns of deficit are clearly relevant to the fact that these two conditions are often present in the same child. We must also emphasize, however, that in the individual case the pattern of neuropsychological deficits described above is a product of both impaired brain functions and environmental influences (which are more adverse in some cases than in others).

Finally, in many cases of persons with normal brain functions, environmental determinants of behavior are of predominant influence in the production of socially unacceptable behavior. These considerations emphasize the importance of neuropsychological testing to assess and describe the influence and interaction of both organic and environmental factors for the individual child, and thereby facilitate an appropriate treatment or remediation program.

Case 21 — GARY

Age:	15-3	**Gender:**	**Male**
Education:	8	**Handedness:**	**Left**

Background Information

Gary was an adolescent who had a life-long history of inappropriate social behavior that had led to several years of supervision by a court-appointed probation officer. At the age of 15 years, 2 months he was committed to a state custodial institution because of incorrigible behavior. Prior to this institutionalization many attempts had been made to assist the parents in supervising Gary, but all interventions had been unsuccessful.

Gary's school attendance had always been very irregular, and his mother frequently wrote notes to the teachers stating that he was ill when this actually was not the case. An investigation by the probation officer indicated that Gary's mother wrote these excuses partially because she wanted to avoid problems with school authorities, but mainly because Gary had threatened to harm her physically if she refused.

Gary's father seemed disinterested and totally ineffective in making any useful contributions to controlling his son's behavior. In a court hearing the judge had threatened the parents with a charge of criminal neglect unless they improved their supervision and control of their son, but they still were not able to effect any change in Gary's behavior.

Gary's mother told us that he often left home for several days at a time. It had been documented that Gary had often used alcohol excessively and had been arrested several times on charges of minor theft. The school authorities reported that he frequently was loud, rude, and verbally abusive toward his teachers, and there were many instances in which Gary was involved in fights. The probation authorities had even used several jail sentences lasting up to seven days as an approach to improving Gary's behavior. A thorough investigation into his school records revealed that Gary had been promoted through the eighth grade only because of his age and size, and his teachers advanced him to the next grade to get him out of their classes.

A review of the extensive records prepared by the juvenile court officials revealed many descriptive statements about Gary. The opinions of the various professionals who had been involved in Gary's case were summarized by his probation officer: "Gary is beyond the control of his parents. He never shows any respect to his parents or to the community or the rights or property of others. Gary has become a law unto himself and feels that anything he does is all right unless he gets caught. He rebels at all authority figures and either totally disregards or laughs at attempts to discipline him. He frequently loses his temper, responds impulsively, and strikes and hurts smaller children with apparently no ability to control his behavior. Gary is unlikely to improve in his behavior because he simply does not want to do what is required or to behave in an acceptable manner."

The only positive reports from authority figures stemmed from situations in which Gary was closely and continuously supervised on a one-to-one basis. In such circumstances it appeared that it was possible to modify Gary's behavior somewhat and elicit constructive efforts in tasks directed toward such activities as cleaning jail quarters, painting walls in the correctional institution, etc. However, predictions of future behavior based on such interactions had invariably turned out to be too hopeful, and had little generalization value to situations in which Gary was less closely supervised.

Neuropsychological Evaluation

Gary had been referred to a neurologist because he had experienced some episodes which were thought to be epileptic seizures. On the basis of the history and EEG the neurologist concluded that Gary was in fact epileptic, and noted that these episodes had been occurring for many years. During these seizures, which were of sudden onset, Gary lost consciousness, collapsed, and demonstrated little in the way of tonic or clonic movement. It appeared that anti-epileptic medication had been effective, at least to a degree, in controlling these seizures. Except for the history and the EEG findings, the physical neurological examination was within normal limits.

Realizing that this type of condition may have serious neuropsychological consequences, the neurologist referred Gary to our laboratory for a complete neuropsychological examination. Since Gary was 15 years, 3 months old at the time of this neuropsychological examination, we administered the Halstead-Reitan Neuropsychological Test Battery for Adults.

Gary's test results demonstrated a mild diffuse impairment of cerebral functions that was chronic and static in nature. However, the principal significance of the neuropsychological findings related to a pattern of scores which clearly indicated the presence of the "terrible triad," and served as a basis for predicting and understanding Gary's behavioral problems.

Wechsler Intelligence Scale for Children — Revised

On the WISC-R Gary earned a Verbal IQ of 68, a value which falls in the range of mild Mental Retardation and exceeds less than 2% of his age peers. However, his Performance IQ of 108 was 40 points higher, falling in the upper part of the Average range and exceeding 70%. These

The Halstead-Reitan Neuropsychological Test Battery for Adults

Name __Gary__   Age __15 – 3__

Gender __M__   Education __8__   Handedness: RH __5__ LH __2__

Neuropsychological Deficit Scale (NDS) Summary

General NDS

Level of Performance	18
Pathognomonic Signs	6
Patterns	3
Right / Left Differences	9

Total G-NDS Score __36__

WISC-R

VIQ	68
PIQ	108
FS IQ	85

Verbal Subtests		*Performance Subtests*	
Information	6	Picture Completion	14
Similarities	5	Picture Arrangement	10
Arithmetic	3	Block Design	12
Vocabulary	5	Object Assembly	13
Comprehension	5	Coding	7
(Digit Span)	(3)		

WRAT

	Grade Equivalent
Reading	3.2
Arithmetic	2.9
Spelling	3.3

Strength of Grip

Dominant hand	(L)	33.5	kg
Non-dominant hand	(R)	37.5	kg

Name Writing

Dominant hand	(L)	15	sec
Non-dominant hand	(R)	37	sec

Category Test

Number of errors __74__

Tactual Performance Test

Dominant hand	(L)	3.9	Total Time	6.2
Non-dominant hand	(R)	1.5	Memory	8
Both hands		0.8	Localization	8

Seashore Rhythm Test

Number correct __27__   3

Speech-sounds Perception Test

Number of errors __11__

Finger Tapping Test

Dominant hand	(L)	48	48
Non-dominant hand	(R)	46	

Impairment Index   0.4

Trail Making Test

Part A	36	sec	1	error(s)
Part B	95	sec	1	error(s)

Bilateral Simultaneous Sensory Stimulation

RH ___ LH ___	Both: RH ___ LH ___	
RH ___ LF ___	Both: RH ___ LF ___	
LH ___ RF ___	Both: LH ___ RF ___	
RE ___ LE ___	Both: RE ___ LE ___	
RV ___ LV ___	Both: RV ___ LV ___	
1		

Tactile Finger Recognition

RH	1 ___	2 ___	3 ___	4 _1_	5 ___	RH 1 / 20	
LH	1 ___	2 ___	3 ___	4 _1_	5 _1_	LH 2 / 20	

Finger-Tip Number Writing

RH	1 _1_	2 ___	3 ___	4 ___	5 ___	RH 1 / 20	
LH	1 _1_	2 ___	3 ___	4 ___	5 ___	LH 1 / 20	

Tactile Form Recognition Test

Dominant hand	(L)	9	sec	0	error(s)
Non-dominant hand	(R)	9	sec	0	error(s)

Reitan-Indiana Aphasia Screening Test

Form for Adults and Older Children

Name __Gary__ Age __15 – 3__

Copy SQUARE	Repeat TRIANGLE
Name SQUARE	Repeat MASSACHUSETTS Massachusess

Spell SQUARE
      S - K - E - R
	Repeat METHODIST EPISCOPAL
	            Methadil Apistiple

Copy CROSS	Write SQUARE
Name CROSS	Read SEVEN Save - - - saven
Spell CROSS	Repeat SEVEN
Copy TRIANGLE	Repeat/Explain HE SHOUTED THE WARNING
Name TRIANGLE	Write HE SHOUTED THE WARNING
Spell TRIANGLE T - R - A - I - G - L - Y	Compute 85 − 27 =
Name BABY	Compute 17 x 3 = 41 5 × 8 = 40
Write CLOCK *See writing of "cluck"*	Name KEY
Name FORK	Demonstrate use of KEY
Read 7 SIX 2 7 - 6 or sex-2 *Ex.?* 7 - 6 - 2	Draw KEY *S said first key was too large and wanted to draw another. Realized he didn't leave enough room for second key and then drew a third key.*
Read MGW	Read PLACE LEFT HAND TO RIGHT EAR
Reading I	Place LEFT HAND TO RIGHT EAR *S placed right hand to right ear.*
Reading II	Place LEFT HAND TO LEFT ELBOW

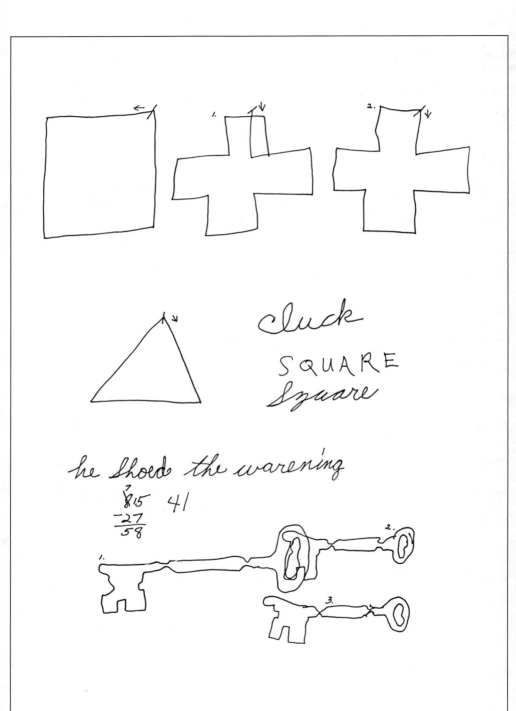

scores yielded a Full Scale IQ of 85, a value in the Low Average range of intelligence. However, the meaningful information obviously relates to the low Verbal IQ as compared with high Performance IQ, which exceeds the 1% confidence band according to Silverstein's tables (1987).

All of Gary's scaled scores on the Verbal subtests tended to be low, ranging from 3 to 6. The Performance subtests were performed adequately except for Coding (7), which might well be expected to be deficient in a child with a low Verbal IQ and evidence of limited academic achievement.

Wide Range Achievement Test

The limitations of Gary's academic progress were clearly manifested by results obtained on the WRAT. On this test he earned the following grade-equivalents: Reading (word recognition), 3.2; Spelling, 3.3; and Arithmetic, 2.9. Although Gary had technically completed the 8th grade in school, it is apparent that he had been promoted without any consideration of his academic competence.

Halstead-Reitan Neuropsychological Test Battery

Neuropsychological Deficit Scale. Since the Adult Battery was administered, the General NDS (G-NDS) for Adults was computed. Gary's test scores yielded a total NDS score of 36, which falls in the range characteristic of mild impairment of cerebral functions. In our original validation studies, we recommended a cut-off score of 25/26, and none of the control subjects had a G-NDS score above 34.

Clinical Evaluation of the Test Results. A clinical analysis of the test results yielded further information about Gary's impairment of brain functions and identified his areas of neuropsychological strengths and weaknesses. We will first consider the four indicators in the HRB other than the G-NDS which are most sensitive to the biological condition of the brain.

Gary's scores on both the Category Test (74) and Part B of the Trail Making Test (95 sec) were in the impaired range. The Impairment Index of 0.4 represented a borderline score, and he performed very well on the Localization component of the TPT (8). These four measures therefore supported the impression suggested by the G-NDS that Gary had mild generalized neuropsychological impairment.

In terms of the Reitan-Wolfson model of neuropsychological functioning, Gary demonstrated fairly adequate abilities at the first level of central processing, concerned with the registration of incoming information. Despite his low Verbal IQ (68), he did quite adequately on the Seashore Rhythm Test (27 correct), and considering his Verbal IQ, performed extremely well on the Speech-sounds Perception Test (11 errors). He also demonstrated that he was capable of perceiving specific stimulus material by performing adequately on the sensory-perceptual measures. Thus, the general indicators demonstrated that Gary performed fairly well at the first level of central processing (attention and concentration), but was significantly impaired at the highest level (abstraction, reasoning, and logical analysis).

Although he did not demonstrate motor or sensory-perceptual problems relating to the left cerebral hemisphere, Gary showed clear evidence of impairment on the Aphasia Screening Test. His deficiencies in spelling were particularly significant. He spelled SQUARE as S-K-E-R, TRIANGLE as T-R-A-I-G-L-Y, and CLOCK as C-L-U-C- K. In scoring the Pathognomonic Signs section of the NDS we assigned a point for spelling dyspraxia.

Gary also demonstrated evidence of dyslexia by his confusion in reading 7 SIX 2 as "7 — 6 or sex — 2." Although he did not make specific mistakes, he had difficulty with the second reading item, HE IS A FRIENDLY ANIMAL, A FAMOUS WINNER OF DOG SHOWS. He also manifested a mild degree of right-left confusion by placing his right hand to his right ear when the instructions requested him to place his left hand to his right ear, and central dysarthria in his mispronunciation of METHODIST.

One might raise a question about whether Gary demonstrated dysgraphia when he wrote a Z instead of a Q in writing SQUARE. Considering the fact that he had previously printed the word correctly, we concluded that he probably had never learned how to write the letter Q. In addition, he was not able to write the sentence HE SHOUTED THE WARNING correctly, but his problem seemed to stem principally from spelling difficulty rather than confusion about forming the letters.

Gary also made an error in multiplying 17 × 3, but his answer of 41 is not a sufficient basis for concluding that dyscalculia was present. Nevertheless, even these minimal deficiencies contribute to the impression of some degree of impairment of left cerebral hemisphere functions.

It appears that Gary's right cerebral hemisphere was more significantly involved than the left, although it must be borne in mind that he was clearly ambidextrous. His grip strength with his left hand (which was the hand he used for writing) was very definitely less (33.5 kg) than with his right hand (37.5 kg). Even though Gary's overall time (6.2) on the TPT was excellent, he was slow with his left hand (3.9 min) as compared with his right hand (1.5 min). In finger tapping speed he was just a little slow with his left hand (48) as compared with his right hand (46).

Finally, on his first drawing of the cross Gary showed definite evidence of constructional dyspraxia, demonstrated by the adjustment and correction that was necessary to complete the upper extremity. After finishing the first drawing of the key, Gary wanted to draw the figure again.

He started the second key in such a location on the paper that it was necessary to overlap the drawing on to the handle of the first key, demonstrating a significant error in his initial judgment about the space that would be required for the second drawing. The third drawing of the key showed some loss of symmetry in the teeth. If considered in isolation, each key by itself might qualify as being marginally acceptable; however, the error in judging the space required for the second drawing must be classified as a sign of right cerebral dysfunction.

This overall configuration of test results is quite convincing in suggesting the presence of mild, chronic, static cerebral damage that is generally distributed and involves both cerebral hemispheres. Despite the low Verbal IQ (68) as compared with the Performance IQ (108), we would estimate that the right cerebral hemisphere is somewhat more impaired than the left. The IQ values almost certainly represent failures of acquisition which, in turn, are based upon an interaction of impaired brain functions and environmental factors. Considering Gary's circumstances, it is very likely that he never experienced adequate development of verbal intelligence through either his academic experiences or home and other environmental influences.

While the test results clearly indicate that Gary has mild though definite indications of impairment of cerebral functions, the more significant information concerns the pattern and relationships of the test scores. Gary clearly meets the criteria for the "terrible triad": (1) a very low Verbal IQ with relation to the Performance IQ, (2) a poor score on the Category Test, and (3) a good score on the Total Time of the TPT. The test results describe an adolescent who is highly proficient in using his hands for complex psychomotor performances, even under the adverse conditions of being blindfolded. He has limited capability for appreciating verbal communication, and is probably influenced very little by this approach. Finally, he has a definite deficiency in drawing meaningful and appropriate conclusions from his observations, and has difficulty understanding circumstances in terms of cause-and-effect relationships.

This pattern of neuropsychological test results is entirely consistent with a child described as one who (1) never showed any respect for his parents, community, or the rights or property of others, (2) disregarded or even mocked attempts to impose disciplinary measures, (3) failed to understand social situations and respond appropriately, and (4) felt that a person could do anything he wished as long as he did not get caught. The authorities believed that "Gary's prospects for eventual development are seriously limited because he simply does not want to do what is required or to behave in an acceptable manner."

It is a serious and very significant error to attribute Gary's behavioral pattern to his own personal motivation and assume that Gary is perfectly normal in terms of his brain-behavior relationships. This adolescent has a particular pattern of neuropsychological deficits which limits his insight and understanding, and predisposes him toward behavior that is considered socially inappropriate and unacceptable. Only with this type of insight into Gary's behavior would it be possible for a therapist to approach his problems in a therapeutic sense that would have any reasonable prospect for success.

In terms of cognitive and behavioral rehabilitation, Gary needs basic training in abstraction, reasoning, logical analysis, and the fundamental analytical ability to translate his observations (which he has the capacity to register quite adequately) into meaningful conclusions. In a conventional description, Gary needs to be taught how to think.

Secondly, after Gary has made progress in the initial area of abstraction and reasoning skills, he needs further development of his verbal intelligence and his academic skills. If these two areas of striking deficiency are remediated, there would be a good prospect that Gary would be able to use his excellent psychomotor skill effectively toward constructive purposes rather than in a socially unacceptable and destructive manner.

Using REHABIT, we would initially work intensively with Gary on Track C. Until he gains some appreciation and understanding about cause-and-effect relationships and the cognitive ability to realize how his behavior impacts on others, Gary will not be able to derive much benefit from any other cognitive retraining exercises. We would integrate material from Track D into Gary's program in order to solidify his gains in abstraction and reasoning skills, using activities in which he already has facility. We would then begin to introduce material from Track B, to relate abstraction and reasoning processes to verbal and language content. Finally, we would use items from Track A for explicit training in developing verbal and academic skills.

Although in this book we do not focus on counseling or behavior modification techniques in our recommendations for rehabilitation, we certainly recognize that these types of intervention must often be integrated into any comprehensive rehabilitation program. Gary's behavior patterns are long-standing and ingrained, and any change in his personality and behavior will be achieved only through an intensive rehabilitation program directed by a neuropsychologist who understands Gary's cognitive ability structure.

In cases such as Gary's, neuropsychological evaluation has the distinct advantage of identifying brain-related deficiencies which need remediation and correction. Compare this to the hopeless inclination, without such information, to identify this child as being totally incorrigible.

It must be pointed out that not every child who has brain-related deficiencies such as Gary's develops the "terrible triad." However, some children who have impaired brain functions also live in a set of environmental circumstances that lead to and foster the development of such behaviors. The ideal approach, of course, is to identify such cognitive limitations early, implement specialized training in order to avoid the development of striking disparities in neuropsychological ability patterns, and thereby avert the need for remediation of deficits after they have already become firmly established.

■

Case 22 — JIM

Age:	12-0	Gender:	Male
Education:	6	Handedness:	Right

Background Information

Jim was referred to a neurologist by his family physician because of his severe behavioral problems in school as well as at home. His argumentative, headstrong, belligerent, hostile, and totally negative behavior had alienated him to the point that he no longer had any friends. Jim's father used to make an effort to do various activities with him, such as assembling model cars and airplanes, attending sporting events, and taking local recreational trips, but he had finally become so frustrated with his son's behavior that he no longer did any of these things, and now essentially ignored Jim.

Jim had a 17-year-old sister of whom he seemed to be extremely jealous. He continually complained that she was allowed to do things that he was not permitted to do, and he refused to accept any explanations relating to their age difference. Jim's mother tried to impose controls and restrictions on his behavior, attempting to explain to him how these regulations related to his unacceptable behavior, but Jim resisted any such explanations and blamed others for doing things which caused him to behave the way he did.

The family situation had deteriorated to the point that Jim's father and sister wanted nothing to do with him. Jim's mother sought professional help, but she, too, has just about exhausted her patience. Jim spends most of his time alone reading comic books, doing puzzles, and listening to records. He says that he does not particularly enjoy these activities, and complains constantly because other children do not like him.

Jim's disruptive behavior was not limited to the family environment. He has had ongoing difficulties in school, and his teachers report that he is constantly arguing, complaining, insisting on having his own way, refusing to co-operate, and blaming others for his problems. Jim had attended the local public school through the fifth grade, and his parents frequently had been called in because of the difficulties he was creating. Finally, he caused such problems that the school authorities recommended enrolling Jim in a private school. He is currently in his second year (7th grade) at a private school. He has improved his grades from C's and B's to a slightly higher level, but his behavior is still a problem, and the school administrator has notified the parents that they will not register Jim for another school year. Jim's sister has done well in school and Jim seems to be very distressed by this, even though everyone in the family makes an effort to downplay these types of comparisons.

Jim's parents told us that their son has exhibited these kinds of behavior problems for most of his life, and about four years before the present referral they had taken Jim to be evaluated by a clinical psychologist. Jim's mother indicated that the psychologist told her that Jim had a serious behavioral problem (which she certainly had been aware of), but offered no other explanation for her son's difficulties. Jim was enrolled in play therapy for a period of time, but showed no improvement and the sessions were discontinued.

The neurologist who referred Jim for neuropsychological examination found no medical evidence of brain disease or damage, and the child's EEG was normal. In the physician's judgment, however, the environmental situation was not sufficient to account for Jim's severe behavioral problems. Since she had had prior experience with our neuropsychological evaluations, she realized that an examination with the HRB often produced findings which were helpful in understanding even children who had no past history or present evidence of brain disease or damage.

Neuropsychological Evaluation

Jim was very co-operative during our day-long examination. After nearly every task he asked whether he had gotten the answer correct and done well, and frequently repeated that he was most eager to do his best. He asked the examiner to tell him if he ever got a wrong answer because he would then try to do better. It was apparent that Jim was somewhat intimidated by the testing situation, but it was also clear that he was trying to perform as well as he possibly could.

Wechsler Intelligence Scale for Children — Revised

The WISC-R yielded both Verbal and Performance IQ values that were in the Average range. Jim's Verbal IQ of 103 was in the upper part of the Average range, exceeding about 58% of his age peers. His Performance IQ was 8 points lower, falling in the lower part of the Average range and exceeding 37%. These values yielded a Full Scale IQ of 100, which falls at the 50th percentile.

The Verbal subtests showed a striking degree of variability, particularly because of the excellent score of 17 on Digit Span. Jim performed somewhat poorly on Information (8), suggesting that he may not be gaining as much information from school and other sources as would be expected. His score of 9 on Comprehension, while almost at the average level when considered with relation to scores on other Verbal subtests, may be related to a mild degree of comparative deficiency in social judgment and comprehension of social situations.

Jim also showed a considerable degree of variability on the Performance subtests, with scores ranging from 5 (Object Assembly) and 7 (Picture Completion) to 13 (Coding). The low scores on Object Assembly and Picture Completion may well suggest that Jim is somewhat limited in his ability

The Halstead-Reitan
Neuropsychological Test Battery
for Older Children

Name __Jim_____ Age __12 – 0__

Gender __M__ Education __6_____ Handedness: RH __7__ LH __0__

Neuropsychological Deficit Scale (NDS) Summary

Level of Performance	Subject's score	Mean for controls	Mean for brain-damaged	Cut-off score
Motor Functions	6	6.29	14.05	
Sensory-perceptual Functions	2	5.15	10.77	
Attention and Concentration	1	1.91	3.78	
Immediate Memory and Recapitulation	2	2.23	3.31	
Visual-spatial Skills	3	4.06	7.69	
Abstraction, Reasoning, Logical Analysis	2	2.63	6.03	
Level of Performance–Total	16	22.27	45.63	33/34
Dysphasia and Related Variables	0	1.37	7.97	3/4
Right / Left Differences	5	6.79	13.74	9/10
Total NDS Score	21	30.43	67.34	43/44

WISC-R

VIQ __103__
PIQ __95__
FS IQ __100__

Verbal Subtests		*Performance Subtests*	
Information	8	Picture Completion	7
Similarities	12	Picture Arrangement	11
Arithmetic	13	Block Design	11
Vocabulary	11	Object Assembly	5
Comprehension	9	Coding	13
(Digit Span)	(17)		

WRAT

	Grade Equivalent
Reading	7.5
Arithmetic	4.9
Spelling	7.4

Strength of Grip

Dominant hand (R) __9.5__ kg
Non-dominant hand (L) __8.0__ kg

Name Writing

Dominant hand (R) __6__ sec
Non-dominant hand (L) __22__ sec

Category Test

Number of errors __62__

Tactual Performance Test

Dominant hand (R) __3.0__
Non-dominant hand (L) __1.4__
Both hands __0.9__   Total Time __5.3__
    Memory __5__
    Localization __3__

Seashore Rhythm Test

Number correct __27__   __3__

Speech-sounds Perception Test

Number of errors __6__

Finger Tapping Test

Dominant hand (R) __49__   __49__
Non-dominant hand (L) __38__

Trail Making Test

Part A __10__ sec   __0__ error(s)
Part B __22__ sec   __0__ error(s)

Bilateral Simultaneous Sensory Stimulation

RH ___ LH ___	Both: RH ___ LH ___
RH ___ LF ___	Both: RH ___ LF ___
LH ___ RF ___	Both: LH ___ RF ___
RE ___ LE ___	Both: RE ___ LE ___
RV ___ LV ___	Both: RV ___ LV ___

Tactile Finger Recognition

RH 1 ___ 2 ___ 3 ___ 4 ___ 5 ___   RH __0__ / __20__
LH 1 ___ 2 ___ 3 ___ 4 ___ 5 ___   LH __0__ / __20__

Finger-Tip Number Writing

RH 1 ___ 2 __1__ 3 __1__ 4 ___ 5 __1__   RH __3__ / __20__
LH 1 ___ 2 __2__ 3 ___ 4 __1__ 5 __1__   LH __4__ / __20__

Tactile Form Recognition Test

Dominant hand (R) __8__ sec   __0__ error(s)
Non-dominant hand (L) __8__ sec   __0__ error(s)

Reitan-Indiana Aphasia
Screening Test

Form for Adults and Older Children

Name __Jim__   Age 12 – 0

Copy SQUARE	Repeat TRIANGLE
Name SQUARE	Repeat MASSACHUSETTS
Spell SQUARE	Repeat METHODIST EPISCOPAL *Methodis Epistacal*
Copy CROSS	Write SQUARE
Name CROSS *Some kind of cross.*	Read SEVEN
Spell CROSS	Repeat SEVEN
Copy TRIANGLE	Repeat/Explain HE SHOUTED THE WARNING
Name TRIANGLE	Write HE SHOUTED THE WARNING
Spell TRIANGLE T - R - I - - - *(long pause)* - - - A - N - G - L - E	Compute 85 − 27 =
Name BABY	Compute 17 x 3 =
Write CLOCK	Name KEY
Name FORK	Demonstrate use of KEY
Read 7 SIX 2	Draw KEY
Read MGW	Read PLACE LEFT HAND TO RIGHT EAR
Reading I	Place LEFT HAND TO RIGHT EAR
Reading II	Place LEFT HAND TO LEFT ELBOW

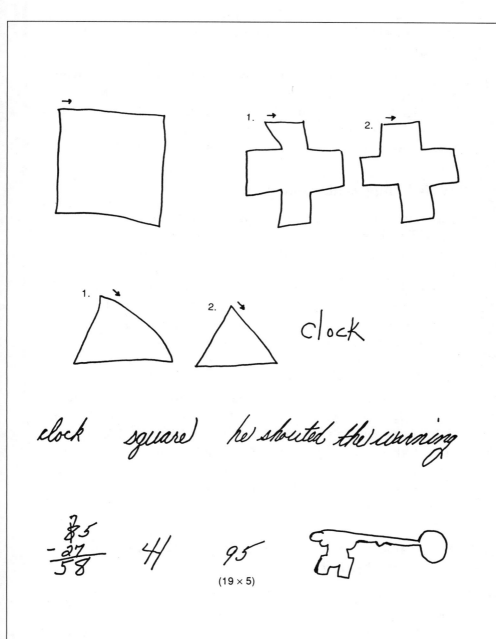

clock   square   he shouted the warning

$$\begin{array}{r} \overset{7}{\cancel{8}}5 \\ -\ 27 \\ \hline 58 \end{array}$$

41   95

(19 × 5)

to use minimal cues as a basis for appreciating and understanding the total problem.

In summary, it would not be possible to conclude from the results obtained on the Wechsler Scale that Jim had any significant impairment of brain functions. However, the variability of the subtests would raise a question about an unevenness in development of various intellectual skills.

Wide Range Achievement Test

Jim was at a grade level of 7.6 when we examined him. The WRAT indicated that he was progressing satisfactorily in terms of Reading (7.5) and Spelling (7.4), but his score of 4.9 on the Arithmetic section suggests that he definitely needs special help in this area. The explanation for his inadequate performance on this section of the WRAT is difficult to discern, even though it is not uncommon to see strikingly disparate scores on the WRAT Arithmetic subtest and the Arithmetic subtest of the WISC-R. Additional selective neuropsychological difficulties to be described below are also difficult to understand etiologically. However, it is almost certain that unless Jim receives remedial assistance in developing specific arithmetical skills, he is likely to fall farther behind in this area as his academic instruction progresses. Such a deficit may have important practical consequences in his future academic training as well as real-life experiences.

Halstead-Reitan Neuropsychological Test Battery for Older Children

Neuropsychological Deficit Scale. Jim earned a total NDS score of 21, a value that falls well within the normal range. In each of the areas of function his scores were at or better than the mean for control subjects. His only scores of 3 (definitely impaired) occurred on Object Assembly and grip strength with each hand. Considering that he did fairly well on most tests concerned with central processing, the finding that his grip strength was reduced on both sides was obviously of little neuropsychological significance. However, Jim made 62 errors on the Category Test, a result that suggests that his basic ability in abstraction, reasoning, and logical analysis is relatively deficient. This is particularly important when viewed in the context of the normal scores he earned on nearly every other measure.

Jim also performed relatively well on tasks concerned with right/left differences. On this section he earned a score of 5, which is somewhat better than the average of 6.79 points for control subjects. Finally, he was able to perform adequately on all of the tasks in the Dysphasia and Related Variables section. His performances produced a total NDS score of 21, which was less than the mean of 30.43 earned by control subjects and well below the cut-off of 43/44 points.

A review of the test data presented up to this point would suggest that Jim had no significant neuropsychological problems, and that the examination could be used only as a basis for reassuring the parents rather than understanding Jim's difficulties.

Clinical Evaluation of the Test Results. A more detailed clinical evaluation of the test results, however, reveals some imbalances in Jim's cognitive ability structure that are of definite significance and almost certainly predispose him to behave in the way he does. In order to understand and appreciate the implications of Jim's test results, it is imperative that careful attention be directed to the comparative neuropsychological strengths and weaknesses.

First, it is apparent that Jim has perfectly adequate ability to pay close attention to stimulus material and register such information at the cerebral level. We can infer this from his scores of 27 correct on the Seashore Rhythm Test, 6 errors on Speech-sounds Perception Test, and no errors in 40 trials on tactile finger localization. In addition, his Total Time of 5.3 minutes on the Tactual Performance Test was very good. His overall quickness and alertness was further demonstrated by excellent scores on Part A (10 sec) and Part B (22 sec) of the Trail Making Test. There is no doubt that Jim is alert, vigilant, and competent in psychomotor performances. His Memory and Localization scores on the TPT also suggest that he understands and remembers the tasks to which he has been exposed.

The key to understanding disparities in Jim's neuropsychological ability structure is to contrast these excellent scores with his deficient scores. Jim performed poorly on Object Assembly (5) and Picture Completion (7), suggesting that he has some difficulty recognizing relevant details and integrating them into a solution of the total problem. More significant, however, was the fact that Jim's score on the Category Test was definitely in the impaired range, nearly reaching a score of 3 on the NDS. He clearly has more difficulty in abstraction, reasoning, and logical analysis than would be expected in consideration of his other abilities. This score would suggest that it is difficult for Jim to analyze complex situations, develop an understanding of the critical nature of problems, attend to recurring similarities and differences in stimulus material (especially in terms of recognizing which details are important to the solution of the problem and ignoring information that is not important), and use these abilities to reach conclusions that accurately reflect the nature of the problem.

Impairment of these neuropsychological abilities predisposes a child to have difficulty behaving in a relevant manner in social situations, which by their very nature are complex and involve many facets and subtleties. It is likely that Jim does not see these social situations in quite the way other people see them, and often fails to understand subtle aspects of interpersonal relationships that others comprehend and take for granted. In addition, Jim seems to have difficulty responding selectively to the appropriate stimuli in the environment. Impairment in this area creates a situation in which the child is constantly exposed to the entire range of incoming stimulus material, and all stimuli essentially compete for his attention. Without being able to differentiate the relevant information from the irrelevant information as well as the normal child, Jim is not able to analyze the overall problem appropriately and respond in a reasonable manner.

We would not propose a generalization that every child with a score of 62 errors on the Category Test would exhibit these types of behavioral problems. As we mentioned above, in order to develop an understanding of the interaction of neuropsychological abilities for the individual child, it is important to recognize the strengths in conjunction with the areas of weakness. In one sense, Jim might be thought of as the victim of his excellent abilities, especially because they exist in the context of impairment of abstraction, reasoning, and logical analysis.

For example, note particularly the excellent score on the Total Time for the TPT (5.3 min), a value that suggests that Jim is very competent in psychomotor performances. Although the TPT ordinarily involves a substantial element of higher-level problem-solving abilities, there are some people (even including professional athletes) who are very good at this kind of task but show a degree of impairment in basic aspects of judgment and reasoning. We would call the reader's attention to the fact that Jim's test scores represent a modified picture of the "terrible triad," with the missing element being a low Verbal as compared with Performance IQ score.

Even though we would not suggest that Jim has any significant brain damage, a conventional interpretation of the test results would be that he has a mild degree of impairment of brain functions. On the TPT he was a little slow with his right hand (3.0 min) compared with his left hand (1.4 min), possibly indicating a mild degree of left hemisphere dysfunction. However, there was no evidence of aphasia and no other left-hemisphere indicators.

There were also findings implicating the right cerebral hemisphere. Jim was a little slow in finger tapping speed with his left hand (38) compared with his right hand (49). In addition, his drawings of the cross, triangle, and key suggest that he has mild impairment in the area of visual-spatial skills (though we were conservative and did not score constructional dyspraxia as being present on the NDS). Both of his attempts to draw the cross show an imbalance of the extremities, especially on the second drawing. In drawing the first triangle, Jim tended to lose the relationship of the lines, and his attempt to compensate tended to distort the figure. On his drawing of the key he demonstrated a lack of appreciation of the stimulus configuration by adding a notch (which was actually in the wrong direction) on the stem.

Summary and Recommendations

Considered within the context of his many good performances, we would not interpret Jim's results as representing any significant type of brain damage. However, his performances do deviate mildly from normal expectancy. Even though such performances would not be detectable by the conventional neurological examination, these types of deficits appear to have significance neuropsychologically.

Finally, having gained some additional insight into the bases of Jim's problems, the neuropsychologist must consider what approaches might be taken to assist him. In light of Jim's good abilities, we would predict that there may be some improvement in his insight, reasoning, and overall behavioral control within the next two or three years as he matures. Nevertheless, it is clear from the history information that Jim has a significant and serious problem with his behavior at the present time, and intervention should be instituted immediately.

In developing a remediation program for Jim, it would first be important to help his parents understand the neuropsychological basis of their son's problems. An understanding of this type can serve to promote communication rather than frustration and rejection. It is sometimes difficult for the parents to understand how a child's neuropsychological impairment contributes to his/her deviant behavior and at the same time not use a label of "brain impairment" to excuse the child's unacceptable behavior. In most cases of this kind, the neuropsychologist must work closely with the parents to develop a behavior modification program that can be integrated into the child's overall rehabilitation plan.

As the second component of the rehabilitation program, Jim needs help in understanding complex situations, sorting out the relevant information from the irrelevant stimuli before responding to a situation, and essentially learning how to behave in a more appropriate and reasonable way. It is likely that Jim's value system has not been adequately developed and he is not fully aware of the basic importance, to himself as well as to others, of having respect for the needs of others. However, we have learned that an approach directed only at this level is usually not sufficient. Jim needs special training in developing his basic abilities of reasoning, logical analysis, and planned organizational behavior.

We would strongly recommend beginning Jim's rehabilitation program with intensive training using Track C of REHABIT to develop and promote his abilities in this fundamental area of central processing. Next, considering Jim's low scores on Object Assembly and Picture Completion (which were largely responsible for the Performance IQ being 8 points lower than the Verbal IQ), we would continue with training in Track D, to integrate abstraction and reasoning abilities with visual-spatial and performance types of problem-solving tasks. Finally, we would use material in Track B to provide even further training in abstraction and reasoning tasks in the area of verbal and language content.

It is apparent that Jim's neuropsychological structure implies a mild degree of brain-related deficits that require remediation. While counseling would be important both for Jim as well as the family members, especially to overcome negative interactions that have accompanied the long-term development of Jim's problems, a direct approach toward remediation of neuropsychological deficits is also required.

We wish to emphasize that rehabilitation of a child like Jim is an extremely complex (and lengthy) process. Besides cognitive rehabilitation, a comprehensive plan encompassing behavior modification techniques and counseling would have to be instituted and involve Jim's family as well as teachers. Progress is likely to be slow, and any definitive and lasting changes in Jim's personality and behavior may take months and even years to achieve.

■

Appendix

Sample of computerized scoring of the Neuropsychological Deficit Scale (NDS) for Older Children.

THE NEUROPSYCHOLOGICAL DEFICIT SCALE

FOR OLDER CHILDREN (9 THROUGH 14 YEARS)

IBM PC/compatible version 1.0
Copyright 1986, 1991 Ralph M. Reitan, PhD

```
CLIENT:               MARGARET I
GENDER:               FEMALE
HANDEDNESS:           RIGHT
AGE:                  9 YEARS 0 MONTHS
EDUCATION COMPLETED:  GRADE 2
DATE OF BIRTH:        03/14/77
DATE OF EXAM:         03/17/86
```

Based on tentative norms presented in
Neuropsychological Evaluation of Older Children
by R.M. Reitan and D. Wolfson (1992)

ALL RIGHTS RESERVED WORLDWIDE

No part of this package may be copied or
distributed in any form without written permission.

RALPH M. REITAN, PH.D.
DEBORAH WOLFSON, PH.D.
REITAN NEUROPSYCHOLOGY LABORATORY
2920 SOUTH 4TH AVENUE
SOUTH TUCSON, ARIZONA 85713-4819
602/882-2022

NEUROPSYCHOLOGICAL DEFICIT SCALE FOR OLDER CHILDREN   PAGE 1

CLIENT: MARGARET I

LEVEL OF PERFORMANCE

	NDS SCORE:	0	1	2	3
MOTOR FUNCTIONS					
1. Finger Tapping — Dominant				35	
2. Finger Tapping — Nondominant . .			32		
3. Grip Strength — Dominant					14.50
4. Grip Strength — Nondominant . . .				13.00	
5. Name Writing — Dominant					22
6. Name Writing — Nondominant . . .					59
7. TPT — Total Time				11.7	
SENSORY-PERCEPTUAL FUNCTIONS					
8. Sensory Imperception				2	
9. Finger Localization — Right . . .				2	
10. Finger Localization — Left . . .			2		
11. Finger-tip # Writing — Right . .		0			
12. Finger-tip # Writing — Left . . .		2			
13. Tactile Form Recognition — Right		0			
14. Tactile Form Recognition — Left .		0			
VISUAL-SPATIAL SKILLS					
15. Picture Arrangement			8		
16. Block Design			9		
17. Object Assembly		11			
18. Trail Making Test — Part A . . .			16		
ALERTNESS AND CONCENTRATION					
19. Seashore Rhythm Test					15
20. Speech-sounds Perception Test . .			6		
IMMEDIATE MEMORY AND RECAPITULATION					
21. TPT — Memory		6			
22. TPT — Localization		6			
ABSTRACTION, REASONING, LOGICAL ANALYSIS					
23. Category Test				58	
24. Trail Making Test — Part B . . .				51	
25. Coding					5

TOTAL SCORE FOR LEVEL OF PERFORMANCE . . . 35

```
╔══════════════════════════════════════════════════════════╗
║  NEUROPSYCHOLOGICAL DEFICIT SCALE FOR OLDER CHILDREN   PAGE 2  ║
║                                                            ║
║  CLIENT: MARGARET I                                        ║
╚══════════════════════════════════════════════════════════╝
```

```
┌────────────────────────────────┐
│     RIGHT-LEFT DIFFERENCES      │
└────────────────────────────────┘
```

NDS SCORE: 0   1   2   3

MOTOR FUNCTIONS

26. Finger Tapping 0.09
27. Grip Strength 0.10
28. TPT . . . .   -1.52
29. Name Writing (Nondom - Dom) . . .   37

SENSORY-PERCEPTUAL FUNCTIONS

30. Sensory Imperception   2
31. Finger Localization   0
32. Finger-tip Number Writing   2
33. Tactile Form Recognition   0

TOTAL SCORE FOR RIGHT-LEFT DIFFERENCES . . . 11

```
NEUROPSYCHOLOGICAL DEFICIT SCALE FOR OLDER CHILDREN    PAGE 3

CLIENT: MARGARET I
```

```
DYSPHASIA AND RELATED VARIABLES
```

```
34. Dysnomia ----------------- 0
35. Constructional Dyspraxia   0
36. Spelling Dyspraxia ------  1
37. Dysgraphia -------------- 0
38. Dyslexia ---------------- 0
39. Visual Number Dysgnosia - 0
40. Visual Letter Dysgnosia - 0
41. Central Dysarthria ------ 0
42. Auditory Verbal Dysgnosia 0
43. Dyscalculia ------------- 0
44. Right-Left Confusion ---- 0
45. Body Dysgnosia ---------- 0
```

TOTAL SCORE FOR DYSPHASIA AND RELATED VARIABLES . . . 1

```
┌─────────────────────────────────────────────────────────────────────┐
│ ╔═══════════════════════════════════════════════════════════════════╗│
│ ║ NEUROPSYCHOLOGICAL DEFICIT SCALE FOR OLDER CHILDREN    PAGE 4      ║│
│ ║ CLIENT: MARGARET I                                                ║│
│ ╚═══════════════════════════════════════════════════════════════════╝│
│                                                                       │
│                      ╔═══════════════════════╗                        │
│                      ║        SUMMARY        ║                        │
│                      ╚═══════════════════════╝                        │
└───────────────────────────────────────────────────────────────────────┘
```

	Subject's Score	Mean for Controls (9-14 yrs)	Mean for Brain-damaged (9-14 yrs)	Cut-off Score
LEVEL OF PERFORMANCE				
Motor Functions	16	6.29	14.05	
Sensory-perceptual Functions	5	5.15	10.77	
Visual-spatial Skills	3	4.06	7.69	
Attention and Concentration	4	1.91	3.78	
Immediate Memory and Recapitulation	0	2.23	3.31	
Abstraction, Reasoning, Logical Analysis	7	2.63	6.03	
LEVEL OF PERFORMANCE TOTAL	35	22.27	45.63	33/34
RIGHT-LEFT DIFFERENCES				
Motor Functions	6	2.61	6.29	
Sensory-perceptual Functions	5	3.09	5.28	
Both Motor and Sensory-perceptual Functions	0	1.09	2.17	
RIGHT-LEFT DIFFERENCES TOTAL	11	6.79	13.74	9/10
DYSPHASIA AND RELATED VARIABLES	1	1.37	7.97	3/4
TOTAL NEUROPSYCHOLOGICAL DEFICIT SCALE SCORE	47	30.43	67.34	43/44

Glossary

A

ABSCESS A localized collection of pus in a cavity, formed by the disintegration of tissues, due to infection by microorganisms (usually bacteria).

ABSTRACT THINKING A style of thinking in which language and symbols are interpreted conceptually, dissociated from any specific situation; the ability to generalize from the similarities among situations; the ability to reason and discern relationships between variables.

ACUTE Term used to describe a condition having a sudden onset, sharp escalation of clinical symptoms, and short course; not chronic.

AGNOSIA Denoting an absence of knowledge. In aphasia, a deficit (due to brain impairment) in the ability to recognize the symbolic meaning of stimulus material.

ANAPLASIA A characteristic of tumor tissue in which there is a loss of differentiation of cells (dedifferentiation) of their orientation to one another, and to their axial framework and relationship to blood vessels. The degree of anaplasia is related to the malignancy of the tumor.

ANGIOGRAPHY A procedure that enables blood vessels to be seen on film after the vessels have been filled with a contrast medium. Angiography is used to detect conditions that alter the appearance or pattern of blood vessels.

ANOXIA A condition in which the cells do not have (or cannot utilize) sufficient oxygen to perform normal functions.

APHASIA A deficit, due to cerebral impairment, in the ability to utilize language symbols (receptively and/or expressively) for communicative purposes.

APRAXIA A deficit, due to brain impairment, in the ability to perform functional or purposeful acts.

ARTERIOVENOUS MALFORMATION (AVM) An abnormal formation of arteries and veins. It may be only a small tangle of vessels or a large collection of abnormal vessels occupying a large area.

ASTEREOGNOSIS A deficit, due to cerebral impairment, in the ability to identify objects or shapes through the sense of touch.

ASTROCYTE A star-shaped neuroglial cell which supports neurons in the brain and spinal cord and attaches the neurons to blood vessels. Collectively, such cells are called *astroglia*.

ASTROCYTOMA A malignant intrinsic tumor of the brain that arises from astrocytes of the neuroglia.

ATAXIA Disordered, uncoordinated movement, affecting balance and gait, limb or eye movements, and/or speech. Ataxia may be caused by damage to the cerebellum or to the nerve fibers that carry impulses to and from the cerebellum.

ATROPHY A wasting away or decrease in size of a cell, tissue, organ, or part of the body.

ATTENTION The ability to focus on a task or set of stimuli.

AUDITORY VERBAL DYSGNOSIA A deficit, due to brain impairment, of the ability to understand the symbolic significance of verbal communication through the auditory avenue (loss of auditory verbal comprehension).

AURA A "warning" sensation that precedes or marks the onset of a seizure in a person who has epilepsy. An aura may be a distorted perception (such as a hallucinatory sound or smell), or a sensation of movement in part of the body.

AUTOMATISM A state in which behavior is not controlled by the conscious mind. The individual carries out movement and activities without being aware of doing so, and later has no clear memory of what happened. The episodes start abruptly and last a few seconds or minutes at the most. Automatisms are a symptom of psychomotor epilepsy.

B

BABINSKI SIGN Extension (instead of flexion) of the big toe, with or without fanning of the other toes, in response to stimulation of the sole of the foot; occurs in persons with lesions of the pyramidal tract.

BILATERAL Pertaining to both the right and left sides.

BILATERAL SENSORY STIMULATION Stimulation of both sides of the body simultaneously, using touch, hearing, or vision, in order to determine whether an individual imperceives the stimulus on one side or the other.

BILATERAL TRANSFER Facilitation of the performance of a task by one hand as a result of having practiced the task with the other hand.

BODY DYSGNOSIA A deficit, due to cerebral impairment, in the ability to identify body parts.

BRAIN LESION Any pathological or traumatic damage of brain tissue.

C

CALLOSTOMY Resection or severing of the corpus callosum.

CAPILLARY A minute blood vessel which connects the arterioles and the venules, forming a network in nearly all parts of the body that effects a transition from arterial to venous blood flow.

CAUSE-AND-EFFECT REASONING The ability to anticipate and understand the consequences of an action or statement.

CENTRAL DYSARTHRIA A deficit, due to brain impairment, in the ability to enunciate words; characterized by an omission, addition, or transposition of syllables.

CENTRAL NERVOUS SYSTEM (CNS) The part of the nervous system made up of the brain and spinal cord.

CEREBELLUM The portion of the brain that lies behind the cerebrum and the pons and fourth ventricle. The cerebellum is concerned particularly with coordination of voluntary movements.

CEREBRAL ATROPHY A wasting away or diminution in the size of cells or tissue structures of the brain.

CEREBRAL HEMISPHERE The large structure representing either half of the cerebrum.

CEREBRAL HEMORRHAGE Bleeding of a blood vessel within the cerebrum.

CEREBROSPINAL FLUID (CSF) The fluid produced in the choroid plexuses of the cerebral ventricles. It acts as a liquid cushion to protect the brain and spinal cord from shock, delivers nutritive substances filtered from the blood, and removes waste and toxic substances produced by brain and spinal cord cells.

CEREBRUM The main portion of the brain which occupies the upper portion of the cranium and consists principally of the two cerebral hemispheres which are united by large masses of tissue fibers (white matter) called the anterior commissure, the corpus callosum, and the posterior commissure. Some anatomists also include the anterior part of the brainstem in the cerebrum.

CHOREOATHETOTIC MOVEMENTS Movements of both a choreic and athetoid nature. Choreic movements are irregular, rapid, jerky fidgets. Athetosis is marked by ceaseless occurrence of slow, sinuous, writhing movements that are involuntary and may be particularly severe in the hands.

CHRONIC Term used to describe a condition or disease characterized by long duration or frequent occurrence; applied to a disease or condition that is not acute.

COMMISSURAL FIBERS See Transverse fibers.

COMPUTERIZED TOMOGRAPHY (CT OR CAT SCAN) An x-ray procedure in which images or "slices," taken by scanners which rotate around the head, are reconstructed through computer-assisted methods. Computed tomography scanning permits identification and differentiation of many soft tissues in the body because of their absorption differences and the thin sections represented by the images in CT scanning.

CONCENTRATION Maintenance of attention to a task or set of stimuli over a period of time.

CONCRETE THINKING A style of thinking in which the individual perceives each situation as unique, and is unable to generalize from the similarities among situations; thinking in which language and symbols are interpreted literally.

CONCUSSION A condition caused by a physical blow to the head or extreme air blast, often resulting in loss of consciousness, vertigo, nausea, weak pulse, and slow respiration.

CONGENITAL LESIONS Lesions present at or dating from birth.

CONSCIOUSNESS The state of awareness of the self and the environment.

CONSTRUCTIONAL DYSPRAXIA A deficit, due to cerebral impairment, in the ability to deal with spatial relationships in either a two- or three-dimensional framework. This symptom is commonly manifested by impaired ability to copy simple shapes, such as a cross.

CONTRALATERAL Pertaining to the opposite side.

CONTRAST RADIOGRAPHY X-ray procedures in which a contrast substance is injected in order to enhance visualization of particular structures. Customarily a contrast substance is injected into the blood circulation of the organ before x-rays are taken.

CONTRECOUP DAMAGE Damage to the opposite side of the brain from the point of injury.

CONTUSION A bruise.

CORPUS CALLOSUM An arched mass of white matter (nerve fibers), located at the bottom of the longitudinal fissure, made up of transverse fibers which connect the cerebral hemispheres.

CORTICAL ATROPHY Wasting, diminution, or shrinkage of the cerebral cortex.

CRANIECTOMY Surgical removal (excision) of a part of the skull.

CRANIOPHARYNGIOMA A tumor that arises from cells derived from the hypophyseal stalk.

CRANIOTOMY Any operation on the cranium.

CRANIUM The skull.

CT SCANNING See computerized tomography.

CYST A closed cavity or sac, lined by epithelium, and usually containing semisolid material.

D

DECEREBRATE POSTURE (DECEREBRATE RIGIDITY) Exaggerated posture of extension as a result of a lesion to the prepontine area of the brain stem.

DECORTICATE POSTURE (DECORTICATE RIGIDITY) Exaggerated posture of upper extremity flexion and lower extremity extension as a result of a lesion to the mesencephalon or above.

DELTA WAVES (ELECTROENCEPHALOGRAPHY OR EEG) Random slow waves of 1 to 3 cps on EEG tracings.

DIPLOPIA Double vision, or seeing one object as if it were two.

DISTAL Toward the periphery or away from the center of the body.

DURA MATER The tough and mostly fibrous outer layer of the meninges or membranes surrounding the brain.

DYSARTHRIA Impaired articulation of speech due to disturbances of muscular control which result from damage to the central or peripheral nervous system.

DYSCALCULIA A deficit, due to cerebral impairment, in the ability to appreciate the symbolic significance of numbers and the nature of arithmetical processes.

DYSDIADOCHOKINESIS Impairment of the ability to arrest one motor impulse and substitute one that is exactly the opposite. The clinical test for this condition is to have the patient hold out both hands and pronate and supinate them as rapidly as possible.

DYSGNOSIA In contrast to agnosia, dysgnosia represents a partial rather than complete loss in understanding the symbolic significance of information reaching the brain.

DYSGRAPHIA A deficit, due to brain impairment, in the ability to form letters when writing.

DYSKINESIA A general term referring to impairment of voluntary movement which may be expressed in a number of specific ways.

DYSLEXIA A deficit, due to brain impairment, in the ability to read and understand the symbolic significance of words.

DYSMETROPSIA A defect in the visual appreciation of the measure of the size of objects.

DYSNOMIA A deficit, due to brain impairment, in the ability to name objects.

DYSPHAGIA A swallowing defect characterized by difficulty in preparing the food for swallowing or in moving the food from the mouth to the stomach.

DYSPHASIA A deficit, due to brain impairment, in the ability to use language symbols for communicational purposes. Technically, a more appropriate term than aphasia, because most persons with this disorder show impairment rather than a complete loss of the ability.

DYSPRAXIA A deficit, due to brain impairment, in the ability to perform coordinated and purposeful movements necessary to accomplish a specific task.

DYSRHYTHMIA A disturbance or irregularity in the rhythm of EEG tracings.

DYSSTEREOGNOSIS A deficit, due to brain impairment, in the ability to recognize objects through touch.

E

EDEMA Swelling caused by accumulation of abnormally large amounts of fluid in the intercellular tissue spaces of the body.

EEG (ELECTROENCEPHALOGRAM) A recording procedure that uses electrodes placed on the scalp to record electrical activity of the brain.

ENCEPHALITIS Inflammation of the brain, usually due to viral infection.

EPIDURAL HEMATOMA An area of bleeding or accumulation of blood outside of the dura mater and in the epidural space. These lesions are usually due to damage of the middle meningeal artery, and may produce compression of the dura mater and thus compression of the underlying brain tissue.

EPILEPSY A disorder characterized by seizures. It may be due to one of many known causes, but frequently is of unknown etiology.

EQUIPOTENTIALITY The capacity for developing in the same way and to the same extent. The *theory of equipotentiality* states that each lesion of equivalent size in the cerebral cortex, regardless of its location, has equivalent effects.

EXTRINSIC BRAIN TUMOR A tumor that arises from tissue surrounding the brain and, when producing brain-related symptoms, does so through compression of brain tissue.

F

FACIAL PARESIS Weakness or partial paralysis of facial muscles.

FIGURE-GROUND The differentiation between the foreground and the background in a sensory system, including vision, hearing, and touch.

FINGER DYSGNOSIA A deficit, due to brain impairment, in the ability to identify individual fingers following tactile stimulation.

FLACCID Relaxed, flabby, or absent muscular tone; limp.

FORAMEN A natural opening or passage from one area to another.

FORAMEN MAGNUM The large opening in the anterior and inferior part of the occipital bone, interconnecting the vertebral canal and the cranial cavity.

FRONTAL LOBE The anterior lobe in each cerebral hemisphere, bound posteriorly by the central fissure.

G

GENERAL DYSPRAXIA A general deficit, due to brain impairment, in the ability to perform coordinated and purposeful acts.

GLIA Neuroglial cells are part of the supporting structure of nervous tissue in the brain. This structure consists of a fine web of tissue made up of ectodermic elements in which are enclosed odd-shape branched cells known as neuroglia or glial cells. These cells are of three types: macroglia or astroglia, oligodendroglia, and microglia.

GLIOBLASTOMA MULTIFORME (ASTROCYTOMA GRADES III OR IV) A rapidly growing glioma originating from astrocytes (star-shaped cells) of the neuroglia.

GLIOMA A brain tumor composed of tissue which represents neuroglia in any of its stages of development.

GRANULOMA A tumor-like mass or nodule of granulation tissue associated with an infectious disease.

GRAY MATTER Cell bodies of neurons in the central nervous system and ganglia, consisting of nonmyelinated nerve tissue.

GLIOSIS An excess of astroglia in damaged areas of the central nervous system.

H

HAPTIC SENSITIVITY Sensitivity to stimuli through touch and proprioception.

HEAD INJURY Damage to living brain tissue caused by an external force.

HEMIANOPIA Blindness for half the field of vision in each eye.

HEMIHYPALGESIA Diminished sensitivity to pain affecting one lateral half of the body.

HEMIPARESIS Partial paralysis or weakness of one side of the body.

HEMIPLEGIA Paralysis of one side of the body. When the affected muscles are stiff and rigid, the disorder is known as *spastic hemiplegia*; when the muscles are limp and wasted, the term *flaccid hemiplegia* is used.

HEMISENSORY DEFICIT Sensory losses, usually including tactile impairment, on half of the body.

HEMISPHERECTOMY Resection of a cerebral hemisphere.

HEMORRHAGE Bleeding that occurs following damage to blood vessels.

HOFFMANN'S SIGN Increased mechanical irritability of the sensory nerves.

HOMEOSTASIS The dynamic processes by which an organism maintains a constant internal environment despite external changes.

HOMOGENEOUS Consisting of or composed of similar elements or ingredients.

HOMOLOGOUS Corresponding in structure, position, origin, etc.

HOMONYMOUS HEMIANOPIA A loss of half of the visual field for each eye with the loss being on the same side (left or right) for each eye.

HOMONYMOUS QUADRANTANOPIA A loss of one quadrant of the visual field (either upper or lower) on the same side (either right or left) for each eye.

HYDROCEPHALUS An abnormal accumulation of cerebrospinal fluid within the skull, usually with dilatation of the cerebral ventricles, caused most often by obstruction of normal cerebrospinal fluid circulation.

HYDROCEPHALUS EX VACUO Replacement of the space lost by cerebral tissue (in atrophy) by cerebrospinal fluid.

HYPALGESIA Diminished sensitivity to pain.

HYPESTHESIA Impairment or lessening of tactile sensitivity.

I

IDIOPATHIC A term referring to conditions of unknown cause.

IDIOPATHIC EPILEPSY Epilepsy of unknown cause.

IMPERCEPTION (TACTILE, AUDITORY, VISUAL) Failure to perceive a sensory stimulus on one side when stimuli are delivered to both sides simultaneously, even though unilateral stimuli on both sides can be perceived correctly.

INFECTION An invasion and multiplication of pathogenic microorganisms in body tissues, resulting in cellular injury.

INTRINSIC TUMOR A tumor arising from tissues within the brain.

IPSILATERAL Referring to (situated on or affecting) the same side, as opposed to the contralateral side.

ISCHEMIA A deficiency of blood in an organ or a part, due to functional constriction or actual obstruction of a blood vessel.

J-K

JACKSONIAN SEIZURES Epileptic seizures which begin with a small, localized group of muscles and gradually spread to involve a larger muscle group.

JUDGMENT The process of forming an appropriate opinion based on an evaluation of a situation; the ability to make appropriate decisions.

KINESTHESIS A sense by which muscular motion and degree of muscular contraction permits perception of weight, bodily position, etc.

L

LEPTOMENINGES The pia mater and arachnoid considered together as one functional unit.

LESION Any damage to bodily tissues as a result of disease or injury.

LETHARGY A condition of drowsiness or indifference in which one is able to be awakened with stimulation.

LOGICAL ANALYSIS A skill characterized by the ability to formulate a general rule or principle in order to solve a problem; the ability to plan, regulate, and control one's activities.

M

MAJOR MOTOR SEIZURES Epileptic seizures characterized by loss of consciousness and tonic-clonic muscular activity. Also referred to as *grand mal epilepsy*.

MANUAL DEXTERITY Proficiency in performances using the hands.

MEDULLOBLASTOMA A rapidly-growing cerebellar tumor composed of undifferentiated neuroepithelial cells.

MENINGES The three membranous tissues (dura mater, arachnoid, and pia mater) that envelop the brain and spinal cord.

MENINGIOMA A tumor of the meninges. These tumors are classified as benign and are usually slowly growing.

MENINGITIS Inflammation of the meninges. When the dura mater is affected the disease is referred to as *pachymeningitis*; when the arachnoid tissue and pia mater are also involved it is called *leptomeningitis.*

MENINGOCORTICAL SCAR Scar tissue that involves the meninges and the cerebral cortex of the brain.

MORBIDITY The state or condition of being diseased. The morbidity ratio is the proportion of diseased to healthy people in a community.

MORTALITY The death rate, or number of deaths per 100,000 (or, occasionally, per 1,000 or 10,000) of the population per year.

MOTOR AREA The precentral gyrus represented in the posterior part of the frontal lobe. This area serves primary motor functions.

MYOCLONIC EPILEPSY An epileptic seizure in which shock-like contractions occur in a portion of a muscle, an entire muscle, or a group of muscles. These seizures are sometimes restricted to one area of the body or appear either in or out of synchrony in several areas.

N-O

NECROSIS The morphological changes occurring as a result of cell death and caused by progressive degrading action of enzymes.

NEOPLASM A tumor; any new, abnormal growth.

NEURON A nerve cell, or the structural unit of the nervous system, including the cell body and the various processes, collaterals, and terminations of the cell.

NUCHAL RIGIDITY Stiffness of the back of the neck.

NYSTAGMUS An involuntary rapid movement of the eyeball, which may be lateral, vertical, rotatory, or a mixed combination.

OBTUNDED A state of consciousness characterized by a mild to moderate reduction in alertness.

OCCIPITAL LOBE The most posterior lobe of each cerebral hemisphere.

P

PAPILLEDEMA Edema or swelling of the optic papilla which gives rise to an elevation of the optic disc ("choked disc"). Papilledema is usually a sign of increased intracranial pressure.

PARESIS A partial or incomplete paralysis.

PARESTHESIA An abnormal tactile sensation such as numbness, burning, prickling, or tickling.

PARIETAL LOBE One of the four lobes of each cerebral hemisphere that is bound by the frontal lobe anteriorly the occipital lobe posteriorly, and the temporal lobe principally inferiorly.

PARTIAL COMPLEX EPILEPSY Epilepsy in which the seizures include inappropriate complex acts and performances for which the patient is amnesic.

PATHOGNOMONIC SIGNS A sign or symptom specifically distinctive or characteristic of a disease or pathological condition and on the appearance of which a diagnosis can be made.

PERCEPTUAL-MOTOR Relating to the interaction of perceptual abilities and motor abilities.

PERINATAL Relating to the period just before or just after birth. Perinatal is often defined more precisely as the period from the 28th week of pregnancy to the end of the first week after birth.

PERIPHERAL Pertaining to or situated at or near the periphery; situated away from a center or central structure.

PERIPHERAL DYSARTHRIA Impaired ability to enunciate characterized by slurring of speech.

PET SCANNING Positron emission tomography, a diagnostic technique based on the detection of positrons (positively charged particles) that are emitted by labeled substances introduced into the body. PET scanning produces three-dimensional images that reflect the metabolic and chemical activity of the tissues being studied.

PETECHIAL HEMORRHAGE A hemorrhage characterized by petechiae or small spots of bleeding.

PETIT MAL EPILEPSY A type of epilepsy seen particularly in children in which there is a sudden and momentary loss of consciousness with only minor myoclonic jerking. After adolescence it may develop into another form of epilepsy.

PHAGOCYTES Any cell that ingests microorganisms or other cells and foreign particles.

PORENCEPHALY The presence of cavities in the brain which developed in fetal life or early infancy, usually resulting from destructive lesions such as small areas of bleeding. These lesions may be cystic and communicate with the arachnoid space.

PREMORBID Characteristics which existed before a disease or injury occurred.

PROBLEM-SOLVING SKILL Ability to appreciate and consider the factors which may influence a situation, and design and select the most appropriate and advantageous solution; a sequential process involving (1) identification of the problem, (2) generation of response options, (3) evaluation of appropriateness of response options, (4) selection and testing of various options, (5) evaluation of response options, and (6) selection of response option most appropriate to the situation.

PROPRIOCEPTION Sensory awareness of the position of body parts, with or without movement. This state is achieved by means of sensory nerve endings within the muscles, tendons, joints, and sensory hair cells in the inner ear. These structures are called proprioceptors ("position sensors"). Information from the proprioceptors passes to the spinal cord and brain and is used to make adjustments in the state of contraction of muscles so that posture and balance are maintained.

PSEUDOTUMOR CEREBRI A condition characterized by the signs and symptoms of a cerebral tumor in the absence of any space-occupying lesion. The condition is caused by cerebral edema, marked by raised intracranial pressure with headache, nausea, vomiting, and papilledema without neurological signs except occasional sixth nerve palsy. Also called *benign intracranial hypertension.*

PSYCHOMOTOR EPILEPSY A condition now referred to as *partial complex epilepsy.*

R

REASONING The ability to recognize multiple meanings in a situation and choose the meaning most appropriate to that situation; the ability to determine the relationship between objects and concepts; the ability to sort or group objects and concepts based on shared attributes; the ability to take information learned in one situation and apply it to another, similar situation.

REDUNDANCY A concept which employs the postulate that undamaged areas of the brain may be involved in the recovery of functions impaired by damage to more discretely identified areas.

REHABIT (REITAN EVALUATION OF HEMISPHERIC ABILITIES AND BRAIN IMPROVEMENT TRAINING) An extensive, organized program of training procedures used for facilitating improvement or recovery of higher neuropsychological functions in both children and adults. Treatment plans are based on an individual's deficits identified through assessment with the Halstead-Reitan Neuropsychological Test Battery.

REITAN-WOLFSON MODEL A neuropsychological concept of brain-behavior relationships that emphasizes (1) input of information to the brain, (2) assimilation and organization of incoming information of varying types and at several levels (central processing), and (3) organization, selection, and direction of responses on the basis of central processing mechanisms.

RESECTION Removal of a portion of an organ or other structure.

RIGHT-LEFT CONFUSION Confusion of the right and left sides of one's own body or of other persons or objects.

ROMBERG TEST A test used for differentiating between peripheral and cerebellar ataxia. In this test the patient is required to stand in a motionless position with the eyes closed. An increase in movements and uncertainty of physical position with swaying indicates the presence of peripheral ataxia. The test is also used more generally to evaluate clumsiness in movements and the width and uncertainty of gait when the patient's eyes are closed. Absence of difficulties with the eyes closed is characteristic of cerebellar ataxia.

S

SCOTOMA An area in the visual field that is characterized by lost or depressed vision and surrounded by an area of less depressed or normal vision. In other words, specific areas of decreased vision or blindness within the visual field.

SEIZURE An uncontrolled discharge of nerve cells in the brain.

SPELLING DYSPRAXIA A deficit, due to cerebral impairment, in the ability to spell words.

STATIC Not dynamic; a chronic, unchanging condition.

STATUS EPILEPTICUS A series of rapidly repeating epileptic seizures that continue without any intervening periods of consciousness.

STEREOGNOSIS The ability to perceive and understand the form and nature of objects by the sense of touch.

STEREOTAXIC SURGERY Surgery in which the purpose is to place a therapeutic lesion in a precise area of the brain. Mechanical equipment and x-rays are used to localize the specific area.

STRABISMUS Involuntary deviation of the eye from the normal position.

SUBARACHNOID HEMORRHAGE Bleeding into the subarachnoid space.

SUBDURAL HEMATOMA Bleeding into the subdural space.

T

TACTILE Pertaining to touch.

TACTILE FORM DISCRIMINATION Ability to discriminate form or shape through the sense of touch.

TEMPORAL LOBE One of the four lobes of the cerebral hemisphere; it lies in an inferior and lateral position.

TENTORIUM A layer of dura mater which forms a partition between the cerebrum and the cerebellum and covers the upper surface of the cerebellum.

THROMBOSIS The formation of a clot (thrombus) in a blood vessel.

TINNITUS A noise in the ears such as ringing, buzzing, roaring, or clicking.

TONIC-CLONIC SEIZURE A seizure characterized by alternate muscular contraction and relaxation in rapid succession.

TRANSVERSE (COMMISSURAL) FIBERS Fibers which interconnect the two cerebral hemispheres.

TUMOR An abnormal mass of tissue that forms when cells in a specific area reproduce at an increased rate.

U-V

UNILATERAL Pertaining to only one side.

VASCULAR Pertaining to the blood vessels.

VIRAL INFECTIONS Any infection of the body resulting from invasion by a virus.

VISUAL AGNOSIA A deficit, due to cerebral impairment, in the ability recognize objects through vision.

VISUAL FIELD The total area in which visual perception is possible while looking straight ahead. The visual fields normally extend outward over an angle of about 90 degrees on either side of the midline of the face, but are more restricted above and below. The visual fields of the two eyes overlap to a large extent, so that a defect in the field of one eye may be concealed if both eyes are open.

VISUAL FIELD DEFECT Inability to see objects located in a specific region of the field of view ordinarily received by each eye.

VISUAL FORM DYSGNOSIA A deficit, due to brain impairment, in the ability to recognize forms or shapes through visual observation.

VISUAL IMPERCEPTION A deficit, due to brain impairment, in the ability to recognize stimuli presented visually on both sides simultaneously, even though the stimulus can be perceived and reported when given unilaterally. The deficit is usually contralateral to the side of cerebral damage.

VISUAL LETTER DYSGNOSIA A deficit, due to brain impairment, in the ability to recognize the symbolic significance of letters of the alphabet through visual perception.

VISUAL NUMBER DYSGNOSIA A deficit, due to brain impairment, in the ability to recognize the symbolic significance of numbers through visual perception.

W

WHITE MATTER Tissue in the nervous system that is made up of nerve fibers (contrasting with gray matter which is made up of cell bodies).

WORD DEAFNESS (SENSORY APHASIA) A deficit, due to brain impairment, in the ability to interpret the meaning of sounds, especially speech, even though the sense of hearing is intact.

References

Adams, J.H., Mitchell, D.E., Graham, D.I., & Doyle, D. (1977). Diffuse brain damage of immediate impact type. Its relationship to "primary brain stem damage" in head injury. *Brain, 100,* 489-502.

Aita, J.A., & Reitan, R.M. (1948). Psychotic reactions in the late recovery period following brain injury. *American Journal of Psychiatry, 105,* 161-169

Annegers, J.F., Schoenberg, B.S., Okazaki, H., & Kurland, L.T. (1981). Epidemiologic study of primary intracranial neoplasms. *Archives of Neurology, 38,* 217-219.

Barnett, H.J.M., Mohr, J.P., Stein, B.M., & Yatsu, F.M. (1986). *Stroke: Pathophysiology, diagnosis, and management* (Vols. 1 and 2). New York: Churchill Livingstone.

Becker, D.P., Miller, J.D., Young, H.F., Selhorst, J.B., Kishore, P.R.S., Greenberg, R.P., Rosner, M.J., & Ward, J.D. (1982). Diagnosis and treatment of head injury in adults. In J.R. Youmans (Ed.), *Neurological surgery* (Vol. 4). Philadelphia: W.B. Saunders Company.

Benda, C.E. (1930). *Developmental disorders of mentation and cerebral palsies.* New York: Grune and Stratton.

Benda, C.E. (1944). The familial imbecile or oligocephaly as a morbid entity. *American Journal of Mental Deficiency, 49,* 11-32.

Benda, C.E. (1949). *Mongolism and cretinism* (2nd ed.). New York: Grune and Stratton.

Bender, L. (1938). The visual motor Gestalt test and its clinical use. *American Orthopsychiatry Association,* [Monograph No. 3].

Bender, L. (1940). The psychology of children suffering from organic disturbances of the cerebellum. *American Journal of Orthopsychiatry, 10,* 287-293.

Bender, L. (1942a). Cerebral sequelae and behavior disorders following pyogenic meningo-encephalitis in children. *Archives of Pediatrics, 59,* 772-783.

Bender, L. (1942b). Post-encephalitic behavior disorders. In J.B. Neal (Ed.), *Encephalitis: A clinical study* (Chapter VIII, pp. 361-385). New York: Grune and Stratton.

Bender, L. (1951). The psychological treatment of the brain-damaged child. *Quarterly Journal of Child Behavior, 3,* 123-132.

Bender, L. (1956). *Psychopathology of children with organic brain disorders.* Springfield, IL: Charles C. Thomas.

Bender, M.B. (1951). *Disorders of perception.* Springfield, IL: Charles C. Thomas.

Bender, M.B., & Teuber, H.-L. (1946). Phenomena of fluctuation, extinction, and completion in visual perception. *Archives of Neurology and Psychiatry, 55,* 627-658.

Benton, A.L. (1955a). Development of finger-localization capacity in school children. *Child Development, 26,* 225-230.

Benton, A.L. (1955b). Right-left discrimination and finger localization in defective children. *AMA Archives of Neurology and Psychiatry, 74,* 583-589.

Benton, A.L. (1955c). Right-left discrimination, finger-localization and cerebral status. *Acta Psychologica, 2,* 165-166.

Benton, A.L. (1958). Significance of systematic reversal in right-left discrimination. *Acta Psychiatrica et Neurologica Scandinavica, 33,* 129-137.

Benton, A.L. (1959a). Finger localization and finger praxis. *Quarterly Journal of Experimental Psychology, 2,* 39-44.

Benton, A.L. (1959b). Right-left discrimination and finger localization. New York: Paul B. Hoeber, Inc.

Benton, A.L. (1964). Developmental aphasia and brain damage. *Cortex, 1,* 40-52.

Benton, A.L. (1973). Minimal brain dysfunction from a neuropsychological point of view. In F.F. de la Cruz, B.H. Fox, & R.H. Roberts (Eds.), *Minimal brain dysfunction* (Vol. 205). New York: New York Academy of Sciences.

Benton, A.L., & Abramson, L.S. (1952). Gerstmann symptoms following electroshock treatment. *AMA Archives of Neurology and Psychiatry, 68,* 248-257.

Benton, A.L., & Cohen, B.D. (1955). Right-left discrimination and finger-localization in normal and brain-injured subjects. *Proceedings of the Iowa Academy of Science, 62,* 447-451.

Benton, A.L., Hutcheon, J.F., & Seymour, E. (1951). Arithmetic ability, finger-localization capacity and right-left discrimination in normal and defective children. *American Journal of Orthopsychiatry, 21,* 756-766.

Benton, A.L., & Menefee, F.L. (1957). Handedness and right-left discrimination. *Child Development, 28,* 237-242.

Birch, H.G. (1964). The problem of "brain damage" in children. In H.G. Birch (Ed.), *Brain damage in children: The biological and social aspects*. Baltimore: Williams & Wilkins.

Birch, H.G., Belmont, I., & Karp, E. (1967). Delayed information processing and extinction following cerebral damage. *Brain, 90*, 113-130.

Black, F.W. (1986). Digit repetition in brain-damaged adults: Clinical and theoretical implications. *Journal of Clinical Psychology, 42*, 770-782.

Blau, A. (1936). Mental changes following head trauma in children. *AMA Archives of Neurology and Psychiatry, 35*, 723.

Boll, T.J. (1972). Conceptual vs. perceptual vs. motor deficits in brain-damaged children. *Journal of Clinical Psychology, 28*, 157-159.

Boll, T.J. (1974). Behavioral correlates of cerebral damage in children age 9-14. In R.M. Reitan & L.A. Davison (Eds.), *Clinical neuropsychology: Current status and application*. Washington, DC: Hemisphere Press.

Boll, T.J., & Reitan, R.M. (1972a). Comparative ability interrelationships in normal and brain-damaged children. *Journal of Clinical Psychology, 28*, 152-156.

Boll, T.J., & Reitan, R.M. (1972b). The comparative intercorrelations of brain-damaged and normal children on the Trail Making Test and the Wechsler-Bellevue Scale. *Journal of Clinical Psychology, 4*, 491-493.

Boll, T.J., & Reitan, R.M. (1972c). Motor and tactile-perceptual deficits in brain-damaged children. *Perceptual and Motor Skills, 34*, 343-350.

Bond, M.R. (1976). Assessment of the psychosocial outcome of severe head injury. *Acta Neurochirurgica, 34*, 57-70.

Bowman, K.M., & Blau, A. (1943). Psychiatric states following head and brain injuries in adults and children. In S. Brock (Ed.), *Injuries of the skull, brain and spinal cord* (2nd ed.). Baltimore: Williams and Wilkins.

Brown, R.D., Jr., Wiebers, D.O., Whisnant, J.P., O'Fallon, W.M., Piepgras, D.G., Marsh, W.R., & Maciunas, R.J. (1987). The natural history of unruptured intracranial arteriovenous malformations. *Stroke, 18*, 282.

Bruce, D.A., Schut, L., & Sutton, L.N. (1990). Supratentorial brain tumors in children. In J.R. Youmans (Ed.), *Neurological Sur-*

gery (3rd ed., Vol. 5, pp. 3000-3015). Philadelphia: W.B. Saunders Company.

Butler, A.B., Brooks, W.H., & Netsky, M.G. (1982). Classification and biology of brain tumors. In J.R. Youmans (Ed.), *Neurological surgery* (Vol. 1). Philadelphia: W.B. Saunders Company.

Carmon, A., & Benton, A.L. (1969). Tactile perception of direction and number in patients with unilateral cerebral disease. *Neurology, 19,* 525-5332.

Chadwick, O., Rutter, M., Shaffer, D., & Shrout, P. (1981). A prospective study of children with head injuries: IV. Specific cognitive deficits. *Journal of Clinical Neuropsychology, 3,* 101-120.

Chadwick, O., Rutter, M., Thompson, J., & Shaffer, D. (1981). Intellectual performance and reading skills after localized head injury in childhood. *Journal of Child Psychology and Psychiatry, 22,* 117-139.

Chapman, L.F., & Wolff, H.G. (1959). The cerebral hemispheres and the highest integrative functions of man. *Archives of Neurology, 1,* 357-424.

Chelune, G.J., & Edwards, P. (1981). Early brain lesions: Ontogenetic-environmental considerations. *Journal of Consulting and Clinical Psychology, 49,* 777-790.

Clements, S.D. (1966). Minimal brain dysfunction in children: Terminology and identification; phase one of a three-phase project. Washington, DC: US Department of Health, Education and Welfare (NINDB Monograph No. 3).

Clements, S.D., & Peters, J.E. (1962). Minimal brain dysfunctions in the school-age child. *Archives of General Psychiatry, 6,* 185-197.

Costa, L.D., Vaughn, H.G., Levita, E., & Farber, N. (1963). Purdue Pegboard as a predictor of the presence and laterality of cerebral lesions. *Journal of Consulting Psychology, 27,* 133-137.

Critchley, M. (1953). *The parietal lobes.* London: Arnold.

Crook, T., Bartus, R.T., Ferris, S.H., Whitehouse, P., Cohen, G.D., & Gershon, S. (1986). Age-associated memory impairment: Proposed diagnostic criteria and measures of change. Report of a National Institute of Mental Health work group. *Developmental Neuropsychology, 2,* 261-276.

Cruickshank, W.M. (Ed.). (1966). *The teacher of brain-injured children.* Syracuse, NY: Syracuse University Press.

de la Cruz, F.F., Fox, B.H., & Roberts, R.H. (1973). *Minimal brain dysfunction*. New York: New York Academy of Sciences [Vol. 205].

Danoff, B.F., Cowchock, F.S., Marquette, C., et al. (1982). Assessment of the long-term effects of primary radiation therapy for brain tumors in children. *Cancer, 49,* 1580-1596.

Denhoff, E., & Robinault, I.P. (1960). *Cerebral palsy and related disorders*. New York: McGraw-Hill Book Company, Inc.

Dikmen, S., & Reitan, R.M. (1976). Psychological deficits and recovery of functions after head injury. *Transactions of the American Neurological Association, 101,* 72-77.

Dodrill, C.B. (1979). Sex differences on the Halstead-Reitan Neuropsychological Battery and on other neuropsychological measures. *Journal of Clinical Psychology, 35,* 236-241.

Dodrill, C.B. (1981). Neuropsychology of epilepsy. In S.B. Filskov & T.J. Boll (Eds.), *Handbook of clinical neuropsychology*. New York: Wiley-Interscience.

Doehring, D.G. (1968). *Patterns of impairment in specific reading disability*. Bloomington: Indiana University Press.

Doehring, D.G., & Reitan, R.M. (1961). Behavioral consequences of brain damage associated with homonymous field visual defects. *Journal of Comparative and Physiological Psychology, 54,* 489-492.

Doehring, D.G., & Reitan, R.M. (1962). Concept attainment of human adults with lateralized cerebral lesions. *Perceptual and Motor Skills, 14,* 27-33.

Doehring, D.G., Reitan, R.M., & Kløve, H. (1961). Changes in patterns of intelligence test performances associated with homonymous visual field defects. *Journal of Nervous and Mental Disease, 132,* 227-233.

Doehring, D.G., Trites, R.L., Patel, P.G., & Fiedorowicz, C.A.M. (1981). *Reading disabilities: The interaction of reading, language, and neuropsychological deficits*. New York: Academic Press.

Dostrovosky, J.O., Millar, J., & Wall, P.D. (1976). The immediate shift of afferent drive of dorsal column nucleus cells following deafferentation. *Experimental Neurology, 52,* 480-495.

Duffy, F.H., & Geschwind, N. (Eds.). (1985). *Dyslexia: A neuroscientific approach to clinical evaluation*. Boston: Little, Brown and Co.

Ebaugh, F. (1923). Neuropsychiatric sequelae of acute epidemic encephalitis in children. *American Journal of Diseases of Children, 25,* 89-97.

Eisenberg, H.M. (1982). Late complications of head injury. In Section of Pediatric Neurosurgery of the American Association of Neurological Surgeons, *Pediatric Neurosurgery* (pp. 321-331). New York: Grune & Stratton.

Ernhart, C.B., Graham, F.K., Eichman, P.L., Marshall, J.M., & Thurston, D. (1963). Brain injury in the pre-school child: Some developmental considerations: II. Comparison of brain-injured and normal children. *Psychological Monographs: Genetic and Applied, 77,* 16-33.

Finger, S., & Stein, D.G. (1982). *Brain damage and recovery: Research and clinical perspectives.* New York: Academic Press.

Finger, S., & Wolf, C. (1988). The 'Kennard Effect' before Kennard. *Archives of Neurology, 45,* 1136-1142.

Finlayson, M.A.J., Johnson, K.A., & Reitan, R.M. (1977). Relationship of level of education to neuropsychological measures in brain-damaged and non-brain-damaged adults. *Journal of Consulting and Clinical Psychology, 45,* 536-542.

Finlayson, M.A.J., & Reitan, R.M. (1976a). Handedness in relation to measures of motor and tactile-perceptual functions in normal children. *Perceptual and Motor Skills, 43,* 475-481.

Finlayson, M.A.J., & Reitan, R.M. (1976b). Tactual perceptual functioning in relation to intellectual, cognitive, and reading skills in younger and older normal children. *Developmental Medicine and Child Neurology, 18,* 442-446.

Fitzhugh, K.B., Fitzhugh, L.C., & Reitan, R.M. (1962). Wechsler-Bellevue comparisons in groups with "chronic" and "current" lateralized and diffuse brain lesions. *Journal of Consulting Psychology, 26,* 306-310.

Fitzhugh, L.C., Fitzhugh, K.B., & Reitan, R.M. (1962). Sensorimotor deficits of brain-damaged subjects in relation to intellectual level. *Perceptual and Motor Skills, 15,* 603-608.

Fulbright, R., & Hom, J. (1987). Neuropsychological correlates of early stage Alzheimer's disease. Unpublished manuscript.

Gaddes, W.H. (1980). *Learning disabilities and brain function.* New York: Springer-Verlag.

Gentry, L.R., Godersky, J.C., & Thompson, B.H. (1989). Traumatic brain stem injury: MR imaging. *Radiology, 171,* 177-187.

Gerstmann, J. (1927). Fingeragnosie und isolierte agraphie, ein neues syndrom. *Ztschr. Neurol. Psych., 108,* 152-177.

Gibbs, C.E. (1930). Behavior disorders in chronic epidemic encephalitis. *American Journal of Psychiatry, 9,* 619.

Goldberg, E., & Costa, L.D. (1981). Hemisphere differences in the acquisition and use of descriptive systems. *Brain and Language, 14,* 144-173.

Goldstein, K. (1936). The significance of the frontal lobes for mental performances. *Journal of Neurology and Psychopathology, 17,* 27-40.

Goldstein, K. (1942a). *Aftereffects of brain injuries in war.* New York: Grune & Stratton.

Goldstein, K. (1942b). The two ways of adjustment of the organism to cerebral defects. *Journal of Mount Sinai Hospital, 9,* 504-513.

Goldstein, K. (1948). *Language disturbances.* New York: Grune and Stratton.

Gomez, M.R. (1967). Minimal cerebral dysfunction (maximal neurologic confusion). *Clinical Pediatrics, 6,* 589-591.

Goodglass, H., & Kaplan, E. (1972). *The assessment of aphasia and related disorders.* Philadelphia: Lea & Febiger.

Goodglass, H., & Kaplan, E. (1979). Assessment of cognitive deficit in the brain-injured patient. In M.S. Gazzaniga (Ed.), *Handbook of behavioral neurobiology* (Vol. 2, Neuropsychology). New York: Plenum Press.

Goodstein, L.D. (1957). Right-left discrimination and finger localization in schizophrenic subjects. *Proceedings of the Iowa Academy of Science, 64,* 504-507.

Green, J.R., Waggener, J.D., & Kriegsfeld, B.A. (1976). Classification and incidence of neoplasms of the central nervous system. *Advances in Neurology, 15,* 51-55.

Greer, M. (1967). Benign intracranial hypertension in children. *Pediatric Clinics of North America, 14,* 819-830.

Greer, M. (1990). Pseudotumor cerebri. In J.R. Youmans (Ed.), *Neurological Surgery* (3rd ed., Vol. 5, pp. 3514-3527). Philadelphia, W.B. Saunders Company.

Gudmundsson, K.R. (1970). A survey of tumours of the central nervous system in Iceland during the 10-year period 1954-1963. *Acta Neurologica Scandinavica, 46,* 538-552.

Haines, S.J., Mampalam, T., Rosenblum, M.L., & Nagib, M.G. (1990). Cranial and intracranial bacterial infections. In J.R. Youmans (Ed.), *Neurological Surgery* (3rd ed., Vol. 6, pp. 3707-3735). Philadelphia: W.B. Saunders Company.

Halstead, W.C. (1940). Preliminary analysis of grouping behavior in patients with cerebral injury by the method of equivalent and nonequivalent stimuli. *American Journal of Psychiatry, 96,* 1263-94.

Halstead, W.C. (1945). Brain injuries and the higher levels of consciousness. Trauma of the central nervous system. Association for Nervous & Mental Disease (Chapter 20). Baltimore: Williams & Wilkins.

Halstead, W.C. (1947). *Brain and intelligence: A quantitative study of the frontal lobes.* Chicago: University of Chicago Press.

Halstead, W.C., & Wepman, J.M. (1949). The Halstead-Wepman Aphasia Screening Test. *Journal of Speech and Hearing Disorders, 14,* 9-13.

Harsh, G.R., & Wilson, C.B. (1990). Neuroepithelial tumors of the adult brain. In J.R. Youmans (Ed.), *Neurological Surgery* (3rd ed., Vol. 5, pp. 3040-3136). Philadelphia: W.B. Saunders Company.

Hathaway, S.R., & McKinley, J.C. (1951). *The Minnesota Multiphasic Personality Inventory Manual* (Revised). New York: Psychological Corporation.

Hays, K.J. (1962). Genes, drive and intellect. *Psychological Reports, 10,* 299-342.

Hécaen, H., & Albert, M.L. (1978). *Human neuropsychology.* New York: Wiley.

Hécaen, H., Penfield, W., Bertrand, C. & Malmo, R. (1956). The syndrome of apractoagnosia due to lesions of the minor hemisphere. *Archives of Neurology and Psychiatry, 75,* 400-434.

Heideman, R.L., Packer, R.J., Albright, L.A., & Freeman, C.N. (1990). Central nervous system tumors. In P.A. Pizzo & D.G. Poplack (Eds.), *Principles and practice of pediatric oncology.* Philadelphia: J.B. Lippincott Company.

Heimburger, R.F., DeMyer, W., & Reitan, R.M. (1964). Implications of Gerstmann's syndrome. *Journal of Neurology, Neurosurgery and Psychiatry, 27,* 52-57.

Herring, S., & Reitan, R.M. (1986). Sex similarities in Verbal and Performance IQ deficits following unilateral cerebral lesions. *Journal of Consulting and Clinical Psychology, 54,* 537-541.

Hohman, L.B. (1922). Post-encephalitic behavior disorders in children. *Johns Hopkins Hospital Bulletin, 33,* 372-375.

Hom, J. (1992). General and specific cognitive dysfunctions in patients with Alzheimer's disease. *Archives of Clinical Neuropsychology, 7,* 121-133.

Hom, J., & Reitan, R.M. (1982). Effect of lateralized cerebral damage upon contralateral and ipsilateral sensorimotor performances. *Journal of Clinical Neuropsychology, 4,* 249-268.

Hom, J., & Reitan, R.M. (1984). Neuropsychological correlates of rapidly vs. slowly growing intrinsic neoplasms. *Journal of Clinical Neuropsychology, 6,* 309-324.

Honig, P.J., & Charney, E. (1982). Distinguishing features in children with brain tumor headache. *American Journal of Disabled Children, 136,* 121-124.

Hynd, C.R. (1986). Educational intervention in children with developmental learning disorders. In J.E. Obrzut & G.W. Hynd (Eds.), *Child neuropsychology.* Vol. 2. Clinical practice (pp. 265-297). New York: Academic Press.

Isaacson, R.L. (1975). The myth of recovery from early brain damage. In N.G. Ellis (Ed.), *Aberrant development in infancy.* New York: Wiley.

Jefferson, A., & Clark, J. (1976). Treatment of benign intracranial hypertension by dehydrating agents with particular reference to the measurement of the blind spot as a means of recording improvement. *Journal of Neurology, Neurosurgery, and Psychiatry, 39,* 627-639.

Jennett, B., & Teasdale, G. (1981). *Management of head injuries.* Philadelphia: F.A. Davis Company.

Johnson, I. & Paterson, A. (1974). Benign intracranial hypertension. Diagnosis and prognosis. *Brain, 97,* 289.

Journal of Learning Disabilities. (1989). Vol. 22, No. 6.

Karzmark, P., Heaton, R.K., Lehman, R.A.W., & Crouch, J. (1985). Utility of the Seashore Tonal Memory Test in neuropsychological assessment. *Journal of Clinical and Experimental Neuropsychology, 7,* 357-374.

Katzman, R., Terry, R., DeTeresa, R., Brown, T., Davies, P., Fuld, P., Renbing, X., & Peck, A. (1988). Clinical, pathological, and neurochemical changes in dementia: A subgroup with preserved mental status and numerous neocortical plaques. *Annals of Neurology, 23,* 138-144.

Kaufman, A.S. (1990). *Assessing adolescent and adult intelligence.* Boston: Allyn and Bacon, Inc.

Kennard, M.A. (1936). Age and other factors in motor recovery from precentral lesions in monkeys. *American Journal of Physiology, 115,* 138-146.

Kennard, M.A. (1938). Reorganization of motor function in the cerebral cortex of monkeys deprived of motor and premotor areas in infancy. *Journal of Neurophysiology, 1,* 477-497.

Kennard, M.A. (1940). Relation of age to motor impairment in man and in subhuman primates. *Archives of Neurology and Psychiatry, 44,* 377-397.

Kennard, M.A. (1942). Cortical reorganization of motor function. *Archives of Neurology and Psychiatry, 48,* 227-240.

Kennard, M.A. (1944). Reaction of monkeys of various ages to partial and complete decortication. *Journal of Neuropathology and Experimental Neurology, 3,* 289-310.

Kennedy, C., & Ramirez, L.S. (1964). Brain damage as a cause of behavior disturbance in children (pp. 13-23). In H.G. Birch (Ed.), *Brain damage in children.* New York: The Williams & Wilkins Company.

Kephart, N.C. (1960). *The slow learner in the classroom.* Columbus, OH: Charles E. Merrill Books, Inc.

Kertesz, A. (1979). Recovery and treatment. In K.M. Heilman & E. Valenstein (Eds.), *Clinical neuropsychology.* New York: Oxford University Press.

Kessler, J.W. (1980). History of minimal brain dysfunctions. In H.E. Rie and E.D. Rie (Eds.), *Handbook of minimal brain dysfunctions: A critical view.* New York: John Wiley & Sons.

Kimble, G.A. (1956). *Principles of general psychology.* New York: Ronald Press.

Kirk, U. (Ed.). (1983). *Neuropsychology of language, reading, and spelling.* New York: Academic Press.

Klonoff, H., & Paris, R. (1974). Immediate, short-term, and residual effects of acute head injuries in children: Neuropsychological and neurological correlates. In R.M. Reitan & L.A. Davison (Eds.), *Clinical neuropsychology: Current status and applications.* Washington, DC: Hemisphere Publishing Corp.

Kløve, H. (1959). Relationship of differential electroencephalographic patterns to distribution of Wechsler-Bellevue scores. *Neurology, 9,* 871-876.

Kløve, H., & Matthews, C.G. (1966). Psychometric and adaptive abilities in epilepsy with differential etiology. *Epilepsia, 7,* 330-338.

Kløve, H., & Reitan, R.M. (1958). The effect of dysphasia and spatial distortion on Wechsler-Bellevue results. *Archives of Neurology and Psychiatry, 80,* 708-713.

Knights, R.M., & Bakker, D.J. (Eds.). (1976). *The neuropsychology of learning disorders.* Baltimore: University Park Press.

Knights, R.M., & Bakker, D.J. (Eds.). (1980). *Treatment of hyperactive and learning disordered children: Current research.* Baltimore: University Park Press.

Kolb, B., & Whishaw, I.Q. (1980). *Fundamentals of human neuropsychology.* San Francisco: W.H. Freeman.

Krynauw, R.A. (1950). Infantile hemiplegia treated by removing one cerebral hemisphere. *Journal of Neurology, Neurosurgery, and Psychiatry, 13,* 243-267.

Laine, E., Pruvet, P., & Osson, D. (1964). Résultats éloignés de l'hémisphérectomie dans les cas d'hémiatrophie cérébrale infantile génératrice d'epilepsie. *Neuro-Chirugerie, 10,* 507-522.

Levin, H.S., Amparo, E.G., Eisenberg, H.M., Miner, M.E., High, W.M., Ewing-Cobbs, L., Fletcher, J.M., & Guinto, F.C. (1989). Magnetic resonance imaging after closed head injury in children. *Neurosurgery, 24,* 223-227.

Luria, A.R. (1970). The functional organization of the brain. *Scientific American, 222,* 66-73.

Marie, Pierre. (1906). Revision de la question de l'aphasie. *Semaine Medicine.*

Marshall, W.C. (1983). Infections of the nervous system. In E.M. Brett. *Paediatric neurology.* Edinburgh: Churchill Livingstone.

Masland, R.L., Sarason, S.B., & Gladwin, T. (1958). *Mental subnormality: Biological, psychological and cultural factors.* New York: Basic Books.

Matarazzo, J.D. (1972). *Wechsler's measurement and appraisal of adult intelligence* (5th ed.). New York: Oxford University Press.

Matson, D.D. (1969). *Neurosurgery of infancy and childhood* (2nd ed.). Springfield, IL: Charles C. Thomas.

Matthews, C.G. (1963). Problem-solving and experiential background determinants of test performances in mentally retarded subjects. *Psychological Reports, 13,* 391-401.

Matthews, C.G. (1974). Applications of neuropsychological test methods in mentally retarded subjects. In R.M. Reitan & L.A. Davison (Eds.), *Clinical neuropsychology: Current status and applications* (pp. 267-280). Washington, DC: Hemisphere Publishing Corporation.

Matthews, C.G., & Kløve, H. (1967). Differential psychological performances in major motor, psychomotor, and mixed seizure classifications of known and unknown etiology. *Epilepsia, 8,* 117-128.

Matthews, C.G., & Reitan, R.M. (1961). Comparison of abstraction ability in retardates and in patients with cerebral lesions. *Perceptual and Motor Skills, 13,* 327-333.

Matthews, C.G., & Reitan, R.M. (1962). Psychomotor abilities of retardates and patients with cerebral lesions. *American Journal of Mental Deficiency, 66,* 607-612.

Matthews, C.G., & Reitan, R.M. (1963). Relationship of differential abstraction ability levels to psychological test performances in mentally retarded subjects. *American Journal of Mental Deficiency, 68,* 235-244.

McFie, J. (1961). Intellectual impairment in children with localized postinfantile cerebral lesions. *Journal of Neurology, Neurosurgery, and Psychiatry, 24,* 361-365.

McFie, J., & Piercy, M.F. (1952). The relation of laterality of lesion to performance on Weigl's sorting test. *Journal of Mental Science, 98,* 299-305.

Menkes, J.H. (1980). *Textbook of child neurology* (2nd ed.). Philadelphia: Lea & Febiger.

Meyers, R. (1947). The relationship between "thinking" and language: An experimental approach using dysphasic patients. *Transactions of the American Neurological Association,* 65-69.

Meyers, R. (1948). Relation of "thinking" and language: An experimental approach using dysphasic patients. *Archives of Neurology and Psychiatry, 60,* 119-139.

Miller, J.D., & Becker, D.P. (1982). General principles and pathophysiology of head injury. In J.R. Youmans (Ed.), *Neurological surgery* (Vol. 4). Philadelphia: W.B. Saunders Company.

Milner, B. (1971). Interhemispheric differences in the localization of psychological processes in man. *British Medical Bulletin, 27,* 272-277.

Mitchell, D.E., & Adams, J.H. (1973). Primary focal impact damage to the brainstem in blunt head injuries: Does it exist? *Lancet, 2,* 215-218.

Molfese, D.L. (1977). Infant cerebral asymmetry. In S.J. Segalowitz & F.A. Gruger (Eds.), *Language development and neurological theory* (pp. 22-33). New York: Academic Press.

Moruzzi, G., & Magoun, H.W. (1949). Brain stem reticular formation and activation of the EEG. *Electroencephalography and Clinical Neurophysiology, 1,* 455-473.

Munn, N.L. (1951). *Psychology* (2nd ed.). New York: Houghton Mifflin Company.

Nelson, D.F., Nelson, J.S., Davis, D.R., et al. (1985). Survival and prognosis of patients with astrocytomas with atypical or anaplastic features. *Journal of Neuro-Oncology, 3,* 99-104.

Nici, J., & Reitan, R.M. (1987). Patterns of neuropsychological ability in brain-damaged versus normal children. *Journal of Clinical and Consulting Psychology, 54,* 542-545.

Oddy, M., Humphrey, M., & Uttley, D. (1978). Subjective impairment of social recovery after closed head injury. *Journal of Neurology, Neurosurgery, and Psychiatry, 41,* 611-616.

Oppenheimer, D.R. (1968). Microscopic lesions in the brain following head injury. *Journal of Neurology, Neurosurgery, and Psychiatry, 31,* 299-306.

Packer, R.J., Atkins, T., Littman, P.A., et al. (1983). Neurological and neuropsychologic sequelae in survivors of childhood brain tumors. *Proceedings of the International Society of Pediatric Oncology, 15,* 71.

Packer, R.J., Schut, L., Sutton, L.N., & Bruce, D.A. (1990). Brain tumors of the posterior cranial fossa in infants and children. In. J.R. Youmans (Ed.), *Neurological Surgery* (3rd ed., Vol. 5, pp. 3017-3039). Philadelphia: W.B. Saunders Company.

Pasamanick, B., & Knobloch, H. (1959). Syndrome of minimal cerebral damage in infancy. *Journal of the American Medical Association, 170,* 1384-1387.

Penfield, W., & Roberts, L. (1959). *Speech and brain mechanisms.* Princeton, NJ: Princeton University Press.

Pennington, H., Galliani, C., & Voegele, G. (1965). Unilateral electroencephalographic dysrhythmia and children's intelligence. *Child Development, 36,* 539-546.

Pirozzolo, F.J. (1979). *The neuropsychology of developmental reading disorders.* New York: Praeger Publishers.

Pirozzolo, F.J., & Wittrock, M.C. (Eds.). (1981). *Neuropsychological and cognitive processes in reading.* New York: Academic Press.

Prigatano, G.P. (1986). *Neuropsychological rehabilitation after brain injury.* Baltimore: Johns Hopkins University Press.

Rapin, I. & Wilson, B.C. (1978). Children with developmental language disability: Neurological aspects and assessment. In M.A. Wyke (Ed.), *Developmental dysphasia.* New York: Academic Press.

Rasmussen, T., & Villemure, J-G. (1989). Cerebral hemispherectomy for seizures with hemiplegia. *Cleveland Clinic Journal of Medicine, 56* (Supplement, Part 1), S-62 - S-67.

Reed, H.B.C, & Reitan, R.M. (1963). Intelligence test performances of brain-damaged subjects with lateralized motor deficits. *Journal of Consulting Psychology, 27,* 102-106.

Reed, H.B.C, Reitan, R.M., & Kløve, H. (1965). The influence of cerebral lesions on psychological test performances of older children. *Journal of Consulting Psychology, 29,* 247-251.

Reed, J.C. (1967a). Lateralized finger agnosia and reading achievement at ages 6 and 10. *Child Development, 38,* 213-220.

Reed, J.C. (1967b). Reading achievement as related to differences between WISC Verbal and Performance IQ's. *Child Development, 38,* 835-840.

Reed, J.C., & Reitan, R.M. (1969). Verbal and performance differences among brain-injured children with lateralized motor deficits. *Perceptual and Motor Skills, 29,* 747-752.

Reitan, R.M. (1953). Intellectual functions in aphasic and non-aphasic brain injured subjects. *Neurology, 3,* 202-212.

Reitan, R.M. (1955a). Certain differential effects of left and right cerebral lesions in human adults. *Journal of Comparative and Physiological Psychology, 48,* 474-477.

Reitan, R.M. (1955b). An investigation of the validity of Halstead's measures of biological intelligence. *Archives of Neurology and Psychiatry, 73,* 28-35.

Reitan, R.M. (1955c). The relation of the Trail Making Test to organic brain damage. *Journal of Consulting Psychology, 19,* 393-394.

Reitan, R.M. (1956). Investigation of relationships between "psychometric" and "biological" intelligence. *Journal of Nervous and Mental Disease, 123,* 536-541.

Reitan, R.M. (1958a). Qualitative versus quantitative mental changes following brain damage. *Journal of Psychology, 46,* 339-346.

Reitan, R.M. (1958b). The validity of the Trail Making Test as an indicator of organic brain damage. *Perceptual and Motor Skills, 8,* 271-276.

Reitan, R.M. (1959a). The comparative effects of brain damage on the Halstead Impairment Index and the Wechsler-Bellevue Scale. *Journal of Clinical Psychology, 15,* 281-285.

Reitan, R.M. (1959b). *The effects of brain lesions on adaptive abilities in human beings.* Tucson, AZ: Neuropsychology Press.

Reitan, R.M. (1959c). Impairment of abstraction ability in brain damage: Quantitative versus qualitative changes. *Journal of Psychology, 48,* 97-102.

Reitan, R.M. (1960). The significance of dysphasia for intelligence and adaptive abilities. *Journal of Psychology, 50,* 355-376.

Reitan, R.M. (1966). A research program on the psychological effects of brain lesions in human beings. In N.R. Ellis (Ed.), *International Review of Research in Mental Retardation* (Vol. 1, pp. 153-218). New York: Academic Press.

Reitan, R.M. (1967). Psychological assessment of deficits associated with brain lesions in subjects with normal and subnormal intelligence. In J.L. Khanna (Ed.), *Brain damage and mental retardation: A psychological evaluation.* Springfield, IL: Charles C. Thomas.

Reitan, R.M. (1970). Sensorimotor functions, intelligence and cognition, and emotional status in subjects with cerebral lesions. *Perceptual and Motor Skills, 13,* 275-284.

Reitan, R.M. (1971a). Sensorimotor functions in brain-damaged and normal children of early school age. *Perceptual and Motor Skills, 33,* 655-664.

Reitan, R.M. (1971b). Complex motor functions of the preferred and nonpreferred hands in brain-damaged and normal children. *Perceptual and Motor Skills, 33,* 671-675.

Reitan, R.M. (1971c). Trail Making Test results for normal and brain-damaged children. Perceptual and Motor Skills, 33, 575-581.

Reitan, R.M. (1972). Verbal problem solving as related to cerebral damage. *Perceptual and Motor Skills, 34,* 515-524.

Reitan, R.M. (1974). Psychological effects of cerebral lesions in children of early school age. In R.M. Reitan & L.A. Davison (Eds.), *Clinical neuropsychology: Current applications* (pp. 53-90). Washington, DC: Hemisphere Publishing Corp.

Reitan, R.M. (1976). Psychological testing of epileptic patients. In P.J. Vinken & G.W. Bruyn (Eds.), *Handbook of clinical neurology: The epilepsies* (Vols. 9 and 10). North Holland Publishing Company.

Reitan, R.M. (1984a). *Aphasia and sensory-perceptual deficits in adults.* Tucson, AZ: Neuropsychology Press.

Reitan, R.M. (1984b). An impairment index of brain functions in children. *Perceptual and Motor Skills, 58,* 875-881.

Reitan, R.M. (1985). *Aphasia and sensory-perceptual deficits in children.* Tucson, AZ: Neuropsychology Press.

Reitan, R.M. (1985b). Relationships between measures of brain functions and general intelligence. *Journal of Clinical Psychology, 41,* 245-253.

Reitan, R.M. (1986). Theoretical and methodological bases of the Halstead-Reitan Neuropsychological Test Battery. In I. Grant & K.M. Adams (Eds.), *Neuropsychological assessment of neuropsychiatric disorders.* New York: Oxford University Press.

Reitan, R.M. (1988). Integration of neuropsychological theory, assessment, and application. *The Clinical Neuropsychologist, 2,* 331-349.

Reitan, R.M., & Boll, T.J. (1971). Intellectual and cognitive functions in Parkinson's disease. *Journal of Consulting and Clinical Psychology, 37,* 364-369.

Reitan, R.M., & Boll, T.J. (1973). Neuropsychological correlates of minimal brain dysfunction. In Annals of the New York Academy of Sciences, *Conference on Minimal Brain Dysfunction* (pp. 65-88). New York: New York Academy of Sciences.

Reitan, R.M., & Davison, L.A. (Eds.). (1974). Clinical neuropsychology: *Current status and applications.* Washington, DC: Hemisphere Publishing Corp.

Reitan, R.M., & Herring, S. (1985). A short screening device for identification of cerebral dysfunction in children. *Journal of Consulting and Clinical Psychology, 41,* 643-650.

Reitan, R.M., Hom, J., & Wolfson, D. (1988). Verbal processing by the brain. *Journal of Experimental and Clinical Neuropsychology,* *10,* 400-408.

Reitan, R.M., Reed, J.C., & Dyken, M.L. (1971). Cognitive, psycho-motor, and motor correlates of multiple sclerosis. *Journal of Nervous and Mental Disease, 153,* 218-224.

Reitan, R.M., & Sena, D.A. (1983, August). The efficacy of the REHABIT technique in remediation of brain-injured people. Paper presented at the meeting of the American Psychological Association, Anaheim, CA.

Reitan, R.M., & Wolfson, D. (1985). *The Halstead-Reitan Neuro-psychological Test Battery: Theory and clinical interpretation.* Tucson, AZ: Neuropsychology Press.

Reitan, R.M., & Wolfson, D. (1986). *Traumatic brain injury. Vol. I. Pathophysiology and neuropsychological evaluation.* Tucson, AZ: Neuropsychology Press.

Reitan, R.M., & Wolfson, D. (1988a). The Halstead-Reitan Neuro-psychological Test Battery and REHABIT: A model for inte-grating evaluation and remediation of cognitive impairment. *Cognitive Rehabilitation, 6,* 10-17.

Reitan, R.M., & Wolfson, D. (1988b). *Traumatic brain injury. Vol. II. Recovery and rehabilitation.* Tucson, AZ: Neuropsychology Press.

Reitan, R.M., & Wolfson, D. (1988c). Neuropsychological func-tions of learning-disabled, brain-damaged, and normal chil-dren. *The Clinical Neuropsychologist, 2,* 278.

Reitan, R.M., & Wolfson, D. (1989). The Seashore Rhythm Test and brain functions. *The Clinical Neuropsychologist, 3,* 70-78.

Reitan, R.M., & Wolfson, D. (1990). The significance of the Speech-sounds Perception Test for cerebral functions. *Archives of Clinical Neuropsychology, 5,* 265-272.

Reitan, R.M., & Wolfson, D. (1992a). *Neuroanatomy and neuropa-thology: A clinical guide for neuropsychologists.* Tucson, AZ: Neuropsychology Press.

Reitan, R.M. & Wolfson, D. (1992b). *Neuropsychological evaluation of young children.* Tucson, AZ: Neuropsychology Press.

Reitan, R.M. & Wolfson, D. (1992c). *The Halstead-Reitan Neuro-psychological Test Battery: Theory and clinical interpretation.* (2nd ed.). Tucson, AZ: Neuropsychology Press.

Rie, H.E., & Rie, E.D. (Eds.). (1980). *Handbook of minimal brain dysfunctions. A critical view.* New York: John Wiley & Sons.

Rosenthal, M., Griffith, E.R., Bond, N.R., & Miller, J.B. (Eds.). (1983). *Rehabilitation of the head-injured adult.* Philadelphia: F.A. Davis Company.

Ross, A.O. (1967). The application of behavior principles in therapeutic education. *Journal of Special Education, 1,* 275-285.

Rourke, B.P. (1975). Brain-behavior relationships in children with learning disabilities: A research program. *American Psychologist, 30,* 911-920.

Rourke, B.P. (1981). Neuropsychological assessment of children with learning disabilities. In S.B. Filskov & T.J. Boll (Eds.), *Handbook of clinical neuropsychology* (pp. 453-478). New York: Wiley-Interscience.

Rourke, B.P. (1982). Central processing deficiencies in children: Toward a developmental neuropsychological model. *Journal of Clinical Neuropsychology, 4,* 1-18.

Rourke, B.P. (Ed.). (1985). *Neuropsychology of learning disabilities. Essentials of subtype analysis.* New York: The Guilford Press.

Rourke, B.P. (1989). *Nonverbal learning disabilities: The syndrome and the model.* New York: The Guilford Press.

Rourke, B.P., & Adams, K.M. (1983). Quantitative approaches to the neuropsychological assessment of children. In R. Tarter & G. Goldstein (Eds.), *The neuropsychology of childhood.* New York: Plenum.

Rourke, B.P, Bakker, D.J., Fisk, J.L., & Strang, J.B. (1983). *Child neuropsychology.* New York: The Guilford Press.

Rourke, B.P., & Brown, G.G. (1986). Clinical neuropsychology and behavioral neurology: Similarities and differences. In S.B. Filskov & T.J. Boll (Eds.), *Handbook of clinical neuropsychology* (Vol. 3, pp. 3-18). New York: John Wiley & Sons.

Rourke, B.P. & Finlayson, M.A.J. (1978). Neuropsychological significance of variations in patterns of academic performance: Motor, psychomotor, and tactile-perceptual abilities. *Journal of Pediatric Psychology, 2,* 62-66.

Rourke, B.P., Fisk, J.L., & Strang, J.D. (1986). *Neuropsychological assessment of children: A treatment-oriented approach.* New York: The Guilford Press.

Rourke, B.P., & Strang, J.D. (1978). Neuropsychological significance of variations in patterns of academic performance: Verbal and visual-spatial abilities. *Journal of Pediatric Psychology,* 3, 62-66.

Rourke, B.P., & Strang, J.D. (1983). Subtypes of reading and arithmetical disabilities: A neuropsychological analysis. In M. Rutter (Ed.), *Developmental neuropsychiatry.* New York: The Guilford Press.

Rudel, R.G. (1978). Neural plasticity: Implications for development and education. In J.S. Chall & A.R. Mirsky (Eds.), *Education and the brain* (Part 2). Chicago: University of Chicago Press.

Runyan, C.W., & Gerken, E.A. (1989). Epidemiology and prevention of adolescent injury. *Journal of the American Medical Association, 262,* 2273-2279.

Russell, J.R., & Reitan, R.M. (1955). Psychological abnormalities in agenesis of the corpus callosum. *Journal of Nervous and Mental Disease, 121,* 205-214.

Russell, W.R., & Nathan, P.W. (1946). Traumatic amnesia. *Brain,* 69, 280-300.

Rutter, M. (1981). Psychological sequelae of brain damage in children. *American Journal of Psychiatry, 138,* 1533-1544.

Rutter, M. (Ed.). (1983). *Developmental neuropsychiatry.* New York: The Guildford Press.

Rylander, G. (1939). Personality changes after operations on the frontal lobes: A clinical study of 32 cases. *Acta Psychiatrica et Neurologica Scandinavica,* (Supplement No. 20), 1-327.

St. James-Roberts, I. (1979). Neurological plasticity, recovery from brain insult and child development. In H.W. Reese (Ed.), *Advances in child development and behavior* (Vol. 14). New York: Academic Press.

Sanders, C. (1970). Terminology and classification. In J. Wortis (Ed.), *Mental retardation. An annual review.* New York: Grune & Stratton.

Sarason, S.B., & Gladwin, T. (1958). Psychological and cultural problems in mental subnormality: A review of research. *American Journal of Mental Deficiency, 62,* 1115-1307.

Satz, P., & Fletcher, J.M. (1981). Emergent trends in neuropsychology: An overview. *Journal of Consulting and Clinical Psychology, 49,* 851-865.

Schilder, P. (1934). Psychiatric aspects of chronic neurological diseases. Institute on Encephalitis, Birth Injury, Epilepsy, arranged by the Committee on Medical-Social Problems of Chronic Neurological Diseases. Medical Social Service Section. The Welfare Council of New York City, December.

Selz, M., & Reitan, R.M. (1979a). Comparative test performance of normal, learning-disabled and brain-damaged older children. *Journal of Nervous and Mental Disease, 167*, 298-302.

Selz, M., & Reitan, R.M. (1979b). Rules for neuropsychological diagnosis: Classification of brain function in older children. *Journal of Clinical and Consulting Psychology, 47*, 258-264.

Semmes, J. (1968). Hemispheric specialization: A possible clue to mechanism. *Neuropsychologica, 6*, 11-26.

Semmes, J., Weinstein, S., Ghent, L., & Teuber, H.-L. (1960). *Somatosensory changes after penetrating brain wounds in man.* Cambridge, MA: Harvard University Press.

Sherer, M., Parsons, O.A., Nixon, S.J., & Adams, R.L. (1991). Clinical validity of the Speech-sounds Perception Test and the Seashore Rhythm Test. *Journal of Clinical and Experimental Neuropsychology, 13*, 741-751.

Silverstein, A.B. (1987). Unusual combinations of Verbal and Performance IQ's on Wechsler's intelligence scales. *Journal of Clinical Psychology, 43*, 720-722.

Spencer, S.S., Spencer, D.D., Williamson, P.D., & Mattson, R.H. (1985). Effects of corpus callosum section on bilateral synchronous EEG discharges. *Neurology, 35*, 1689-1702.

Sperry, R.W. (1974). Lateral specialization in the surgically separated hemispheres. In F.O. Schmitt & F.G. Worden (Eds.), *The neurosciences. Third Study Program.* Cambridge, MA: Massachusetts Institute of Technology Press.

Spreen, O., Tupper, D., Risser, A., Tuokko, H., & Edgell, D. (1984). *Human developmental neuropsychology.* New York: Oxford University Press.

Squire, L.R. (1975). Short-term memory as a biological entity. In D. Deutsch & J.A. Deutsch (Eds.), *Short-term memory.* New York: Academic Press.

Stage, W.S., & Stein, J.J. (1975). Treatment of malignant astrocytomas. *American Journal of Roentgenology, Radiation Therapy, and Nuclear Medicine, 120*, 1551-1557.

Stein, D.G., Rosen, J., & Butters, N. (Eds.). (1974). *Plasticity and recovery of function in the central nervous system.* New York: Academic Press.

Stewart, W.A. (1941). Electroencephalographic changes associated with different forms of experimentally produced increased intracranial pressure. *Bulletin of Johns Hopkins Hospital, 69,* 240-265.

Storrie, M.C., & Doerr, H.O. (1980). Characterization of Alzheimer type dementia utilizing an abbreviated Halstead-Reitan Battery. *Clinical Neuropsychology, 2,* 72-82.

Strang, J.D., & Rourke, B.P. (1983). Concept-formation/nonverbal reasoning abilities of children who exhibit specific academic problems with arithmetic. *Journal of Clinical Child Psychology, 12,* 33-39.

Strauss, A.A., & Kephart, N.C. (1955). *Psychopathology and education of the brain injured child. Volume II. Progress in theory and clinic.* New York: Grune & Stratton, Inc.

Strauss, A.A., & Lehtinen, L.E. (1947). *Psychopathology and education of the brain-injured child.* New York: Grune & Stratton.

Strauss, A.A., & Werner, H. (1941). The mental organization of the brain-injured mentally defective child. *American Journal of Psychiatry, 97,* 1194-1203.

Strauss, A.A., & Werner, H. (1942a). Disorders of conceptual thinking in the brain-injured child. *Journal of Nervous and Mental Diseases, 96,* 153-172.

Strauss, A.A., & Werner, H. (1942b). Experimental analysis of the clinical symptom "perseveration" in mentally retarded children. *American Journal of Mental Deficiency, 27,* 185-187.

Strauss, A.A., & Werner, H. (1943). Impairment in thought processes of brain-injured children. *American Journal of Mental Deficiency, 47,* 291-295.

Strecker, E., & Ebaugh, F. (1924). Neuropsychiatric sequelae of cerebral trauma in children. *Archives of Neurology and Psychiatry, 12,* 443-453.

Taylor, E.N. (1959). *Psychological appraisal of children with cerebral defects.* Cambridge, MA: Harvard University Press.

Terman, L.M. (1921). Intelligence and its measurement: A symposium. *Journal of Educational Psychology, 12,* 123-147.

Teuber, H.-L. (1969). Neglected aspects of the posttraumatic syndrome. In A. Walker & K. Akert (Eds.), *The late effects of head injury.* Springfield, IL: C.C. Thomas.

Teuber, H.-L. (1976). Neural plasticity: Extents and limits. Paper presented at the Ninth Winter Conference on Brain Research, Keystone, Colorado.

Tinuper, P., Andermann, F., Villemure, J-G., Rasmussen, T.B., & Quesney, L.F. (1988). Functional hemispherectomy for treatment of epilepsy associated with hemiplegia: Rationale, indications, results, and comparison with callosotomy. *Annals of Neurology, 24,* 27-34.

von Bonin, G. (1962). Anatomical asymmetries of the cerebral hemispheres. In V.B. Mountcastle (Ed.), *Interhemispheric relations and cerebral dominance.* Baltimore: Johns Hopkins University Press.

Walker, A.E., Robins, M., & Weinfeld, F.D. (1985). Epidemiology of brain tumors: The national survey of intracranial neoplasms. *Neurology, 35,* 219-226.

Watson, J.B. (1924). *Behaviorism.* New York: People's Institute.

Wechsler, D. (1955). *Manual for the Wechsler Adult Intelligence Scale.* New York: The Psychological Corporation.

Wechsler, D. (1974). *Manual for the Wechsler Intelligence Scale for Children-Revised.* New York: The Psychological Corporation.

Weisenburg, T., & McBride, K.E. (1935). *Aphasia: A clinical and psychological study.* New York: The Commonwealth Fund.

Werner, H., & Bowers, M. (1941). Auditory-motor organization in two clinical types of mentally deficient children. *Journal of Genetic Psychology, 59,* 85-99.

Werner, H. & Strauss, A.A. (1939). Types of visuo-motor activity in their relation to low and high performance ages. *American Association on Mental Deficiency, 44,* 163-168.

Werner, H., & Strauss, A. (1940). Causal factors in low performance. *American Journal of Mental Deficiency, 45,* 213-218.

Werner, H., & Strauss, A.A. (1941). Pathology of figure-background relation in the child. *Journal of Abnormal and Social Psychology, 36,* 236-248.

Werner, H., & Thuma, B.D. (1942a). Critical flicker frequency in children with brain injury. *American Journal of Psychology, 55,* 394-399.

Werner, H., & Thuma, B.D. (1942b). A deficiency in the perception of apparent motion in children with brain injury. *American Journal of Psychology, 55,* 58-67.

Wheeler, L., Burke, C.J., & Reitan, R.M. (1963). An application of discriminant functions to the problem of predicting brain damage using behavioral variables. *Perceptual and Motor Skills*, [Monograph supplement], *16*, 417-440.

Wheeler, L., & Reitan, R.M. (1962). The presence and laterality of brain damage predicted from responses to a short Aphasia Screening Test. *Perceptual and Motor Skills, 15*, 783-799.

Wheeler, L., & Reitan, R.M. (1963). Discriminant functions applied to the problem of predicting cerebral damage from behavior tests: A cross validation study. *Perceptual and Motor Skills, 16*, 681-701.

White, H.H. (1961). Cerebral hemispherectomy in the treatment of infantile hemiplegia: Review of the literature and report of 2 cases. *Confinia Neurologica, 21*, 1-50.

Wilson, B.C., & Risucci, D.A. (1986). A model for clinical-quantitative classification. Generation 1: Application to language-disordered preschool children. *Brain and Language, 27*, 281-309.

Wilson, B.C., & Wilson, J.J. (1978). Language disordered children. A neuropsychologic view. In B.F. Feingold & C.L. Banks (Eds.), *Developmental disabilities of early childhood*. Springfield, IL: Charles C. Thomas.

Woods, B.T., & Carey, S. (1979). Language deficits after apparent clinical recovery from childhood aphasia. *Annals of Neurology, 6*, 405-409.

Wyke, M.A. (Ed.). (1978). *Developmental dysphasia*. New York: Academic Press.

Zangwill, O.L. (1978). The concept of developmental dysphasia. In M.A. Wyke (Ed.), *Developmental dysphasia*. New York: Academic Press.

Zigler, E. (1967). Familial mental retardation: A continuing dilemma. *Science, 155*, 292-298

Author Index

A

Abramson, L.S., 16
Adams, J.H., 673
Adams, R.L., 117
Aita, J.A., 644
Albert, M.L., 27
Albright, L.A., 561
Andermann, F., 609, 610
Annegers, J.F., 544
Atkins, T. 529

B

Bakker, D.J., 22, 283, 736
Barnett, H.J.M., 31
Bartus, R.T., 99
Becker, D.P., 32
Belmont, I., 308
Benda, C.E., 2, 292
Bender, L., 2, 187
Bender, M.B., 86, 308
Benton, A.L., 13, 14, 15, 16,
    17, 25, 203, 275
Birch, H.G., 8, 9, 308
Black, F.W., 775
Blau, A., 2
Boll, T.J., 41, 42, 43, 101, 192,
    239, 241, 242, 275, 280,
    281, 283
Bond, M.R., 674
Bond, N.R., 225
Bowers, M., 6
Bowman, K.M., 2
Brooks, W.H., 31
Brown, G.G., 188
Brown, R.D., Jr., 627
Brown, T., 31
Bruce, D.A., 546, 561, 562
Burke, C.J., 258, 304
Butler, A.B., 31
Butters, N., 27

C

Carey, S., 40
Carmon, A., 275
Chadwick, O., 18
Chapman, L.F., 274
Charney, E., 561
Chelune, G.J., 27, 28, 39
Clements, S.D., 24, 270
Cohen, G.D., 99
Costa, L.D., 48, 49, 50, 51, 52,
    53, 59, 110
Cowchock, F.S., 530
Critchley, M., 308
Crook, T., 99
Crouch, J., 97

D

Danoff, B.F., 530, 536
Davies, P., 31
Davis, D.R., 562
de la Cruz, F.F., 24, 25
DeMyer, W., 17
Denhoff, E., 2
DeTeresa, R., 31
Dikmen, S., 42
Dodrill, C.B., 8, 539, 656, 658
Doehring, D.G., 22, 42, 54, 55,
    60, 67, 112, 165, 265, 736
Doerr, H.O., 99
Dostrovsky, J.O., 36
Duffy, F.H., 736
Dyken, M.L., 42

E

Ebaugh, F., 2
Edgell, D., 736
Edwards, P., 27, 28, 39
Eisenberg, H.M., 676

F

Farber, N., 59
Ferris, S.H., 99
Fiedorowicz, C.A.M., 22, 736
Finger, S., 31, 32, 39
Finlayson, M.A.J., 42, 53, 251, 279
Fisk, J.L., 22, 283, 736
Fitzhugh, K.B., 42, 266, 310
Fitzhugh, L.C., 42, 266, 310
Fletcher, J.M., 28, 39
Fox, B.H., 24, 25
Freeman, C.N., 561
Fulbright, R., 99
Fuld, P., 31

G

Gaddes, W.H., 22, 203, 212, 736
Galliani, C., 267
Gentry, L.R., 673
Gerken, E.A., 674
Gershon, S., 99
Gerstmann, J., 86
Geschwind, N., 736
Ghent, L., 275
Gibbs, C.E., 2
Gladwin, T., 292, 293
Godersky, J.C., 673
Goldberg, E., 48, 49, 50, 51, 52, 53, 110
Goldstein, K., 7, 55, 104, 164, 233, 235, 237, 238
Gomez, M.R., 25
Goodglass, H., 188, 254
Goodstein, L.D., 16, 225
Graham, D.I., 673
Green, J.R., 543, 544
Greenberg, R.P., 32
Greer, M., 580
Griffith, E.R., 225
Gudmundsson, K.R., 544

H

Haines, S.J., 594
Halstead, W.C., 20, 21, 48, 55, 62, 94, 100, 164, 235, 236, 237, 274, 299, 303, 315, 316, 333, 351
Harsh, G.R., 544
Hathaway, S.R.
Hays, K.J., 288
Heaton, R.K., 97
Hécaen, H., 27
Heideman, R.L., 561
Heimburger, R.F., 17
Herring, S., 42, 262
Hohman, L.B., 2
Hom, J., 47, 58, 99, 120, 160, 527
Honig, P.J., 561
Humphrey, M., 674
Hynd, C.R., 736

I-J

Isaacson, R.L., 28, 39
Jennett, B., 51
Johnson, I., 581
Johnson, K.A., 42

K

Kaplan, E., 188, 233, 254
Karp, E., 308
Karzmark, P., 97
Katzman, R., 31, 97
Kaufman, A., 300
Kennard, M.A., 26, 28, 38, 39, 43, 44
Kennedy, C., 226
Kephart, N.C., 9, 10, 11, 12, 13
Kertesz, A., 27
Kessler, J.W., 2, 24
Kimble, G.A., 101
Kirk, U., 736
Kishore, P.R.S., 32
Klonoff, H., 18

Kløve, H., 42, 188, 191, 192, 264, 265, 299, 657
Knights, R.M., 22, 736
Knobloch, H., 24
Kolb, B., 56, 57, 58, 59, 61
Kriegsfeld, B.A., 543, 544
Krynauw, R.A., 608
Kurland, L.T., 544

L
Laine, E., 609
Lehman, R.A.W., 97
Lehtinen, L.E., 7, 8
Levita, E., 59
Littman, P.A., 529
Luria, A.R., 48, 233, 234, 235, 274

M
Maciunas, R.J., 627
Magoun, H.W., 62
Mampalam, T., 594
Marie, P., 104
Marquette, C., 530
Marsh, W.R., 627
Marshall, W.C., 640
Masland, R.L., 292
Matarazzo, J.D., 300
Matson, D.D., 674
Matthews, C.G., 22, 291, 294, 295, 296, 298, 657
Mattson, R.H., 610
McBride, K.E., 102
Mcfie, J., 18, 55
Menkes, J.H., 580
Meyers, R., 101, 102
Millar, J., 36
Miller, J.B., 225
Miller, J.D., 32
Milner, B., 97
Mitchell, D.E., 673
Mohr, J.P., 31
Molfese, D.L., 65

Moruzzi, G., 62
Munn, N.L., 102

N
Nagib, M.G., 594
Nathan, P.W., 96
Nelson, D.F., 562
Nelson, J.S., 562
Netsky, M.G., 31
Nici, J., 283
Nixon, S.J., 117

O
Oddy, M., 674
O'Fallon, W.M., 627
Okazaki, H., 544
Oppenheimer, D.R., 673
Osson, D., 609

P-Q
Packer, R.J., 529, 561
Paris, R., 18
Parsons, O.A., 117
Pasamanick, B., 24
Patel, P.G., 22, 736
Paterson, A., 581
Peck, A., 31
Penfield, W., 102
Pennington, H., 267
Peters, J.E., 24
Piepgras, D.G., 627
Piercy, M.F., 55
Pirozzolo, F.J., 736
Prigatano, G.P., 785
Pruvet, P., 609
Quesney, L.F., 609, 610

R
Ramirez, L.S., 226
Rapin, I., 202, 203
Rasmussen, T.(B.), 608, 609, 610
Reed, H.B.C., 42, 188, 191, 192
Reed, J.C., 42, 267, 275, 280

Reitan, R.M., 10, 17, 20, 21, 23, 25, 27, 28, 30, 32, 37, 38, 39, 40, 42, 43, 47, 51, 52, 54, 55, 58, 59, 60, 62, 64, 65, 67, 76, 77, 80, 82, 89, 96, 97, 98, 102, 103, 104, 105, 106, 107, 112, 117, 118, 119, 120, 122, 124, 125, 134, 160,165, 174, 176, 188, 191, 192, 193, 196, 198, 199, 204, 214, 221, 222, 226, 229, 235, 236, 237, 238, 239, 241, 242, 245, 251, 252, 254, 256, 257, 258, 259, 260, 261, 262, 263, 264, 265, 266, 267, 272, 274, 275, 277, 279, 281, 283, 286, 288, 294, 295, 296, 299, 303, 304, 305, 310, 312, 313, 314, 325, 326, 328, 460, 471, 481, 526, 527, 543, 591, 607, 631, 632, 642, 644, 656, 658, 674, 676, 703, 718, 720, 737, 741, 743, 768

Renbing, X., 31

Rie, E.D., 25, 26

Rie, H.E., 25, 26

Risser, A., 736

Risucci, D.A., 18, 19

Roberts, L., 102

Roberts, R.H., 24, 25

Robinault, I.P., 2

Robins, M., 544

Rosen, J., 27

Rosenblum, M.L., 594

Rosenthal, M., 225

Rosner, M.J., 32

Ross, A.O., 227

Rourke, B.P., 22, 52, 53, 54, 55, 56, 110, 188, 280, 283, 736, 737, 739, 741

Rudel, R.G., 27

Runyan, C.W., 674

Russell, J.R., 27, 51

Russell, W.R., 96

Rutter, M., 18, 736

Rylander, G., 55

S

Saint James-Roberts, I., 28

Sanders, C., 288

Sarason, S.B., 292, 293

Satz, P., 28, 39

Schilder, P., 2

Schoenberg, B.S., 544

Schut, L., 546, 561, 562

Selhorst, J.B., 32

Selz, M., 193, 204, 222, 258, 259, 260, 261, 741

Semmes, J., 50, 51, 275

Sena, D.A., 283

Shaffer, D., 18

Sherer, M., 117

Shrout, P., 18

Silverstein, A.B., 538, 553, 600, 682, 795

Spencer, D.D., 610

Spencer, S.S., 610

Sperry, R.W., 165

Spreen, O., 736

Squire, L.R., 96

Stage, W.S., 546

Stein, B.M., 31

Stein, D.G., 27, 31, 32

Stein, J.J., 546

Stewart, W.A., 581

Storrie, M.C., 99

Strang, J.D., 22, 53, 54, 283, 736

Strauss, A.A., 3, 4, 6, 7, 8, 9, 10, 19, 30, 183

Strecker, E., 2

Sutton, L.N., 546, 561, 562

T
Taylor, E.N., 17, 18
Teasdale, G., 51
Terman, L.M., 293
Terry, R., 31
Teuber, H.-L., 27, 30, 86, 275
Thompson, B.H., 673
Thompson, J., 18
Thuma, B.D., 5
Tinuper, P., 609, 610
Tupper, D., 736
Trites, R.L., 22, 736
Tuokko, H., 736

U-V
Uttley, D., 674
Vaughan, H.G., 59
Villemure, J-G., 608, 609, 610
Voegele, G., 267
von Bonin, G., 48

W
Waggener, J.D., 543, 544
Walker, A.E., 544
Wall, P.D., 36
Ward, J.D., 32
Watson, J.B., 101
Wechsler, D., 121, 123, 299, 300, 301
Weinfeld, F.D., 544
Weisenburg, T., 102
Weinstein, S., 215
Wepman, J.M., 303
Werner, H., 3, 4, 5, 6, 7, 9, 19, 30, 183, 187

Wheeler, L., 10, 59, 65, 106, 165, 258, 304
Whishaw, I.Q., 56, 57, 58, 59, 61
Whisnant, J.P., 627
White, H.H., 608
Whitehouse, P., 99
Wiebers, D.O., 627
Williamson, P.D., 610
Wilson, B.C., 18, 19, 202, 203
Wilson, C.B., 544
Wilson, J.J., 18, 19
Wittrock, M.C., 736
Wolf, C., 39
Wolff, H.G., 274
Wolfson, D., 28, 30, 32, 38, 47, 76, 77, 80, 82, 96, 97, 98, 117, 118, 119, 120, 160, 174, 176, 188, 198, 214, 221, 226, 254, 256, 257, 274, 283, 286, 312, 313, 314, 325, 328, 460, 481, 526, 543, 591, 607, 631, 642, 674, 676, 703, 720, 737, 741
Woods, B.T., 40
Wyke, M.A., 201

X-Y-Z
Yatsu, F.M., 31
Young, H.F., 32
Zangwill, O.L., 202
Zigler, E., 288

Subject Index

A

Abstraction
    as a basic neuropsychological ability, 164-167
    as expressed in spatial and sequential tasks, 176-181
    impairment of, and learning disabilities
    significance of degree of impairment among mentally
        retarded subjects, 296-298
Abstraction and reasoning abilities, 67
    as related to "personality change", 68
    Category Test, as a measure of, 111-113, 115, 124-126
    in clinical case interpretations, 471-814
    significance of, in mentally retarded subjects, 294-294
Abstraction, reasoning, logical analysis, flexibility,
    and planning
    as related to the Halstead-Reitan Battery, 111-116
Academic achievement, 76
Academic deficits
    and normal neurological findings, 505-515
Academic readiness
    training procedures for, 139-144
Adult neuropsychology, 1, 11, 16, 20, 23-24
    historical foundations of, 23-24
    Verbal vs. Performance IQ values, 263, 268-269
    vs. child neuropsychology, 11, 29-30, 39-40, 42-43, 74, 186,
        190-191, 196, 238-242, 283
Age effects
    and Finger Tapping Test, 251-252
    and Finger-tip Number Writing Perception results, 251-252
    and grip strength, 251-252
    and Tactile Finger Recognition Test, 251-252
    and tactile-perceptual deficits, 280
    and Trail Making Test, 245-247
    evaluation in clinical case interpretations, 471-814
    on brain plasticity, 37
Age-related improvements
    in test scores, as related to the Halstead-Reitan Battery,
        242-252

Aphasia, 59, 60
    evaluation in clinical case interpretations, 471-814
    expressive deficits in, 343-344, 346
    receptive deficits in, 343-344, 346
    retraining procedures for, 133-134, 155
Aphasia Screening Test. See *Reitan-Indiana Aphasia Screening Test.*
Arithmetic readiness
    training procedures for, 152-154
Arithmetic subtest, 300
Arithmetical relationships
    training procedures, 162-163
Arteriovenous malformations of the brain
    description, 626-628
    case illustration, 629
Astrocytoma, 543-578
    case illustrations, 548-578
    description, 543-547
Attention and alertness, 63
Attention and concentration
    evaluation in clinical case interpretations, 471-814
    impairment of, in learning disability, 286-288
Attention, concentration, and memory, 94-101
    as related to the Halstead-Reitan Battery, 94-101
Attention deficit disorder, 271-272
Auditory verbal comprehension
    and learning disability, 134-136
    evaluation in clinical case interpretations, 471-814
    training procedures for, 134-139
Auditory verbal dysgnosia, 206-207, 342
    evaluation in clinical case interpretations, 471-814
    examples of deficits and NDS scoring guide, 373-375
Axonal sprouting, 35

B
Behavioral changes
    in encephalitis lethargica, 2
Behavioral disorders
    as related to "terrible triad", 783, 786-788, 791, 798, 811
    illustrations in clinical case interpretations, 760-773, 789-801

Behavioral neurology, 188
   vs. clinical neuropsychology, 188
Behavioral problems
   and approaches to cognitive rehabilitation, 799-801, 812
   and learning disability, 744, 760-761, 770-773, 783, 788
   as related to cerebral damage or dysfunction, 785-814
   case illustrations, 760-773, 789-801, 802-814
   description, 785-788
   use of REHABIT with, 800-801, 813-814
Benign intracranial hypertension
   and pseudotumor cerebri, 580
Bilateral simultaneous sensory stimulation, 82-84, 323
   and homonymous visual field defects, 387
   description, 306-309
   evaluation in clinical case interpretations, 471-814
   instructions for administration, general, 385-388
   instructions for administration and scoring, specific, 388-397
Bilateral transfer
   as represented in the Tactual Performance Test, 93
Birth injury, 2
Block Design subtest, 106-107, 109, 300
   and right cerebral damage, 124
   sensitivity of, vs. other tests, 280-283
Body dysgnosia, 205, 206-207, 354
   examples of deficits and NDS scoring guide, 371
Booklet Category Test, 324-325
Brain-behavior relationships, developmental theories of
   Goldberg and Costa's theory, 48-52
   Kolb and Whishaw's theory, 56-61
   Reitan and Wolfson's theory, 62-70
   Rourke's theory, 52-56
Brain damage
   and personality changes, 226
   and Reitan-Indiana Aphasia Screening Test, 204-212
   and Trail Making Test, 249-251
   as related to behavioral problems, 785-814
   as related to learning disability, 204-212
   clinical evaluation of, 471-814

effects of
 as related to the Halstead-Reitan Battery, 190, 192-196
 clinical evaluations of, 471-814
 in young children, 193
 on the Category Test, 190
 on the Finger Tapping Test, 190, 276-277, 278-279
 on the Finger-tip Number Writing Perception Test, 192-193,
  276-277, 278-279
 on the Grip Strength Test, 192-193, 276-277, 278-279
 on the Name Writing Test, 192-193, 196-200
 on the Seashore Rhythm Test, 190
 on the Speech-sounds Perception Test, 190
 on the Tactile Finger Recognition Test, 192-193, 276-277,
  278-279
 on the Tactile Form Recognition Test, 192-193, 276
 on the Tactual Performance Test
  Time, Memory and Localization components, 190, 276-277
 on the Trail Making Test, 190
 on the Wechsler Scale, 190-191, 193-195, 196
 on the Wide Range Achievement Test, 192-193
evidence of, in mentally retarded subjects, 292
five most sensitive measures of, 124
sensitivity of Tactile Form Recognition Test to, vs. other
 tests, 280-286
WISC-R, effects of brain damage on, 190
Brain functions
 and language abilities, 101-104
 as related to Verbal and Performance IQ differences,
  109-110
 clinical evaluation of, 471-814
 general measures of, 126-127
 higher-level and lower-level, 274
 specific measures of, 126-127
Brain injury
 and IQ values in children, 41-43
 and tactile functions, 51
 clinical evaluation of, 471-814
 developmental consequences of, 44-45
 outcome of, 31-45
 perinatal, 18
 primary effects of, 32-33

recovery process after, 32-38
    long term, 35-38
    sprouting of neurons, 35
    short term, 33-34
  secondary effects of, 32-33
  traumatic, 17
Brain lesions
  and chronicity, 266-267
  as related to VIQ and PIQ differences, 266-267
Brain retraining
  clinical evaluation as a basis for prescribing a program, 471-814
  for subjects with encephalitis, 651-654
  sequence of approaches, 114

C

Category Test, 54, 60-61, 67, 324, 325
  and comparative neuropsychological deficits, 283-286
  as a measure of abstraction and reasoning, 111-113, 115, 124-126
  as related to sensorimotor functions, 277-279
  clinical interpretation in individual cases, 471-814
  degree of impairment, significance of, among mentally retarded subjects, 296-299
  description, 318-321
  effects of cerebral damage on, 190
  instructions for administration, general, 444-450
  instructions for administration and scoring, specific, 450-453
  modifications of adult version, 327
  sensitivity to brain damage vs. other tests, 280-286
Central dysarthria, 207-208
  examples of deficits and NDS scoring guide, 367-368
  in clinical case interpretations, 471-814
Central processing, 80, 94-116
  as related to higher- and lower-level brain functions, 94
  as related to memory, 94-96, 98-101
  sequential nature of, as related to the Reitan-Wolfson model, 175
Central processing functions
  as related to the Halstead-Reitan Battery, 94-116

Cerebral abscess, 592-607
case illustration, 595-607
description, 592-594
Cerebral hemisphere, left
theoretical developmental characteristics, 49-52, 53-56
Cerebral hemisphere, right
theoretical developmental characteristics, 49-52, 53-56
Cerebral hemispherectomy
and superficial cerebral hemosiderosis, 608-610
as treatment for epilepsy, 608-610
case illustration, 611-625
discussion of, 608-610
Cerebral impairment
screening devices for, 252
Cerebral palsy, 2, 18
Cerebral tumors, 561-578
as related to subtentorial and thalamic tumors, 526-527,
533-534
case illustration, 563-578
description, 561-562
improper diagnosis and psychological counseling, 561-562
Child neuropsychology, 1-30
and mental retardation, 3
developmental theories, 47-70
early approaches toward identifying deficits, 2
early concepts
critique of, 8-9, 11-17, 23-23
of brain-related deficits, 3-18
early therapeutic recommendations, 7-10
critique of, 8-9
early vs. late brain damage, 26-29
history of, 1-30
neuropsychological correlates, 22-23
neuropsychological deficits, 10-17, 22
vs. adult neuropsychology, 11, 29-30, 39-40, 42-43, 74, 186,
190-191, 196, 283
Clinical assessment, 605-607
examples of, 471-814
Clinical interpretation
and the NDS, 472-479
clinical illustrations, 471-814

guidelines, 471-484
Clinical neuropsychology
    vs. behavioral neurology, 188
    vs. experimental neuropsychology, 30
Coding subtest, 112, 115-116, 122-123, 125, 191, 300, 301
Cognitive rehabilitation. See also *Cognitive retraining.*
    and behavioral problems, 799-801, 812
    and "terrible triad", 799-801
Cognitive retraining, 129-184
    and learning disability, 738, 756-758, 770-773, 783-784
    and traumatic brain injury, 686, 720-721, 733
    as prescribed from neuropsychological evaluation, 471-814,
        605
    as related to the Halstead-Reitan Battery, 184
Commissurotomy, 51
Comparative neuropsychological deficits in children,
        273-288
    methodological considerations, 273-274
Comprehension subtest, 300
Concept formation, 55-56, 60
    and mental retardation, 7
Conceptual deficits in brain-damaged children
    compared with perceptual deficits and motor deficits,
        280-282
Constructional dyspraxia, 60, 210
    as related to Wechsler measurements, 264-265
    clinical evaluation in individual cases, 471-814
    evaluation using guidelines for the NDS, 361-363
Corpus callosum
    congenital absence of, 51
Corpus callosotomy
    and seizure control, 610
Cretinism, 2
Critical flicker fusion
    and mental retardation, 5

D
Developmental dysphasia, 201-204
    and learning disability, 203-204
Developmental language disorder, 18-19

Developmental theories of brain-behavior relationships
and child neuropsychology, 47-70
and specialized functions of the brain, 47-48, 52, 53, 61, 65
Goldberg and Costa's theory, 48-52
Kolb and Whishaw's theory, 56-61
Reitan and Wolfson's theory, 62-70
Rourke's theory, 52-56
Digit Span subtest, 300
Digit Symbol subtest, 107, 122-123
Down's syndrome, 2
Dyscalculia, 207-208
and clinical case interpretations, 471-814
examples of deficits and NDS scoring guide, 368-369
Dysgnosia
receptive deficits, 343-344
Dysgraphia, 207-208
and clinical case interpretations, 471-814
examples of deficits and NDS scoring guide, 360, 364
Dyslexia, 208-209
and clinical case interpretations, 471-814
examples of deficits and NDS scoring guide, 365-367
Dysnomia, 205, 207-208, 343
and clinical case interpretations, 471-814
examples of deficits and NDS scoring guide, 355-357
Dysphasia, 201-212
as related to Wechsler measurements, 264-265
examples of deficits and NDS scoring guide, 355-375
Dyspraxia
examples of deficits and NDS scoring guide, 355-375
expressive deficits, 343-344
Dysstereognosis, 87
impairment of tactile form recognition, and the
NDS scoring guide, 455-470

E
Emotional problems of adjustment
as related to neuropsychological impairment, 224-232
Encephalitis, 18
approaches to brain retraining in, 651-654
case illustration, 643-654
description, 640-642

lethargica, 2
   epidemic, 2
   behavioral changes in, 2
Endogenous mental retardation, 3-8
Epilepsy
   case illustrations, 611-625, 659-671
   description, 659-671
   treatment by cerebral hemispherectomy, 608-610
Equipotentiality of cerebral cortical tissue, 70
Exogenous mental retardation, 3-10
Experimental neuropsychology, 29
   vs. clinical neuropsychology, 30
Expressive deficits
   dyspraxia, 343-344
   in aphasia, 343-344, 346

F
Figure ground effects
   and mental retardation, 6
Finger agnosia. See *Tactile Finger Recognition Test.*
Finger localization, 13, 58
   and NDS scoring guide, 455-470
   and psychosis, 15-16
   neuropsychological correlates, 16-17
Finger Tapping Test, 63, 88, 323, 325, 335
   and clinical case interpretations, 471-814
   comparative performances of older and young children,
      251-252
   description, 306
   effects of cerebral damage on, 190, 276-277, 278-279
   instructions for administration, general, 376-378
   instructions for administration and scoring, specific,
      376-381
   normative evaluation using the NDS, 455-470
   sensitivity to brain damage vs. other tests, 280-286
Finger-tip Number Writing Perception Test, 84, 323
   and clinical case interpretations, 471-814
   and comparative neuropsychological deficits, 283-286
   comparative performances of older and young children,
      251-252
   description, 310-311
   effects of cerebral damage on, 192-193, 276-277, 278-279

instructions for administration, general, 402-404
instructions for administration and scoring, specific, 404-408
normative evaluation using the NDS, 455-470
Functions of the brain, specialized
and developmental theories, 47-48, 52, 53, 61, 65
of left and right hemispheres, 47-48, 52, 53

G
Gender effects, 88-89
on the Grip Strength Test, 251-252
on the Trail Making Test, 245-249
General measures of brain functions, 126-127
relationship to screening devices, 254-255
General neuropsychological tests, 76-77
General and specific neuropsychological tests
as related to rehabilitation, 607
importance in clinical assessment, 605-607
Generalized neuropsychological abilities
as related to specialized neuropsychological abilities, 164-165
Glioblastoma multiforme, 561
Goldberg and Costa's theory of brain-behavior
relationships, 48-52
Grip Strength Test
and clinical case interpretations, 471-814
and comparative neuropsychological deficits, 283-286
comparative scores of older and young children on, 251-252
description, 306
effects of cerebral damage on, 192-193, 276-277, 278-279
gender effects on, 251-252
instructions for administration, general, 382-383
instructions for administration and scoring, specific, 383-384
normative evaluation using the NDS, 455-470

H
Halstead-Reitan Battery
findings in mental retardation, 290-298
Halstead-Reitan Neuropsychological Test Battery for
Older Children, 74, 77, 79
abstraction, reasoning, logical analysis, flexibility, and planning, 111-116

age-related improvements in test scores, 242-252
age-related changes, clinical interpretation and, 242-245
as related to the Reitan-Wolfson model of
    neuropsychological functioning, 80-81, 117-127
attention, concentration, and memory, 94-101
central processing functions, 94-116
cerebral damage, effects on, 190, 192-196
clinical interpretation of, 471-814
cognitive retraining (REHABIT), relationship to, 184
cognitive, conative, and emotional factors, relationships of,
    224-232
description of tests included in, 80-116, 299-322
deficits, quantitative vs. qualitative, 232-242
evaluation using the NDS, 455-479
historical and conceptual development, 185-188, 326
importance of a comprehensive and balanced assessment,
    651-654
instructions for administration and scoring, 323-453
modifications of the adult battery, 326-327
motor functions, 88-94, 275-277
Reitan-Indiana Aphasia Screening Test, 105-106, 109
Reitan-Wolfson model, relationship to, 117-127
sensory-perceptual functions, 81-87, 275-277
sensorimotor vs. higher-level functions, 277-287
suggestions for proper test administration, 329-333
verbal and language skills, 101-106
visual-spatial and sequential abilities, 106-111
Halstead-Wepman Aphasia Screening Test, 303
Hand preference
    effects on motor and tactile-perceptual skills, 251-252
Handedness, 79
Hemispherectomy
    as treatment for epilepsy, 608-610
    case illustration, 611-625
    description, 608-610
Higher-level brain functions
    and central processing, 94
    as related to sensory imperception, 278-279
Higher-level and lower-level brain functions, 274
    and learning disability, 741-742

Homonymous visual field defects, 83
    and testing for bilateral simultaneous visual stimulation,
        387
Hydrocephalus, 18

I-J-K

Impaired brain functions
    and mental retardation, 786
Impairment Index, 124
Impairment Index for Children, 255
    development and validation of, 258-261
    NDS, as a replacement for, 260-261
Imperception
    of bilateral simultaneous sensory stimulation, 387
    significance of in clinical case interpretations, 471-814
Incidental learning, 100
Information subtest, 300
Interpretation of neuropsychological test data
    evaluation of the individual subject, 471-814
    methods of inference, 77-79
IQ
    and brain injury in children, 41-43
Kaufman Assessment Battery, 71
Kennard principle, 26-29, 38-44
Kolb and Whishaw's theory of brain-behavior
    relationships, 56-61

L

Language abilities
    and brain functions, 101-104
Language disorder
    developmental, 18-19
Lateral dominance, 79
    importance for test administration, 301-303
Lateralization effects
    as related to Verbal IQ vs. Performance IQ, 568-569
    in Rhythm Test, 312
    in Speech-sounds Perception Test, 313
Learning capacity
    of mentally retarded subjects, 294-295

Learning disability, 22, 24, 53-54, 55, 174
    and abstraction, impairment of, 114-115, 165-166
    and behavioral problems, 744, 760-761, 770-773, 783, 778
    and developmental dysphasia, 203-204
    and higher- and lower-level brain functions, 741-742
    and neuropsychological impairment, frequency of, 260
    and REHABIT, 738, 756-758, 772-773, 784
    and Reitan-Indiana Aphasia Screening Test, 204-212, 743
    approaches to cognitive retraining, 738, 756-758, 770-773,
        783-784
    as related to known brain damage, 204-212
    case illustrations and clinical neuropsychological
        evaluation, 736-784
    comparisons of brain-damaged and control groups, 193-195
    comparisons of normal, learning-disabled, and
        brain-damaged children, 741-743
    description, 736-743
    from a neuropsychological perspective, 736-784, 786
    impairment of attention and concentration in, 286-288
    importance of auditory verbal comprehension in, 134-136
    nature of neuropsychological impairment in, 221-224
    subtypes of, 736-741, 771-773
    theories of, 736-741
Learning, incidental, 100
Left cerebral hemisphere
    theoretical developmental characteristics, 49-52, 53-56
Litigation
    and traumatic brain injury, 722-735
Logical analysis
    as a basic neuropsychological function, 164-167
Logical thinking
    training procedures for, 161
Lower-level brain functions
    and central processing, 94
Luria-Nebraska Neuropsychological Battery, 126

M
Marble Board Test
    and mental retardation, 6
Marching Test, 279
Mazes subtest, 301

Medulloblastoma, 528-542
    case illustration, 531-542
    description, 526-527
Memory
    as an aspect of central processing, 94-96, 98-101
Meningitis, 18
Mental retardation
    abstraction, significance of degree of impairment of,
        in mentally retarded subjects, 296-298
    and child neuropsychology, 3
    and concept formation, 7
    and critical flicker fusion, 5
    and figure-ground effects, 6
    and impaired brain functions, 786
    and Marble Board Test, 6
    and musical pattern reproduction, 6-7
    and phi-phenomenon, 5
    and right-left orientation, 10
    and Tactual Performance Test, 295-296
    and visual perception, 5-6
    Category Test, significance of degree of impairment on,
        among mentally retarded subjects, 296-299
    comparative psychomotor abilities of mentally retarded
        subjects, 295-296
    diagnostic and classification systems of, 288-289, 298
    endogenous, 3-8
    evidence of brain damage in the mentally retarded, 292
    exogenous, 3-10
    familial, 3
    findings using the Halstead-Reitan Battery, 290-298
    hereditary, 3
    learning capacity of mentally retarded subjects, 294-295
    limitations of intelligence tests for classification of, 289-290
    methodological approaches in evaluating retarded subjects,
        290-292
    significance of abstraction and reasoning abilities in,
        294-295
    neuropsychological findings in, 288-298
Methods of inference, 186
    and interpretation of neuropsychological test data, 77-79
Miles ABC Test of Ocular Dominance, 340

Minimal brain dysfunction (MBD), 24-26
  critique of concept of, 24-26
Minnesota Multiphasic Personality Inventory (MMPI), 72
  as related to sensorimotor functions, 277-279
Motor deficits
  and perceptual deficits, compared with conceptual deficits,
    280-282
Motor functions
  as related to the Halstead-Reitan Battery, 88-94
Motor skills
  effects of hand preference on, 251-252
Musical pattern reproduction
  and mental retardation, 6-7

N
Name Writing Test, 89-90
  effects of cerebral damage on, 192-193, 196-200
Neoplasms of the brain
  astrocytoma, 543-578
  clinical neuropsychological evaluation, 526-278
  description, 526-527
  differences in subtentorial, thalamic, and cerebral tumors,
    526-527, 533-534
  medulloblastoma, 528-542
  supratentorial tumors, 543-591
Neurological findings
  and academic deficits, 505-515
  and neuropsychological impairment, 497-504
Neurological signs
  "soft" signs, 4
Neuropathological correlates
  of finger localization, 16-17
  of right-left orientation, 16-17
Neuropsychological Deficit Scale (NDS), 104-105, 124, 198,
    333, 176, 258-259
  and clinical case interpretations, 471-814
  as related to the Reitan-Indiana Aphasia Screening Test, 354
  as related to the comprehensive neuropsychological
    examination, 480-481
  as related to the WISC-R, 479-480
  auditory verbal dysgnosia, examples of, in scoring guide,
    373-375

body dysgnosia, examples of, in scoring guide, 371

central dysarthria, examples of, in scoring guide, 367-368

comparisons of brain-damaged and control children, 213-221

constructional dyspraxia, examples of, in scoring guide, 361-363

deficits of brain-damaged and learning disabled groups as compared to controls, 213-224

description, 213-214

dyscalculia, examples of, in scoring guide, 368-369

dysgraphia, examples of, in scoring guide, 360, 364

dyslexia, examples of, in scoring guide, 365-367

dysnomia, examples of, in scoring guide, 355-357

illustration of clinical interpretation, 472-479

Impairment Index for Children, as a replacement for, 260-261

Left NDS, 176

organizational content, 455-460

Reitan-Indiana Aphasia Screening Test, evaluation of responses and scoring on, 355-375

Right NDS, 176

right-left confusion, examples of, in scoring guide, 370

sample of computerized scoring, 815

scoring procedure, 455-470

screening devices, relationship to, 255

spelling dyspraxia, examples of, in scoring guide, 357-360

usefulness in research analysis, 221-224

visual letter dysgnosia, examples of, in scoring guide, 372

visual number dysgnosia, examples of, in scoring guide, 371-373

Neuropsychological deficits

and Finger-tip Number Writing Perception Test, 283-286

and grip strength, 283-286

and Tactile Finger Recognition Test, 283-286

and Tactual Performance Test, 283-286

and Trail Making Test, 283-286

clinical evaluation of, 471-814

Neuropsychological evaluation of children

basic purposes of, 251

Neuropsychological impairment
  as related to emotional problems of adjustment, 224-232
  in learning disability, 221-224, 260
  with normal neurological findings, 497-504
Neuropsychology
  adult, 1, 11, 16, 20, 23-24
    historical foundations of, 23-24
    vs. child neuropsychology, 11, 29-30, 39-40, 42-43, 74
  and mental retardation, 288-298
  child
    clinical evaluation, 471-814
    historical development of, 1-30
    vs. adult neuropsychology, 190-191
  research and clinical methodology, 20-22
Neuropsychology, clinical
  vs. experimental neuropsychology, 30
Neuropsychology, experimental, 29
  vs. clinical neuropsychology, 30
Normal (control) children
  academic deficits but normal neurological findings in
    505-515
  and the Reitan-Indiana Aphasia Screening Test, 204-212
  frequency of neuropsychological impairment in
    "neurologically normal" children, 483-484
  neurologic involvement without specific neurological
    findings, 516-525
  neuropsychological findings with, 482-486
  neuropsychological impairment without neurological
    deficits in, 497-504
  relevance of neuropsychological assessment to, 253-254

O
Object Assembly subtest, 106-107, 109, 301
Older as compared to young children
  neuropsychological significance of tactile-perceptual
    deficits, 280
Organic mental deficiency, 3

P
Papilledema
  and pseudotumor cerebri, 580

Pathognomonic signs
    Reitan-Indiana Aphasia Screening Test, 304-305
    strengths and weaknesses of, 304-305
    use in clinical case interpretations, 471-814
Perceptual deficits
    and motor deficits, compared with conceptual deficits, 280-282
Perinatal brain lesions, 18
Personality changes
    and brain damage, 226
    and cognitive impairment, 112
    as related to abstraction and reasoning, 67
Phi phenomenon
    and mental retardation, 5
Phonics
    training procedures, 138-143, 158
Picture Arrangement subtest, 106-107, 109, 179, 301
Picture Completion, 107, 301
Plasticity of the brain, 26-29, 31-32, 38-45
    age-related differences, possible, 37
Primary effects
    of traumatic brain injury, 32-33
Pseudotumor cerebri, 579-591
    and benign intracranial hypertension, 580
    and papilledema, 580
    case illustration, 581-591
    description, 579-581
Psychomotor abilities
    comparative, of mentally retarded subjects, 295-296
Psychosis
    and finger localization, 15-16
    and right-left orientation, 15-16
Purdue Pegboard, 59

R
Reading comprehension
    training procedures, 145-147
Reading disabilities, 22
Reading skill
    development of, and visual-form perception, 140-141

Reasoning
    as a basic neuropsychological function, 164-167
Receptive deficits
    dysgnosia, 343-344
    in aphasia, 343-344, 346
Recovery processes
    long term, 35-38
    short term, 33-34
Redundancy of brain tissue, 37-38
Regional localization in the cerebral cortex, 70
Rehabilitation of brain functions, 129-184
    as related to general and specific neuropsychological tests,
       607
REHABIT
    as related to clinical case interpretations, 471-814
    as related to the Reitan-Wolfson theory, 62, 69, 184
    description, 129-132
    Track A
        academic readiness training, 139-144
        developing arithmetic skills and number concepts, 152-155
        developing printing and cursive writing skills, 151
        developing reading skills, 144-151
        developing verbal, language and academic skills, 123-126
    Track B
        developing abstraction and reasoning abilities in the
           language area, 157-163
    Track C
        abstraction and reasoning as a basic neuropsychological
           function, 164-166
        developing abstraction and reasoning abilities, 167-175
    Track D
        developing abstraction and reasoning abilities in the area
           of spatial, sequential, and manipulatory skills, 176-181
    Track E
        developing basic abilities in spatial relationships, 182, 183
        use with behavioral problems, 800-801, 813-814
        use with "terrible triad", 800-801
Reitan-Indiana Aphasia Screening Test, 194, 105-106,
       205-212, 323, 325, 330
    and clinical case interpretations, 471-814
    and learning disability, 743

as related to the Halstead-Reitan Battery, 105-106, 109

as related to the NDS, 354

comparison of brain-damaged, learning-disabled, and control groups, 204-212

content, description of, 303-305

evaluation of responses on, and scoring the NDS, 355-375

instructions for administration, general, 342-347

instructions for administration, specific, 347-354

strengths and weaknesses of a pathognomonic sign approach, 304-305

Reitan-Kløve Lateral Dominance Examination, 79, 251

description, 301-303, 323, 325

instructions for administration and recording, 335-341

Reitan-Wolfson model of neuropsychological functioning, 254

as related to the Halstead-Reitan Battery for Older Children, 80-81, 117-127, 471-814

sequential nature of central processing, 175

Reitan-Wolfson theory of brain-behavior relationships, 62-70

Retraining of neuropsychological abilities, 129-184

Retraining procedures

for aphasia, 133-134, 155

Rhythm Test. See *Seashore Rhythm Test.*

Right cerebral damage

and Block Design subtest, 124

Right cerebral hemisphere

theoretical development characteristics, 49-52, 53-56

Right-left confusion, 209-210, 370

and clinical case interpretations, 471-814

Right-left orientation, 10

and mental retardation, 10

and psychosis, 15-16

neuropathological correlates of, 16-17

Rourke's theory of brain-behavior relationships, 52-56

S

Screening devices for cerebral impairment, 252, 255

critique of, 252-257, 263

development and validation, 261-263

purpose of, 255-256

Seashore Rhythm Test, 96-97, 117-120, 174, 324, 325
   and clinical case interpretations, 471-814
   as related to sensorimotor functions, 277-279
   description, 311-312
   effects of cerebral damage on, 190
   instructions for administration, general, 418-419
   instructions for administration and scoring, specific,
      419-422
   lateralization effects, 312
   sensitivity to brain damage vs. other tests, 280-283
Secondary effects
   of traumatic brain injury, 32-33
Seizure control
   and corpus callosotomy, 610
Sensorimotor functions
   and the Category Test, 277-279
   and clinical case interpretations, 471-814
   and the Trail Making Test, 277-279
   as related to the MMPI, 277-279
   as related to the Seashore Rhythm Test, 277-279
   as related to the Speech-sounds Perception Test, 277-279
   as related to VIQ and PIQ, 277-279
Sensory imperception
   and clinical case interpretations, 471-814
   as related to higher level brain functions, 278-279
Sensory-perceptual Examination, 323, 325
   and clinical case interpretations, 471-814
   description, 306-311
   instructions for administration and scoring, 385-408
   suggestions regarding administration, 331-332
Sensory-perceptual functions
   as related to the Halstead-Reitan Battery, 81-87
Similarities subtest, 300
   and Category Test, 123
   and Vocabulary subtest, 123
Smedley Hand Dynamometer, 88, 382
"Soft signs"
   on the neurological examination, 4
Specific measures of brain functions, 126-127
Specific neuropsychological tests, 76-77

Specialized functions of the brain
  and developmental theories, 47-48, 52, 53, 61, 65
  of left and right hemispheres, 47-48, 52, 53
Specialized neuropsychological abilities
  as related to generalized neuropsychological abilities,
    164-165
Speech-sounds Perception Test, 85, 96-98, 117-120, 174, 324,
    325
  and clinical case interpretations, 471-814
  as related to sensorimotor functions, 277-279
  description, 312-313
  effects of cerebral damage on, 190
  instructions for administration, general, 413-414
  instructions for administration and scoring, specific,
    414-417
  lateralization effects, 313
  modifications of adult version, 327-328
Spelling dyspraxia, 205, 209-210
  and clinical case interpretations, 471-814
  examples of deficits and NDS scoring guide, 357-360
Spelling skills
  training procedures for, 150-151
Stereognosis, 58
Superficial cerebral hemosiderosis
  and cerebral hemispherectomy, 608-610
Supratentorial brain tumors, 543-578
  as related to subtentorial tumors, 526-527, 533-534
  case illustrations, 526-578
  cerebral tumors, 561-578
  pre- and postoperative comparisons, 560, 563-578
  thalamic tumors, 543-560

T
Tactile Finger Recognition Test, 84, 323
  and clinical case interpretations, 471-814
  and comparative neuropsychological deficits, 283-286
  comparative performances of older and young children on,
    251-252
  description, 309-310
  effects of cerebral damage on, 192-193, 276-277, 278-279
  instructions for administration, general, 398

instructions for administration and scoring, specific, 398-402

Tactile Form Recognition Test, 86-87, 324

and clinical case interpretations, 471-814

description, 311

effects of cerebral damage on, 192-193, 276

instructions for administration, general, 409-410

instructions for administration and scoring, specific, 410-412

sensitivity to brain damage vs. other tests, 280-286

Tactile functions

and brain injury, 51

Tactile-perceptual skills

effects of hand preference on, 251-252

relationship to WRAT scores, 280

Tactual Performance Test, 79, 90-93, 108-109, 178, 324, 325, 335

ability levels of mentally retarded subjects on, 295-296

and clinical case interpretations, 471-814

and comparative neuropsychological deficits, 283-286

bilateral transfer, as represented in, 93

description, 314-318

instructions for administration, general, 432-436

instructions for administration and scoring, specific, 436-443

Memory and Localization components, 99-101, 124, 126, 436

and clinical case interpretations, 471-814

effects of cerebral damage on, 190, 2766-277

modification of adult version, 327

neurological model and, 92-93, 316-318, 435-436

Telling time

training procedures for, 160-161

Terminology

to identify neuropsychological deficits, 270

"Terrible triad"

approaches to cognitive rehabilitation, 799-801

as related to behavioral disorders, 783, 786-788, 791, 798, 811

use of REHABIT, 800-801

Thalamic tumors, 543-547

as related to subtentorial tumors and tumors of the cerebral hemispheres, 526-527, 533-534 case illustration, 548-560

Theories
of learning disability, 736-741

Trail Making Test, 109, 111-113, 115, 124-126, 324, 325
and clinical case interpretations, 471-814
and comparative neuropsychological deficits, 283-286
and improvement of scores with age, 245, 247
as related to sensorimotor functions, 277-279
description, 313-314
differences between girls and boys, 245-249
effects of cerebral damage on, 190
instructions for administration, general, 423
instructions for administration and scoring, specific, 423-431
modifications of adult version, 327-328
performances of brain-damaged children vs. controls on, 249-251

Training procedures
for academic readiness, 139-144
for auditory verbal comprehension, 134-139
for arithmetic readiness, 152-154
for arithmetical relationships, 162-163
for logical thinking, 161
for phonics, 138-143, 158
for spelling skills, 150-151
for telling time, 160-161
for visual form perception, 180-181, 183
for vocabulary development, 149-150
for word building, 149

Traumatic brain injury (TBI), 17
and cognitive retraining, 686, 720-721, 733
and litigation, 722-735
case illustrations, 677-693, 694-710, 711-721, 722-735
description, 672-676
primary effects of, 32-33
secondary effects of, 32-33

Tumors
clinical case interpretations, 528-578
differences in subtentorial, thalamic, and cerebral tumors, 526-527, 533-534

V

Verbal and language skills
  as related to the Halstead-Reitan Battery, 101-106
Verbal and Performance IQ differences
  as related to age when brain damage was sustained, 266-267
  as related to chronicity of brain lesion, 266-267
  behavioral criteria and, 264-265
  EEG criteria and, 264
  homonymous visual field defects and, 265-266
  in adult and child neuropsychology, 263, 268-269
  in cases of lateralized cerebral lesions, 568-569
Visual field defects
  homonymous, 83
Visual-form perception
  and development of reading skill, 140-141
  training procedures for, 180-181, 183
Visual letter dysgnosia, 207-208
  examples of deficits and NDS scoring guide, 372
Visual number dysgnosia, 206-207, 371-373
Visual perception
  and mental retardation, 5-6
Visual-spatial and sequential abilities
  as related to the Halstead-Reitan Battery, 106-111
Vocabulary development
  training procedures for, 149-150
Vocabulary subtest, 120-122, 300

W

Wechsler Adult Intelligence Scale (WAIS), 74
Wechsler Intelligence Scale for Children-Revised (WISC-R), 71, 74-75, 324
  and clinical case interpretations, 471-814
  effects of cerebral damage on, 190
Wechsler measurements
  as related to constructional dyspraxia, 264-265
  as related to dysphasia, 264-265
Wechsler Scales
  behavioral criteria and VIQ-PIQ differences, 254-265
  Block Design subtest, sensitivity of, vs. other tests, 280-283
  description, brief, 300-301
  EEG criteria and VIQ-PIQ differences, 264

effects of cerebral damage on, 190-191, 193-195, 196
homonymous visual field defects and VIQ-PIQ differences,
    265-266
VIQ and PIQ as related to sensorimotor skills, 277-279
VIQ and PIQ differences, 263-269
Wide Range Achievement Test (WRAT), 72
    effects of cerebral damage on, 192-193
Wide Range Achievement Test (WRAT) scores
    and comparative neuropsychological deficits, 283-286
    as related to tactile-perceptual skills, 280
Word building
    training procedures for, 149
Word Finding Test, 120-122, 160